FIFTY PLAYS
for
HOLIDAYS

Fifty Plays
for
Holidays

*A collection of royalty-free,
one-act children's plays for
holidays and special occasions*

Edited by

SYLVIA E. KAMERMAN

Publishers   PLAYS, INC.   Boston

Contents

Columbus Day

BEYOND MUTINY   Mary Nygaard Peterson   3
Turning point of a fateful voyage
FOR THE GLORY OF SPAIN   Helen Roberts   13
Columbus in the court of Ferdinand and Isabella
THE GHOST FROM GENOA   Earl J. Dias   24
Football player follows example of Columbus

Halloween

TEST FOR A WITCH   Esther MacLellan
and Catherine V. Schroll   40
Learning the lessons of witchcraft
NOBODY BELIEVES IN WITCHES!
Martha Swintz Watkins   50
How to convince a prince
THE WONDERFUL WITCHWARE STORE
Elinor R. Alderman   62
New styles in broom travel

Book Week

THE HAUNTED BOOKSHOP   Jessie Nicholson   71
Favorite story characters lead a treasure hunt
THE BOOK THAT SAVED THE EARTH   Claire Boiko   80
A science fiction comedy-spoof

v

BOOKS A LA MODE   Mildred Hark
                              and Noel McQueen   96
        Making friends for the library

                    Election Day

RUNNING THE COUNTRY   Janice Auritt Oser   121
        Understanding the idea behind voting

                American Education Week

THE THREE ROYAL R's   Mary Thurman Pyle   128
    Young Tom Jefferson foresees free public schools
WELCOME, PARENTS   Eva Cole   143
                A back-to-school skit

                    Thanksgiving

THE PILGRIM PAINTING   James Rawls   150
    A "living" portrait brings the message of Thanksgiving
IN THE NAME OF MILES STANDISH   Helen Ramsey   162
            Dramatization of a famous proposal
TURKEY, ANYONE?   Juliet Garver 173
    Too much of a good thing almost spoils a family tradition
THE THANKSGIVING SCARECROW   Eleanor D. Leuser   191
        A kind word brings an unexpected reward
GOVERNOR BRADFORD'S SCISSORS   Graham DuBois   197
        A dramatic event threatens the First Thanksgiving

                     Christmas

HAND-ME-DOWN HILDY   Sara E. Sagoff   216
        Rediscovering the true meaning of Christmas
ONE NIGHT IN BETHLEHEM   Deborah Newman   226
            A moving drama of the Christmas story
SANTA AND THE EFFICIENCY EXPERT
                              Frances B. Watts   235
            Bringing Christmas up-to-date

THAT CHRISTMAS FEELING   Mildred Hark
                              and Noel McQueen   246
    Preparing for an old-fashioned Christmas
TWO STRANGERS FROM NAZARETH   Graham DuBois   264
    When there was "no room at the inn"
LONG LIVE CHRISTMAS   Islay Benson   277
    Attempts to banish Christmas are foiled
THE BROWNIE WHO FOUND CHRISTMAS
                                Adele Thane   294
    Children reveal the Christmas spirit

Lincoln's Birthday

LOOKING FOR LINCOLN   Deborah Newman   304
    A vote for Abe Lincoln
VISITOR TO GETTYSBURG   Earl J. Dias   312
    When Lincoln made the Gettysburg Address
YOUNG ABE LINCOLN   Aileen Fisher   327
    Revealing scenes from Lincoln's early life

Valentine's Day

THE VALENTINE TREE   Marjorie Barrows   346
    A silver penny turns up an unusual Queen of Hearts
VALENTINE STARDUST   Jessie Nicholson 355
    A special ingredient for a change of heart
THE TINIEST HEART   Frances B. Watts   369
    Finding a proper name for a Prince of Hearts

Washington's Birthday

THE HANDWRITING ON THE WALL   Jessie Nicholson 382
    Washington contributes to a modern restoration
MARTHA WASHINGTON'S SPY   Earl J. Dias   402
    An historical drama
GEORGE SLEPT HERE, TOO   Anne Coulter Martens   417
    One Washington too many

Brotherhood Week

THE OTHER SIDE OF THE WALL   Patricia Clapp   431
Removing the barriers to friendship

St. Patrick's Day

THE LAST SNAKE IN IRELAND   Mary Malone   445
A traditional play about St. Patrick
ST. PATRICK SAVES THE DAY   Graham DuBois   455
A practical joker gets his comeuppance
THE LEPRECHAUN'S POT OF GOLD   Frances B. Watts   471
Long ago in Ireland

Easter

CINDER-RABBIT   Constance Whitman Baher   484
Cinderella in an Easter setting
THE CHOOSING OF EASTER RABBIT   Sally Werner   499
The Easter Fairy makes a surprising selection

Pan-American Day (April 14)

FIESTA   Jean McArthur   506
Getting to know our Latin-American neighbors
THE BELL OF DOLORES   Camilla Campbell   518
The struggle for Mexican independence

Arbor Day

WEEPING WILLOW'S HAPPY DAY   Janice Auritt Oser   534
The beauty and value of trees
THE TREE FRIENDS   Sara Sloane McCarty   541
How aspens help their pine tree friends

May Day

MAY WITCH   Margaret Wylie Brydon
                          and Esther E. Ziegler   548
          Choosing the Queen of the May

Mother's Day

MOTHER'S CHOICE   Mildred Hark McQueen   565
              The right gift for Mother
TIME FOR MOM   Aileen Fisher   580
          What every mother needs most
A HAT FOR MOTHER   Marguerite Kreger Phillips   588
              Mother's crowning touch

Patriotic Holidays

WE, THE PEOPLE   Myriam Toles   598
              Framing our Constitution
THE YANKEE DOODLE KITTEN   Deborah Newman   615
              A patriotic cat saves the flag
AMERICA IS A SONG   Paul T. Nolan   623
    A dramatic setting for the songs of our pioneers

Production Notes   635

FIFTY PLAYS
for
HOLIDAYS

Beyond Mutiny

by Mary Nygaard Peterson

Characters

CHRISTOPHER COLUMBUS
PEDRO DE SALCEDO, *his cabin boy*
JUAN DE LA COSA, *Master of the "Santa Maria"*
PERALONSO NINO, *Pilot of the "Santa Maria"*
CHACHU, *a boatswain*
JOSÉ ⎤
BARTOLOME ⎟
RODRIGO ⎬ *seamen*
VINCENTE ⎦
OTHER SEAMEN
HELMSMAN (*Offstage voice*)

TIME: *At night, early October, 1492.*
SETTING: *The deck of the "Santa Maria." The quarter-deck is a raised platform at left of stage. There is a railing marking the edge of the quarter-deck.*
AT RISE: *The stage is in semi-darkness.* COLUMBUS *and* PEDRO *stand on the quarter-deck, talking.*

COLUMBUS: Have you ever known a finer night for sailing, Pedro?
PEDRO: The stars look almost low enough for us to touch them.

3

COLUMBUS: The waves of the sea are so gentle and regular —almost as if the ocean were breathing.

PEDRO (*Apprehensively; pointing to barrels at right*): Did you see something move between those barrels just now, Captain Columbus?

COLUMBUS: Probably only a sailor finding himself a place to sleep.

PEDRO (*Doubtfully*): I don't know, sir.

COLUMBUS: Hadn't you better go and find a place for yourself, Pedro? It is getting late.

PEDRO: I'd rather stay with you, sir.

COLUMBUS: I appreciate that, son, but it isn't necessary. Do get some sleep.

PEDRO: I feel uneasy, sir.

COLUMBUS: How so?

PEDRO: There has been so much whispering among the men, sir. They look at you with such black looks.

COLUMBUS: I have been telling myself that I only imagined it.

PEDRO: Oh, no, sir. Today I overheard José talking to Bartolome and Rodrigo. He opened his shirt to show them something—I saw it also, sir. It was a wicked knife he had concealed there.

COLUMBUS: Did you hear what the men were talking about?

PEDRO: Only a few words here and there, sir—I couldn't get close enough. Bartolome said that the ocean sea was a great cloak that could hide a multitude of things.

COLUMBUS: It is true. The sea has many secrets.

PEDRO: José showed them the knife, and then he said, "Some dark night soon there will be a quick stab in the back, a splash in the water, and then the ships will turn back because the foreigner has fallen overboard while looking at the stars."

COLUMBUS: Mutiny. I have felt it in the air.

PEDRO: It is no longer safe for you to walk alone, Captain Columbus.

COLUMBUS: No one walks alone, Pedro. Now you go curl up somewhere and go to sleep.

PEDRO: You are brave, Captain Columbus, but I am not. José and his friends saw me watching them this afternoon. If I were to sleep somewhere on the deck, perhaps there would be a quick stab in the back for me, also.

COLUMBUS: Very well, son. Stay with me, if you like. But why not go into my cabin, then, and sleep awhile?

PEDRO: Unless you command it, sir, I prefer to stay at your side.

COLUMBUS (*Wearily*): Very well—as you wish. (*There is silence for a moment. José enters stealthily right, softly crosses stage as close to upstage wall as possible and crouches in the corner between quarter-deck and upstage wall. Suddenly, COLUMBUS leans over the railing and peers into the shadows. Sharply*) Who goes there?

JOSÉ (*In an ingratiating voice*): It is only José, Captain Columbus. Just taking the air.

COLUMBUS: I think the air would be the same if you were to lie down and sleep until your watch is called.

JOSÉ: I was about to sleep, Captain, when I noticed a queer lightness in the water. I wish you would come down and take a look at it, sir. It gives one a peculiar feeling, sir, to see it—not quite natural, if you know what I mean.

COLUMBUS (*Curtly*): I know what you mean well enough, José. As for the light, it comes from tiny plants and animals in the sea. It is natural enough. Now, I suggest that you go to bed.

JOSÉ (*Suddenly*): Bed is a place I never expect to see again, Captain Columbus.

COLUMBUS: That is nonsense. (RODRIGO *and* BARTOLOME *enter and join* JOSÉ.) Who are those other fellows? Why are they not asleep? *(Peers down, strikes one hand in other)* Who are you, I say!

RODRIGO: Rodrigo Sanchez, Columbus.

COLUMBUS *(Sharply)*: *Captain* Columbus.

RODRIGO *(Sullenly)*: Captain Columbus.

COLUMBUS: And who is that with you?

BARTOLOME: Bartolome de Torres, Captain Columbus.

COLUMBUS: Why are you wandering about when you should be sleeping?

RODRIGO: We are afraid to sleep, Captain.

BARTOLOME: We want to turn back to Spain, Captain Columbus, before it is too late.

COLUMBUS *(Impatiently)*: Too late for what?

JOSÉ: We know that the compass no longer points to the North.

RODRIGO: It is the Devil's hand, pushing it off course so that we will never find our way back to Spain.

BARTOLOME: We are lost. Before long, we will be tangled in the mass of seaweed that spreads thick all about us. We are in a trap. As soon as we are held fast, the sea monsters will come and tear our ships apart with their mighty arms.

COLUMBUS: There are no sea monsters, Bartolome.

JOSÉ: We know better, Captain.

COLUMBUS: You dare to dispute my word, José?

JOSÉ: Will you not admit that there has been no wind at all, all day today?

COLUMBUS: I will admit that.

RODRIGO: The sails have hung like wet rags, with not a breath to stir them.

JOSÉ: Yet the sea heaves and swells under our feet. What would cause that except the movement of monsters beneath the sea of weeds?

COLUMBUS: There is no wind now, but no doubt the movement of the sea is caused by winds somewhere else.

There will be wind soon, I promise it. As for monsters
—there are no monsters. There is nothing at all to
be afraid of. Now find yourselves a place to lie down
and go to sleep.

José: We want you to promise us that you will turn the
ships around and go back to Spain.

BARTOLOME (*Threateningly*): Turn back, Columbus.

COLUMBUS (*Wearily*): Listen, men. It is late. Go to sleep.
Come and see me in the morning. We will talk about
it then. Bring the rest of the men with you, if you like.
Everyone may speak his mind.

RODRIGO: You will see—everyone wants to turn back.

José: We will wait till morning, Columbus, but no longer.
(*The three men exit right.*)

COLUMBUS: I think we will be safe for the night, Pedro.
Please get some sleep.

PEDRO: They may change their minds and come back, sir.
I prefer staying with you.

COLUMBUS: Very well, stay. As you said, the men may
change their minds and come back—they are like little
children and must constantly be reassured. Rest now,
son. You are too young to go without your sleep—
especially when tomorrow may see our dreams come
true. (PEDRO *rests his head on his arms, which are placed
on the railing, and gradually falls asleep.* COLUMBUS
*paces back and forth on the platform. The light grad-
ually becomes brighter, signifying the dawn. Eventually,
there is full light.*)

PERALONSO (*Entering right*): Good morning, Captain
Columbus. You are awake already?

COLUMBUS: Good morning, Peralonso. I have not slept.

PERALONSO: Not slept, sir? Is something wrong?

COLUMBUS (*Softly*): I think that if we are not very careful,
we may have mutiny on our hands.

PERALONSO (*Horrified*): Mutiny!

COLUMBUS: Hush, someone is approaching. (*He looks to the left*)

JUAN DE LA COSA (*Entering left*): Good morning, Peralonso. All is well?

PERALONSO: Good morning, Juan. All is well. (*He motions toward the quarter-deck.* JUAN *comes to quarter-deck.*)

JUAN: Captain Columbus! You are awake early.

COLUMBUS: I have not slept, Juan.

PERALONSO: Captain Columbus says there is mutiny in the air.

JUAN: Mutiny!

COLUMBUS: Last night, I firmly believe, José was prepared to take my life.

JUAN: I hope you are mistaken, sir. Still—José is a bad one. Was he alone?

COLUMBUS: Two of his friends were with him—Rodrigo Sanchez and Bartolome de Torres.

PERALONSO: They are all of the same stripe, beyond a doubt.

JUAN: Why don't we hang the three of them, Captain? The King's marshal would do it. That would put an end to all thought of mutiny.

COLUMBUS: No, not that, Juan. I think it might make matters worse. You know that as it is, I am called "the foreigner." I am Genoese—not Spanish. They all resent it.

JUAN: You are my brother, sir.

PERALONSO: Mine, also, Captain.

COLUMBUS: Thank you—both of you. It is good to know that I may rely on someone. (PEDRO *stirs in his sleep.* COLUMBUS *looks down on him fondly, smiles, puts his hand on the boy's head.*) You see, I have another loyal friend—my cabin boy.

PEDRO (*Awakens with a start*): Oh! Where am I? (*Getting*

clumsily to his feet) I'm sorry, I didn't mean to fall asleep.

COLUMBUS (*Kindly*): It's all right, son—I am glad you did.

PEDRO: Have the men—José and the others—have they come back?

COLUMBUS: No, they have not returned yet, but I imagine they soon will. Why don't you go and get us a bucket of water so that we can wash up? These gentlemen and I will retire to my cabin for a short time.

PERALONSO (*Significantly*): Yes. we'll need to make some plans.

PEDRO: I'll have the water for you in a minute, sir. (*Exits right*)

COLUMBUS: Come, gentlemen. (*They exit upstage center just as* JOSÉ, RODRIGO, BARTOLOME, CHACHU, *and* OTHER SEAMEN *enter right.*)

JOSÉ (*Looking around angrily*): He's not here.

RODRIGO (*Also sullen*): He promised to talk to us.

BARTOLOME: He'd better keep his promise and not put us off. (PEDRO *enters right with bucket of water. He is frightened at the sight of the men.*)

JOSÉ (*Pointing at* PEDRO): You, there—

PEDRO (*Frightened, but trying to be brave*): Yes?

JOSÉ: What have you got there?

PEDRO: Water, by order of the Captain. For the Captain to wash with.

JOSÉ: Tell him we're waiting to talk to him. The washing can wait.

PEDRO (*Frightened, but bold*): I'll tell the Captain you *request* an audience.

JOSÉ (*Advancing menacingly*): Get along, you—and hurry!

PEDRO (*As calmly as he can*): Very well. (*He walks slowly toward center exit past the menacing crew. A few feet before reaching the exit, he turns to look at crew, then hurries out.*)

CHACHU: I still say you men should be at your work. Leave the running of the ship to the Captain.

BARTOLOME: Be quiet, Chachu.

CHACHU: It is not my job to be quiet. My job is to see that the work gets done.

BARTOLOME (*Threateningly*): Be quiet, or you will have no job at all.

JOSÉ (*Persuasively*): You like being boatswain, Chachu?

CHACHU (*Defiantly*): Yes, I like being boatswain.

JOSÉ (*Significantly*): Then be quiet, Chachu, and you may still be boatswain. (COLUMBUS, PERALONSO *and* JUAN *enter center and step from behind onto quarter-deck.*)

COLUMBUS (*Speaking pleasantly from railing*): Good morning, men.

CHACHU: Good morning, Captain Columbus. (*The other men merely grumble and murmur.*)

COLUMBUS (*Looking about at sky and sea*): A wonderful morning, isn't it? We couldn't ask for a finer day.

JOSÉ: A fine day for turning back to Spain, Columbus.

JUAN (*From quarter-deck*): *Captain* Columbus, José.

COLUMBUS: Thank you, Juan.

JOSÉ (*Sullenly*): We are not here to argue about titles.

BARTOLOME: We want to go home, Captain.

RODRIGO: Turn back, Columbus.

COLUMBUS: Why turn back now? The wind is fair, just as I promised you, José. (*He wets a finger in his mouth and holds it up to the wind.*) A true northeast wind. We could not ask for a better.

RODRIGO: The men say you are in league with the Devil, Captain—you command the wind and it comes to your order.

COLUMBUS (*Pleasantly*): That is nonsense, Rodrigo. I merely know the winds. I do not command them. I planned this voyage to take advantage of them.

BARTOLOME: Since we left Spain the wind has been from the northeast. How will we ever get back against this wind? It will blow us over the western edge of the world.

COLUMBUS: The earth is round, Bartolome. It has no edges. There is one wind to bring us, another to take us back. You will see.

JOSÉ: What is to keep us from being caught in the seaweed? It stretches like a meadow on every hand. There is no end to it. (*He sweeps his arm about.*) We will never get through it.

COLUMBUS: You can all see that the seaweed is not holding us. The water is deep beneath it. We all watched Peralonso take the sounding yesterday—he did not find bottom anywhere. See, the weeds part easily for the ships to pass through. (*He motions to the right. All heads turn to watch. Some nod at what they see.*)

JOSÉ: Even if the weeds do not hold us, how can we know where we are going? The compass no longer works—it does not point to the North Star.

COLUMBUS: The compass still works, Pedro. It is only that the North Star moves. All the stars move. Didn't you know that? (*The sailors look at each other in consternation.*) There are many things about navigation you don't know, my friends. But I know them, for that is my business. (*The sailors mutter, look at each other, appear uncertain.*)

CHACHU: Shall I have the men get to their tasks, Captain?

COLUMBUS: Just a minute, Chachu. (*To the men*) Give me a few more days of your faith, men. I—wait, who is coming? (*All listen, as running footsteps are heard approaching from offstage.*)

PEDRO (*Running onstage right*): Captain! Captain!

COLUMBUS: What is it, Pedro!

PEDRO (*Panting*): Over on the starboard side—I saw birds flying—large flocks of them! (*Men murmur excitedly,*

"Birds! Do you think that means land?" etc.)

COLUMBUS: Birds—that *is* good news, but nothing more than I expected. Men, do you know what that means?

BARTOLOME (*Hesitantly*): It—it may mean land nearby, Captain. (VINCENTE *runs onstage right, holding a dripping tree branch.*)

VINCENTE (*Excitedly*): Captain Columbus! Look what came floating on the water!

JOSÉ (*Wonderingly*): Why, it's from a tree.

RODRIGO: And look how fresh the leaves are. It—it couldn't have been floating very long.

COLUMBUS: Land must be within reach! Would you turn back now? Do you want some other country to have the honor of finding the western route to the Indies?

CREW (*Ad lib*): Land must be near; perhaps the Captain is right. Why turn back now? (*Etc.*)

COLUMBUS: Think of the rewards that are waiting for you, just ahead. (*He points right and men all strain to see.*) In India, the roofs of the houses are tiled with gold. There are mountains of gold and streams of jewels. There are silks and spices—all yours. And the glory! (*He waits a moment to let them think. Then he speaks briskly.*) Well, what do you say? Shall we turn back, men?

ALL: No. No.

CHACHU: Sail on.

ALL: Sail on, Columbus!

COLUMBUS (*Vigorously*): Very well, we will. We will sail on—on to the West. (*He calls loudly to the* HELMSMAN *offstage*) Ho, Helmsman! Sail on to the West. Not to the North, not to the South, but to the West.

HELMSMAN (*Voice heard from offstage*): To the West. Not to the North. Not to the South. But to the West. (*Curtain*)

THE END

For the Glory of Spain

by Helen Roberts

Characters

KING FERDINAND
QUEEN ISABELLA
TALAVERA, *Archbishop of Granada*
CHANCELLOR
JUAN DE COLOMA
COLUMBUS

TIME: *Spring 1492.*
SETTING: *The Alhambra. Council Chamber.*
AT RISE: KING FERDINAND *sits on a special throne-like seat at right end of table.* QUEEN ISABELLA *at left.* TALAVERA, *the new Archbishop of Granada, is seated near* FERDINAND. *The* CHANCELLOR *hovers near* ISABELLA. JUAN DE COLOMA *is standing halfway between door rear and tables.*

JUAN DE COLOMA (*Approaching* QUEEN): Your Majesty, he says you have promised him an audience.
FERDINAND (*Irritably*): Who? What? Where? What are you talking about, Juan?
JUAN: Why, about Christopher Columbus, Your Majesty. He's waiting in the anteroom. He was pacing the floor, talking to himself when I went past there.
FERDINAND: Let him pace the floor! Exercise won't hurt

13

him any. (*To* TALAVERA) What was it we were planning, Talavera? A big celebration in honor of you, the new Archbishop of Granada. Wasn't that it?

TALAVERA: Indeed, yes, Your Majesty. I see no reason why our conference should be interrupted by a mere hanger-on of the court.

JUAN: Especially one so full of hairbrained ideas.

ISABELLA: Juan! You've said enough. Show Columbus in.

JUAN (*Subdued*): Yes, Your Majesty. (*Exits*)

CHANCELLOR (*Smiling broadly*): I am glad you are giving the poor fellow his chance. After all, he's been waiting for this opportunity for years.

ISABELLA: Of course, he has. We've been so overburdened with wars and troubles of every sort.

FERDINAND: And now you give your permission for further trouble to come in that door. My dear, it seems to me you've handled this in a rather high-handed manner, when you know *I* had other plans.

ISABELLA: Sometimes, things have to be done that way. If I weren't convinced that this Columbus person knew what he was talking about, it might be different.

JUAN (*At door with* COLUMBUS): Christopher Columbus! (*They enter.*)

COLUMBUS (*Approaching throne and bowing*): Your Majesties! . . . King Ferdinand! Queen Isabella! I am highly honored that you have at last given me a hearing.

FERDINAND (*Interrupting, after yawning openly*): State your business, man, and be done with it.

COLUMBUS: Certainly, Your Majesty. That is my very great desire! All the world knows of your great wealth and power. Your recent victory over the Moors which gave you Granada and this beautiful Alhambra made the world notice you more than ever.

FERDINAND (*Tapping the table impatiently*): Yes, yes! *We* know all about that! What of it?

COLUMBUS: Just this. I have come to show you how you can become the greatest monarchs in all the world, perhaps for all time.

FERDINAND (*Surprised*): What?

ISABELLA (*Kindly*): My dear Christopher Columbus, how would you suggest that we gain this added fame?

FERDINAND (*Wearily*): My dear, can't you ever be satisfied with your conquests?

JUAN: But, Your Majesty, surely they are your conquests, too.

FERDINAND: Of course. But I would have given up long ago except for my interest in Granada.

CHANCELLOR: You may well be proud of Granada. It was a mighty task to drive the Moslems from our country after they had been here eight hundred years.

ISABELLA (*Approaching* CHANCELLOR *with enthusiasm*): And now, Christopher Columbus promises us even greater renown and wealth.

TALAVERA (*Sarcastically*): Promises! Why, any fool knows promises are good for nothing except the fun of breaking them.

CHANCELLOR (*Aside to* QUEEN): Maybe that's the way with *his* promises.

TALAVERA: How does this . . . this man expect to give us renown and wealth?

COLUMBUS (*Ignoring* TALAVERA, *addresses* QUEEN): Your Majesty. Through my years of careful study and practical seamanship, I have figured a new route to the wealth of India and China and to their vast mountains of gold. I ask the privilege of bringing this to you and laying it at your feet.

TALAVERA: A mountain of gold at your feet! Wouldn't that be wondrous? (*Bursts out laughing*) What kind of fairy tale is this? It's too much! This man should be thrown out and put in chains as a madman.

FERDINAND (*Nodding approval*): And that would be the end of him and his wild schemes. (*Consults with* TALAVERA *while* COLUMBUS *pleads with* QUEEN.)

COLUMBUS (*To* QUEEN): Your Majesty, if you will approve my plans, I assure you that you will never regret it. Never! For eight long years now I have been waiting for your promised help.

TALAVERA: Eight more years might temper your madness! (*To* KING) Send him away! He has been receiving royal support too long as it is. We can't afford to give him any more charity.

ISABELLA (*Severely*): Talavera! Who gave you the authority to issue such orders in our presence?

FERDINAND: I don't know that I blame him. (*Pompously*) After all, Talavera is interested only in the country's welfare.

ISABELLA (*Aside*): I wonder! (*To* KING) There's no reason why he should take such liberties just because you've appointed him Archbishop of Granada.

FERDINAND (*Mildly*): Come, come, my dear. Let's not make an issue of this Columbus fellow.

CHANCELLOR (*To* QUEEN): Your Majesty is perfectly right. We have been putting the poor man off for years. He has followed us around from place to place waiting for the help we promised him.

TALAVERA (*Laughing heartily*): Then a few more days surely won't make any difference.

FERDINAND (*Placatingly*): If you feel you must hear him, let him have his say—and be gone.

ISABELLA: If he can show us how to become still greater, we must hear him out. Ever since I came to the throne I have had nothing but war, war, war. Now that it's over at last, we can plan for a greater Spain.

FERDINAND (*Showing pleasure at last of her speech*): Excellent, my dear. Excellent! (*To* TALAVERA) What do you consider suitable plans for Spain, Talavera? Our people can't afford another war.

TALAVERA (*Strutting before* KING): Indeed they cannot, Your Majesty. For too many years of war they have been forced to practice economy. Now that we have no more wars to fight, *I* suggest a period of great court splendor. One that will be unparalleled in all history.

ISABELLA (*Indignantly*): So that's your suggestion, is it?

TALAVERA (*Blustering*): Well—what's wrong with that?

ISABELLA (*Facing him in anger*): You have just refused to listen to plans Columbus has made. Then, without even hearing them, you say they are too costly! Now, you suggest a period of great court splendor.

TALAVERA: Which is quite a different matter.

FERDINAND (*Nodding*): Obviously.

CHANCELLOR: Noble Queen! There is some truth in what they say. The common people would reflect some of the glory of the court, while an unknown venture might distress them.

ISABELLA: My dear Chancellor. I do respect your counsel, but this time I cannot follow your advice. We have promised this hearing for a long time to Christopher Columbus. (*Steps defiantly to the table*) And what's more, he shall have it right now!

FERDINAND: By all means let him have his say, so we can make an end of all this dull discussion. (*Nervously strums on the table.*) It has gone on too long as it is.

COLUMBUS: Thank you for such permission, Your Majesties. For many years now, I have been thoroughly convinced that China, India, and Japan can be reached by sailing west instead of east.

TALAVERA (*Derisively*): Sheer nonsense! Who ever heard of such a thing?

CHANCELLOR (*Approaching* COLUMBUS *kindly and fingering the maps and globes*): It is not quite clear to me just how you expect to reach these eastern lands by travelling in a westerly direction.

COLUMBUS: That's what I have been waiting for a chance to explain. I shall be only too glad to show you. (*Goes to table by maps and globes*) I have constructed these globes and maps accurately as a result of my years of study. With their help I believe I can convince you of the truth of what I say. (*Takes globe*) Now, here is Europe, and here you see Spain. (*Turns it left*) And here is China, as well as India and Japan.

FERDINAND: What of it? That's nothing new.

TALAVERA: Where is your wonderful discovery?

COLUMBUS (*Unperturbed*): Now, watch. (*Turning globe*) Here is our Spain. (*Turns it to right*) And here in the west we have India again.

FERDINAND: The man's positively a magician! I should have him perform my court tricks.

TALAVERA (*Scornfully*): It would take more than a magician to sail in that crazy fashion.

COLUMBUS (*Proudly*): Yes, indeed! Much more than a magician! It requires an expert mariner—and ships.

TALAVERA: And what would be gained by such a voyage?

COLUMBUS: Great honor to Spain and to the Holy Church.

TALAVERA: Yes! The conversion of unknown people who stand on their heads. (*He goes over to the globe.*) You find that hard to believe? It's really very simple. Here you see Spain, don't you? (*They nod agreement, and he points to under side of globe.*) And here you see India, don't you? (*They nod.*) Then, all these people living in China and India must be standing on their heads. What possible use have we for people who go around on their heads? (*He sits down satisfied. Several laugh and applaud.*)

FERDINAND: Why, you are a better orator than Columbus, Talavera. That explodes his whole theory, and we won't have to make the troublesome voyage after all. (*Yawns loudly*) What is next for discussion?

COLUMBUS: Pardon me, Your Majesty. I'm not finished yet. The argument Talavera suggested is no new one. Fortunately it's long since been disproved, and even ridiculed. One point he neglected to make is that I would bring back gold to Spain.

FERDINAND (*Interested*): Gold!

COLUMBUS: There are mountains of gold in these countries, and rivers flowing with precious stones.

TALAVERA (*Still unwilling to give in*): I have heard that the seas boil in the tropics, and that no sailor can avoid those burning whirlpools.

COLUMBUS (*Patronizingly*): I fear, Talavera, that you have been so occupied with your holy wars against the Moors that you are quite out of date. Perhaps you are not aware that the Portuguese have already sailed the tropic seas. My younger brother, Bartholomew, made the trip with the famous Portuguese explorer. They sailed around the southern tip of Africa for the first time six long years ago!

FERDINAND: And did the waters boil?

COLUMBUS (*Significantly*): Certainly not. But they would never fear sailing through boiling water any more than through heat and storms. Rest assured, these Portuguese are great explorers, and fearless, far-seeing men.

ISABELLA (*Proudly*): But Spain shall be greater! Never let it be said that Spain lacked the courage to chart a new route.

COLUMBUS (*Incredulous*): Then you mean you are ready to furnish ships for the voyage?

ISABELLA (*Decisively*): This shall be taken care of immediately.

COLUMBUS (*Kneeling in gratitude*): Your Majesty! I am overcome with joy! Your kindness has rewarded my years of waiting. They have disappeared like a bad dream. You have been brave in war and peace, Your Majesty. Now, you have shown even greater courage, in making this momentous decision.

FERDINAND (*Getting up to argue*): Without consulting me! Where do you think the money for these ships is coming from? Perhaps you know where it grows on trees.

TALAVERA: And how do you think the people will like such added expense?

CHANCELLOR (*Eloquently*): Don't you realize how the Portuguese have become a united people? They are much more loyal and prosperous since their recent discoveries and explorations. If this new route is discovered, the glory will belong forever to our beloved Spain.

ISABELLA: Can we raise the money for such a voyage, Chancellor?

FERDINAND: You should have thought of that before you gave your word. (*Aside*) Just like a woman to speak first and think later—if she thinks at all.

TALAVERA: And what of ships?

COLUMBUS: Here is a letter from Prior Juan Perez at Palos. He declares his faith in my proposed voyage. He also mentions several prominent men of Palos who are convinced of the value of the trip.

FERDINAND: What right have they to express themselves? It's easy enough for them to do a lot of talking when it doesn't cost them anything.

COLUMBUS (*With compelling dignity*): But it will cost them something. The three Pinzon brothers, well-known sea captains, are willing not only to contribute to the expense, but also to go along on the expedition.

TALAVERA: I little thought to hear of so many fools in one day.

CHANCELLOR (*Taking letter and reading it*): It says here

that the Pinzons have convinced many others in Palos of the value of the trip.

TALAVERA: Simple people are easily convinced.

CHANCELLOR: They are not common sailors, but rather people who understand the dangers—perhaps better than we do.

TALAVERA: These Pinzons may be ever so foolhardy, but it will take one hundred fifty men for such a trip. Had you thought of that?

FERDINAND: And a great quantity of provisions besides.

TALAVERA: Perhaps Columbus will have some answer for this, too. Perhaps he can twirl a globe that will produce men by the magic twist of his wrist.

FERDINAND: I have a better plan than that. Since the city of Palos has shown such—such public interest in the voyage, they will have to furnish a ship. It will serve as punishment for their disobedience in the Moorish war.

ISABELLA (*Doubtfully*): But one ship—would that be enough?

COLUMBUS: No, Your Majesty. We should have at least three. If one became disabled, we could still carry on.

TALAVERA: Humph! He talks of providing ships as if they were—mere maps.

ISABELLA: What do you say, Chancellor? I would gladly pledge my jewels for the expedition, but alas, they were needed for the Moorish War.

CHANCELLOR (*Figuring busily on paper*): We can arrange a loan, Your Majesty, sufficient to equip two other ships.

COLUMBUS: Then with the ships pledged, it should be a small matter to get a crew for them.

TALAVERA (*Mockingly*): Certainly! Certainly! A very small matter. Just open up the jails, and there you are. A fine crew for a fine madman.

FERDINAND (*Pounding the table in glee*): Not such a bad

idea at that! If we cannot get enough men any other way, we shall release all the prisoners convicted of minor offenses—that is, if they'd rather go on the expedition— which I doubt.

COLUMBUS: And now may we draw up a contract for the voyage?

ISABELLA: You have heard the terms, Juan de Coloma?

JUAN: Yes, Your Majesty.

ISABELLA: That is well. Since there's nothing further, pre-pare the document for our signatures immediately. (JUAN *begins writing at small table*.)

COLUMBUS: But there is something else.

ISABELLA: How can that be? (*Checks them off on her fingers*.) We have provided ships, men, and provisions. Surely that takes care of everything.

COLUMBUS: There are certain terms necessary.

ISABELLA (*Displeased*): Terms? What do you mean? What are these terms?

COLUMBUS (*Grandly, as if long rehearsed*): That I, Chris-topher Columbus, be made Admiral of this fleet; that I be Viceroy and Governor General of all islands I dis-cover. . . .

FERDINAND (*Choking with anger*): Are you finished, im-pertinent villain?

COLUMBUS (*Calmly, ignoring the interruption*): And lastly, that to me and my heirs the title of Don be given . . . with the rank of Lord for succeeding genera-tions.

ISABELLA (*Putting her head in her hands*): Poor Colum-bus! Why have you suddenly become so demanding?

TALAVERA: You have overstepped this time.

ISABELLA (*Sadly*): Go, Columbus! You have lost your chance! Go! Get out of my sight!

COLUMBUS (*Dramatically*): Your Majesty, farewell! I thought for a time I had a true friend in you. (*Starts off*)

Perhaps some other monarch will put you to shame!

CHANCELLOR: Wait! (*To* KING *and* QUEEN) Do not be so hasty in dismissing him. We were ready to give this help to Columbus until he made his demands. They are not really so ridiculous nor excessive. Don't you see he will only get these rewards when and if he discovers new lands for Spain?

ISABELLA (*Still hurt*): But why must he be so unreasonable?

CHANCELLOR (*Pleading*): Surely Columbus is entitled to something if he succeeds. He is staking everything on the venture. Do not let him go to some other monarch for help. If you missed such an opportunity as this, you would reproach yourself forever.

ISABELLA: You are right, Chancellor. Go ahead with the document, Juan.

JUAN (*Aside*): It still seems ridiculous to me. (*Continues writing*)

COLUMBUS (*Returning excitedly*): You will never regret your decision, my Queen. (*He kneels before her.*)

JUAN: The contract is ready.

ISABELLA: That is well. Bring it to me. (JUAN *brings it to her. She reads it carefully.*) It seems to be all in good order; therefore, I, Queen Isabella of Spain, do hereby sign my name. (*Signs*) Ferdinand? (JUAN *takes it to* KING).

JUAN (*Indicating where to sign*): Here, Your Majesty. (KING *signs reluctantly*)

ISABELLA: Arise, Christopher Columbus, and accept this contract.

COLUMBUS: It is almost too much to believe, Your Majesty.

ISABELLA (*Gaily*): Now, Admiral Christopher Columbus, your part of the bargain lies on the horizon ahead of you.

COLUMBUS: I shall make arrangements to sail as early as possible. (*Kisses her robe*) Your Majesty! This is the greatest moment of my life. The moment I have lived for.

ISABELLA: Then arise . . . the best wishes of our court shall go with you to the end of your journey.

COLUMBUS (*Dramatically*): Everything I gain in wealth, fame and fortune, I do for the glory of Spain, the Church, and (*bowing deeply*) for your most gracious Majesties, Queen Isabella and King Ferdinand. (*Exits grandly. Curtain.*)

THE END

The Ghost from Genoa

by Earl J. Dias

Characters*

MRS. HARRIS
SALLY HARRIS
MR. HARRIS
BOB HARRIS
SAM BENSON
CHRISTOPHER COLUMBUS
PEDRO MENDOZA, *former first mate on the "Nina"*
QUEEN ISABELLA

SCENE 1

TIME: *The present. Late afternoon, October 11.*
SETTING: *The Harris living room.*
AT RISE: MRS. HARRIS *is seated at left of table, glancing through a magazine.* SALLY HARRIS *lies on sofa.*

MRS. HARRIS (*Looking at magazine and shaking her head*):
I just can't see any sense to some of these new fall
fashions. Why, some of these women's suits look like
boxes. (*Rises and goes to sofa to show* SALLY *a magazine
illustration*) Look at this, Sally.

*NOTE: For reasons obvious in the script, the roles of Columbus, Mendoza,
and Queen Isabella should be played respectively by the same performers
who play Bob, Sam, and Mrs. Harris.

25

SALLY (*Raising herself on her elbow*): Why, Mother, I think it's just dreamy.

MRS. HARRIS: Dreamy! Nightmarish would be more like it!

SALLY (*Relaxing once more*): After all, some of the styles you wore when you were a girl were pretty horrible, too.

MRS. HARRIS (*Returning to chair*): Maybe, but at least they were feminine. (*Looking at watch*) Hm-m. Four o'clock. Bob should be home from school by now.

SALLY: Don't forget he has football practice.

MRS. HARRIS: That's right, he does. Let's just hope he comes home whole then. Every year it's either a sprained ankle or a puffed eye or a bruised leg.

SALLY: You know what the song says. You've got to be a football hero to get along with the beautiful girls.

MRS. HARRIS: Don't you believe it. Your father was a football hero of sorts, and all he got from it was a trick knee that plagues him whenever the weather is damp.

SALLY: But he also got himself a beautiful girl, didn't he?

MRS. HARRIS: Now, spare my blushes!

SALLY: It's so wonderful just to lie back here and relax with the thought that there's no school tomorrow because it's Columbus Day. Thank heaven for Christopher! (MR. HARRIS *enters quickly at left. He is carrying a brief-case.*)

MR. HARRIS: Boo!

MRS. HARRIS: Heavens! You startled me!

SALLY: Hi, Dad! We didn't hear you come in!

MR. HARRIS: It's the Indian in me. Silent Sam Harris, they call me—the most successful stalker on the frontier since Daniel Boone. (*He places briefcase on table*)

MRS. HARRIS (*Pointing toward briefcase*): That certainly looks as though it's bulging at the seams. Do you intend to spend your holiday working? (MR. HARRIS *goes to chair and sits.*)

Mr. Harris: The law can't stop—even for Christopher Columbus. I have a couple of important cases coming up in court day after tomorrow. After all, my clients pay me to work. Bob home yet?

Mrs. Harris: He's at football practice.

Mr. Harris: Still, the coach might let the boys off a bit early, since tomorrow's a holiday. (*The bang of a door and the sound of voices are heard offstage.*)

Sally: That sounds like Bob now. He always just about takes the door off its hinges when he comes in.

Mr. Harris: The trouble with these football players is that they just don't know their own strength. (Bob Harris *enters at left followed by* Sam Benson. Bob *is limping and looks somewhat unhappy.*)

Bob: Hi, folks. (*He goes to sofa.*) Get your feet out of the way, will you, Sally? I'm tired.

Sally: I knew this was too good to last. (*She shifts her feet, leaving room for* Bob *to sit down*) How are you, Sam?

Sam: Fine, Sally. It's Bob who's under the weather.

Mrs. Harris: Did I see you limping just now, Bob?

Bob: Yes. Joe Baron stepped on my foot with his cleats in a scrimmage.

Sam: I'll say he did.

Sally: Joe Baron! That must be like being trampled on by a dinosaur.

Bob: It is. Joe weighs two hundred pounds.

Sam: It was all a mistake, anyway.

Bob: That's a laugh.

Mr. Harris: This conversation is becoming very obscure. Why don't you fellows let us in on the secret?

Sam: Bob was playing right end in scrimmage. He got his signals mixed, pulled out of the line, grabbed the ball from Danny Felder, the quarterback, and ran with it.

BOB: I made eleven yards, too, before I collided with that steamroller, Joe Baron.

SAM: It was still a mistake. You shouldn't have been carrying the ball.

MRS. HARRIS: This is all Greek to me, but I do know that if Bob made eleven yards, that was a pretty good gain, wasn't it?

BOB: You bet it was. The second team wasn't expecting anything like that at all.

SAM (*Laughing*): Neither was Coach Carson. He called Bob a lunkhead.

MRS. HARRIS: He did? Well, I don't think he has any right to call my son such an unflattering name.

MR. HARRIS: Now, Mother, keep your temper. Lunkhead is mild compared to what my coach used to call me years ago.

SAM: Anyway, Bob made a mistake. We don't have any play in which an end pulls out of the line to carry the ball.

MRS. HARRIS: Well, if such a mistake gains eleven yards, maybe you *should* have such a play.

BOB: That's what I told all the fellows, and that's what I told Coach Carson. They all just laughed at me. They probably think I was just trying to cover up my mistake. But I really wasn't. A play like that would have the element of surprise in it.

SAM: That's a good story, Bob. You stick to it.

BOB (*Wearily*): Sam, why don't you just go home now.

MR. HARRIS: That's not very hospitable, Bob.

SAM: Oh, that's all right, Mr. Harris. Bob's pride has been hurt as well as his foot. Anyway, I just walked home with him to make sure he got here with that wobbly foot.

BOB: My foot will be all right.

MRS. HARRIS: It was very nice of you, Sam, to take all that trouble.

SAM: No trouble at all. Glad to do it. Well, I'll be getting along. Hope your foot's better tomorrow, Bob.

BOB: Thanks, Sam. (SAM *goes to door left.*)

SAM: See you all later. (SAM *exits.*)

BOB: You see how it is. I took quite a riding out on the field today. But I still think that that play, even though I discovered it by accident, would be a good one.

MRS. HARRIS: Of course it would, dear.

MR. HARRIS: And Mother knows best—particularly about football matters. Anyway, cheer up, Bob. There's no school tomorrow.

BOB: That's a laugh.

MR. HARRIS: What do you mean?

BOB: To my English teacher, Miss Wainwright, there is no such animal as a holiday. I've got to write a five-hundred-word composition. And guess what the dizzy subject is. (*Disgustedly*) "What Christopher Columbus Means to Me." Now I ask you, isn't that a beauty?

MR. HARRIS: It's timely, to say the least.

SALLY: Anyway, it's a change from stuff like "How I Spent My Summer Vacation" or "My Greatest Ambition in Life."

BOB: I can tell you one thing. My greatest ambition in life is not to write a composition about Christopher Columbus.

MRS. HARRIS: This is all beyond me. What in the world do you have against Columbus? You sound as if he were a contagious disease.

BOB: I'm just sick to death of hearing about Columbus every year since I was in kindergarten. It's the same old stuff all the time. The same old poem (*Mockingly*): "Sail on," he said. And the same old applesauce about the *Nina*, the *Pinta*, and the *Santa Maria*. And Queen Isabella. And all for a guy who made a mistake, thinking he had reached India when all the time he was in the West Indies.

MR. HARRIS: You certainly seem bitter about the whole thing. After all, good old Christopher made a natural mistake. Seems to me you made a mistake yourself this afternoon at practice, didn't you, Bob?

BOB: My biggest mistake was getting Miss Wainwright for an English teacher.

SALLY: She's a very nice woman.

BOB: Hm-m.

MRS. HARRIS: Of course, she is. I know Sarah Wainwright well. She's a very brilliant girl. And anything she asks you to do, Bob, you can be sure is for your own good.

BOB: I wouldn't exactly call her a girl.

MR. HARRIS: Now let's not get sarcastic.

BOB: I'm sorry.

MR. HARRIS: Don't forget, it always is best to practice a bit of chivalry.

SALLY: And Bob is such a Sir Galahad anyway.

MR. HARRIS: To get to a less dangerous subject, what's for dinner?

MRS. HARRIS: Lamb chops.

MR. HARRIS (*Standing up*): Good. Well, I think I'll go upstairs and freshen up a bit. (*Takes briefcase from table*) I can also do a little work before dinner.

MRS. HARRIS: The kitchen calls. Want to help, Sally?

SALLY (*Stretching*): I'll be in in a minute, Mother.

MRS. HARRIS: And don't look so gloomy, Bob. I think your idea about your surprise football play is excellent.

BOB: Thanks, Mother. (MR. *and* MRS. HARRIS *exit left.* BOB *turns to* SALLY) You're good in English. Can you tell me how I can possibly say anything new about Columbus?

SALLY (*Yawning*): It's not my assignment. It's all yours.

BOB: You're a big help.

SALLY: It's my Girl Scout training that does it.

BOB: Christopher Columbus! Everything's been said that ever needs to be said about him and his gallant crew. (*Sarcastically*) They were probably all jailbirds, anyway.

SALLY: That's a nice thing to say about a national hero. Your experience at football practice this afternoon seems to have left you very bitter. (*Sighing*) Well, I'll leave you to your beautiful thoughts, and your wonderfully cheerful mood. (*She rises.*) Why don't you write a long poem about Columbus? Fifty or sixty stanzas would be about right—in nice, swingy rhythm to imitate the motion of the sea. (*Laughing*) Maybe Miss Wainwright will get seasick when she reads it. That ought to make you happy.

BOB (*Hollowly*): Ha! Ha! Very funny. You ought to be on television.

SALLY (*Going toward door left*): See you later. (*Dramatically*) "Sail on—and on—and on!" (*She exits.*)

BOB: Phooey! (*He stretches out on the sofa, his hands behind his head.*) What a day! (BOB *closes his eyes, and falls asleep. The lights dim, and the curtains close.*)

*   *   *

SCENE 2

TIME: *Later the same afternoon.*

SETTING: *Same as Scene 1.*

AT RISE: BOB *is sleeping on the sofa. The lights are dim.* COLUMBUS *and* MENDOZA *enter left and watch* BOB. *(Since* BOB *himself will appear as* COLUMBUS *in the dream sequence to follow, the director should have another boy of about the same height and build as* BOB *in* BOB's *place on the sofa. If that is not feasible, a dummy figure can be arranged, covered perhaps by an afghan. If this is done,* BOB *should have covered himself with the afghan at the close of Scene 1. It should be obvious to the audience that* COLUMBUS *is* BOB, MENDOZA *is* SAM BENSON, *and* QUEEN ISABELLA *is* MRS. HARRIS.)

MENDOZA: This is the fellow who says such nasty things about you, Admiral. (*Hand on dagger*) You want me to take care of him?

COLUMBUS (*Placing a deterring hand on* MENDOZA's *shoulder*): Now, Mendoza, that's not what we're here for. Control yourself.

MENDOZA (*Wistfully*): I could do it in just a few seconds. A good, quiet job.

COLUMBUS (*Sharply*): Mendoza! I said no!

MENDOZA: All right, Admiral.

COLUMBUS: He's a pleasant-looking boy.

MENDOZA: But he has the tongue of a snake.

COLUMBUS: Don't be harsh, Mendoza. Youth is always an impulsive time.

MENDOZA: He's impulsive all right. I don't like to be called a jailbird, and I know you don't either, Admiral.

COLUMBUS: Steady now, Mendoza. Pull in your sails and drift quietly. In this modern world, everybody, like Bob here, seems to be bored. It seems to be the fashion to scoff at everything—including me.

MENDOZA: You remember his words? He said you were a "guy who made a mistake, thinking he had reached India when all the time he was in the West Indies."

COLUMBUS: Yes, I remember.

MENDOZA: And he himself made a big mistake this afternoon out on the football field. The coach gave him a hard time, and his fellow players laughed at him.

COLUMBUS *(Sadly)*: He has my sympathy. I know what it is to be laughed at.

MENDOZA: So you do, Admiral. But this young jackanapes does not seem to want to forgive mistakes in others.

COLUMBUS: Oh, well. Perhaps I was mistaken, but what does it matter in the long run? I opened the way to a new continent, did I not?

MENDOZA: Indeed, you did.

COLUMBUS: And this boy has no idea of how it feels to sail off into the unknown—to go on for days and days with only faith to be your guide and support. To him, it may sound like "old stuff," but to us, it was new and frightening.

MENDOZA: You bet it was. We never knew when we might come upon a sea monster, or sail right off the top of the world and go down, down, down into nothingness. Even I, Pedro Mendoza, a man known throughout Italy and Spain for his courage, was sometimes a bit frightened.

COLUMBUS *(Chuckling)*: I remember one day how you pleaded with me to turn back.

MENDOZA *(Sheepishly)*: Now, Admiral, you promised you'd never mention that again.

COLUMBUS: I'm sorry, Mendoza.

MENDOZA: And, anyway, that was the only time I lost faith in you, Admiral. Most of the others were far worse. You remember when the compass needle varied so much, the crew was ready to mutiny. I remember a big hulk of a man, Carlos Sequeira—as big as an ox but with the heart of a chicken—who whimpered with fear.

COLUMBUS: Those were difficult times, Mendoza. And the men made me promise that if we did not sight land in three days, we would turn back.

MENDOZA: And then on that glorious third day, we sighted San Salvador. And yet this young fellow here, from the peak of his sixteen years, can scoff at our remarkable feat.

COLUMBUS: Avast now. Mind your temper.

MENDOZA: Well, the Queen didn't like what he said, either.

COLUMBUS: Ah, the good Queen Isabella. Is she nearby, Mendoza?

MENDOZA: She said she might drop in later.

COLUMBUS: Splendid. (*The lights dim for an instant. When they brighten,* QUEEN ISABELLA, *dressed in an elaborate gown and wearing a crown, has entered. She is obviously* MRS. HARRIS, BOB'S *mother.* COLUMBUS *and* MENDOZA *bow low.*)

COLUMBUS: Your Majesty.

MENDOZA: Your Majesty.

ISABELLA: Is this the boy?

MENDOZA: He's the one, Your Majesty.

ISABELLA: He's a nice-looking young fellow.

MENDOZA: Looks can be deceiving, Your Majesty. He wags his tongue too freely.

ISABELLA: Of course, I don't approve of the unflattering things he has been saying about you, Admiral—but the boy does not look as though he really has much harm in him. After all, he has had a trying day, what with his mistake on the football field and the ridicule he has received for it.

COLUMBUS: Does it not strike you as strange, Your Majesty, that his mistake and what he calls mine actually had beneficial results?

ISABELLA: What do you mean?

COLUMBUS: My mistake discovered a new world; his— now what was the expression he used—ah, yes, gained eleven yards.

ISABELLA: That is true, Admiral. As a result, I feel that when he thinks over what he has said, he will see the light. (*Looking closely at* Bob) He is a pleasant and intelligent-looking boy. All he needs to be made to realize is that if yours was a mistake, it was a natural one, considering the limited geographical knowledge of the time. It was a glorious mistake, in other words— and one that has proved to be most profitable for the world at large.

COLUMBUS: Thank you, Your Majesty.

MENDOZA: That boy will never see the light. He's as stubborn as a stable full of mules.

ISABELLA: Don't be harsh, Mendoza. (MENDOZA *goes to easy chair and sits down.*)

MENDOZA: Ah, what comfort. We had nothing like this aboard the *Nina.* That young scamp lives in the lap of luxury, but I'll wager he doesn't appreciate it.

COLUMBUS: After all, he is young, Mendoza. And the young seldom have an appreciation of the blessings that surround them.

ISABELLA: And, what is more, the young do not give credit enough to the trailblazers that have gone before them.

MENDOZA: Right!

ISABELLA: But I have high hopes for this boy. Well, I must be on my way. There is still another young person on my list whom I must visit. Are you coming, Admiral? And you, Mendoza?

COLUMBUS: We shall follow soon, Your Majesty.

MENDOZA: After I rest my tired feet a bit longer, Your Majesty. I am not so young as I once was.

ISABELLA: Then I shall see you both later. Goodbye.

COLUMBUS (*Bowing*): Goodbye, Your Majesty.

MENDOZA (*Rising and bowing*): Goodbye, Your Majesty. (QUEEN ISABELLA *exits left.* MENDOZA *sits down again with a sigh.*) A fine woman.

COLUMBUS: And a true queen. She seems to like the boy.

MENDOZA: Even queens suffer from the maternal instinct.

COLUMBUS: Don't be bitter, Mendoza. All this boy needs to know is this: that in every age, someone has to have the will and the courage to dare, to venture into the unknown. In this boy's own century, for example, there have been the Wright brothers. People laughed at them. "How can men fly?" they sneered. But the Wright brothers dared to take the risk.

MENDOZA: You're right, Admiral. And look at all these new developments—television and home permanents and high-fidelity phonographs. (*Sighing*) Sometimes I think I was born too soon. I'd have looked good on the television screen.

COLUMBUS: Be modest now, Mendoza.

MENDOZA: The ladies of Genoa and in my own city of Madrid always told me I was a fine figure of a man.

COLUMBUS: Before we go, I hope we can leave with this boy the lesson we came to bring. Everything that seems old and boring was once fresh and new, and if one uses his imagination, it is still fresh and new. All one has to do is to brush off the dust.

MENDOZA: Let's hope, too, he sees that a mistake, like his own on the football field, can sometimes lead to good results.

COLUMBUS: Amen to that. And now, are you ready, Mendoza?

MENDOZA (*Sighing*): I suppose so, Admiral. How I wish I could take this chair with me!

COLUMBUS (*Laughing*): The disappearance of a chair might cause considerable confusion, Mendoza.

MENDOZA (*Standing up*): You're right as usual, Admiral.

COLUMBUS (*Looking down at* BOB *once more*): Goodbye, my boy. We take our leave. Come, Mendoza. (*They exit left as the lights dim and the curtains close.*)

CURTAIN

*   *   *

Scene 3

Time: *Later.*
Setting: *Same as Scene 2.*
At Rise: Bob *is lying on sofa. He awakens and gradually looks about.*

Bob: Gone! (*He looks thoughtful for a moment, then says slowly*) "The will and the courage to dare." That's it. (Sally *enters left*)
Sally: Talking to yourself, hey. Well, Shakespeare, you look as if you've been having a snooze.
Bob: I guess I have.
Sally: That Columbus composition was just too much, I guess, for what we laughingly refer to as your brain.
Bob: Say, Sally, the library's open tonight, isn't it?
Sally: Yes, until nine, I think.
Bob: Good. I'm going down there to get some really solid material for my theme. What's the name of the book about Columbus, anyway? Some Harvard professor wrote it.
Sally: You're probably thinking of "Admiral of the Ocean Sea." Samuel Eliot Morison wrote it.
Bob: That's the one. I hope it's in.
Sally: Golly, you've certainly become industrious all of a sudden. That nap did wonders for you.
Bob: You don't know the half of it. (Mr. Harris *enters left.*)
Mr. Harris: Hi, folks. Sally, how's dinner coming?
Sally: It ought to be ready in a minute, Dad.
Mr. Harris: Fine. I can do justice to it.
Bob (*Rising from sofa*): Me too. (Mrs. Harris *enters left.*)
Mrs. Harris: Dinner is ready.
Bob (*Bowing*): Your Majesty.
Mrs. Harris: What?

BOB: Oh, nothing. Nothing at all.

MRS. HARRIS: Hunger seems to be going to your brain.

BOB: You know what? I've been thinking about football practice this afternoon. I still think I was right about that play. I made a mistake, I know, but it's a mistake that can be made to pay off. After all, it would have the element of the unexpected and unusual in it.

MRS. HARRIS: That's just what I said.

BOB: I know you did, and I appreciate it. I think the coach ought to use it. After all, "in every age, someone has to have the will and the courage to dare, to venture into the unknown."

MR. HARRIS: That sounds like a quotation.

BOB: It is.

MR. HARRIS: I don't recognize the source, though.

BOB: And if I told you, you wouldn't believe it. You know what? I'm going to get hold of Mendoza tonight—

MRS. HARRIS: Mendoza?

BOB: I mean Sam Benson. And I'm going to persuade him I'm right about that play. Tomorrow I'll celebrate Columbus Day by going over to the coach's house, and I'll try to persuade him, too. "The will and the courage to dare"—that's what the team needs.

MRS. HARRIS: Good for you! (MRS. HARRIS *exits left, looking somewhat bewildered.*)

BOB: I'm glad we're eating early. That will give me plenty of time in the library and then time enough to see Mendoza—I mean Sam Benson. By golly, I'm going to write a composition that will make Miss Wainwright sit up and take notice. I have a new slant on Columbus. (*Goes to left.*) Lamb chops, here I come! (BOB *exits.*)

MR. HARRIS (*Scratching his head*): Is that my son who just said that?

SALLY: I was about to ask the same question.

MR. HARRIS: Did your brother say that Joe Baron stepped

on his foot this afternoon at football practice—or on his head?

SALLY: I'm beginning to wonder about that, too.

MR. HARRIS: Well, life in this household offers its share of mysteries. Let's eat.

SALLY: An excellent idea, Dad.

MR. HARRIS: And let's not question too closely the unexpected blessings that come our way. (SALLY *and* MR. HARRIS *exit left, laughing, as the curtain closes.*)

THE END

Test for a Witch

by Esther MacLellan and Catherine V. Schroll

Characters

GRIZZY ⎫
TIZZY ⎬ *two witches*

LIZZY, *their sister, a witchette*

POLLY

PETER

SNAP ⎫
SLY ⎬ *members of the Witches'*
STUMBLE ⎭ *Council*

GREY ⎫
GLUM ⎬ *visiting Goblins*
GLOOMY ⎭

OTHER WITCHES AND GOBLINS

TIME: *Halloween.*

SETTING: *A small park with a picnic table and benches. A stone fireplace is at the rear of the stage.*

AT RISE: *The park is deserted.* GRIZZY *bustles on, waving a large book which she places on the table.*

GRIZZY: Come, Tizzy, come, Lizzy! I've found the place, the very place we've been looking for. (TIZZY *enters, carrying a book, dishes, spoons, and cups.* LIZZY *follows, with a large kettle and a bottle.*)

TIZZY: Excellent! Excellent! A table, chairs and a fireplace.

GRIZZY: Near a village, too. Now, Lizzy, you ought to do very well here. Remember, this is your big chance. You've been a witchette long enough. If you pass your test today, you'll be a witch, a real witch, just like us. (*Shakes head*) But if you fail . . .

TIZZY: You'll have to wait till next Halloween.

GRIZZY: Tests are given only once a year.

TIZZY: And you certainly don't want to be a witchette forever! You've been taking the test for the last fifty years.

LIZZY (*Miserably*): I know! I know!

GRIZZY: It's giving our family a bad reputation. Fail once, fail twice, fail twenty times—that's not bad. But fifty!

LIZZY (*Wailing*): It's awful! It's awful!

TIZZY: It certainly is. You must keep your mind on what you're doing, Lizzy. Hand and head, that's the test. To be a witch you must prove that you have a clever hand and a clever head.

GRIZZY: Make a good dinner. That will show your clever hand.

LIZZY: Oh, I will, I will. Here's my kettle. I'll get the fire started—right away, right away. (*She rushes around the stage waving her kettle.*)

TIZZY: Then you must show you have a clever head, Lizzy. But don't try anything fancy. Work an easy spell. (*Paces up and down*) Change a girl into a cricket. That's the first lesson in *The Witch's Primer*. Anybody can do that.

LIZZY: Oh, yes! Oh, yes! I'll pass the test this time. Cook a good cricket and change a girl into a dinner. That's what I'll do.

TIZZY: No! No! Cook the *dinner*.

GRIZZY: Change the *girl*.

LIZZY: Oh, yes! Oh, yes! I'll remember.

TIZZY: We have to leave you now, Lizzy. There's lots to be done before dinner.

GRIZZY (*Shaking her finger*): But we'll be back—with all the witches in the council.

TIZZY: And the visiting goblins, too.

GRIZZY: Be sure to have a good dinner, Lizzy. No more of that Chicken a la Witch you had last Halloween.

TIZZY: Imagine anyone being so stupid as to cook a chicken with all the feathers on!

LIZZY: The cook book didn't say . . .

TIZZY: Great pumpkins, Lizzy! You're supposed to have some sense. Don't fail again or you'll be a witchette for another year.

LIZZY: Oh, I'll pass. I'll pass.

GRIZZY: See that you do. Come, Tizzy, we must go. (*Exit* GRIZZY *and* TIZZY)

LIZZY (*Picking up a book from table*): Let's see, now. Here's the Witch's Cook Book. (*Turns pages hurriedly*) Goblin Goulash? That sounds good, and I've never tried it. (*Reads*) "Remove the bones from two pounds of mosquitoes." (*Closes book*) First, I'd better catch the mosquitoes. No, maybe I should read over the rules for turning girls into crickets. I may see a girl before I catch the mosquitoes. (*Puts one book down and picks up the other. Turns pages. Reads.*) "To turn a girl into a cricket: hop on the left foot three times, hop on the right foot four times . . ." That's easy enough. What next? "Shake head from left to . . ." (*Enter* POLLY, *carrying a large basket.*)

POLLY: How heavy this basket is! I'll sit and rest for a few minutes.

LIZZY (*Aside*): A girl! So early, too. I can get the Head part of the test finished early, and have all the rest of the time to get dinner. (*Walking back and forth across the stage*) Now, what was I supposed to do first? Oh, I remember. Remove the bones! (*To* POLLY) Hello, Girl.

POLLY: Hello, Madam.

LIZZY: Stand up, Girl, stand up!

POLLY: Why?

LIZZY: Don't argue, Girl. Stand up. It will make everything much easier.

POLLY: Will it? All right. (*She stands.*)

LIZZY (*Tugging at her shoulders*): My, my, they're in tight. What's your name, Girl?

POLLY: Polly.

LIZZY: What's the matter with your bones, Polly?

POLLY: They're fine, thank you.

LIZZY: Oh, no, they're not. They should come out. See, the book says so. (*Shakes book under* POLLY's *nose*)

POLLY (*Reading*): "Goblin Goulash: Remove the bones from two pounds of mosquitoes."

LIZZY: Mosquitoes! Oh, *mosquitoes.* I must be a little mixed up.

POLLY: I should say so. There's quite a difference between a girl and a mosquito.

LIZZY: Indeed?

POLLY: Indeed. And why do you want to make Goblin Goulash? It sounds terrible.

LIZZY: Does it? I thought it might be good.

POLLY (*Reading*): "Remove the bones from two pounds of mosquitoes, add three large beetles and seven sour pickles." Ugh! Nobody could eat that!

LIZZY (*Wringing hands*): What shall I do? What shall I do? (*Pacing back and forth*) I must cook something. All the witches' council and the visiting goblins will be expecting dinner and I'll have nothing but an empty kettle. (*Sobbing*) I'll fail again.

POLLY: Fail?

LIZZY: I'm only a witchette. I can't be a witch till I do something with my *hands.* I must have a good dinner.

POLLY (*Crossing to her basket*): You poor thing! I'll help. I've just been to the store. (*Hands* LIZZY *a package*)

Here's a piece of beef. Put that in your kettle and cover it with water.

LIZZY: Oh, yes. Oh, yes. (*Runs to fireplace*)

POLLY (*Looking after her*): Take off the paper. You don't cook paper.

LIZZY: Do you eat it raw?

POLLY: You don't eat paper cooked *or* raw. Now you need vegetables.

LIZZY: Do I? (*She gets a cup of water from faucet, adds it to kettle.*)

POLLY: Of course. Vegetables contain vitamins. No one can do without vitamins. I'll run home and get you some vegetables from my garden. Keep the kettle simmering. I'll be right back. (*Exits right*)

LIZZY (*Running after her*): Don't forget, don't forget. (*Returning to center of stage*) Well, that takes care of dinner, I suppose. But vegetables? Will witches like vegetables? Oh, dear! Oh, dear! They'll have to like vegetables. (*Picks up book from table*) Now, I'll have to find a new spell. I can't change Polly into a cricket when she's been so nice. (*Opens book*) "Lesson Two: How to turn a boy into a grasshopper—Face the North and bow three times, face the South and bow four times." (*Closes book*) Dear, dear! What if another girl comes? Can I turn a girl into a grasshopper? What does the book say? (*Opens book again and turns pages hurriedly. Enter* PETER *carrying a large paper bag.*)

LIZZY (*Closing book*): Thank goodness! I don't need to find out. Here's a boy. Hello, Boy.

PETER: Hello.

LIZZY: What's your name, Boy? I may have to know it. I haven't read very far in the book.

PETER: I'm Pete.

LIZZY: Stand still, Pete. This isn't easy. "Face the North

and bow four times." (*She bows*) Four? Or was it three?
Open the book, Pete, and see what it says.

PETER (*Taking book*): Where?

LIZZY: Lesson Two. How to change a boy into a grasshopper.

PETER (*Turning pages*): Here it is. (*Reads*) "Face the
North and bow . . ." Say! Who's turning whom into a
grasshopper?

LIZZY: Why, I'm turning you.

PETER (*Shutting book*): No, thank you.

LIZZY: But you have to be a grasshopper. If I don't cast a
spell, I can't pass the Witch Test. And I've been trying
for fifty years.

PETER: Fifty years! That's a long time.

LIZZY: Yes, it is. So please help me. Be a grasshopper.

PETER: I don't want to be a grasshopper.

LIZZY: You might like it very much.

PETER: No! (*He pounds fist on table and knocks over
bottle.*)

LIZZY: Now see what you've done!

PETER: I'm awfully sorry. What have I done?

LIZZY (*Sobbing*): You've spilled the vinegar and I'm in
charge of dinner and now there's nothing to drink.
Nothing!

PETER: You weren't going to drink vinegar?

LIZZY: Certainly. What else is there?

PETER (*Opening his bag*): What else? Here's what—*milk!*

LIZZY (*Looking at it doubtfully*): But that's white.

PETER: It's good. And it's good *for* you. You don't know
what you've been missing.

LIZZY: Don't I? (POLLY *enters breathlessly.*)

POLLY: Now for the dinner! Look at the vegetables I
brought. (*Removes them from basket*) Potatoes, onions,
string beans, and carrots.

Lizzy (*Picking up carrots*): Carrots? They're pretty.

Peter: They're better than pretty. They're delicious!

Polly (*Glancing toward fireplace*): The meat is simmering. The vegetables are washed. All I have to do is cut them up and toss them into the kettle.

Peter: I'll help. (*They cross back and forth putting vegetables into kettle.*)

Polly: Dinner will be ready in a jiffy. Such a dinner! You'll pass your Witch Test easily.

Lizzy (*Clapping her hands*): Really?

Peter: Sure! And when your friends taste that delicious milk, they'll make you a Super Witch!

Lizzy (*Starting to sob*): No, they won't. The dinner is only one part. Witches have to pass a double test, Hand and Head. Now the Hand's all right, but what about the Head?

Polly: Head?

Peter: She means she has to do something brainy. That's why she wanted to change me into a grasshopper.

Polly: And me into a cricket. (*Shakes her head*) It doesn't seem clever to me.

Lizzy: But it is, it is. (*Doubtfully*) Isn't it?

Peter: Of course not. I'm doing all right as a boy. How do you know what kind of a grasshopper I'd make?

Polly: I'm sure I'd have been a miserable cricket.

Peter: I think that changing girls into crickets and boys into grasshoppers is just plain silly.

Lizzy: It is?

Peter: Definitely.

Lizzy: Oh, oh, what shall I do? I must pass. I can't go on being a witchette forever!

Polly: No, fifty years is long enough.

Peter: I have an idea. The dinner is Hand, but it's Head, too.

LIZZY: How's that?

PETER: Take milk, for instance. When you drink milk you're changing milk into rosy cheeks and energy. Pep, you know. I'll bet you've often been tired.

LIZZY: Oh, I have!

POLLY: No wonder, drinking vinegar! Wait till you've started on milk. What a difference you'll see! No more dragging your feet around; you'll be dancing like a fairy.

LIZZY: Really?

POLLY: I think so—not just at once, but soon.

PETER: Tell *that* to the witches and I'm sure you'll pass. After all, changing witches to fairies is smarter than changing girls into crickets.

POLLY: Or boys into grasshoppers.

LIZZY: I must remember.

POLLY: And now, goodbye and good luck.

PETER: Pass your test. You can be a witch as well as the others.

LIZZY: I'll try. I'll try hard.

POLLY: Don't worry, you'll pass easily—with vegetables and milk. (PETER *and* POLLY *exit left*)

LIZZY: I hope Peter and Polly are right. I hope milk and vegetables are as good as they say. (*She goes to fireplace and tastes stew.*) Why, this is delicious! (*She dances around stage.*) I've made something wonderful! (WITCHES *and* GOBLINS *enter, if possible, through the audience. They talk as they parade to the stage.*)

GOBLIN GREY: Another Halloween, and another of Lizzy's meals!

GOBLIN GLOOMY: I can't stand the thought.

SLY: Witches are supposed to feast on Halloween.

SNAP: And we haven't had a decent dinner for fifty years.

GOBLIN GLUM: Remember Lizzy's cobweb pie?

ALL: Ugh!

STUMBLE: I don't think that was as bad as her corn-cob croquettes.

GOBLIN GREY: Or her moss pudding with stewed leaves.

ALL: Ugh!

SLY (*Pausing and sniffing*): Wait a minute! I smell something good.

GOBLIN GLUM: Impossible. (*They march on stage.*)

SLY: Something *does* smell good.

STUMBLE: Delicious.

GRIZZY: I told you that tonight Lizzy was going to pass the test.

SNAP: Bring on the dinner!

GOBLIN GREY: Quick! Quick! Quick! (GRIZZY, TIZZY, *and* LIZZY *serve and pass dishes and spoons to* WITCHES *and* GOBLINS *who sit at picnic table.*)

STUMBLE: This is the best meal I ever ate.

GLUM: Delicious!

SNAP: Delightful!

STUMBLE: I say Lizzy's passed the Hand test. She's half a witch at least.

GLOOMY: Aye!

ALL: Aye! Lizzy's passed the Hand test.

SLY: And how about the Head test?

GRIZZY: Did you change a boy into a grasshopper, Lizzy?

TIZZY: Or a girl into a cricket? They are the easiest spells. Beginner stuff.

LIZZY: Well, no.

SLY: Somebody pass the vinegar. I'm thirsty.

GLOOMY: Pass the vinegar, pass the vinegar.

SNAP (*Holding up bottle*): Why, this is white . . . Lizzy made white vinegar.

LIZZY: Oh, no.

STUMBLE (*Pouring milk into cup and drinking*): It's good.

Much better than brown. (*Others pour milk into cups and drink.*)

GREY: Delicious! So sweet! Changing brown vinegar to white is a splendid piece of work!

LIZZY: But I didn't. You're drinking milk.

SNAP: I never knew Lizzy was so smart. Imagine her inventing a new drink—and a good one.

LIZZY: I didn't invent it. Cows did, I think.

SNAP: Well, you discovered it. I didn't know cows did anything but eat grass.

STUMBLE: Hurrah for Lizzy! She's cooked the best meal we ever ate.

GREY: Hurrah for Lizzy! And give me another glass of milk.

SLY (*Raising* LIZZY's *hand*): You've passed the test. Your days as a witchette are over.

LIZZY: Am I really a witch, a real witch?

ALL: You certainly are.

GLOOM: Now bring more stew, bring more vegetables and pass the milk. This is the best Halloween I've ever had.

LIZZY: Me, too. I'm a witch at last, thanks to Peter and Polly and vegetables and milk. (*Curtain*)

THE END

Nobody Believes in Witches!

by Martha Swintz Watkins

Characters

MATILDA WITCH
LILLY WITCH, *her sister*
PRINCE EDWARD
KING
QUEEN
PRIME MINISTER
COURTIERS

BEFORE RISE: MATILDA WITCH *enters and stands before curtain.*

MATILDA (*To audience*): How do you do? I am Matilda Witch, known to my friends as Mattie. Now, I can see many of you out there saying to yourselves, who believes in witches? There is nothing that makes my cauldron bubble or my steam rise more than folks who don't believe in witches. This is very discouraging to us witches. . . . Well, I'd like to tell you a little story about what happened one day when a certain young man came to our house. He didn't believe in witches either—at least not then. (*Starts to exit*) My sister, Lilly, and I were sitting at home catching up on the latest news of who was enchanting whom when we were interrupted. . . . (*Exits.*)

50

Scene 1

SETTING: *The witches' den, containing two chairs and a stove with a kettle on it.*

AT RISE: LILLY WITCH *and* MATILDA *are seated.* MATILDA *is reading a newspaper.*

LILLY: You mean Hettie Witch really turned herself into that?

MATILDA: She did, and it says here that anyone who can break the spell will be named "Witch of the Month" because Hettie's tired of being a doorbell.

LILLY: Well, that's what she gets for showing off. Remember the time you changed yourself into a rocket and were almost shot to the moon?

MATILDA: I'll always be sorry that I never made the trip. Those boys on the launching pad won't forget me for quite a while, I'll bet. Oh well, you can't do everything. (*Rises*) There's a man at the door.

LILLY: How do you know?

MATILDA: How do I know? I'm a witch! I'll bet my crow's feet to your bat wings that I'm right.

LILLY: It's a bet. (*There is a knock on door.*) Come in. (PRINCE EDWARD *enters.*)

EDWARD (*Gazing about in bewilderment*): How do you do?

MATILDA (*To* LILLY): Two bat wings, please.

EDWARD: I beg your pardon?

MATILDA: Two bat wings. I've just won two bat wings.

EDWARD: I'm afraid I haven't any with me.

LILLY: Oh, not your bat wings—*my* bat wings.

EDWARD (*Completely baffled*): Oh, yes, certainly, *your* bat wings. (*To* MATILDA) I'm sorry to intrude like this, but, you see, I'm lost. I was going through these woods when the road suddenly disappeared in front of me.

LILLY: Disappeared? Right in front of you?

EDWARD: Yes. It was most strange, as it really was quite a large road. (MATILDA *chuckles*.) It kept getting narrower and narrower until suddenly—nothing. I had an awful time finding this place.

MATILDA: Fancy that!

EDWARD: I might have suspected something rather frightening except, of course, I don't believe in that magic nonsense.

MATILDA: You don't.

EDWARD: Of course not.

MATILDA: Well, what if I told you that I was a witch and that I made that road disappear?

EDWARD: That's ridiculous. Besides, nobody believes in witches.

MATILDA: Say that again.

EDWARD: Nobody believes in witches!

MATILDA (*Furious*): Well, what do you think I am? And my sister, Lilly, there, she's a witch, too.

LILLY: Only part-time.

MATILDA: A part-time witch is just as real as a full-time one.

EDWARD: What you say may indeed be true, ladies, but if you will just direct me on my way again, I must be going.

MATILDA: Not so fast, dearie. You have to believe in me first. (*Goes about showing items in room*) Look, here's my steaming kettle, my book of magic spells. (*Looks under chair*) There's a black cat around here someplace. (*Picks up broom*) Now this is my pride and joy. The very latest model. Look at those clean lines, even has an automatic shift for high-speed flying. Why, when the seat belts come. . . . Want to try it, dearie?

EDWARD: No, thank you. Look, just put that thing away, and put the road back in the forest where it belongs, if you really have it here, and I'll take your word for the rest.

LILLY: Oh, please don't go. We never have visitors any more.

EDWARD: *That* I can understand.

MATILDA: Stay for supper. We're having our specialties, owl soup and black-cat stew.

EDWARD: That's impossible. I'm expected at the castle before dark.

LILLY: The castle. You live at the castle with the King and Queen?

EDWARD: Yes, I'm Prince Edward, and I really must be going.

LILLY: I've never met a prince before.

MATILDA: Princes are good for only one thing. (*To* LILLY) What shall we change him into?

LILLY: Why change him? He's very nice now.

MATILDA: But he's a prince, and we *must* change him into something. Then he'll be an enchanted prince, and there's nothing better than that. (*Walks around* EDWARD)

LILLY: I think he's quite enchanting the way he is now.

MATILDA: Come on, Lilly, think! He's tall enough to be a tree.

LILLY: Someone might cut him down.

MATILDA: Perhaps a bear—he looks strong enough.

LILLY: A hunter might find him.

MATILDA: Well, I absolutely refuse to do the frog thing. Everybody changes princes into frogs these days. Lack of imagination, if you ask me.

EDWARD (*Angrily*): If you have quite finished, I'll be going. Since you will not—or cannot—put the road back or give me directions, I will find my own way.

LILLY: Oh, please don't go.

EDWARD: I'm sorry, but your sister brings out the worst in me.

MATILDA: And I didn't even try!

LILLY: She's really a very good witch.

EDWARD: If you say so. Goodbye, Lilly. (*He exits.*)

LILLY: My, he was nice.

MATILDA: Nice! You call him nice? He didn't believe in us.

LILLY: I don't mind.

MATILDA: That's the trouble with you part-time witches. No pride in your work.

LILLY: That's not true. It's just that sometimes I like to treat people as people, not as possible tricks or spells.

MATILDA: That takes the fun out of it. (*Gets her book of magic spells*)

LILLY: What are you doing?

MATILDA: I'm going to teach Prince Edward a lesson. Get the kettle.

LILLY: Oh, no. Please don't do anything to him.

MATILDA: Now let's see—hm-m-m-m—let's have him wander around in the woods for a few days and . . .

LILLY: Mattie, don't do that.

MATILDA: Maybe I'll send him in circles. (*Spinning around dizzily*) Round and round he goes.

LILLY: Please, not that.

MATILDA: I know! I'll put him in the old cave. Then, when he's good and scared, I'll let him out again. That will teach him.

LILLY: Oh, Mattie, you won't hurt him?

MATILDA: I promise. Now, get my things. (*They bring the kettle downstage.* LILLY *gets the other things as* MATILDA *calls for them.*) Where's my magic stick? (LILLY *gets tree limb.*) There we are. Now, Lilly, water from the magic well. A little dried toad and rattlesnake. Just a touch of crow's feathers—not too much! And, finally, my own special touch. (*Reaches into her pocket*) A pinch of dried cat whiskers. Ah, that's just right. Now, stand back. Here we go!

LILLY: I wish you wouldn't.

MATILDA (*Stirring kettle*):
Bubble, water from the well,
Work into my magic spell,
Let the Prince now walk and wander,
Till he comes to dark cave yonder.
Let him enter, let him shout,
But he'll find he can't get out.
When he thinks his case is tragic,
I'll release him with my magic.
Then we'll see if he's so sure,
Witches really don't occur.
(*Laughs triumphantly*)

CURTAIN

*   *   *

SCENE 2

SETTING: *The castle dining room.*

AT RISE: *The table is set for dinner.* KING *and* QUEEN *are standing in front of the table.* COURTIERS *may be grouped around.*

QUEEN: I just know something terrible has happened to Edward. He should have been home by now.

KING: Now, dear, you mustn't worry. Edward can take care of himself.

QUEEN: But he had to cross that dark forest . . . and he promised to be here for dinner.

KING: I'm sure he is all right. (*With pride*) There's an excellent road through that forest. I had it built myself at considerable expense. Now, don't fret. (PRIME MINISTER *enters.*)

PRIME MINISTER: Your Majesty?

KING: Yes, yes. What is it? Has the Prince returned?

PRIME MINISTER: No, Sire. But there is someone—or something—at the door who wants to see you.

KING: What's so strange about that?

PRIME MINISTER: She says that she's a witch.

KING: A witch! That's impossible. Nobody believes in witches.

PRIME MINISTER: I thought so, too, but then, there's the broom . . .

KING: What broom?

PRIME MINISTER: Well, it's chromeplated with headlights. All at once she just appeared on that thing.

QUEEN: She was *on* it?

PRIME MINISTER: Yes, Your Majesty. You see, it has this very interesting saddle. She explained that her seat belts hadn't come yet. . . .

KING: Just a moment. You really saw all of this?

PRIME MINISTER: I agree it's hard to believe, Sire, but when she mentioned Prince Edward's being away, I was pretty well convinced.

QUEEN: The Prince! Show her in at once.

PRIME MINISTER: Yes, Your Majesty. (*Bows and exits*)

KING: This is outrageous. Chromeplated brooms with seat belts! (MATILDA *enters, wearing a bright-colored cloak.*)

MATILDA: How do you do? I'm Matilda Witch, known to my friends as Mattie.

QUEEN: Uh—how do you do?

KING: That's quite a Halloween costume, Mattie.

MATILDA: Matilda to you, sir! This is my calling cloak, used only for special occasions. Very potent, too. I wouldn't stand too close.

KING (*Stepping back*): Oh, yes, of course. Well, I'm sure we appreciate your dropping by, but at the moment we are quite busy with court affairs.

MATILDA: Aren't you forgetting something, dearie?

KING: I don't believe so.

MATILDA: You do have a son, Prince Edward?

QUEEN: Oh, yes, yes. Do you know him? Where is he?

MATILDA: You might say he came to call on me. He lost his way in the forest.

QUEEN: I knew it.

KING: That's impossible. There is an excellent highway. I had it built myself.

MATILDA: You built it—I took it!

KING: You can't do that.

MATILDA: I can and I did. It always just lay there. It never did anything, so I took it.

KING: You can't take a road and put it in your pocket.

MATILDA: You're right. I put it in the hall closet.

QUEEN: And my son, the Prince?

MATILDA: Oh, the closet is pretty crowded with all that road in there. Edward is in the cave.

QUEEN: Oh, dear. I think I'm going to faint. (*She starts to slump to the floor.*)

KING: Not yet, dear. We don't know where the cave is.

QUEEN (*Straightening up*): Oh, all right.

MATILDA: I've come to offer you my terms.

KING: Your terms? What nonsense is this?

MATILDA: Do you want the Prince back?

QUEEN: Yes, of course we do.

MATILDA (*Pointing to* KING): Then you had better make him listen to me.

QUEEN (*To* KING): Please, dear?

KING: I still say this is nonsense. (*Calling*) Prime Minister, come in here and take this down.

PRIME MINISTER (*Entering with pad and pencil*): Yes, Your Majesty. (*Preparing to take notes*) This should be good.

MATILDA: Things haven't been going too well with me

lately. People just don't believe the way they used to. (*To* QUEEN) Do they?

QUEEN: Oh, yes, yes.

MATILDA: Well, they don't. If you knew what I've been through in the last six months—anyway, I want a nice permanent job here at the castle.

KING: A permanent job—here?

MATILDA: That's right, dearie. I want to be the official, number one witch of the kingdom, by special appointment of His Majesty!

KING: I refuse!

MATILDA: I'd think it over if I were you. Why, there are lots of little things I can do around here. Who gets rid of your old spider webs, bats, and strange noises in the night?

QUEEN: Why, no one right now.

MATILDA: Then, there are the grocery bills.

QUEEN: The grocery bills?

MATILDA: It must take a lot of food to feed everybody around here. (*Points to* PRIME MINISTER) Especially him. Well, I can put a stop to all that. (*To* PRIME MINISTER) You there, sit down at the table.

PRIME MINISTER: Do I have to, Sire?

KING: Yes. I'd like to see if anything can slow down your appetite. (PRIME MINISTER *sits.*)

MATILDA: Now then, dearie, just help yourself. (*As* PRIME MINISTER *reaches for food,* MATILDA *says spell.*) Abracadabra, kazaam! (PRIME MINISTER *freezes in position.*) Now then—everybody sits down but nobody eats.

KING: That's really something.

MATILDA: Nothing to it when you know how.

KING: You know, it might be handy to have a witch around the place. You never can tell what might turn up.

MATILDA: Then it's arranged! I really don't need much space. Just a room to work in for my sister and me.

QUEEN: Your sister?

MATILDA: Yes, Lilly Witch. Only she's just a part-time witch. I've sent her to look after Edward.

QUEEN: Now I *am* going to faint.

KING: Not yet, dear. Just where is Edward, Matilda?

MATILDA: You can call me Mattie, dearie. He's safe and sound in the cave. Not a bit hurt, but I hope he's learned his lesson by now.

KING: His lesson?

MATILDA: He didn't believe in me. But I guess he will now. After all, I'm the official, number one witch of the kingdom. (*To* KING) Say, dearie, you couldn't have a little badge made up with that printed on it? Just in case somebody should ask?

KING: I'm sure it can be arranged.

MATILDA: Oh, hoppy toads and spider webs, I don't know when I've been so happy. Come on, I'll take you to the Prince. (*To* QUEEN) You'll have to ride sidesaddle, honey. I do wish those seat belts would come.

QUEEN: Don't you think we ought to do something about the Prime Minister?

MATILDA: Oh, yes. (*Snaps fingers*) There you go, dearie. (PRIME MINISTER *begins to move again.*) Enjoy your dinner. Come on, folks, all aboard! (*They start to exit as* EDWARD, *followed by* LILLY, *suddenly enters.*)

EDWARD: Just a minute, you!

KING *and* QUEEN: Edward!

EDWARD: Yes, Mother.

MATILDA: Great horned owls, the spell came undone!

EDWARD: Nothing came undone, Matilda. I was released.

MATILDA: Well, that's something. My professional standing, you know. Only, how did . . . Lilly! What have you done?

LILLY: Now, Mattie, don't be cross.

MATILDA: Don't be cross! Do you know what's happened?

I've just gotten us both good steady jobs here at the castle and now you've ruined everything.

EDWARD: Jobs at the castle? Father, have you agreed to anything?

KING (*Hesitating*): Well, I did rather promise Mattie—a little something.

MATILDA: He certainly did. Number one witch, that's what he said, and it still holds, doesn't it, Sire?

KING: Well, now that Edward is home safely . . .

QUEEN: How did you get home, dear?

EDWARD: Lilly came and let me out of the cave. (*Brings* LILLY *forward*) Then she waved her cloak three times and here we are. Just like that.

MATILDA: Just like that! (*To* LILLY) Sometimes I think you don't deserve to be a witch, Lilly. You ought to turn in your spell book and cloak. (MATILDA *takes cloak from* LILLY, *revealing for the first time that* LILLY *is very young and pretty.* KING, QUEEN, *and* EDWARD *all speak at once.*)

KING: My goodness!

QUEEN: Gracious me!

EDWARD (*Delighted*): She's lovely!

MATILDA: Now I've really done it!

EDWARD: You certainly have, Matilda, only why did it take so long! Lilly, you are the loveliest girl I've ever seen.

LILLY: Oh, Prince Edward, you are too kind.

KING: Yes, yes, my dear, you are truly a lovely girl.

MATILDA: And she's *my* sister!

KING: Now there's real magic for you.

EDWARD: Father, perhaps we ought to reconsider about having Lilly and Matilda here.

MATILDA: You mean the number one witch business might still be available?

EDWARD: I think it is an excellent idea.

MATILDA *and* KING: You do?

EDWARD: I certainly do. In fact, I think Lilly and Matilda ought to move in right now. Come, Lilly, I'll show you around the castle. I want you to feel at home here—very much at home. (*They exit.*)

QUEEN: Oh, isn't that romantic! I think I'll faint. (*Pause*) No, there isn't time. I'd better arrange for your rooms, Matilda—that is if you want to stay.

MATILDA: Oh, yes, we'll stay. (QUEEN *exits.*)

KING: Now, Matilda, about that road through the forest. It is really a very good road, and I want it put back.

MATILDA: I'll put it back very first thing, Your Majesty. You can count on me. Yes, sir. And you won't forget about my badge?

KING: I promise you shall have it. (*Glances around to see if anyone is listening*) Say, Mattie, the Prime Minister tells me you have a very unusual broom parked outside.

MATILDA: Absolutely the latest thing. Come on, dearie, I'll take you for a spin. (PRIME MINISTER *looks alarmed.* MATILDA *speaks as she and* KING *exit*) Let me tell you how I was nearly shot to the moon. . . .

PRIME MINISTER (*Starting to follow after* KING): Oh, Your Majesty, do you really think you ought to? (*Stopping and shrugging shoulders*) It's too late now. (*Shaking his head*) I should have stopped him. (*Running to window*) She's getting on the broom! *He's* getting on! (*Looking up, then turning front*) It flies! The thing really flies! (*Curtain*)

THE END

The Wonderful Witchware Store

by Elinor R. Alderman

Characters

MR. GOBLIN, *owner of the Witchware Store*
MRS. GOBLIN, *his wife*
GRACE GRUESOME, *a haughty witch*
GERTRUDE GRUESOME, *her timid sister*
A GLOOMY GHOST
WITCHES

TIME: *Early Halloween night.*
SETTING: *The Witchware Store.*
AT RISE: MR. *and* MRS. GOBLIN *are straightening up the counter of their store.*

MRS. GOBLIN: What time is it now?
MR. GOBLIN (*Looking at his watch*): It's just half past five. In another hour we will have to close the shop for this season. All the witches will be getting ready to fly by then.
MRS. GOBLIN: I just can't understand it. (*Looking at the row of brooms*) Those models are so pretty and yet we haven't been able to sell a single one.
MR. GOBLIN (*Pointing to counter*): And these bandages —even on special sale the witches won't buy them. You know, I think they are insulted at the idea that they

might *need* bandages. And yet everyone knows that once in a while even the best witch drivers fall off their brooms. (*Shakes head, puzzled*)

MRS. GOBLIN: I know—and with all the new hazards these days, too. So many houses with television antennas!

MR. GOBLIN (*Goes over to brooms*): I didn't want to worry you, but I might as well tell you now that if we don't sell some of these things soon, we'll have to go out of the Witchware business.

MRS. GOBLIN: Oh, no! Not after a hundred and fifty years! Surely it can't be that bad!

MR. GOBLIN (*Nodding*): I'm afraid so, my dear. That slick ghost salesman from the city persuaded me to put all of our money into a new line of brooms. He convinced me that ours were out of style.

MRS. GOBLIN: Well, these *are* pretty, and they say this two-tone effect is very popular with People. But it doesn't seem to go over at *all* with witches.

MR. GOBLIN (*Shaking his head*): No, I don't think it's that so much as the new Power Glide feature. These can fly very fast, you know. I think the witches are really afraid they *will* fall off.

MRS. GOBLIN (*Pointing*): Then they should buy bandages!

MR. GOBLIN (*Laughing*): Maybe you can convince them —I certainly haven't had any luck. (*A bell tinkles as* GRACE *and* GERTRUDE *enter.*)

MR. AND MRS. GOBLIN: Good evening!

WITCHES (*Together*): Good evening. We're the Gruesome sisters!

MRS. GOBLIN (*Cordially, going over to them*): How nice!

GRACE GRUESOME (*Stiffly*): I am Grace.

GERTRUDE GRUESOME (*Meekly*): And I'm Gertrude.

MR. GOBLIN (*Coming over to them, too*): And what can we do for you ladies this evening?

GRACE: Oh, we just stopped in to pick up an extra bottle of Witches' Brew. The girls are having a party tonight after they get through riding, and I am on the refreshment committee.

MR. GOBLIN: Yes, certainly. What flavor would you like? We have Bat's Wing, Frog's Tongue and Serpent's Tooth— (*Making a face*) all *very* tasty.

GRACE: Well, I don't know. What do you think, Gertrude?

GERTRUDE: Oh! (*Fluttering*) I think Serpent's Tooth is always nice. So refreshing after a hard night's ride.

GRACE: All right, we will take a bottle of that, then. The large size, please.

MR. GOBLIN: I'll just go and get it for you. Excuse me. (*He nods to his wife and points to the brooms, then back to the witches. She understands and nods back. GRACE and GERTRUDE are looking at the bandage display.*)

MRS. GOBLIN (*Moving over behind counter*): I see you are admiring our bandages. Could you use some perhaps?

GRACE (*Insulted*): Well!

MRS. GOBLIN: Oh, dear—I didn't mean any harm. It's just that accidents *will* happen you know. I'm sure you are both wonderful drivers, I mean riders . . .

GRACE (*Drawing herself up*): Three hundred and forty-seven years without an accident!

MRS. GOBLIN: Amazing!

GERTRUDE (*Trying to be insulted, too, but less sure of herself*): And I've had only one accident—you remember, Grace, that Halloween we flew to Bridgeport and that horrid Ghost made a left turn right in front of me. (*Getting agitated*) It really wasn't my fault!

GRACE: There, there, dear. Of course it wasn't your fault, and we certainly did not come here to be insulted. We can buy our brew elsewhere, I'm sure! Come along,

Gertrude. (*They exit, and* MRS. GOBLIN *starts to cry.* MR. GOBLIN *re-enters with gallon jug.*)

MR. GOBLIN (*Cheerfully*): Well, any luck, my dear? (*Looks around*) Why—where did they go?

MRS. GOBLIN (*Crying*): Oh, dear! They left because I tried to sell them some bandages. (*Cries harder*) Oh, I'm a terrible salesman and now we really will have to go out of business. That awful Grace Gruesome will tell all the witches I insulted her and—

MR. GOBLIN (*Consoling her*): Now, now, never mind, my dear. It's not so bad—we'll think of something. (*Thoughtfully*) But just in case we do have another customer, it might be better to show the new brooms *first.*

MRS. GOBLIN: Yes, dear. (*Sniffs*) I'm awfully sorry. I was just trying to help. (*Bell tinkles.*)

MR. GOBLIN (*Happily*): Another customer! (GHOST *enters.*)

MRS. GOBLIN (*Disappointed*): Oh, it's only a ghost.

MR. GOBLIN: Sh-h. (*To* GHOST, *politely*) Good evening, sir! This is a pleasant surprise. We seldom have the honor of a ghostly customer. May I help you?

GHOST (*Gloomy and very dignified*): I really don't know. I came here only because all the ghost stations seem to be closed. I am looking for a new shroud for my wife.

MR. GOBLIN: Why, yes, certainly. I'm sure we can help you. As a matter of fact, I have the latest thing in shrouds—the New Look! (*From behind counter he pulls out a folded colored sheet*) Isn't this lovely?

GHOST (*Shudders*): Oh, ectoplasm! Take it away; that won't do at *all!* If there is anything I cannot stand, it's a loud shroud.

MR. GOBLIN (*Crushed*): Oh. (*Puts it away*) Well, perhaps in that case—let me see . . . (*Brings out plain white sheet*) Would this do, sir? (MRS. GOBLIN *comes over, too, standing beside her husband, ready to be helpful.*)

GHOST: Hm-m-m. (*Fingers sheet*) That is more what I had in mind—

MRS. GOBLIN (*Helpfully*): I'm sure your wife would like it, sir. This is a very discreet sheet!

GHOST (*Nodding*): Hm-m-m-m. Yes. All right, I'll take this one. No need to wrap it, my wife is waiting out in the fog. She'll want to wear it tonight.

MR. GOBLIN: Fine. Will there be anything else?

MRS. GOBLIN (*Eagerly*): How about a nice new broom?

GHOST (*Shocked*): Really, Mrs. Goblin! What would my friends say if I were to appear on a broom?

MRS. GOBLIN: Oh, I don't know—they might think it was very dashing of you. They might even want to try it, too. You could start a whole new trend!

GHOST (*Hesitates, then shakes his head firmly*): No, I'm afraid not. Brooms just aren't dignified enough for ghosts. Our own Floating Action suits us best. (*To* MR. GOBLIN) How much do I owe you for the shroud?

MR. GOBLIN: That will be $2.98.

GHOST (*Pays him and takes sheet*): Good night.

MR. GOBLIN: Thank you. Good night, sir.

MRS. GOBLIN: Happy haunting! (GHOST *exits.*) Well! He was a stuffy one, wasn't he!

MR. GOBLIN (*Sighs*): Yes, I'm glad we deal mostly with witches. They may be scary, but they're a lot more cheerful about it.

MRS. GOBLIN: And they do use brooms—maybe we can still sell some of them before it's too late. (*Voices heard offstage*) What's that? (*Bell jangles violently, and several* WITCHES *enter, laughing and talking together.*)

MR. GOBLIN (*To his wife*): And maybe this is our chance. Better let me handle it. (*Coming forward*) Good evening. Happy Halloween to you all! May we help you?

1ST WITCH: Happy Halloween! We're just looking, thank you. (*They look around, some go to counter, others to brooms.*)

MR. GOBLIN (*Backing away, disappointed*): Help yourselves. We carry a full line of witchwares, you know.

2ND WITCH (*Looking at the brooms*): Oh, girls—come look at these! (*To* MR. GOBLIN) Are these the new models, Mr. Goblin?

MR. GOBLIN: Yes, they're—

2ND WITCH (*Interrupting*): Oh, they're just lovely. I suppose they can fly terribly fast?

MR. GOBLIN: Yes, they're—

2ND WITCH (*Interrupting again*): But then I guess they're awfully dangerous?

MR. GOBLIN: Well, no—

MRS. GOBLIN (*Brightly, at the same time*): Well, yes— (*Both stop talking and he gives her a look. She is embarrassed.*) What I meant was—they might be a *little* more dangerous but they are very easy to handle, really, and then we do have a complete line of— (*Indicates bandages*)

MR. GOBLIN (*Hurriedly*): What Mrs. Goblin means is that—

1ST WITCH: It really doesn't matter, Mr. Goblin. (*Gestures toward* 2ND WITCH) She couldn't manage one anyway. Why, last year she almost had an accident just flying that poky old model she has now. (*Dramatically*) Would have fallen right in the ocean if her skirt hadn't caught at the last minute and saved her!

OTHER WITCHES: Oh! Oh, my goodness! What a narrow escape! (*They all begin to walk away from the brooms, seeming to be no longer interested.*)

MR. GOBLIN: Just a minute! You say her skirt caught and kept her from falling off the broom?

2ND WITCH (*A little ashamed*): Yes, it did. She's right, I would never feel safe on one of those. . . . (*Pointing to brooms*)

MR. GOBLIN: Well, now, ladies, just a minute. (*All turn, including* MRS. GOBLIN) First of all, am I correct in assuming that each one of you would really like to buy one of these beautiful new models? If you felt they were safe, I mean.

WITCHES (*Ad lib*): Oh, yes. Of course. Certainly! (*Etc.*)

MR. GOBLIN: Well then. (*He moves to bandages, picks one up.*) Your problems are solved, ladies! (*As if to himself*) And mine too, I hope. (*Louder again and very dramatically*) I have here in my hand the latest invention of the Society for the Preservation of Witches. It is intended for use with *all* the latest broom models. (*Unrolls a bandage with flourish*) A Safety Belt!

WITCHES: Oh! Ah! How wonderful! Imagine that! (*They crowd closer to see.*)

MR. GOBLIN (*To* 2ND WITCH): May I show you how this works?

2ND WITCH (*Excitedly*): Oh, yes!

MRS. GOBLIN (*Running over and getting a broom*): Here —try this one.

MR. GOBLIN: Thank you. If you will just get on the broom, madam. (2ND WITCH *does so.*) And now— (*He wraps bandage around her waist and ties it to front of the broom.*) There you are! Would you care to try once around the block?

2ND WITCH: Yes, I would. It seems fine but maybe I had better try it up in the air once before I decide. I'll be right back. (*She exits, on the broom.*)

OTHER WITCHES (*Taking brooms and bandages and helping each other tie themselves on*): Oh, how wonderful. Aren't they lovely? (*When each* WITCH *has a broom and a bandage, there is one of each remaining.*)

1st Witch (*On broom*): Mr. Goblin, you are a genius—
I have never felt so secure on any broom.

2nd Witch (*Re-enters running*): It's wonderful! (*To
Witches*) You'll all want one. I even tried a loop-the-
loop. Didn't even muss my hair! (*To Mr. Goblin*)
How much do we owe you, Mr. Goblin? It's getting
very late, almost take-off time!

Other Witches (*Very excited and happy*): On our new
models!

Mr. Goblin: That's all right, ladies. You just ride them
out of here and I'll charge them to you.

Witches: Oh, thank you. Good night. Happy Halloween!
(*They leave. Mr. and Mrs. Goblin follow them to door,
waving good-bye, etc.*)

Mrs. Goblin (*Happily, returning to center stage*): Well,
that certainly was a wonderful idea!

Mr. Goblin: Yes, it worked out fine, didn't it? I think
we should celebrate.

Mrs. Goblin: Yes, let's. (*Goes to remaining broom*) But
what are you going to do with this one?

Mr. Goblin: That's no problem—I'll take it around to
that Used Broom Dealer, "The Happy Haunter."

Mrs. Goblin: But it isn't used! (*Picks up broom.*)

Mr. Goblin: He won't care; lots of them aren't. That's
why he's happy!

Mrs. Goblin (*Fondly*): Silly! I'm serious—it's a shame
to waste it. Do you suppose you could fly it?

Mr. Goblin (*Firmly*): My dear wife, Goblins do not fly.

Mrs. Goblin (*Mocking*): You sound like that stuffy old
ghost!

Mr. Goblin (*Laughing*): Or that witch you insulted?

Mrs. Goblin (*Making a face*): Oh—Grace Gruesome!
(*Thoughtfully*) I wonder what she would think if she
saw a Goblin riding a broom.

Mr. Goblin: Probably fall right off her own.

MRS. GOBLIN (*Hopefully*): You really think so? (*She gets on broom.*)

MR. GOBLIN: You aren't serious about riding that, are you?

MRS. GOBLIN (*Riding slowly around the stage, testing broom*): Well, I would rather scare witches than children. (*Riding faster*) Oh, come on! It's easy!

MR. GOBLIN (*Tempted but still doubtful*): I'm not sure we should . . .

MRS. GOBLIN (*Exasperated*): Oh! (*Rides to face him and then sings or talk-sings*) Goblin, Goblin, give me your answer do! Please stop squabblin'—I can't wait all night for you!

MR. GOBLIN (*To audience*): She won't be a stylish flyer — (*Grinning and climbing onto broom*) But I'm not too proud to try her!

BOTH (*Together, exiting on broom*):
And witches will shout
As we chase them about
On our broomhandle built for two!
(*Curtain*)

THE END

The Haunted Bookshop

by Jessie Nicholson

Characters

HANK	TOM SAWYER
CHET, *his pal*	AUNT POLLY
BILLY BONES	INJUN JOE
BLACK DOG	PENROD
OLD PEW	JODY
JIM HAWKINS	MA BAXTER
LONG JOHN SILVER	FORRESTER BROTHERS } *voices*
HUCKLEBERRY FINN	PENROD'S MOTHER

TIME: *Late evening.*

BEFORE RISE: *The drop is painted to represent a row of shops. Between two street lights is a shop whose sign reads in large print that can be seen by the audience "The Haunted Bookshop—Drop In and Browse Around —Become Acquainted with Your Favorite Characters —in Person." Two boys emerge from right wing, strolling along slowly.*

CHET: Boy, oh boy, was that a swell movie! I never heard so many good old guns going bang, bang, bang, all at once.

HANK: Me either. And I nearly missed going out tonight,

71

too. If my father had known my book report for school wasn't finished yet, I never would have seen that picture.

CHET (*In disgust*): Book reports—I'm sick of them—always another book report every time there's a new western at the Paramount or a television show I want to see.

HANK: Yeah—I know. And what's so educational about reading a book? Words, words, words! No real, live people—just words! (BILLY BONES' *voice is heard offstage behind partly opened "doorway" of bookshop.*)

BILLY BONES (*In a very hollow tone*): Shiver my timbers —what stupidity!

CHET (*Startled*): What was that?

HANK: I didn't hear anything. Now, listen to me—what's so educational about a book? You take the movie we saw tonight—a boy could learn a lot from that.

CHET: Sure could—bang, bang, bang!

BILLY BONES (*Off*): Pooh, pooh—mere child's play!

HANK (*Jumping*): Holy smokes, who said that?

CHET (*Uneasily, looking all about*): G-Gosh, I don't know. I told you I heard something. (*Suddenly spying the sign above the bookshop and pointing a trembling finger*) I n-never saw that before. (*Reading*) "The Haunted Bookshop—Drop In and Browse Around—Become Acquainted with Your Favorite Characters—in Person!" You don't t-t-think—

HANK (*Nervously*): Ha, ha, ha! People out of books can't talk, silly.

BILLY BONES (*Commandingly*): Silence there between decks!

CHET: Ye-ow—I'm going home!

HANK (*Fearfully*): Me too!

BILLY BONES: Not so fast, mateys—not so fast. (*A long arm reaches out and drags first CHET and then HANK,*

*who have been too frightened to move, inside the door-
way. The curtain rises slowly.*)

* * *

SETTING: *The interior of a bookshop.*

AT RISE: *Fierce-looking* BILLY BONES *has both boys by the
scruff of the neck and is gazing from one to the other
suspiciously.*

BILLY BONES: Now which one of ye wooden-headed land
lubbers was so misinformed as to say we weren't real,
live folks—which one, I say? (*Glaring first at one boy
and then the other*) Come, speak up or I'll be forced to
knock your wooden heads together.

HANK (*Falteringly*): I—I guess I said it, s-s-sir.

BILLY BONES (*Disgustedly*): Well, you're a nice one, to be
sure. Pinch me if I'm not real. Pinch me, I say.

HANK (*Trying to draw away*): Not me, sir.

BILLY BONES (*To* CHET): Well, you then. You look like a
promising young scamp. You pinch old Billy Bones.

CHET (*Fearfully*): Billy B-B-Bones!

BILLY BONES: That's me, mate, and don't ever tell me
you haven't heard of Billy Bones, the bold buccaneer.
There's none so fierce and daring as Billy Bones—not
Black Dog—not Old Pew—not— (*In a husky, terrifying
stage whisper*) not even Long John Silver himself. May
I walk the plank if it is not so. (*Then threateningly*)
Pinch me, I say. (*Both boys cautiously pinch the buccaneer on either arm at which he lets out a bloodcur-
dling yell. The boys break away from him in fright as he
shouts loudly.*) "Fifteen men on a dead man's chest,
Yo, ho, ho and a bottle of rum!" (*From behind book
cover entitled "Treasure Island" comes* OLD PEW, *who
is hunched over and old-looking. He feels his way with a*

crude stick. BLACK DOG, *who is as fierce in appearance as* BILLY BONES, *springs out also from behind book cover.*)

BILLY BONES: (*Gasping*): Pinch me if it's not B-B-Black Dog!

BLACK DOG: The same. We as was shipmates in a sight o' plundering, Billy Bones. (*He shakes his fist under* BILLY BONES' *nose.* BILLY *backs away.*) Come now to share the spoils of our last voyage together as is only right and proper. Out with it, matey, where have you got the treasure map concealed?

BILLY BONES (*Furiously shaking his fist in the air*): Share with you? Never! You scoundrel, wretch, blackhearted rogue! Can't keep what you got and now want to lay hands on another's.

BLACK DOG (*Craftily*): And will, too. Would you have the Black Spot put on you, Billy Bones?

BILLY BONES: By thunder, I'll run you through first. (*He draws his cutlass and rushes at* BLACK DOG, *who follows suit but he is quickly brought down and scuttles back behind the cover of "Treasure Island." In the meantime,* OLD PEW *has been dodging about trying to keep out of harm's way.* BILLY BONES *notices him for the first time. He starts backing away, a terrified expression on his face.*)

OLD PEW (*Feeling his way toward him with his stick*): Don't move, Billy Bones! Old Pew can hear if his eyes can't see. (*He pins* BILLY *to a counter with the end of his stick.*) I've fetched you something and if it is not to your fancy, 'tis no fault of mine. (*Snickering*) Give me your hand— (*And as* BILLY BONES *hesitates*) Give it to me, I say! (BILLY BONES *holds out a trembling hand and* OLD PEW *puts something into it. Then, with a high, cackling laugh, he hobbles back into book, his cane tapping his way across the floor.*)

BILLY BONES (*Hoarsely, looking down into his hand*):

By the powers—the Black Spot! (*He falls gasping to the floor and then becomes quiet.*)

HANK (*Going over and peering down at him aghast*): He's deader than a doornail!

CHET: Without even being struck a blow!

HANK: That was the Black Spot, silly, don't you see? Old Pew put the Black Spot on him. There it is in his hand —a wad of black paper.

CHET: Poor Billy Bones—I kind of liked him, too, didn't you, Hank? (*On these words* BILLY BONES *suddenly bounces up off the floor, while the boys dodge back in astonishment.*)

BILLY BONES (*Cheerfully*): Well, how did I do, mates? Am I real or am I not? (JIM HAWKINS *comes out from behind the cover of "Treasure Island."*)

JIM HAWKINS: Get back where you belong, Billy Bones. Dead men tell no tales. From here on the story's mine. (BILLY BONES *slinks back behind the cover of the book and* LONG JOHN SILVER *strides out on stage.*)

LONG JOHN (*Growling*): And mine, Jim Hawkins. Don't forget Long John Silver—him what saved your life on Treasure Island.

JIM HAWKINS: And very near made me lose it too, as well as the treasure. If ever a man should have a black conscience 'tis you, Long John Silver.

LONG JOHN: Thank ye kindly, Jim Hawkins. I admire a man what speaks his mind!

CHET (*In awed tone, plucking* JIM's *sleeve*): Did you really find treasure—buried treasure on an island?

LONG JOHN: He asks if we really found treasure, mate. (*Guffawing*) By the great horn spoon, did we find treasure or didn't we?

JIM HAWKINS: Stow the talk, Long John Silver. 'Tis me that tells the tale, not you.

LONG JOHN: Aye, aye, Jim Hawkins, and a hearty tale it

is, too. I pities them that hasn't had the good fortune to read it.

HANK: What of the buried treasure, Jim Hawkins—tell us how you found the buried treasure.

JIM HAWKINS (*Cagily*): 'Tis all there for those that care to read it. (*Pointing to the volume of "Treasure Island."*)

LONG JOHN (*Slapping his thigh and laughing noisily*): By all the fish in the sea, that's tellin' 'em, matey. Let's you and I batten down the hatches and set sail for Treasure Island. As for those that are minded to go along—a stormy voyage and a dangerous one, ho, ho, ho! (*They exit. Out of the book titled "The Adventures of Tom Sawyer" dart* TOM *and* HUCK FINN. HANK *and* CHET, *grinning at each other, seat themselves on the floor, their backs against a counter, their hands clasped around their knees.*)

TOM: Sh-h! (*Glancing all around suspiciously*) Did you hear someone mention buried treasure—huh—did you, Huck Finn?

HUCK (*Cautiously*): What kind o' treasure, Tom? I 'low there's different kinds of treasure—your Aunt Polly's cookie jar, wriggly worms and tadpoles (*Waxing enthusiastic*), a fine, big, dead rat on a string—

TOM: Aw, shucks, nothin' like that, Huck. I figure it might be a rotten ole chest full of diamonds or a brass pot spillin' over with gold. Now, you and I could form a partnership and go digging for that treasure in the dark of night.

HUCK: How are we gonna see where we're diggin' if it's the dark of night, Tom?

TOM (*In exasperation*): You always ask so many questions.

HUCK: Well, I gotta git things straight in my mind. How *are* we gonna see where we're diggin' in the dark of the night?

TOM: All right, then, *you* can have a little moonlight if you're so fussy.

HUCK: You mean I'll dig in the moonlight and you'll dig in the dark? (*Puckering his brow and scratching his head*) How we gonna fix that up?

LONG JOHN (*Thrusting his head out*): Stow the talk, mates, or somebody else will have dug up the treasure whilst you're sparrin' around with words.

TOM (*Shakily*): I could almost a-swore I heard somebody mention treasure then, couldn't you, Huck?

HUCK (*Peering about fearfully*): Nope—didn't hear anything—I don't think.

TOM (*Sighing with relief*): I figure talking about mysterious, hidden treasure sorta makes a fella see and hear things that really aren't there—like—like spooks, for instance. Don't you, Huck? (INJUN JOE *appears stealthily from behind cover of "Adventures of Tom Sawyer," and sneaks across stage, carrying a pick and shovel. He mumbles to himself as he exits.*)

HUCK: That weren't a spook. That were Injun Joe, the robber. Probably goin' to dig up another dead body in the graveyard for some old sawbones.

TOM: I'll bet he's gonna dig up hidden treasure—that's what I'll bet. C'mon, let's follow him. Maybe he'll go down to the old haunted house in the hollow. There's no place like a haunted house for buried treasure.

HUCK: There's no place like a haunted house for Huckleberry Finn to keep away from. You won't ketch me goin' down there. I'm skeered o' haunts. (*A shrill, feminine voice is heard calling from behind book cover*)

AUNT POLLY: Tom—Tom Sawyer! (*The two boys shrink down beside book shelves.*)

HUCK (*Hoarsely*): That's your Aunt Polly, sure as shootin'.

AUNT POLLY (*In great annoyance*): Land o' Goshen,

where in tunket has that boy gone to? Tom—you, Tom!

HUCK: C'mon, what are we waitin' for? Let's git down to the haunted house. I'd ruther be chased by a spook than your Aunt Polly! (*They exit on the run.* INJUN JOE *comes trudging back, still muttering, a chest brimming over with old coins hoisted on his shoulder. He disappears behind book cover.* LONG JOHN SILVER's *head and shoulders have appeared again, a fearsome expression on his face.*)

LONG JOHN (*Bitterly*): I warned those young landlubbers somebody would get there a-fore 'em! Them and their talk. This is a fine kettle of salt fish! (AUNT POLLY *emerges from behind book cover, peering over the top of her steel-rimmed spectacles.*)

AUNT POLLY (*Suspiciously*): Who said somethin' about fish? Tom Sawyer, come out of hidin' this instant or I'll box your ears when you do. You're not goin' fishin' this time o' night.

LONG JOHN: Shiver my timbers—I can see this is no place for a bold buccaneer! (*He withdraws his head abruptly.*)

AUNT POLLY: I heard that, Tom Sawyer, and your language isn't befittin' a Sunday School boy. Come out, I say, wherever you are. The longer you hold back, the longer it gives me to figure out a proper punishment. (HANK *and* CHET *try to sneak away but* AUNT POLLY *spies them and drags them out by the ears to center of stage.*)

CHET: Ouch!

HANK: Ouch, ouch, ouch!

AUNT POLLY (*Grimly*): No more than you deserve. (*Then observing them more closely*) Why, land sakes, you're not Tom and Huck. I declare it's so dark I came near makin' a mistake. (*With a final tweak, she releases their ears.*)

HANK (*Ruefully, rubbing his ear*): You sure did, Aunt —Aunt Polly.

AUNT POLLY: My, butter wouldn't melt in your mouth, would it—Aunt Pollyin' me! I'll warrant you've both been up to some mischief.

HANK: Oh, no, ma'am, not us.

AUNT POLLY: You mean to say you haven't been playin' hooky today?

CHET: No, *ma'am!*

AUNT POLLY: Or neglectin' your studies?

HANK (*Shifting uneasily from one foot to the other*): Well, not exactly—that is—

AUNT POLLY: Just as I thought. (*Giving his ear a fresh tweak*) Now, what is it you haven't done—readin', writin' or 'rithmetic?

HANK: It's sort of writin'—a book report.

AUNT POLLY: Book report, eh? Well, you sure have come to the right place then. You can take your pick here. Why don't you choose "The Adventures of Tom Sawyer," by Mark Twain? (*Pointing to it with pride*) Now that's a book I can *really* recommend. I'm in it.

HANK: Would we find out more about the buried treasure and what happens to Injun Joe?

AUNT POLLY: Land sakes, yes, and you'd read about Tom runnin' away from home and turnin' up at his own funeral, and the best way to whitewash a fence of a Saturday morning without doing a lick of work yourself. And how Tom and Becky Thatcher got lost in McDougal's cave and was near given up for lost. I declare, I think it's the most excitin' book that ever was written.

LONG JOHN (*Thrusting his head out again*): If that's not just like a woman—trying to take all the credit!

HANK: It sure sounds interesting.

LONG JOHN (*In an injured tone*): What—you're not goin' back on your old mates?

CHET: Yeah—how about that, Hank? I sorta wanted to set sail on that voyage for Treasure Island.

HANK: Well . . .

AUNT POLLY (*Tapping her foot in annoyance*): Seems I've been wastin' my voice. All that talk for nothing. It would take a real detective to figure out how a boy's mind works. (*From behind cover of "Penrod Jashber" comes* PENROD, *a large magnifying glass in his hand, scanning the floor inch by inch with great care.*) Land sakes, what are you up to?

PENROD (*Raising his head and looking around cautiously*): Sh-h—I'm looking for clues.

AUNT POLLY: Clues—fiddlesticks—more 'an likely you should be home vexin' your brains over your book learnin'. Who are you, anyway?

PENROD: Penrod Scho—that is (*Clearing his throat and assuming a tone of superiority*) I'm George J. Jashber, Private Detective, Operator Number 103. My badge— (*Whisking open his coat to display a large, nickel badge attached to his shirt*) Put your case in my hands, madam, and it's as good as solved by the greatest detective in the world.

AUNT POLLY: Well, I never.

PENROD: Right now I'm on the trail of Harold Romorez, the handsome bandit, for whose capture I will get a reward of $5,000.

HANK: Gosh—$5,000! Maybe we could catch a bandit or two, huh, Chet?

PENROD (*Disdainfully*): Not unless you were real detectives with a badge pinned on your shirt. (*Rubbing his badge with his coat sleeve in great pride.*)

CHET (*Faltering*): How—how could we get one?

PENROD: Couldn't, I expect. I had to pay a lotta money

for this good ole badge. Course if I were to tell you to go and shadow some good ole crooks for me, you'd have to do it. That's the law. (*With a very wide, bored yawn,* LONG JOHN SILVER *has dropped his head in his hand and gone to sleep.*)

HANK: Do you shadow crooks all the time?

PENROD: I should say so. I hardly get any time left to go to school.

CHET: Say, that sounds all right.

AUNT POLLY: I never heard such poppycock. Don't go fillin' up my Tom with any such ideas. No time for school indeed! (*She flounces back behind book cover.*)

HANK (*Mysteriously*): We might just happen to have a couple of prospects for you.

PENROD (*Cautiously*): Like who, for instance? (INJUN JOE *sneaks across the stage again from behind book cover, pick and shovel in hand, his old felt hat pulled down over his eyes.*)

HANK (*Hoarsely*): Like him. That's Injun Joe, the robber. He digs up dead bodies and buried treasure.

CHET (*In stage whisper*): And then there's Long John Silver, whose conscience is as black as the Black Spot that was put on poor old Billy Bones.

LONG JOHN (*Awaking in terror*): Black Spot—who said Black Spot? (*Running a finger suggestively across his throat*) I can see this is no place for me! (*He withdraws his head hastily.*)

HANK (*Eagerly*): Well—what do you say?

CHET: Yeah—how about it Pen—that is, Mr. George Jashber?

PENROD (*Sternly*): Private detective— number 103.

CHET (*Humbly*): Private detective—number 103.

PENROD (*Condescendingly*): Um—well yes, they're pretty good prospects. I might let you in. (*Voice of* PENROD'S MOTHER *calling from behind cover of "Penrod Jashber."*)

MOTHER: Penrod—Penrod Schofield! Come in the house this instant and get ready for bed, or you won't want to get up when it comes time for school in the morning.

PENROD (*Disgustedly*): Oh, all right. (*Becomes absorbed in peering through the magnifying glass again.*)

MOTHER (*In no uncertain tone of voice*): Pen—ROD!

PENROD (*With alacrity*): Yes'm. (*He straightens up promptly and moves on the run behind book cover.*)

HANK: Shucks—just when we were getting somewhere, too.

CHET (*Looking wistfully at book*): I'd certainly like to know how he operates—$5,000 reward—whew!

HANK (*Sighing heavily*): School can sure interfere with your life. (JODY *springs from behind book cover entitled "The Yearling."*)

JODY: That's one thing I don't worry about—school! My pa, Penny Baxter, teaches me my sums and how to read and write, in the evening after the candle's lit. But then 'fore you know it he's off on a tale—no one kin tell a tale like my pa. Oh, yes, I've had a heap o' learnin' from Pa—

CHET (*Enviously*): Sure sounds fine.

JODY: Iffen I take a notion to follow the honey bees to their bee-tree or go for a ramble and build myself a flutter-mill down at the sink hole or maybe go off huntin' ole Slewfoot with Pa, there's nobody to stop me. (*Voice of* MA BAXTER *from behind cover of "The Yearling."*)

MA BAXTER: Jody Baxter—git to yer chores!

JODY (*Ruefully*): That is, nobody exceptin' Ma. Well, I got to fetch in a load of wood now 'fore she gits really riled.

HANK: Wait a minute—who's ole Slewfoot?

CHET: Yeah, who's ole Slewfoot?

JODY (*In amazement*): You mean to say you never heard of ole Slewfoot? (HANK *and* CHET *shake their heads. From*

*behind cover of "The Yearling" are heard several fierce
male voices.*)

FORRESTER BROTHERS (*Chanting slowly and distinctly in
obvious disgust*): They never heerd of ole Slewfoot! Sech
ignorance. And they bin to school!

CHET (*A little fearfully*): Who was that?

JODY: Jest them fightin' Forrester brothers. There's six
of 'em, not countin' Fodder-wing. They're big and
black and they got fine black beards. Ma says we should
have no truck with 'em. She says their hearts are as
black as their beards. But Pa thinks different and so do
I. I'd ruther go to the Forresters than eat. Fodder-wing's
my best friend.

CHET: Fodder-wing? What a funny name.

JODY (*Defensively*): It's a right fine name. He came by it
aimin' to fly one time. He tied a bundle of fodder to
each arm and took off from the barn roof.

HANK: And what happened?

JODY (*Sadly*): He got himself a powerful lot of broken
bones! Some folks call him witless, but he's my friend.
He's got more pets than you kin shake a stick at, fox
squirrels and rabbits, a baby coon and an ole fat possum
and a fine, big eagle.

CHET: Whew—I sure would like to see those.

JODY (*Eagerly*): Fodder-wing would make you right welcome, and then happen-chance you could come and see
my yearling. Fodder-wing named him for me—Flag. Isn't
that a pretty name? (*Tenderly*) I declare he's the
sweetest, prettiest little creature you could ever want to
see.

MA BAXTER (*From inside book cover*): Jody Baxter, come
git this pesky animal out o' my kitchen. He's upset the
mush, eaten my fresh baked corn pone whilst my back
was turned and slopped over a bucket o' milk on my
clean floor!

JODY: He didn't mean no harm, Ma. Flag was just aimin' to be playful. I'll clean it up straight off. (*He exits hurriedly behind book cover.*)

HANK: A fine thing! We didn't even get to know what kind of a pet Flag was!

CHET: Nor ole Slewfoot.

HANK: Somehow I don't think he's anybody's pet. (*Cautiously*) You know something, Chet. I figure there's only one way to find out all these things we want to know.

CHET (*Equally cautious*): I—I figure you're right. Where'll we start? (*From out behind their respective book covers rush* LONG JOHN SILVER *and* AUNT POLLY.)

AUNT POLLY (*Excitedly, pushing* LONG JOHN *aside*): Remember I told you "The Adventures of Tom Sawyer" was the most excitin' book ever written. You'll find out all about buried treasure in a haunted house and get lost in a cave with Tom and Becky.

LONG JOHN (*Pleadingly*): You wouldn't listen to a woman, matey? Come with Long John Silver to Treasure Island, where the stakes are high and the rum flows like water. (*Then fiercely*). "Fifteen men on a dead man's chest, Yo, ho, ho and a bottle of rum!" (*Enter* PENROD *with a small megaphone in his hand.*)

PENROD (*Hawking through megaphone*): Learn all about being a detective in twenty-two exciting chapters. Learn how to capture a handsome, dangerous bandit and win a reward of five million dollars! Learn all about it.

CHET (*Huskily*): Five *million* dollars! I thought it was only five thousand. Jumping grasshoppers, Hank, we have to get in on this for sure. (*Enter* JODY, *jumping up and down excitedly.*)

JODY: Whoopee!

CHET: What's the matter with him?

JODY (*Tossing the cap he is now wearing in the air*): Whoopee!

LONG JOHN (*Growling*): Silence there between decks!

AUNT POLLY: What's ailin' you, boy? Speak up!

JODY: Me and Pa brought down ole Slewfoot—the meanest, orneriest creature in the whole of Floridy—whoopee!

MA BAXTER (*From inside book cover*): Git in this house, Jody Baxter, directly. Flag's upset the whole pan of peas I bin shellin' and they're gone every which-a-way!

JODY: Comin', Ma. (*He exits. Book characters withdraw backwards slowly into covers as if fading from view*)

HANK: You see what I mean. We just have to find out.

CHET (*Looking around wonderingly*): Gosh, Hank, look at all these books. I didn't know there were so many books in the whole world.

HANK: Me either. Why, we could write millions of good old book reports! (*Walking around examining the titles*) "Kidnapped," "Robinson Crusoe," "Penrod," "Penrod and Sam"—oh, boy, more books about good ole George Jashber—"Hans Brinker and the Silver Skates," "My Friend Flicka," "Adventures of Huckleberry Finn"—

CHET: Say—that was Tom Sawyer's friend, wasn't it? What do you suppose they're up to in that book?

HANK (*Very earnestly*): You know something, Chet? We have an awful lot of reading to catch up on!

THE END

The Book That Saved the Earth

by Claire Boiko

Characters

HISTORIAN
GREAT AND MIGHTY THINK-TANK
APPRENTICE NOODLE
CAPTAIN OMEGA
LIEUTENANT IOTA
SERGEANT OOP
OFFSTAGE VOICE

BEFORE RISE: *Spotlight shines on* HISTORIAN, *who is sitting at table down right, on which is a movie projector. A sign on an easel beside him reads:* MUSEUM OF ANCIENT HISTORY: DEPARTMENT OF THE TWENTIETH CENTURY. *He stands and bows to audience.*

HISTORIAN: Good afternoon. Welcome to our Museum of Ancient History, and to my department—curiosities of the good old, far-off twentieth century. The twentieth century was often called the Era of the Book. In those days, there were books about everything from anteaters to Zulus. Books taught people how to, and when to, and where to, and why to. They illustrated, educated, punctuated and even decorated. But the strangest thing a

NG.)

NOODLE (*Bowing*): O Great and Mighty Think-Tank, most powerful and intelligent creature in the whole universe, what are your orders?

THINK-TANK (*Peevishly*): You left out part of my salutation, Apprentice Noodle. Go over the whole thing again.

NOODLE: It shall be done, sir. (*In a singsong*) O Great and Mighty Think-Tank, Ruler of Mars and her two moons, most powerful and intelligent creature in the whole universe— (*Out of breath*) what-are-your-orders?

THINK-TANK: That's better, Noodle. I wish to be placed in communication with our manned space probe to that ridiculous little planet we are going to put under our generous rulership. What do they call it again?

NOODLE: Earth, your Intelligence.

THINK-TANK: Earth—of course. You see how insignificant the place is? But first, something important. My mirror. I wish to consult my mirror.

NOODLE: It shall be done, sir. (*He hands* THINK-TANK *a hand mirror.*)

THINK-TANK: Mirror, mirror, in my hand. Who is the most fantastically intellectually gifted being in the land?

OFFSTAGE VOICE (*After a pause*): You, sir.

THINK-TANK (*Smacking mirror*): Quicker. Answer quicker next time. I hate a slow mirror. (*He admires himself.*) Ah, there I am. Are we Martians not a handsome race? So much more attractive than those ugly Earthlings with their tiny heads. Noodle, you keep on exercising your mind, and someday you'll have a balloon brain just like mine.

NOODLE: Oh, I hope so, Mighty Think-Tank. I hope so.

THINK-TANK: Now, contact the space probe. I want to invade that primitive ball of mud called Earth before lunch.

NOODLE: It shall be done, sir. (*He twists knobs and adjusts levers on switchboard. Electronic buzzes and beeps are heard as the curtains open.*)

*   *   *

SETTING: *The Centerville Public Library.*

AT RISE: CAPTAIN OMEGA *stands at center, opening and closing card catalogue drawers in a puzzled fashion.* LIEUTENANT IOTA *is up left, counting books in a bookcase.* SERGEANT OOP *is at right, opening and closing a book, turning it upside down, shaking it, and then riffling the pages and shaking his head.*

NOODLE (*Adjusting knobs*): I have a close sighting of the space crew, sir. (THINK-TANK *puts on a pair of huge goggles and turns toward the stage to watch.*) They seem to have entered some sort of Earth structure.

THINK-TANK: Excellent. Make voice contact.

NOODLE (*Speaking into a microphone*): Mars Space Control calling the crew of Probe One. Mars Space Control calling the crew of Probe One. Come in, Captain Omega. Give us your location.

CAPTAIN OMEGA (*Speaking into a disk which is on a chain around his neck*): Captain Omega to Mars Space Control. Lieutenant Iota, Sergeant Oop and I have landed on Earth without incident. We have taken shelter in this (*Indicates room*)—this square place. Have you any idea where we are, Lieutenant Iota?

IOTA: I can't figure it out, Captain. (*Holding up a book*) I've counted two thousand of these peculiar things. This place must be some sort of storage barn. What do you think, Sergeant Oop?

OOP: I haven't a clue. I've been to seven galaxies, but I've never seen anything like this. Maybe they're hats. (*He opens a book and puts it on his head.*) Say, maybe this is a haberdashery!

OMEGA (*Bowing low*): Perhaps the Great and Mighty Think-Tank will give us the benefit of his thought on the matter.

THINK-TANK: Elementary, my dear Omega. Hold one of the items up so that I may view it closely. (OMEGA *holds a book on the palm of his hand.*) Yes, yes, I understand now. Since Earth creatures are always eating, the place in which you find yourselves is undoubtedly a crude refreshment stand.

OMEGA (*To* IOTA *and* OOP): He says we're in a refreshment stand.

OOP: Well, the Earthlings certainly have a strange diet.

THINK-TANK: That item in your hand is called a "sandwich".

OMEGA (*Nodding*): A sandwich.

IOTA (*Nodding*): A sandwich.

OOP (*Taking book from his head*): A sandwich?

THINK-TANK: Sandwiches are the main staple of Earth diet. Look at it closely. (OMEGA *squints at book.*) There are two slices of what is called "bread," and between them there is some sort of filling.

OMEGA: That is correct, sir.

THINK-TANK: To confirm my opinion, I order you to eat it.

OMEGA (*Gulping*): Eat it?

THINK-TANK: Do you doubt the Mighty Think-Tank?

OMEGA: Oh, no, no. But poor Lieutenant Iota has not had his breakfast. Lieutenant Iota, I order you to eat this— this sandwich.

IOTA (*Dubiously*): Eat it? Oh, Captain! It's a very great honor to be the first Martian to eat a sandwich, I'm sure, but—but how can I be so impolite as to eat before my Sergeant? (*Handing* OOP *the book; brightly*) Sergeant Oop, I order you to eat the sandwich.

OOP (*Making a face*): Who, sir? Me, sir?

IOTA *and* OMEGA (*Slapping their chests in a salute*): For the glory of Mars, Oop!

OOP: Yes, sirs. (*Unhappily*) Immediately, sirs. (*He opens his mouth wide.* OMEGA *and* IOTA *watch him breathlessly. He bites down on a corner of the book, and pantomimes chewing and swallowing, while making terrible faces.*)

OMEGA: Well, Oop?

IOTA: Well, Oop? (OOP *coughs.* OMEGA *and* IOTA *pound him on the back.*)

THINK-TANK: Was it not delicious, Sergeant Oop?

OOP (*Slapping his chest in salute*): That is correct, sir. It was *not* delicious. I don't know how the Earthlings can get those sandwiches down without water. They're dry as Martian dust.

NOODLE: Sir, sir. Great and Mighty Think-Tank. I beg

your pardon, but an insignificant bit of data floated into my mind about those sandwiches.

THINK-TANK: It can't be worth much, but go ahead. Give us your trifling bit of data.

NOODLE: Well, sir, I have seen surveyor films of those sandwiches. I noticed that the Earthlings did not *eat* them. They used them as some sort of communication device.

THINK-TANK (*Haughtily*): Naturally. That was my next point. These are actually communication sandwiches. Think-Tank is never wrong. Who is never wrong?

ALL (*Saluting*): Great and Mighty Think-Tank is never wrong.

THINK-TANK: Therefore, I order you to listen to them.

OMEGA: Listen to them?

IOTA *and* OOP (*To each other; puzzled*): Listen to them?

THINK-TANK: Do you have marbles in your ears? I said, listen to them. (*Martians bow very low.*)

OMEGA: It shall be done, sir. (*They each take two books from the case, and hold them to their ears, listening intently.*)

IOTA (*Whispering to* OMEGA): Do you hear anything?

OMEGA (*Whispering back*): Nothing. Do you hear anything, Oop?

OOP (*Loudly*): Not a thing! (*OMEGA and IOTA jump in fright.*)

OMEGA *and* IOTA: Sh-h-h! (*They listen intently again.*)

THINK-TANK: Well? Well? Report to me. What do you hear?

OMEGA: Nothing, sir. Perhaps we are not on the correct frequency.

IOTA: Nothing, sir. Perhaps the Earthlings have sharper ears than we do.

OOP: I don't hear a thing. Maybe these sandwiches don't make sounds.

THINK-TANK: What? What? Does someone suggest the Mighty Think-Tank has made a mistake?

OMEGA: Oh, no, sir. No, sir. We'll keep listening.

NOODLE: Please excuse me, your Brilliance, but a cloudy piece of information is rolling around in my head.

THINK-TANK: Well, roll it out, Noodle, and I will clarify it for you.

NOODLE: I seem to recall that the Earthlings did not *listen* to the sandwiches. They opened them, and watched them.

THINK-TANK: Yes, that is quite correct. I will clarify that for you, Captain Omega. Those sandwiches are not for ear communication, they are for eye communication. Now, Captain Omega, take that large, bright-colored sandwich over there. It appears to be important. Tell me what you observe. (OMEGA *picks up a very large copy of "Mother Goose", holding it so that the audience can see the title.* IOTA *looks over his left shoulder, and* OOP *peers over his right shoulder.*)

OMEGA: It appears to contain pictures of Earthlings.

IOTA: There seems to be some sort of code.

THINK-TANK (*Sharply interested*): Code? Code? I told you this was important. Describe the code.

OOP: It's little lines and squiggles and dots. Thousands of them, next to the pictures.

THINK-TANK: Code. Perhaps the Earthlings are not so primitive as we have thought. We must break the code. We must.

NOODLE: Forgive me, your Cleverness, but did not the chemical department give our spacemen pills to increase their intelligence?

THINK-TANK: Stop! A thought of magnificent brilliance has come to me. Spacemen, our chemical department has given you pills to increase your intelligence. Take them immediately and then watch the sandwich. The meaning of the code will slowly unfold before you.

OMEGA: It shall be done, sir. Remove pill. (*Crew take pills from boxes on their belts.*) Present pill. (*They hold pills out in front of them, stiffly.*) Swallow pill. (*They pop the pills into their mouths and gulp simultaneously. They open their eyes wide, their heads shake, and they put their hands to their foreheads.*) The cotangent of a given angle in a right triangle is equal to the adjacent side divided by the hypotenuse.

IOTA: *Habeas corpus ad faciendum et recipiendum!*

OOP: There is change of pressure along a radius in curvilinear motion.

THINK-TANK: Excellent. Now, decipher that code.

ALL: It shall be done, sir. (*They frown over the book, turning the pages.*)

OMEGA (*Brightly*): Aha!

IOTA (*Brightly*): Oho!

OOP (*Bursting into laughter*): Ha, ha, ha.

THINK-TANK: What does it say? Tell me this instant. Transcribe, Omega.

OMEGA: Yes, sir. (*He reads with great seriousness.*)
Mistress Mary, quite contrary,
How does your garden grow?
With cockle shells and silver bells
And pretty maids all in a row.

OOP: Ha, ha, ha. Imagine that. Pretty maids growing in a garden.

THINK-TANK (*Alarmed*): Stop! This is no time for levity. Don't you realize the seriousness of this discovery? The Earthlings have discovered how to combine agriculture and mining. They can actually *grow* crops of rare metals such as silver. And cockle shells. They can grow high explosives, too. Noodle, contact our invasion fleet.

NOODLE: They are ready to go down and take over Earth, sir.

THINK-TANK: Tell them to hold. Tell them new information has come to us about Earth. Iota, continue transcribing.

IOTA: Yes, sir. (*He reads very gravely.*)

Hey diddle diddle! The cat and the fiddle,
The cow jumped over the moon,
The little dog laughed to see such sport,
And the dish ran away with the spoon.

OOP (*Laughing*): The dish ran away with the spoon!

THINK-TANK: Cease laughter. Desist. This is more and more alarming. The Earthlings have reached a high level of civilization. Didn't you hear? They have taught their domesticated animals musical culture and space techniques. Even their dogs have a sense of humor. Why, at this very moment, they may be launching an interplanetary attack of millions of *cows!* Notify the invasion fleet. No invasion today. Oop, transcribe the next code.

OOP: Yes, sir. (*Reading*)

Humpty Dumpty sat on the wall,
Humpty Dumpty had a great fall;
All the King's horses and all the King's men,
Cannot put Humpty Dumpty together again.

Oh, look, sir. Here's a picture of Humpty Dumpty. Why, sir, he looks like—he looks like—(*Turns large picture of Humpty Dumpty toward* THINK-TANK *and the audience.*)

THINK-TANK (*Screaming and holding his head*): It's me! It's my Great and Mighty Balloon Brain. The Earthlings have seen me. They're after me. "Had a great fall!"—That means they plan to capture Mars Central Control and me! It's an invasion of Mars! Noodle, prepare a space capsule for me. I must escape without delay. Spacemen, you must leave Earth at once, but be sure to remove all traces of your visit. The Earthlings must not know that I know— (OMEGA, IOTA *and* OOP *rush about, putting books back on shelves.*)

NOODLE: Where shall we go, sir?

THINK-TANK: A hundred million miles away from Mars. Order the invasion fleet to evacuate the entire planet of Mars. We are heading for Alpha Centauri, a hundred million miles away. (OMEGA, IOTA *and* OOP *run off right as* NOODLE *helps* THINK-TANK *off left and the curtain closes. Spotlight shines on* HISTORIAN *down right.*)

HISTORIAN (*Chuckling*): And that's how one dusty old book of nursery rhymes saved the world from a Martian invasion. As you all know, in the twenty-fifth century, five hundred years after all this happened, we Earthlings resumed contact with Mars, and we even became very chummy with the Martians. By that time, Great and Mighty Think-Tank had been replaced by a very clever Martian—the Wise and Wonderful Noodle! Oh, yes, we taught the Martians the difference between sandwiches and books. We taught them how to read, too, and we established a model library in their capital city of Marsopolis. But as you might expect, there is still one book that the Martians can never bring themselves to read. You've guessed it—*Mother Goose!* (*He bows and exits right.*)

THE END

Books *a la* Mode

by Mildred Hark and Noel McQueen

Characters

MISS KENDALL, *the new librarian*
MISS BROWN, *assistant librarian*
CHARLIE, *student part-time helper*
MR. GREGG, *chairman of library board*
BOB GREGG, *his son*
SALLY NELSON, *a new girl*
JIM
MYRA
PETE } *other boys and girls*
JANET
PROFESSOR MARTIN
MAN
WOMAN

TIME: *The present. Friday afternoon.*
SETTING: *A library, in a medium-sized town. Upstage center is a display of new books. At left is a large reading table. The library counter is at right, with the two librarians' desks behind it.*
AT RISE: MISS KENDALL *and* CHARLIE *are near the display table, and* MISS BROWN *sits at one desk.*

MISS KENDALL (*Straightening one of the signs and stepping back*): There, Charlie, I think our display looks wonderful.

CHARLIE: Yes, so do I, Miss Kendall. It's good to see some new books in this library. How did you ever get old Gregg to pay for them?

MISS KENDALL: Now, Charlie, he isn't so old and you mustn't be disrespectful in speaking of Mr. Gregg. He's the head of our library board.

CHARLIE: You're telling me? I've helped part time in this library since I was in eighth grade, but when Miss Stacy was librarian she never ordered anything but encyclopedias and dry old stuff like that.

MISS KENDALL: They're important too, Charlie, but we have enough of them. When Miss Stacy retired and Mr. Gregg hired me as the new librarian, I told him I thought we needed some new books.

CHARLIE: What did he say to that?

MISS KENDALL: The second day I was here I got a check in the mail.

CHARLIE: It's hard to believe, but here are the books to prove it. Boy, look at them—how-to-do-it books, career novels, science fiction—I guess the old saying is true. A new broom sweeps clean.

MISS KENDALL (*Laughing*): Charlie, I suppose you mean I'm the new broom. Oh, I do hope my campaign will be successful. Mr. Gregg said he wished the young people would use the library more—get interested in books—and this is the only way I know. (*She moves a sign a little.*)

CHARLIE: Yes, this display ought to help—and all those posters you had me put in the windows and at school, too.

MISS KENDALL: What about some of your classmates? Do

you think I can get the high school crowd interested in books?

CHARLIE: Well, just since you've been here, you got *me* interested, and if you got *me* interested, I figure you can get anyone.

MISS KENDALL (*Laughing*): It's not as bad as all that, Charlie.

MISS BROWN (*Comes from desk carrying a piece of paper*): Miss Kendall, this note of yours saying to make out the file cards in a different way—now, all the years Miss Stacy was here—

MISS KENDALL: Yes, I know, Miss Brown, you did it another way, but now I want it done as I've suggested.

MISS BROWN (*Shaking her head as she goes back to desk and sits, still shaking her head*): All right, Miss Kendall, but I've worked in this library for years and we never did it this way.

CHARLIE (*Going on*): No fooling, Miss Kendall, about the books. All the time I've worked here, I hardly ever opened one. I'd get 'em out of the stacks and then when they came back, put 'em away again. But as far as I was concerned, I guess books were just something that collected dust.

MISS KENDALL (*Laughing*): It didn't take you long to become interested in these new books. While you were unpacking them, you got so involved in one of them that I had to remind you there was work to do.

CHARLIE (*Indicating book*): That was this how-to-do-it book. And you know what? I was reading about making model airplanes and the author mentioned another book about the Wright brothers. So I looked on the shelves, and there it was—right here in the library. It's very good, too.

MISS KENDALL: Of course it is. There are many others as well. You like to make things with your hands and the how-to-do-it book got your attention first. Other boys and girls will become interested in different ways. (*Sound of voices and chattering off.*)

CHARLIE (*Nodding toward windows*): Say, Miss Kendall, here come some of the high school crowd now.

MYRA (*Off*): I could do with a coke.

JANET (*Off*): Or a double chocolate sundae.

JIM (*Off*): Don't look at me.

BOB (*Off*): Or me either. It's Friday and I'm broke.

MYRA (*Giggling*): Look at the new sign—"Welcome to the library." Maybe they're serving refreshments.

JIM: Fat chance, but let's go in anyway. At least we'll be in out of the rain.

MISS KENDALL (*Happily*): Oh, Charlie, they're coming in!

CHARLIE: You'd better not get too optimistic, Miss Kendall. The gang's come in here before on Friday and just sat around.

MISS KENDALL: What does Friday have to do with it?

CHARLIE: You heard what they said. It's the end of the week, and their allowances have run out. So they can't go to the Snack Shop. (MYRA, JANET, JIM, PETE, *and* BOB *enter left, wearing school clothes—jackets, raincoats, etc. They all carry schoolbooks. They hesitate a little at door.*)

MISS KENDALL: Good afternoon. Welcome to the library.

JIM: Welcome? Oh, thanks. We—we just thought we'd come in and use the table to study. Hi, Charlie.

CHARLIE: Hi, gang.

MISS KENDALL: Make yourselves at home and feel free to use the books as much as you like. I'm Miss Kendall, the new librarian.

MYRA: I'm Myra Hodge, and this is Janet Penn.

CHARLIE: The others are Jim and Pete and Bob Gregg.

MISS KENDALL: Hello, all of you. Charlie and I just finished setting up this display of the new books. I'm sure you'll want to look at them. (*She motions toward display table of books. The boys and girls hesitate a moment and then move toward table and look at books.*) Here are the how-to-do-it books and books on developing hobbies (*Pointing as she speaks*), books on problems boys and girls may have—making friends and getting along with others, career novels, science fiction—well, why don't you look through them? Take some over to the reading table if you like.

MYRA: Well—er—

JIM (*Being polite*): They look nice, all with their bright covers.

JANET: Yes, the bright-colored covers are certainly pretty.

PETE: They sure are, but—we have some books, Miss Kendall (*Showing schoolbooks*), and I—I guess we ought to get studying. (*He starts toward reading table and others follow.*)

OTHERS (*Ad lib*): Yes, we have to study. I have an exam coming up Monday. Yes, we'd better get at our studying. (*Etc.*) (*Boys and girls all go to reading table, sit down and open their books. They start to giggle. MISS KENDALL goes to upstage desk with CHARLIE following her.*)

MISS KENDALL (*Sighing*): Well, Charlie, I don't seem to be a very good salesman. (*She sits at desk.*)

CHARLIE (*Looking disappointed*): They're not going to study any more than I am. You watch, if they read anything, it'll be movie or TV magazines they have hidden in their notebooks.

MISS KENDALL: Charlie, that boy named Gregg—is he any relation to Mr. Gregg, our director?

CHARLIE: Relation? He's his son.

MISS KENDALL: He is? Surely you'd think he'd be interested in the library—with his father on the board—

CHARLIE: They don't seem to like the same things, Miss Kendall. See, Bob's mother died when he was little, and *my* mother says Mr. Gregg has been too strict. Now he says Bob has to study to be a lawyer just as he is, but Bob doesn't want to. He's a whiz at math and science and that sort of stuff. He wants to go into nuclear physics.

MISS KENDALL: He does? Well, that's wonderful.

CHARLIE: Yes. Well, I guess I'd better straighten some books in the stacks.

MISS KENDALL: All right, Charlie. (CHARLIE *goes into stacks as* MISS BROWN *rises from typewriter with two or three small file cards in her hand. She shows them to* MISS KENDALL. *The boys and girls are talking and giggling and have already taken out some movie magazines from inside their books.*)

MISS BROWN: I've done them your way, Miss Kendall. Is this right?

MISS KENDALL (*Looking at cards*): Yes, that's fine, Miss Brown. Now, don't you think this new system will make it easier to classify the books?

MISS BROWN: I don't know. Maybe. I'll try it. (*She sits at desk again.* MISS KENDALL *picks up a catalogue.*)

MISS KENDALL: Good—and I want to look over some of these new lists for future ordering.

MISS BROWN (*As she types slowly*): Well, I wouldn't order any more books if I were you. I don't know what Mr. Gregg is going to say about all these you've *already* ordered.

MISS KENDALL: Nonsense, he sent the check, didn't he? (*There is a burst of laughter from reading table.* MISS BROWN *looks over disapprovingly as boys and girls giggle and show each other pictures in magazines.*)

MYRA: Look, isn't he a dreamboat, Janet?

JIM: I don't think he's so hot.

JANET: Did you see him on TV the other night?

MISS BROWN: How a body can hear herself think with that noisy bunch in here—

MISS KENDALL: But I'm glad they *are* here, Miss Brown— (*Looking toward left as a* MAN *enters with five or six books*), and here comes someone else. (*She rises smiling and stands at counter.*) Did you want to return the books? I'll take them.

MAN: Yes'm. (*Putting books on counter*) And they're a bit overdue, I guess. I got a notice.

MISS KENDALL: Yes, they are. And five books—let's see, that's seventy-five cents.

MAN (*Taking change from pocket and handing it to* MISS KENDALL): O.K. Hardly seems worth it, though.

MISS KENDALL: If you kept them so long, you must have enjoyed them.

MAN: I tell you, we borrowed 'em for my daughter. She was sick a few weeks ago, but I don't think she even read 'em. All she wants to do is watch TV.

MISS KENDALL: Oh, I see. There are some new books you might be interested in. (*Motioning toward display table as* MAN *starts left. A* WOMAN *enters left and goes to counter.*)

MAN: Haven't time today. (*Exits.*)

MISS KENDALL (*Disappointed*): Oh.

MISS BROWN (*To* WOMAN): May I help you?

WOMAN: The truth is I need some historical facts.

MISS KENDALL (*Brightening*): Historical facts? There's a very good reference on the shelf there, Miss Brown— "Facts of History," number 942. Why don't you get that one for her? (MISS BROWN *goes into stacks and brings back book as* WOMAN *opens her purse and takes out card.*) I take it you're interested in history?

WOMAN: I wouldn't say that exactly, but I have to be if I want to win the thousand dollars.

MISS KENDALL: The—the thousand dollars?

WOMAN: It's the puzzle in the newspaper. I surely hope I can win the prize. (MISS KENDALL *stamps card and puts it in book.*)

MISS KENDALL: Yes, of course. (*As the* WOMAN *starts out*) Would you like to look at our new books?

WOMAN: Not unless they'd help with the contest—

MISS KENDALL: No, I suppose not. (WOMAN *goes out.*)

MISS BROWN (*Who is looking at books* MAN *brought back*): You'll get used to her. Sometimes she even wants me to find the answers for her. And look at this book that man brought back. (*Holding it up*) Water-marked!

MISS KENDALL: Oh, dear, that's too bad.

MISS BROWN: Guess someone was using it to stand a vase of flowers on. That's what they do with books in this town. They don't read 'em.

MISS KENDALL: Miss Brown, I'm not going to be discouraged. (*Sits down*) We've made a start—with our display, and there's no reason we can't get more people interested in books.

MISS BROWN (*Sitting down*): You watch. We'll just have the same old ones. The puzzle fans, and a few old ladies who like romantic novels—

MISS KENDALL: There's no reason why we can't build up our library. They're doing it in other towns. More people are using libraries now than they ever did before. Statistics show it.

MISS BROWN: You can prove anything by statistics. Anyhow, you mark my words. You won't get 'em to read— not in this town. They'll go to movies and watch TV but they won't read. They're too lazy to use their heads.

MISS KENDALL: I'm afraid you're just being pessimistic, Miss Brown. I know we can do it. We'll get the young people interested.

MISS BROWN: Humph, you mean that bunch over there?

MISS KENDALL: Certainly, I do. (*There is giggling and then loud laughter from group at table. MISS BROWN rises quickly and steps to counter.*) Miss Brown, don't.

MISS BROWN (*Tapping bell several times. Then angrily*): Quiet, quiet, all of you. Don't you children know how to behave in a library? (*They all quickly turn to their books and pretend to study.*)

MISS KENDALL: Miss Brown, aren't you forgetting yourself? When I'm here, it's my place to discipline the young people.

MISS BROWN: Yes, yes, I'm sorry. (*She sits again.*) But they do get on my nerves. (*She goes back to her typing.*)

CHARLIE (*Entering right*): You ring for me, Miss Kendall?

MISS KENDALL: No, I didn't, but as long as you're here, those books can be put away. (*She points to stack of books on counter.*)

CHARLIE: O.K. (*He walks around front and picks up books. SALLY enters left hesitantly, looks around and walks slowly to table.*)

SALLY (*Shyly, to group at table*): Hello.

JIM *and* JANET: Hello, Sally.

MISS KENDALL: Well, here comes someone else. And she's young, too. Do you know her, Charlie?

CHARLIE: Sure, I guess I know her as well as anyone does. She's kind of shy. Her name is Sally Nelson.

MISS KENDALL: Sally Nelson. Is she a new girl?

CHARLIE (*As SALLY moves to stage center and looks at books on display table*): Yes, she started this semester, but she doesn't seem to be in with the crowd.

MISS KENDALL: Hm-m-m. And she's pretty.

CHARLIE: Yes, I guess she is, now that you mention it. (*Goes off into stacks.*)

MISS KENDALL: She seems interested in the books, too, but if she's so shy, I don't suppose I'd better push her.

MISS BROWN: She just came in out of the rain like the others and is too shy to sit with them. (MISS KENDALL *and* MISS BROWN *go back to their work for a few moments as* SALLY *picks up two or three books and looks at them. Group at table talk quietly. Then* SALLY *turns and approaches the counter.*)

MISS KENDALL (*Smiling*): Hello, Sally. I'm Miss Kendall, the new librarian.

SALLY: Oh, how do you do. How did you know my name?

MISS KENDALL: I asked Charlie. He goes to school, but he works here, too, helping keep the books straight. I guess most boys know the names of the pretty girls.

SALLY (*Smiling a little*): Oh.

MISS KENDALL: Do you like our display of new books?

SALLY: Yes, they're very nice, but I was wondering if you had a book—well, that would—well, Miss Kendall, you'll think this is silly, but a book that would show a girl how to make people like her. (*Then blurting out*) That might even get someone to ask her to the school dance next month—or something like that.

MISS BROWN (*Looking at* MISS KENDALL): See.

MISS KENDALL (*Taking no notice*): Why, Sally, my dear. (*Rising*) I don't think you are silly at all. Books can help people in many ways. Let's go look at some of these new ones. (*She goes to display table and* SALLY *follows her.*) You want something that will show you how to make friends. And (*Picking up book*) here's one with that very title, *How to Make Friends*. It discusses the qualities that are important in friendship and shows how you can learn to be more friendly. For instance (*Leafing through the book*), here's a whole section on "Showing Interest in the Things Other People Are Interested In." Now, suppose the boy— (*Smiling*) Is it a boy?

SALLY: Well, yes, mainly.

MISS KENDALL: That's quite natural. Well, then, suppose he's interested in baseball. You'd do well to show an interest in that.

SALLY: Oh, but it isn't baseball, Miss Kendall. He's going to study law and be a lawyer. But I don't know how to get interested in law.

MISS KENDALL: No—no, of course, you don't. (*She glances over at table where the boys and girls are laughing and talking again.*) And somehow, in your case, I don't think an interest in law would help. Now, you take these science fiction books—

SALLY: But, why?

MISS KENDALL: Well, it's because so many people who go in for subjects like law often like to relax with fiction and —and such a person would very probably like science fiction. (*Picking up book*) Now, here's one called *Into Space with Atom Power.* Now, if you were to read that and then talk to the person about it, you might find that he'd be fascinated.

SALLY: Well, I—I don't quite see why, but if you say so, I'll try.

MISS KENDALL: Good, good, that's fine. You'll want to take the one on friendship, too. I'll sign them out for you. (SALLY *takes books, hands* MISS KENDALL *a library card, and* MISS KENDALL *goes to counter and stamps it.*) Now, why don't you sit at the table with the rest of them? (*The phone rings and* MISS BROWN *rises and answers it.*)

SALLY: I don't know if they want me.

MISS KENDALL: Of course they do. You know, Sally, if you want to make friends, often you have to take the first step yourself, even if it's difficult. (*She goes left again with* SALLY *following.*)

MISS BROWN (*Into phone*): Yes, yes. Oh my. I certainly will. (*Hangs up*) Miss Kendall, Miss Kendall.

MISS KENDALL: Just a minute, Miss Brown.

MISS BROWN: This is important, Miss Kendall. That call was—

MISS KENDALL: Please, Miss Brown. Boys and girls, you can find room for Sally, can't you? She's found a book she wants to read.

BOYS *and* GIRLS: Why—why, sure . . . Sure.

MISS KENDALL (*Pulling out chair next to* BOB GREGG): Sit down, Sally, and read your book with the rest. (*She pretends not to notice others putting their magazines into notebooks. She smiles and goes back to desk.*) Now, Miss Brown, what is it?

MISS BROWN: Oh, Miss Kendall, that was Mr. Gregg's secretary! And Mr. Gregg is on his way here—and—and he'll be here any minute and—oh, dear, what'll we do?

MISS KENDALL: Isn't that nice? I'm so glad we got the display ready in time.

MISS BROWN: You don't know Mr. Gregg—

MISS KENDALL: Of course, I know him.

MISS BROWN: Not as well as I do. I don't think he'll like the display.

MISS KENDALL: Why not?

MISS BROWN: He always finds something wrong, Miss Kendall, and, oh dear, we ought to be getting ready—

MISS KENDALL: We *are* ready.

MISS BROWN: But Mr. Gregg is coming, and there ought to be something else we can do—

MISS KENDALL (*Sitting at desk*): I, for one, am going to look over my list of books. It will be a good chance to ask him about ordering some more.

MISS BROWN: I wouldn't talk about ordering any more. Oh dear, oh dear! (*She sits and turns back to her typewriter, shaking her head.*)

BOB (*Looking over at book* SALLY *is beginning to read*): Hm-m-m, science fiction. Are you interested in science?

SALLY: Well—yes, a little. That is, I'm *getting* interested. Are you?

MYRA: Is he interested? He's had nothing but straight A's in science all year.

SALLY: Oh, then, maybe you'd like to look at this. (*Shoving book toward* BOB.)

BOB: No, thanks, I—say, that picture is the latest thing in atomic reactors.

SALLY: It—it is?

BOB: Sure, let's look. (*He takes book and leafs through and reads a little to himself*) Yes, and that's a good description of a reactor. Whoever wrote this knows something about atomic science all right. Say, are there other books like this in that display?

SALLY: Why, yes, I think so.

BOB: Let's go look them over. (*He rises.*)

SALLY: Well, all right. (*She rises and follows* BOB *right to table.*)

JANET (*Looking after them*): Can you imagine that?

PETE (*Laughing*): Maybe little Sally isn't as dumb as we thought she was.

MYRA: It's the first time I've ever seen a girl get a tumble out of Bob Gregg. Now, why didn't I think of something like that?

JIM: Because you're my steady, that's why.

MYRA: Oh, all right, but darned if they don't seem to be really interested in the old books. (MISS KENDALL *looks over at them and then smiles at* MISS BROWN.)

BOB (*He has picked up two or three books and glanced through them, then he hands one to* SALLY): Here's one I'd like to read. It has a lot of stuff on jet airplanes.

SALLY: Yes—yes, and the story looks exciting.

BOB: I suppose you would think of the story first, but I'll enjoy checking up on the scientific facts the author uses. (*Taking book from* SALLY *and going toward desk.*) Miss

Kendall, may I borrow this book, to take home, I mean?

Miss Kendall: If you have a library card, of course you may.

Bob (*Taking card from his wallet and laughing*): Sure, I have a card. (*He hands book and card to* Miss Kendall.) I guess I've never used it much, but this book looks good.

Miss Kendall (*Stamping card and then smiling and handing* Bob *the book*): I hope you'll like it.

Bob (*Returns to display table where* Sally *has been looking at several other books*): Find anything else?

Sally: Not that I want right now, but look, there are all kinds of things, hobbies and how to find out the kind of work you want to do and—

Bob: Yes, I looked at that one, and it would be just the thing for Jim. I'm going to start to read this one.

Sally: Yes, I—I guess I'll read mine, too. (*They go back to reading table and sit down.*)

Myra: Well, here are the bookworms.

Bob: You can laugh if you want, but there are really some good books over there. For instance, Jim, you're always saying you have to go to work after high school—

Jim (*Grinning*): I suppose there's a book that will find me a job.

Bob: No, but there's a book on vocations that looks good. In the introduction, it says it shows people how to find out what they are best fitted for.

Jim: You intrigue me. (*Stands up*) Maybe I'll take a look. Come on, Myra, maybe we can find a book that will get you a good enough job to support me in my old age.

Myra (*Standing up*): All right, but don't talk as though we're engaged. Going steady is one thing but being engaged is another. (*As they go to display table*) Besides, I may not ever get married. I'm going to be a career girl.

SALLY (SALLY *and* BOB *have been reading*): Bob.

BOB (*Looking up from book*): Yes?

SALLY: What's uranium 235?

BOB: If you don't know that, I guess you really don't know much about science, do you?

SALLY: I—I guess not.

BOB: What do you want to read a book like that for, anyway?

SALLY: Well, I—I have a kid brother who is always spouting this kind of stuff and—so I wanted to learn something about it.

BOB: Oh, so that's it! Well, for instance, in common uranium—uranium 238—the atom can't be split, but 235 has three less neutrons, and it can be split.

SALLY: Oh, I see.

BOB: Just ask me if you run into things like that.

SALLY: Yes, thanks. (*They go back to reading.*)

JANET: This erudite atmosphere is getting too much for me, Pete. Let's go look at the books.

PETE: O.K. (*As they rise, looking toward counter where* JIM *is standing with book*) It looks as though Jim's found something he's going to borrow. (*They go to display table.*)

JIM (*Handing book and card to* MISS KENDALL): I'd like to borrow this one because I guess I'll have to go to work next year.

MISS KENDALL (*Looking at cover of book*): *Choosing Your Vocation.* Yes, that's a very useful book. But Jim, are you sure you'll have to stop school?

JIM: Yes. I don't want to stop, but—well, there just isn't the money, Miss Kendall.

MISS KENDALL: Maybe you could get a scholarship somewhere.

JIM (*Laughing a little*): I don't know if I'm prize-winning material.

MISS KENDALL: You just wait a minute. *(She taps bell.)*

CHARLIE *(Appears from right)*: Yes, Miss Kendall?

MISS KENDALL: Charlie, bring me *Carroll's Guide to Scholarships,* please. (CHARLIE *goes off right.* MYRA *comes from table with a book.*) You found something, Myra?

MYRA: Yes, I haven't read a book for ages, but I've always been interested in interior decorating and this is about a girl who goes into that field. *(Hands book and card to* MISS KENDALL.*)*

MISS KENDALL: You'll find that these career novels contain a lot of useful information as well as an interesting story. *(Gives book back to* MYRA.*)*

MYRA: Thank you. *(She goes back to reading table.)*

MISS KENDALL *(As* CHARLIE *appears and hands her a book)*: Thank you, Charlie. *(He goes off right again.)* Look at this, Jim. *(She reads from cover.)* *Carroll's Guide to Scholarships.* This book has helped many, many students to continue with their education. It lists millions of dollars worth of scholarships that are given out every year, and it shows how and where to apply for them. Then there are valuable hints on preparing for examinations and—oh, all sorts of information.

JIM: Say, I never knew there were books like that. I'll take that one instead.

MISS KENDALL: Why not take them both? This one on choosing your vocation may help you decide what program you want to pursue in college in preparation for a specific job.

JIM: O.K. I'll read them both. *(He grins.)* And if I can figure some way to go to school next year, I'll tell everyone that Miss Kendall at Gregg Public Library is putting me through college.

MISS KENDALL *(Laughing)*: You won't tell them anything of the sort. That book shows you how to put yourself through college. (As JIM *goes back to reading table)*

Miss Brown, now what do you think Mr. Gregg will have to say?

MISS BROWN: I don't know. I do hope he's satisfied, because I have to admit—well, Miss Kendall, you do have such a way with the youngsters.

MISS KENDALL: Thank you, Miss Brown, coming from you, that is a real compliment. (JANET *and* PETE *leave display table, each carrying a book.*)

PETE: This book has some good stuff on color photography under artificial light. Already I can see where I've been doing a couple of things wrong. (*Reaching counter and handing book and card to* MISS KENDALL.) I'd like to borrow this one, Miss Kendall.

MISS KENDALL (*Smiling*): Very well. (*She stamps card and hands book and card back. Then to* JANET) You have one, too?

JANET: Yes. (*Smiling*) Everyone else seems to be reading so I didn't want to be lonesome.

MISS KENDALL (*Looking at book*): Well, now, I happen to have read this book myself, and I'm sure you'll enjoy it. We have several more in the stacks by the same author so when you've read this one, let me know if you want some more.

JANET: I will, thank you. (*They go back to reading table.*)

JIM: Say, Myra, I may go back to school next year after all. Look at this list of foundations and other outfits that grant scholarships.

MYRA: Why, there are hundreds of them. How do you go about getting one?

JIM: It tells how to go about it in here. (*Grinning*) There's only one drawback. You have to work hard.

MYRA: Jim, you've always worked hard and had good marks.

JIM: You can bet I'm going to from now on. (*Looking up*

as GREGG *enters left)* Say, isn't that Bob's father? Bob, look who's here.

BOB: For Pete's sake!

GREGG: Hello, Bob.

BOB: Hello, Dad.

GREGG: I didn't expect to find you here. It's good to see young people take an interest in reading. *(He goes toward counter.)*

MISS KENDALL *(Standing up and walking to the front of counter)*: Good afternoon, Mr. Gregg. I'm so glad you've come. (MISS BROWN *also stands, with some hesitation.)*

GREGG: Thank you, Miss Kendall, and I'm delighted to see that you have coaxed some of the boys and girls into the library. *(He nods at* MISS BROWN) How do you do, Miss—Miss—

MISS BROWN: Brown. How do you do, Mr. Gregg.

GREGG: Ah, yes, Miss Brown. (MISS BROWN *sits.)*

MISS KENDALL *(Still smiling)*: I haven't really done anything, Mr. Gregg. It's because of those new books we bought.

GREGG: New books, what new books?

MISS KENDALL: The ones you told me to order. *(From now on, young people look up and all watch.)*

GREGG: I didn't tell you to order anything.

MISS KENDALL: But you sent the check.

GREGG: Of course, I sent the check. And my letter said that I'd be in as soon as possible to go over the lists and help you select—didn't you read the letter, Miss Kendall?

MISS KENDALL: Well—well, I must have. But I was so excited and pleased to get the check that perhaps I didn't read the letter very carefully. I did notice that you'd be in soon.

GREGG: It seems most irresponsible to me. I'm not used to having people ignore my letters.

MISS KENDALL: Oh, I'm sorry, Mr. Gregg, but the books are already here, and we just finished setting up this display. (*She starts toward the display and* GREGG *follows.*)

GREGG: Display? (*Looking toward display*) Books all stacked up like cans in a supermarket. Well, we'll have to get rid of the whole cheap business. Professor Martin from the university is coming to meet me here and see the library.

MISS KENDALL: Who is Professor Martin?

GREGG: He happens to be a professor who taught me in college, and I've often asked him to visit the library. Today he agreed to come and help us select books.

MISS KENDALL: Oh. Well, we've saved him the trouble. Look, you can see from the signs the variety we have. Career novels, do-it-yourself books, science fiction—

GREGG: Science fiction? Why, that's a lot of trash!

MISS KENDALL: Not the titles I've selected, Mr. Gregg. Lots of professors read science fiction. (*Picking up book*) Now you take this one. It's well written and contains a great many scientific facts. Librarians today know that it is exactly the sort of thing that can get young people interested in reading.

GREGG: Nonsense! And career novels! What earthly use can they be?

MISS KENDALL: A great deal of use. They help young people to find out the type of vocation they might like and—

GREGG: Vocations! Those children don't have enough sense at their age to choose. They need to be told what to do. You take my boy over there. He has some bug in his head about being a scientist, but I know better. I'm going to make a lawyer out of him.

MISS KENDALL: Mr. Gregg, this is the twentieth century —you talk as though you were living in the Dark Ages.

If I remain as head of this library, I'm going to operate it as an up-to-date institution.

GREGG: Why, I— (*Quiet and angry*) Miss Kendall, I'm afraid I made a grave mistake in hiring you as librarian for my library. I don't often make mistakes but—

MISS KENDALL: No, I'm sure you don't. At least in your own estimation. But I wasn't aware that this was *your* library. I thought your grandfather presented it to the town as the Gregg *Public* Library.

GREGG (*Most displeased*): That's neither here nor there. Miss Kendall, you've taken a great deal of authority upon yourself—acted in a very high-handed way, and I'm not pleased—not pleased at all. I suppose you know what this means— (BOB *comes forward and in a moment* SALLY *follows him.*)

BOB: Dad, wait—you can't—

GREGG: What's the matter with you, Bob?

BOB: If you fire Miss Kendall, you're crazy.

GREGG: Bob, go back to the table. This isn't your business.

BOB: I think it is, Dad. You can't talk to Miss Kendall this way. She's O.K. We've all felt at home here in the library today—

MISS KENDALL: Thank you, Bob. It's true, Mr. Gregg. For the first time, the young people are using the library. They're really interested in the books.

GREGG: What kind of books are they?

SALLY (*Forgetting herself*): They're—they're wonderful books, Mr. Gregg. Bob likes the science ones.

GREGG: Science? That's just science fiction.

BOB: Fiction or not, there's a lot of good stuff in them. And it's made me realize one thing—I'm going to be a scientist. It's the only work I want to do.

GREGG: Bob, this is a closed subject. You and I have talked—

BOB: Dad, I can't be a lawyer. You like law, but I like science.

GREGG: Now, Miss Kendall, perhaps you see how much damage can be done with this sort of book. (JIM *comes forward followed by* MYRA.)

JIM: Damage? Say, you're off the beam, Mr. Gregg. Miss Kendall's helped us all today. Why, she's even shown me how I can go to college.

GREGG: Jim, you know your folks can't afford to send you to college.

MYRA: He can get a scholarship, Mr. Gregg. The book tells all about it. It says no bright boy need stay out of college just because of financial reasons.

GREGG: Miss Kendall, these books are more dangerous than I thought—putting all sorts of nonsense into young people's heads— (PROFESSOR MARTIN, *an elderly gentleman with twinkling eyes, enters left. Boys and girls move back toward table a little.*)

PROFESSOR: Busy day in the library, I see. Hello, Harry, I'm a little late as usual.

GREGG (*Flustered*): Professor Martin. You're here.

PROFESSOR: Yes, quite obviously. (*Smiling at* MISS KENDALL) You must be Miss Kendall, the new librarian.

MISS KENDALL: Yes. How do you do, Professor Martin. We've been having a little discussion about the new books. (*She indicates display.*)

PROFESSOR: Oh, so you've already ordered them? (*Looking at books*) Hm-m-m. (*Then to* GREGG) Harry, I always thought you'd have a stuffy old library. I'm surprised to find books like these.

GREGG: I should think so. You're no more surprised than I am. These books were ordered by mistake. They're going to be returned. I'm going to get them out of here—

MISS KENDALL (*Angry again*): Mr. Gregg, I happen to be the librarian. If these books go, I go, too.

GREGG: That's fine. Miss Kendall, you're fired.

PROFESSOR: Dear me, dear me. It seems I've walked in on a little argument. (*To* MISS KENDALL) You mustn't mind Harry, Miss Kendall. I've known him a long time—had him in my classes. Always a little set in his ways—inclined to think he was right in everything. But really a nice fellow, you know. Some excellent qualities.

MISS KENDALL: I guess I haven't seen that side of him.

GREGG: Professor Martin, I don't think this is quite fair. I may have done some things when I was young—

PROFESSOR: Yes, but Harry, you don't seem to have changed very much and that means you really haven't grown up yet. (BOYS *and* GIRLS *giggle.* MISS BROWN, *who has been listening, beside herself with anxiety, nervously taps bell.* CHARLIE *enters and listens, too.*) You know, Harry, if you fire Miss Kendall, I doubt if she'll have much trouble obtaining another position. She obviously knows how to select books that young people like.

GREGG: But, Professor—

PROFESSOR: Now, you let me talk a minute. (*Picking up books*) Young people need books like these. (*Smiling*) They are, we might say, books *a la mode.*

GREGG (*Crossly*): What do you mean? Books with ice cream?

PROFESSOR: Certainly not, Harry, remember your French. *A la mode* really means "in the fashion"—in the popular style. These books are up-to-date—and practical, too. They help young people with their problems—they show them how to live. Through them, they get interested in other types of books—the classics, the fine biographies—the kind of books you prefer, Harry.

MISS KENDALL: I tried to explain that to Mr. Gregg but—

PROFESSOR (*Picking up another book*): Yes, you've made a fine selection, Miss Kendall—why, dear me, you've even got one by Mike Parrish.

MISS KENDALL: Yes, there are two or three by him, and they're all good titles.

GREGG: Mike Parrish—a silly-sounding name, isn't it?

PROFESSOR: Well, perhaps it is—perhaps it is. Maybe I can think of a better one, but I've used it for so many books that it's rather well known. It's a pseudonym of mine. (BOB *goes to reading table.*)

MISS KENDALL (*Laughs*): An author—right here in our library!

GREGG: You've been writing books like these?

PROFESSOR: Yes, Harry, I've been writing them for years. When I'm not teaching young people, I'm writing books for them, and I must admit that I enjoy it. (BOB *picks up book* SALLY *has been reading and goes to* PROFESSOR.)

BOB (*Holding up book*): Mike Parrish is your pen name? Then you wrote this one, too, Professor.

PROFESSOR (*Looking at book*): *Into Space with the Atom* —yes, that's one of mine.

BOB: See, Dad, and you called it trash.

PROFESSOR: Oh, he did, did he? Let me tell you, Harry Gregg, it takes some brains to write that sort of trash.

BOB: I'll say. I know something about atomic science and the Professor knows his stuff.

PROFESSOR: Thank you, Bob. You see, Harry?

GREGG: This is all most incredible.

BOYS *and* GIRLS (*Ad lib*): Think of having a real author right here! How exciting! What a thrill! (*Etc.*)

MISS KENDALL: Yes, it certainly is thrilling. Why, Professor, if we had only known you were coming, I'd have arranged for an autographing party.

BOYS *and* GIRLS (*Gather around* PROFESSOR *with pieces*

of paper and notebooks): Please, Professor, may I have your autograph? (*Etc.*)

PROFESSOR (*As he autographs*): Miss Kendall, we seem to be having an autographing party. Now, which do you want? Professor Martin, Ph.D., or Mike Parrish?

BOYS *and* GIRLS (*Laughing*): Both of them! Both of them! (CHARLIE *has joined group and gets an autograph.*)

PROFESSOR (*As he finishes autographing*): You know, I seldom get a chance to have such an enthusiastic group of admirers about me. It makes me want to celebrate —have a real party. Where can we get some refreshments —to go with our books *a la mode?*

BOB: Well—there's the Snack Shop, but this is Friday.

PROFESSOR: Ah, yes. I know something about students' finances on Friday. So you show me the way and I'll treat.

BOYS *and* GIRLS (*Rushing and picking up their books*): Hooray for Professor Martin! Hooray for Mike Parrish!

SALLY: But how about Miss Kendall? Can't she come, too?

PROFESSOR: Of course she can.

MISS KENDALL: Thank you, but I don't think I'd better leave the library—that is, if I'm still librarian.

GREGG: Miss Kendall, I—

PROFESSOR: How about you, Harry? Will you come?

GREGG: No, I doubt if I'll be missed. The young people didn't ask me.

BOB: Oh, but, Dad, sure, we—

GREGG: Besides, there's something I want to say to Miss Kendall.

PROFESSOR: Very good. I'll see you later, Harry. You, too, Miss Kendall. Now, let's go find this Snack Shop. Goodbye, all of you. (*He goes out left with the* BOYS *and* GIRLS.)

BOYS *and* GIRLS (*Ad lib*): Goodbye, Miss Kendall. Thanks a lot. We'll be back again. (*Etc.*)

GREGG (*Looking at* MISS KENDALL): Miss Kendall, I—

MISS KENDALL: Yes, Mr. Gregg?

GREGG: This is a bit difficult for me, but I—I apologize. I'm afraid I've made another mistake. And, of course, you *are* still librarian if you'll stay after what—

MISS KENDALL: I want to stay.

GREGG: Thank you. I'm—I'm sorry for everything. I guess Professor Martin is right. I have a great deal to learn.

MISS KENDALL (*Smiling a little*): Well, we have a number of books. Perhaps a reference work—

GREGG (*He goes to display table and looks at two or three books*): No, I guess I need something on—well, understanding myself or understanding others or—perhaps I haven't been a very good father. You seem to understand young people a great deal better than I do. Would you help me, Miss Kendall?

MISS KENDALL (*Coming to table, smiling.* MISS BROWN, *sitting at her typewriter watching, smiles, too*): I'll be glad to help. And you know, you can learn almost anything from books.

GREGG (*He is looking through one book and now turns to her, holding one finger in a place in it*): Yes, so I gather, and for now, I've selected this one. (*He opens it.*) I notice there is a section here on how a gentleman asks a young lady to have dinner with him. It says that if you use this approach, she will be almost sure to accept. (*He smiles.*)

MISS KENDALL (*Smiling and looking at book*): That is a very reliable source of information, Mr. Gregg. (*Quick curtain.*)

THE END

Running the Country

by Janice Auritt Oser

Characters

TIM, *a safety patrolman*
JOHNNY, *a newsboy slightly older than the others*
MARILYN
PEGGY
BILLY
FRED
JANET
TOMMY
SUSAN
JIMMY
MISS WINSLOW, *a teacher*

SETTING: *A street corner.*
AT RISE: *Children stand waiting to cross the street.* TIM *bars their way.* JOHNNY *comes by selling newspapers.*

MARILYN: Look, Peggy, here comes Johnny. He really *is* selling papers.
PEGGY (*Looking proudly at* JOHNNY): He says he'll run a paper some day.
JOHNNY: Extree, extree, read all about it! President calls on all citizens to aid new 'ministration!
JIMMY: What are you doing, Johnny?

JOHNNY: Can't you see?

BILLY: Show us a paper, Johnny!

JOHNNY (*Proudly*): Got a dime?

BILLY (*Taking money from his pocket*): Oh, gee. All I have is seven cents.

FRED: I have three cents. Let us see, Johnny.

JOHNNY (*Collecting*): Sure. (*Pockets money and goes out*) Extree, extree, read all about it!

FRED (*Others gather around him as he reads slowly*): "Tells Congress nation must (*Spells out*) u-n-i-t-e to meet problems . . ." The print gets too small.

MARILYN: My father says the paper's always full of problems. He says even grown-ups don't always run things right.

PEGGY: I'll bet Miss Winslow could teach them how to run things. She teaches us everything.

JANET: Why don't they ask Miss Winslow?

BILLY: Miss Winslow can't do everything. She's only a girl.

FRED (*Manfully*): We could help her.

PEGGY: What could we do?

FRED: Why, lots of things. I could be President.

TOMMY: And I could be Congress.

SUSAN: You can't be Congress, silly. Congress is lots of people.

TOMMY: Well, I have lots of friends.

BILLY: I'll be a judge, like my father. I'll be Chief Judge.

MARILYN: You boys always want to run everything. But I have to be Treasurer, 'cause I'm class treasurer.

JIMMY: I'll be the messenger.

JANET: What for? We're all together.

JIMMY: No, I mean to England and France and all those places.

SUSAN: That's not a messenger. That's an ambassador. I

can be an ambassador, too. You can't keep running to England *and* France.

TIM (*Turning around to show way is clear*): You can go now. (*Children ignore him and go on talking; he shrugs his shoulders and listens to conversation.*)

PEGGY: I'll help Johnny run a newspaper.

JANET: I want to be a nurse. I'll be head nurse.

FRED: This isn't a hospital we're running, this is the country!

SUSAN: You can be head of the Red Cross, Janet.

TIM: And I'll be Chief of Police!

FRED: As President, I say no more homework.

SUSAN: You can't just *say* that. You have to pass a law.

FRED (*Turning to* TOMMY): Congress, pass a law.

JANET: Miss Winslow wouldn't like that.

FRED: And we'll have a party on Saturday. A big party, with ice cream for everyone!

TOMMY: I can't come on Saturday. I have to go to the dentist.

FRED: The whole country can't go without a party just because *you* can't come!

TOMMY: Well, you can't have it. I won't pass a law to give you the money to have a party.

MARILYN: What money? We haven't any money.

FRED: How can we run a country without money?

PEGGY: I have a nickel.

SUSAN: So do I. Let's collect from everyone. We'll be paying taxes.

MARILYN: Good. Everybody put money in the Treasury. (*Holds out her hand, all dig in pockets for nickels and pennies*)

FRED: How much do we have?

MARILYN (*Counting*): Five, ten, eleven, fourteen . . . no, I mean (*Counting on her fingers*) twelve, thirteen, fourteen, fifteen, sixteen . . . (FRED *drops part of paper,* JIMMY *picks it up and starts to read the comics.*) Let's see . . . twenty-one, thirty-one, five and one are six, thirty-six . . . thirty-seven cents!

FRED: Good. We'll put it towards the party.

TOMMY: But I can't come on Saturday. And anyway, I'd rather go to a baseball game. (*Winds up and pitches to* BILLY)

PEGGY: We can use it to buy newspapers. We ought to know what's happening to the country.

JANET: We have a newspaper.

PEGGY: But new ones come out every day. (JIMMY *starts to laugh.*) What's so funny?

JIMMY: It's a riddle . . . Why does the moron tip-toe past the medicine cabinet?

TIM: Why?

JIMMY: So he won't wake up the sleeping pills. (*Others laugh.*)

PEGGY (*Scornfully*): You shouldn't be reading the funnies, you should be reading the political news.

FRED: Aw, the print's too small. And the words are too long. I say, have a party!

TOMMY (*Having a catch with* BILLY): Baseball game!

FRED: Who's running this country anyway?

BILLY (*Letting ball go into street*): Not you. When there's a fight, the judge decides. And I'm Chief Judge. The Judge says we go to the movies.

JANET: I'd rather have a party.

TIM (*To* BILLY, *who starts to run into the street after the ball*): Wait a minute! There may be a car coming. You can't go now. (*Bars the way*)

BILLY: You can't tell me what to do! I'm Chief Judge!

TIM: Well, I'm Chief of Police! (*They stare at each other angrily.*)

MARILYN: This is terrible. We're acting like grown-ups!

JANET: Here comes a grown-up. It's Miss Winslow! (MISS WINSLOW *enters right.* TIM *looks up and down the street and motions to* BILLY *to retrieve the ball.*)

MARILYN (*Going up to* MISS WINSLOW): Miss Winslow, we're in a terrible fix! The President wants a party and the Judge wants to go to the movies and Congress wants to go to a baseball game! And we don't have enough money anyway!

MISS WINSLOW: What's all this? Congress wants to go to a baseball game?

SUSAN: We're running the country.

MARILYN: To help the grown-ups out.

MISS WINSLOW (*Laughing*): Oh, I see. And you're having trouble?

MARILYN (*Holding out money*): You see, we have thirty-seven cents. I'm Treasurer.

JIMMY: And I'm an am—am—

SUSAN: Ambassador. To England. I'm ambassador to France.

TOMMY: And I'm Congress.

FRED: And I'm President, and I say we ought to have a party.

JANET: And he wants to pass a law against homework!

MISS WINSLOW: Oh ho! Presidents don't just give parties, Fred. What else do you do?

FRED: Well . . . run things. Run the country.

MISS WINSLOW: That's a big job, running the country. Presidents have to know a great deal. And if you're President, I'll expect you to know all the answers in that history test next week.

TOMMY: Oh-oh, Fred. You'd better stay home and study next Saturday. I think I'll skip the dentist and go to the baseball game.

MISS WINSLOW: Oh, but if you're Congress, Tommy, you have a big job, too. You have to pass all kinds of laws, and you won't know if a law is good or bad if you don't know your history, too—and citizenship and . . . oh, many, many things. Congress had better get busy in school.

BILLY: My father says a judge is always going to school.

MISS WINSLOW: That's right, Billy. He may not come to school exactly and sit in a classroom, but he keeps right on learning.

JIMMY: I'm glad I'm only an am—am—

SUSAN: Ambassador. To England.

MISS WINSLOW: Yes, but if you want England to be our friend you should know a lot about England . . . how the country's run and what kind of a country it is.

PEGGY: We thought you could teach us. I want to learn how to run a newspaper—to help Johnny.

MISS WINSLOW (*Smiling*): Well, I'll try. But it will take time. It will take 'til way past high school—*and* some homework, I'm afraid.

FRED: But we don't have to wait that long to have a party.

MARILYN: We have some money for it now.

TOMMY: But I can't come Saturday.

BILLY: You tell us, Miss Winslow. Who decides what we do with the money?

MISS WINSLOW (*To* TOMMY): Well, you have to pass a law, Congress. (*To* FRED) And the President has to approve it. (*To* BILLY) And you have to see if it's Constitutional. Because if you're going to be Chief Judge, you'll have to know all about the Constitution.

SUSAN: But we don't all want the same thing.

MISS WINSLOW: People have different ideas about how to run the country. In this country, when that happens, we take a vote.

PEGGY: Good! We'll have an election!

MISS WINSLOW: Why don't we round up some more voters? We could get the whole class in on it. Maybe we can have a party in school—on the last day, when we've learned a little more about running the country.

JIMMY: That'd be great! Let's go tell everybody! (*Starts to cross street*)

TIM (*Barring way*): Wait! The way isn't clear. (*Turns after a moment*) O.K., you can go now!

MISS WINSLOW: Thank you, Tim. We may be running the country but we still have to obey the law! (*All cross street. Curtain.*)

THE END

The Three Royal R's

by Mary Thurman Pyle

Characters

REV. RALPH EVERETT, *the teacher*
EDWARD TANNER, *a wheelwright*
GEORGE HIGGS, *a constable of the nearby town*
JOHN EVANS, *a Quaker*
WIDOW GRAY
MRS. PHILLIPS
THOMAS, *an aristocratic boy*
NICHOLAS, *son of the Widow Gray*
MARGARET
RICHARD, *her brother*
FRANCIS
ABIGAIL, *his younger sister*   } *pupils*
BETSY
MATILDA, *her sister*
OTHER CHILDREN

TIME: *Early morning on a September day—the opening day of school—about the middle of the Eighteenth Century.*
SETTING: *A "field school" in Virginia.*
AT RISE: MR. EVERETT *is just finishing writing the alphabet*

THE THREE ROYAL R'S

on the chart with black crayon, and begins to count the
slates and pencils. WIDOW GRAY *and her son* NICHOLAS
stand outside. They are poorly but neatly dressed.

EVERETT: Good morning. Be so good as to come in.

WIDOW (*As she and* NICHOLAS *enter*): Good morning,
your Reverence. I'm the Widow Gray, of your parish, sir,
and this is my son, Nicholas.

EVERETT: I recall your visit this summer to the parish
house, Widow Gray. I'm happy to see you again. Please
be seated.

WIDOW: Oh, no, sir, thank you kindly. It's only about Nick
I've come.

EVERETT (*Holds out his hand to* NICHOLAS): So this is the
lad. I trust you are well?

NICHOLAS (*Formally*): My health is good, sir, and I trust
yours is the same. (*Bursting out eagerly*) I'm coming to
your school, Mr. Everett! My Ma says I am, and she says
it has all been properly arranged with Mr. Tanner, the
wheelwright.

EVERETT (*Smiling*): That is good news, indeed, Nicholas.

WIDOW: Nick is bound out to Edward Tanner, the wheelwright, sir, as I told you when I came to see you last
summer. The papers were drawn up last week, and Nick
begins his apprenticeship in a few days. I'm that relieved,
sir. (THOMAS, *a tall, slender, aristocratic boy wearing*
riding clothes, enters.)

THOMAS: Good morning, Mr. Everett. Faith, 'tis a morning fit for a king. I rode my new sorrel and mare over
from the plantation— (*Realizes the presence of others*
and stops) Oh, I ask your pardon. I—I did not know
anyone was here but you, sir.

EVERETT: Good morning, Thomas. (*Dryly*) I am pleased
you are so abounding in good spirits for the opening
morning of school! Will you show Nicholas, our new

scholar, where to leave his hat and where he is to sit, while I consult further with his mother?

THOMAS: Most assuredly, sir. (*To* NICHOLAS) My name's Thomas. (*The boys go to the table, where* THOMAS *shows* NICHOLAS *the books and slates.*)

EVERETT: You were saying, Widow Gray—?

WIDOW (*Smiling at the boy's friendliness*): Oh, yes, your Reverence. The indenture papers are drawn up, and I pleaded with my boy's new master that he be allowed to attend your school for three hours each weekday morning, working at his trade from noon until bedtime, and all day of a Saturday; and that the cost of the schooling be paid from Nick's earnings—or what he would earn if he were to be paid.

EVERETT: And Mr. Tanner consented?

WIDOW: He seemed loath at first; declared schooling was for the rich and not for poor folk like myself and my fatherless boy, who, poor lad, must learn a trade to support himself. But I told him I'd keep Nick at home and work my fingers to the bone before I'd bind him out with no chance to get book learning. Oh, sir, his father meant Nick to have advantages— (*She hastily takes a large handkerchief from a reticule hanging from her belt, and begins to cry into it softly.* NICHOLAS *quickly rises and goes to his mother, putting an arm round her shoulder.* THOMAS *rises and looks on with interest and sympathy.*)

EVERETT: There, there, ma'am. Compose yourself.

NICHOLAS: Come, Ma, there's no use crying *now*. You're a great one—crying because things are coming about as you want 'em.

WIDOW (*Drying her eyes and smiling at* NICHOLAS): Womenfolk are like that, Nick, lad. Now go back to your writing, for I see you've begun to learn something already, thanks to the fine young gentleman there.

THOMAS: Oh, I *like* to see people learn to read and write. It is wonderful when you know how. (*The boys go back to their seats and sit down and are quickly intent on the slates and books.*)

EVERETT: And now tell me what Mr. Tanner finally said, ma'am. He agreed to the plan?

WIDOW: Yes, finally, sir, though none too willingly, I'll confess. He wrote it all down in the indenture papers. The money will be paid by him, sir, and if you'll render your account to Edward Tanner, the wheelwright, I'll be obliged.

EVERETT: Allow me to make an entry in my account book. (*He goes behind table and makes a notation in a large book.* WIDOW *looks around the room, pausing curiously before the writing chart.*)

THOMAS: You say you cannot write your *name*? How old are you?

NICHOLAS: Twelve years old. (*Quickly*) But I've never been to school, for my mother's a widow and has no means of paying for a tutor, and I suppose *you* couldn't write, either, if nobody had ever taught you.

THOMAS (*Laughing*): No, I suppose not.

WIDOW: Tut, tut, Nick, that's no way to speak to the young gentleman.

THOMAS: Oh, no offense, ma'am. I like a lad with spirit. He can make wheels and I can't, so we're even. And besides (*To* NICHOLAS), you'll soon learn to write, and read and cipher, too, if you are indeed coming here to Mr. Everett's school. Look! We all practice on our slates and then write our exercises on this chart. I'll write something for you, in beautiful, tall letters, as Mr. Everett taught me. (*He takes the crayon from the table, goes to the chart, and writes "Thomas" in large, ornate script.*)

EVERETT (*Closing account book*): Remember, Thomas, "Fools' names, like fools' faces, do oft appear in public places." I advise you to display your orthography by something more interesting than your name.

THOMAS (*Laughing good-naturedly*): Everyone learns to write his name first, sir. But I'll write more interesting things before I'm through, I hope. (*To* NICHOLAS) I'll write *your* name on your slate and then you can copy it. (*He writes on the slate and* NICHOLAS *tries to copy it.*)

WIDOW: It warms my heart to see him so happy. He was that eager to come, sir! And now I'll say good day to ye.

EVERETT: You may remain for a bit and watch the children at their work, if it so pleases you.

WIDOW: I have a fair day's work to do, sir—and besides, Nick will fare better without his mother here, I'm thinking. I'll miss him sore, with him away from me except for a visit on Sundays. (*She wipes her eyes again.*) But I'll not be minding the separation so much, sir, knowing he's here with you each morning, learning what neither I nor his father ever knew—for I cannot read or write, sir.

EVERETT: We shall take the best care of him, never fear. (*She goes out, with another pleased glance toward the boys.*) Thomas, you may ring the bell. Our scholars must be loitering on their way. 'Tis nigh to eight o'clock— high time to open school.

THOMAS: Very well, sir. (*He takes the bell from the table and goes out, meeting* MRS. PHILLIPS *and her niece and nephew,* MARGARET *and* RICHARD. *He nods to them, and then goes out. The bell is heard ringing loudly.*)

MRS. PHILLIPS (*Out of breath*): Land sakes, I told you children to hurry. Do you hear that bell a-ringing?

RICHARD (*Giggling*): It was you who couldn't hurry, Aunt Harriet.

MARGARET: Hush now, Richard.

MRS. PHILLIPS: And take your cap off.

MARGARET (*Curtsying to* EVERETT): Good morning, sir.

EVERETT (*Going to door to greet them*): Good morning, Mrs. Phillips. Good morning, Margaret and Richard. I trust I find you well?

MRS. PHILLIPS: Good morning, Mr. Everett. My brother asked me to bring the children to school. We would have been here long before, but young Richard—well, you know how boys are these days.

EVERETT: Indeed. (*Sternly, to children*) Get slates and readers from the table and take your places, children.

MARGARET: Yes, sir. (*She hangs her hat and her brother's cap on nails at left, and gets slates, pencils and books, giving one set to* RICHARD. MRS. PHILLIPS *looks on, smiling and fanning herself occasionally.* THOMAS *re-enters, places bell on table and joins children. There is ad lib whispering and giggling.*)

EVERETT: I trust your brother is well, Mrs. Phillips?

MRS. PHILLIPS: He's in right good health, thank you kindly. He sends his compliments to you, and he asked me to tell you that old Zeb would be by to call for the children at the proper time.

EVERETT: Very well.

MRS. PHILLIPS (*To* MARGARET *and* RICHARD): Now, you children behave yourselves and act the way your father would like to have you act. It isn't every child who has the privilege of getting some learning into his head. When you grow up, you're going to need those "three R's"—so pay attention.

EVERETT (*Bowing slightly*): We call them the "three *royal* R's." That's even better. (FRANCIS *and* ABIGAIL *enter, exchange greetings with* EVERETT, *hang up their hats and take their places on the benches.*)

MRS. PHILLIPS: I'd better be getting along. Excuse me for taking up so much time, but I'd like to see those children be a credit to their father. It's costing him several hundred pounds of his best cotton for this schooling. Good day, Mr. Everett. (*She goes out.*)

EVERETT (*Laughing in a kindly manner*): It will be worth that cotton, Mrs. Phillips. (RICHARD *and* MARGARET *run to door and call "goodbye" to their aunt.*)

EVERETT: Places, children, please. (*The children go to seats and gradually quiet down.*) I wish to greet you all on this opening day of school.

CHILDREN (*Together*): Good morning, sir. (JOHN EVANS *enters with his nieces,* MATILDA *and* BETSY.)

EVANS: Good morning, Friend Everett.

EVERETT: Good morning to you, sir. (*Children all look up and begin to whisper.*) Mind your manners, children— else my birch stick will see service before our visitors.

EVANS: I am John Evans, who wrote thee concerning my nieces.

EVERETT: Ah, yes, Friend Evans. I'm happy to see you. And these are the little girls.

EVANS: Matilda and Betsy, my sister's orphaned children. I'm placing them in thy school, as I wrote.

EVERETT: Yes, Friend Evans, I was expecting you.

EVANS: I'm pleased and thankful to place my beloved nieces under thy care, Friend Everett. 'Tis my wish to give them every possible advantage.

EVERETT: It will be a pleasure and a privilege to have them in my school, I assure you.

EVANS: I have arranged to have someone call for them at the end of each day, and I shall bring them each morning myself.

EVERETT: We welcome you, Matilda; we are pleased to have you with us, Betsy.

MATILDA (*Neither she nor her sister curtsies*): We thank thee, schoolmaster.

BETSY: We do, indeed, schoolmaster.

EVERETT: Margaret, take these new scholars to their places. (MARGARET *comes forward graciously and takes the newcomers to hang up their hats, and then guides them to their places.*)

EVANS: My sister would have been proud to see her girls in such good hands, schoolmaster.

EVERETT: And proud to see such kindly thought of them on the part of their good uncle. Truly, your beneficence warms the heart, Friend Evans.

EVANS: So long as I have a penny, my sister's children shall have their schooling. Now, let me see. I wish to pay thee for the first quarter. (*He takes coins from his pocket and counts them out into the schoolmaster's hand.*) That is correct, I believe, Friend Everett?

EVERETT: It is indeed, Friend Evans.

EVANS: Send me the accounting for the second quarter, and I will settle it promptly. And now I'll slip out quietly. Goodbyes to the children might distress them. Goodbye and God's blessing upon thee and thy charges.

EVERETT: Good day, Friend Evans. (EVANS *goes out, and* EVERETT *returns to the table and opens his account book to make an entry.*) You will please study the first lesson in the readers, the younger children from the primers and the others from the advanced reader. (*The children immediately begin to "drone," as they study out loud.* EVERETT *works on his books. He straightens his papers, then looks around.* NICHOLAS *comes up to desk.*)

NICHOLAS: Will you help me, sir?

EVERETT: Of course, Nicholas. Sit down. (NICHOLAS *does so, and they bend quietly over book, speaking in low voices.* FRANCIS *pulls a long feather from his pocket and begins to tickle* RICHARD, *who sits in front of him.* RICHARD *brushes feather away, and the other children begin to giggle.* MARGARET, *annoyed, pushes* FRANCIS *off the bench onto the floor, and the children laugh out loud.*) Silence!—Silence, I say. (*The laughing and the "droning" both cease.*) Take your seat, Nicholas. I will assist you shortly. We are having some difficulty in settling down to study after our summer holiday. I wish to be lenient today and not to put my friend here (*Taking up his birch*) to active service the very first day of school. Thomas, you will read the first page of the lesson to us. (THOMAS, *seated near door, has been gazing dreamily out. He "comes to" with a start, rises, fumbles with his book, tries to find the right page, etc.*)

THOMAS: Oh, yes, sir . . . Of course, sir. At once, sir.

EVERETT (*As the children titter again*): Thomas, will you be so good as to shut the door. The lessons of nature seem of more interest to you this morning than those in your reader. (THOMAS *shuts door and goes back to fumbling with his book.*) Come! Perhaps a spelling lesson will help to settle us down to work. We will begin with you, Thomas. (*Opens book and reads*)" Constantinople!"

THOMAS: C-o-n, con; s-t-a-n, stan, constan; t-i, ti, constanti; n-o, constantino; p-l-e, p'l—Constantinople. (*He sits down.*)

EVERETT: Correct. Francis! (FRANCIS *rises.*) "Unnecessary."

FRANCIS (*Starting off in a cocksure manner*): U-n, un; n-e-c, nec, unnec; (*Not so sure now*) c-e-s, ces, unneces; a-r-y, ary, unnecessary. (*He finishes triumphantly and sits down.*)

EVERETT: Incorrect! Margaret!

MARGARET (*Rising*): U-n, un; n-e-c, nec, unnec; e-s, es, unneces; s-a-r-y, sary, unnecessary.

EVERETT: Correct! (MARGARET *sits down.*) That is one of our difficult words, Francis. I recommend that you apply yourself to your studies and leave such childish matters as playing with feathers to the younger children. (ABI-GAIL *lifts her hand timidly.*) What is it, Abigail?

ABIGAIL: Please, sir, I can spell "Necessary." My mother taught me.

EVERETT: Very well. Abigail, let us hear you.

ABIGAIL (*Rising*): N-e-c, nec; e-s, es, neces; s-a-r-y, sary, necessary.

EVERETT: That was *very* good. (ABIGAIL *sits*.) Now, Francis, we'll let you spell "Mediterranean."

FRANCIS (*Rising*): M-e-d, med; m-e- no, m-i— (*There is a loud, authoritative knock at the door.*)

EVERETT: Who can that be, I wonder? You will all practice your writing exercises. Let me see if you've made progress during the summer months. (*The children settle down to work, and* EVERETT *goes to the door and opens it.* EDWARD TANNER, *a burly, red-faced man in workman's clothes and a burlap apron, stands outside, accompanied by* GEORGE HIGGS, *a constable.*)

TANNER (*In a loud, disagreeable voice before the schoolmaster can speak*): This is the Reverend Ralph Everett's school, I take it?

EVERETT (*With dignity*): It is, sir. Whom am I addressing?

TANNER (*Forcing his way in, followed by* HIGGS): You're addressin' none other than Edward Tanner, wheelwright. And this is George Higgs, representin' the law.

EVERETT: You are interrupting school hours. Surely your business, whatever it is, can wait till a more opportune time.

TANNER: No time like the present (*Laughing disagreeably*), especially when it's time you're payin' for. (*To* HIGGS) That there's the boy, Constable. (*He points to* NICHOLAS.) Seize him.

HIGGS (*Grasping the boy's collar*): That I will! Teach you to run off from your lawful master.

NICHOLAS: I didn't run off! My mother brought me here. She had everything arranged with Mr. Tanner—I heard her say so. (*He tries to squirm out of* HIGGS' *clutches*.)

HIGGS: Not so fast there! You're comin' with me, you young knave.

EVERETT (*With authority*): Let the boy loose!

HIGGS (*Letting go of* NICHOLAS *but standing near him threateningly*): I'm here in the name of the law! It's my duty to take the lad back to his work.

EVERETT (*To* TANNER): The Widow Gray brought her son here in all good faith. He is to study with me three hours each week day and work for you the remaining hours.

TANNER (*Sneeringly*): So the apprentice to a wheelwright must learn readin' and writin' and 'rithmetic, must he? And who's to pay for such fine doin's, I ask ye? I didn't take him on to learn the three "R's"—along with these fine young gentlemen.

THOMAS (*Springing up angrily and facing* TANNER): I think *you* might learn something from a *gentleman!*

EVERETT: Be seated, Thomas. You can do no good, my boy. (THOMAS *still stands defiantly before* TANNER.) Be seated, I say! At once! (THOMAS *slowly takes his seat*.)

HIGGS (*Grasping* NICHOLAS *again and pulling him along*): No use resistin' the law.

EVERETT: One moment! Tanner, this boy's mother informed me that you had agreed to pay for his schooling while he is serving his indenture.

TANNER (*With derisive laughter*): Oh, well, it isn't writ in our agreement. It isn't in the young scoundrel's papers. You can see for yourself. (*Slyly*) The widow must have got my meaning wrong, and since she can't read what's really writ down, she'll have to accept what's there.

EVERETT: And how am I to know you're telling the truth?

HIGGS: I've read this lad's indenture papers. There's no provision for time out of work hours for schoolin', nor for any payment by Mr. Tanner for schoolin'. (NICHOLAS

twists out of HIGGS' *grasp and stands away from him and*
TANNER)

NICHOLAS (*Fiercely*): Then you tricked my mother! She
thought it was in the papers! (*Half crying in his dis-
appointment and fury*) She wants me to learn things—
besides how to make wheels. I was going to study hard
to learn to write and cipher—and read! If *she* could
read, you couldn't have tricked her like this. (*He buries
his head in his arm and sobs openly.*)

EVERETT (*Going to him and putting a kindly hand on his
shoulder*): There, my boy. Let me attend to this. Be
brave.

THOMAS (*Jumping up again and going to* NICHOLAS, *he
angrily pushes* EVERETT'S *hand from his shoulder*): Be
brave! Be brave! That's all people know how to say!
Why should we be brave and just *stand* things that are
all wrong? I'm going to help you some way, Nicholas. I
don't know how yet—but I'm going to!

EVERETT: That's easier said than done, Thomas.

HIGGS: That it is! The law's the law!

THOMAS (*Vehemently*): Then we'd best change the laws
and make better ones!

TANNER: I've no more time to waste. Fetch him along,
Higgs. (*Menacingly*) *I'll* teach him a few things he needs
to know. (*He and* HIGGS *again take* NICHOLAS *roughly
by the arms.*)

NICHOLAS: I *won't* go! I *won't!*

THOMAS (*Earnestly, to* TANNER): Oh, sir, please don't take
him away. We were going to be such friends. If he wants
to come to school, he should be allowed to do so.

TANNER: And who's to pay for such luxuries as book
learnin', my fine young sir?

THOMAS (*With much earnestness and vehemence*): I don't
know but somebody ought to. He's a boy like me—and
Francis here—and Richard. He ought to have the same

chances. Why—why— (*Struggling for words to express his sudden overpowering emotions*) we're all created free and equal, are we not? We all should have the same opportunities for liberty—and—and—happiness! How can a boy be happy if he can't make something of his life? And one cannot be really free if one can't read and write! (*Turns to* TANNER *with boyish fury and indignation*) You could not have tricked Nick's mother if she could *read!* You're a trickster—and a coward! That's what you are. (*He begins to beat at* TANNER'S *broad chest and to try to pull* NICHOLAS *from his clutches.* EVERETT *quickly intervenes, forcing* THOMAS *out of the way.* TANNER *and* HIGGS *grab* NICHOLAS' *arms and drag him struggling toward the door, while* EVERETT *holds* THOMAS *firmly.*)

TANNER (*Taken aback, but keeping up a show of sarcasm*): A fine school you have here, Mr. Everett. You're training rebellious speakers, I see! (*He grabs* NICHOLAS' *arm.*) I've wasted near a morning over this foolishness. You'll pay for this, you sniveling knave.

HIGGS: No use to struggle, boy. It's all legal and accordin' to His Majesty's laws.

THOMAS (*Shouting in his excited anger*): But it won't always be! Some day you will see. I'm just a boy now, but when I'm a man, I'll show you. I'll get laws passed!

EVERETT: Thomas, lad, be quiet. (*To* TANNER, *with quiet dignity and authority*) Let the boy loose, Tanner. He need not be dragged away like an animal. For shame— two grown men handling a young lad like this! Be more gentle in your treatment of him, else I'll preach a sermon from my pulpit on Sunday next that will give your fellow townspeople much to think of! (*HIGGS and* TANNER *sulkily let go of* NICHOLAS *and drop back a few steps.*) You must go quietly, Nicholas. But you *can* be brave, in spite of Thomas' anger at my use of that word.

NICHOLAS: My Ma'll be dreadful unhappy, sir.

EVERETT: I'll call by and explain things to her—and do my best to comfort her.

NICHOLAS: Thank you kindly, sir. (*To* THOMAS) Goodbye.

THOMAS: Goodbye.

NICHOLAS (*Smiling shyly*): I'll practice writing my name, as you showed me.

THOMAS: Take my slate with you.

NICHOLAS (*Eager for it but afraid of* TANNER): I—don't know whether—I'd be allowed to do that.

EVERETT (*Quickly with a warning look at* TANNER): Indeed you may take it! Give it to him, Thomas. (THOMAS *gets the slate and hands it to* NICHOLAS.)

NICHOLAS (*Happily*): Oh, I thank you! (*He looks at the slate.*) I don't know your last name. You've written only "Thomas." (THOMAS *quickly goes to the chart and writes "Jefferson" in large letters after the "Thomas".*)

THOMAS (*Turning to* NICHOLAS): Goodbye, Nick.

NICHOLAS: Goodbye, Thomas. (*He turns and goes to the door where* TANNER *and* HIGGS *stand.*)

TANNER (*Looking at* THOMAS *with a mixture of servility and defiance*): The fine young gentleman who believes in readin' and writin' and 'rithmetic for everybody—but it won't be Edward Tanner who pays for it. (*He and* HIGGS *go out, taking* NICHOLAS *with them, firmly but not so roughly as before.*)

THOMAS (*Calling after* TANNER): How do you know you won't pay for it? Maybe you'll be *taxed* to pay for children to go to school! It would serve you right! (THOMAS *stands at door, waving to* NICHOLAS. EVERETT *also stands there, looking off rather sadly.*)

EVERETT: Practice your writing lesson, children. (*The children, who have been frightened and upset, settle down.* EVERETT *puts his hand on* THOMAS' *shoulder, as they stand near door. They walk towards center.*)

THOMAS: Pray forgive me, sir, for my ungentlemanly rudeness to you—and for my temper. Mother tells me that is because of my red hair.

EVERETT: There's nothing for me to forgive. Indeed, you've taught me something. Out of the mouths of babes. . . . "Liberty—happiness—equal opportunity"—those were inspired words you used, my boy.

THOMAS (*With a boyish smile at the master*): And "reading, writing, and arithmetic," sir—don't forget them! They are important, too—and some day they are going to be *free*—for *everybody!* (*Curtain*)

THE END

Welcome, Parents

by Eva Cole

Characters

MRS. SMITH
MR. SMITH
TOM ⎤
DAVID ⎟
JACK ⎟
ALICE ⎬ *their children*
DIANE ⎟
SUSAN ⎟
NANCY ⎦
MRS. PARKER, *a neighbor*
MARY ⎤
JANE ⎦ *Nancy's friends*

TIME: *Breakfast time, the present.*
SETTING: *The dining room of the Smith home.*
AT RISE: MRS. SMITH *is setting the table for breakfast. From offstage come the sounds of various instruments being played.* MR. SMITH *enters, dressed in trousers and a bathrobe, and sits down at the table, holding his ears.*

MRS. SMITH (*Calling loudly as the music dies away*): Children, time for breakfast. Breakfast is ready! Breakfast! (*The music stops.*)

143

MR. SMITH: What a racket to wake up to. Do the children *have* to practice at this time in the morning?

MRS. SMITH: They need to practice for the Open House program at school tonight. They're playing for the parents.

MR. SMITH (*Nodding*): Oh, yes. Another Open House at school.

MRS. SMITH: I hope you'll be able to come home on time for dinner tonight. We'll have to leave for school at seven. (TOM *enters and sits down at the table.*)

TOM: Good morning, Mom. Hi, Dad. Say, could I have some macaroni?

MRS. SMITH (*As she serves* MR. SMITH): No, Tom, I'm sorry. I don't serve macaroni for breakfast.

TOM: Oh, I didn't mean to *eat*. I have to take some to school. We're making designs with macaroni in art class. We're going to paint them, too. The art teacher told us all about it last week when she came.

MRS. SMITH: And *I* find out the morning you have to have the macaroni. Well, I don't know if I have any. Eat your breakfast and I'll see. (TOM *eats. Doorbell rings.*) Now, who can that be so early in the morning? (*She exits, and returns a moment later with* MRS. PARKER.)

MR. SMITH: Good morning, Mrs. Parker.

MRS. PARKER: Excuse me for disturbing you so early. I wouldn't bother you at breakfast time, but Susie is frantic. She needs two egg cartons for school, and I don't have any.

MR. SMITH: Egg cartons! What are they using egg cartons for?

MRS. PARKER: If I have it straight, they are learning multiplication and division by studying egg cartons.

MRS. SMITH: Sit down, Mrs. Parker. I'll see if I can find any cartons for you. (*She goes out.*)

MRS. PARKER (*Sitting down and sighing*): The mornings

are always so hectic. I just gave Michael his father's last pair of socks to make hand puppets in school.

MR. SMITH: That sounds familiar. I find *my* socks have been turned into hand puppets, too. (JACK, ALICE *and* DIANE *enter, sit at table, and eat.*)

DIANE: I have to take some paper plates to school today, and some ribbons, and some flowers, and any other pretty things.

MR. SMITH: Paper plates and ribbons! What a combination. What for?

DIANE: Well, it's a big secret —but it's for a fashion show. It's something to wear. You'll see at Open House tonight. (MRS. SMITH *enters. She has one and one-half egg cartons.*)

MRS. SMITH: Here, Mrs. Parker. I found one carton in the wastepaper basket, and this one in the incinerator. It's half-burned, but maybe it will help a little. (MRS. PARKER *takes cartons.*)

MRS. PARKER: Oh, thank you so much, Mrs. Smith. Now I have to go home and find a large box for Mary so that she can make a puppet theater for her puppets. Goodbye, everyone. (*She exits.*)

ALICE: That reminds me, Mother. *My* puppet has to have something to wear. The teacher said to bring some old pieces of cloth left over from sewing to make Roman togas for our puppets. I said you had a lot of material— you sew so much.

MRS. SMITH: But Alice, I just gave away a pile of those left-over scraps to a woman who's making a quilt. I suppose you need the material this morning?

ALICE: Oh, yes, Mother. We have to work on it first thing.

MRS. SMITH: Such a pleasant morning! Looking for macaroni, finding egg cartons in the incinerator. . . .

DIANE: And I need paper plates, Mother.

MRS. SMITH: Oh, Diane! You used up the paper plates last

week. I bought fifty of them—and you used them all up.

MR. SMITH: Now, now, calm yourself, Mother. There's really nothing to get upset about.

MRS. SMITH: If you had to collect all these things for the children to take to school, maybe you'd get upset, too. Remember when I had to produce six paper towel tubes in one morning? I've hoarded them ever since, and nobody's ever wanted any again. And I'm saving aluminum foil tubes, cleanser containers, milk bottle caps, empty spools and old Brillo pads.

ALICE: Oh, I remember the beautiful llama I made with the Brillo pads. That was when we were studying mountain countries.

JACK: I don't need any Brillo pads, but, Dad, there is something I do need. We're going to germinate some beans in wet sawdust to study embryos and stuff like that. I remembered that pile of sawdust on the floor in your workroom, so I said I'd bring a lot in today.

MR. SMITH (*Shaking his head*): I'm sorry, Jack. Your mother nagged me into sweeping up that sawdust and throwing it away just yesterday.

JACK: You'll make some more, won't you, Dad? With that new electric saw of yours?

MR. SMITH: You don't think I'm going to saw up my expensive boards just to make you some sawdust, do you?

MRS. SMITH: Now, now, calm yourself, dear. Let's all have something to eat and we'll talk about it. (MR. SMITH *gets up.*)

MR. SMITH: I'd better finish getting dressed, and then we'll talk about it. (*He goes out as* SUSAN *enters, with some yellow material draped over her shoulders.*)

SUSAN: Good morning, Mommy. Look what I just found near your sewing machine. It will make a good costume for our jungle play. I'm going to be a leopard. It will be easy to paint black spots on this material.

MRS. SMITH: No, Susan. I'm going to make myself a nice new dress out of that material.

SUSAN: But I have to have a costume. We're having dress rehearsal this morning.

MRS. SMITH: I'll find something else for you. I'll try to bring it to you when I pick up Linda after kindergarten this morning. Now, eat your breakfast. (DAVID *enters slowly. He wears shorts and has a fur stole draped over one bare shoulder. He carries a club. He pounces on* SUSAN, *who screams and drops the material. Everybody jumps.*) David, stop that!

DAVID (*Yelling*): I'm a caveman, I'm a caveman. I kill leopards with my club.

MRS. SMITH: Stop this instant! (*Goes over to* DAVID, *gasps*) Why, that's my mink stole! (*She grabs it from him and drapes it around herself for safekeeping.*)

DAVID: An old mink is perfect for a caveman costume, don't you think?

MRS. SMITH: I will count to ten before I tell you what I think. (*She counts to ten as she picks up material* SUSAN *has dropped.*) David, my mink is positively *not* going to school today. Now, sit down and eat your breakfast. (DAVID *sits dejectedly.* MR. SMITH *enters.*)

MR. SMITH: There isn't a white shirt in this house. (*Stops and stares at* MRS. SMITH) Katherine, are you wearing mink at the breakfast table these days?

MRS. SMITH: Sometimes it's a good idea. Especially if you have a caveman for a son. Besides, I don't have much chance to wear it in the evening, so perhaps I *should* wear it at breakfast. At least the family can enjoy it.

MR. SMITH: Sounds pretty silly to me. But I really don't care. All I *do* care about right now is something I can wear. Like a shirt.

MRS. SMITH: Look in the second drawer. I'm sure there are some nice colored shirts there. (*He exits.*) Drink your milk, Susan. I wonder where Nancy is. She said she wanted to paint a poster. (*Shakes her head, puzzled*) I can't understand it. I know I saw a white shirt in your father's drawer yesterday. That was why I decided I could wait until today to pick up the clean shirts at the laundry.

TOM: Mother, Nancy had something white on her arm when she went up to the attic to paint. Maybe she took the shirt. Our art teacher says shirts with the sleeves cut off make the best smocks for messy art classes. Of course, the teacher says to use *old* shirts. Maybe Nancy couldn't find an old shirt. (*Eagerly*) Shall I go get her?

MRS. SMITH: Yes, please do, Tom. Right away. (TOM *exits.* MR. SMITH *enters, dressed as before, holding up three mismatched socks in one hand.*)

MR. SMITH: Someone's taken the cardboards from my colored shirts and you should see them. They're all wrinkled. I have an important business call to make— and look at me—without a shirt, and not even two socks that match. (*Holds up socks.* ALICE *reluctantly holds up the mates and hands them to her father. The doorbell rings.* MRS. SMITH *goes out and returns with* JANE *and* MARY, *who wear coats.* JANE *carries an armload of milk cartons and* MARY *has a huge cardboard box.*)

MRS. SMITH: Tom has gone to find Nancy, girls. She should be down in a minute.

MR. SMITH: Good morning, girls. Ah, Jane, I see *your* mother had milk cartons.

JANE: My mother made everybody drink lots and lots of milk for breakfast so I could have these. Everybody was so angry with me. They shouldn't be. Milk is good for you.

MARY: My mother had a lot of junk stored in this box, but I knew if I begged long enough, she'd give the box to me. It will make a fine puppet theater. (TOM *enters with*

NANCY. *NANCY wears a white shirt covered with paint, and has some paint on her hands and nose, too. She carries a big piece of paper, folded up.*)

MRS. SMITH: Nancy, look at you!

MR. SMITH: Look at my shirt!

NANCY: Good morning, everyone. Hi, Jane. Hi, Mary. Mom, I'll wash up in a minute. I've just finished my sign for Open House, and I want to show it to you. O.K.?

MRS. SMITH: Yes, dear. But hurry. You haven't had breakfast, and you *do* have to go to school. (*With everyone's help,* NANCY *unfolds a long piece of paper that says,* WELCOME, PARENTS. *All hold it up. A welcoming song might be sung as the curtains close.*)

THE END

The Pilgrim Painting

by James Rawls

Characters

BONNIE BROWN
EDDIE, *her brother*
MRS. BROWN, *their mother*
MR. BROWN, *their father*
MR. MARKS, *chairman of the school board*
PILGRIM GIRL
PILGRIM BOY
PILGRIM MOTHER
PILGRIM FATHER

TIME: *Thanksgiving Day.*
SETTING: *The living room of the Brown home. Two folding screens hide the back center wall.*
AT RISE: BONNIE BROWN *is seated in an armchair, bouncing a ball on the floor.* EDDIE *stands near her holding an old doll upside down.* MRS. BROWN *is entering from the kitchen to place a bowl of fruit on the table.*

EDDIE: Bonnie, I'm telling you, you won't have any doll at all unless you fix this one. Look at it: its leg is half off, its face is all dirty and its dress is in rags. (*Tosses doll onto table*)
BONNIE: I don't care, Eddie. I'm sick of that old doll. I've

150

had it forever. Why can't I have a new one? (*Tosses ball to* EDDIE)

EDDIE: Why can't I have a baseball bat? All I have to play with is this old rubber ball. (*Puts ball in his pocket*)

MRS. BROWN (*Arranging table*): Now, children, that's no way to talk. Remember this is Thanksgiving, and you have a great deal to be thankful for. You're young and healthy; you go to a nice school (BONNIE *and* EDDIE *groan.*), and you're going to have a good Thanksgiving dinner in just a little while.

EDDIE: A good dinner! I know what we'll have —boiled cabbage and a hambone! I can smell it cooking.

BONNIE: Most people have turkey. Why, everyone has a turkey on Thanksgiving. That's what Thanksgiving is for!

MRS. BROWN (*Sadly*): You know we can't afford a turkey.

EDDIE: We can't afford a lot of things. Look at this old sweater I'm wearing. I can hardly get it on any more, I've worn it so long.

BONNIE: My dress is worse! It's the newest one I have, and it's already over a year old. Oh, Mother, why do we have to be so poor? (*She starts to cry.*)

MRS. BROWN (*Crossing to* BONNIE *to stroke her hair*): There, there, children. No crying on Thanksgiving. (*She puts an arm around* EDDIE.) Why, my darlings, I know how you feel. Bonnie, you do need some pretty new clothes and a new doll and a carriage, too—and, Eddie, a real baseball with a bat and a glove to go with it.

BONNIE: Isn't Daddy ever going to sell a picture?

EDDIE: All he does is paint, paint, paint, but no one ever buys one. Why doesn't he stop painting pictures and paint houses or something? People pay for that.

MRS. BROWN (*Suddenly angry*): Now stop it this instant! I will not have you children criticizing your father. He's an artist, and he works hard. Some day he will be famous; and we must all help him. Now stop this grumbling and be thankful for what you do have. (*She goes to kitchen.* MR. BROWN *enters from side, carrying a palette and brush.*)

MR. BROWN: Well, my pets, have you seen my latest painting? I finished it this morning.

BONNIE (*Listlessly*): Did you, Daddy?

EDDIE (*Without enthusiasm*): That's nice.

MR. BROWN: It's the best picture I've ever painted.

BONNIE: Is it pretty, Daddy?

MR. BROWN: I don't know if it's "pretty," but it's very life-like. It's right behind there. (*Points to screens*) Why don't you look at it?

BONNIE: It's just awful that the school board no longer wants to buy it.

EDDIE: It would look wonderful hanging in our lunchroom at school. That picture's big enough to cover the whole side of the lunchroom.

MR. BROWN: Yes, it's life-size, all right, and it's taken hard work to finish it by Thanksgiving. But, as you say, Mr. Marks of the school board says they no longer want to buy it. (*He shakes his head as he goes to the kitchen.*)

BONNIE: So what good is it? All that work for nothing.

EDDIE: Do you want to see it, now that it's finished?

BONNIE: What for?

EDDIE: Oh, come on, let's take a look. Dinner isn't ready yet.

BONNIE: All right, but what's the use? It's not going to bring us a Thanksgiving turkey. (*They fold back the screens and move them out of the way. Revealed is a framed living tableau of a Pilgrim family sitting with bowed heads at a wooden table.* PILGRIM FATHER *and* MOTHER *are at right and left ends of the table, and* PILGRIM GIRL *and* BOY *are side by side behind the table facing front. On the table is a cooked turkey.*) Eddie, those Pilgrims look almost real.

EDDIE: Yes, they do. You know something, Bonnie?

BONNIE: What?

EDDIE: Something else looks real, too.

BONNIE: What?

EDDIE: That turkey!

BONNIE: Mm-m-m, I wish it were. If only we could have one like that.

EDDIE: You know, the longer you look at them the more real they seem. Boy, I wouldn't be a bit surprised if they just raised their heads and said hello to us.

BONNIE: Oh, Eddie! (PILGRIMS *slowly raise their heads, then the* PILGRIM BOY *and* GIRL *smile at* BONNIE *and* EDDIE.)

PILGRIM GIRL: Would you share our meal?

PILGRIM BOY: Pray join us. (BONNIE *and* EDDIE *scream and cling to each other.*)

BONNIE: Eddie! I thought I heard them speak!

EDDIE: So did I! But I don't believe it!

PILGRIM BOY (*Rising*): I pray you, do not run from us. We are as real as you.

PILGRIM GIRL (*Rising*): Aye, in faith. As surely as this day is Thanksgiving Day, 1628.

BONNIE: But it isn't! I mean, it's Thanksgiving Day, but this is 1969.

EDDIE: You're a painting. You're not real. My father painted you.

PILGRIM GIRL (*Coming around table into the room, as* PILGRIM MOTHER *rises and exits*): He painted us well, too. Do but feel the texture of my cape.

PILGRIM BOY (*Coming into the room as* PILGRIM FATHER *also exits, taking the turkey out with him.*): And my jacket. Prithee, feel the warmth of it.

PILGRIM GIRL: Do not be afraid. Give me thy hand. (BONNIE *and* EDDIE *touch the clothing.*)

BONNIE: It feels rough and coarse. It's nice, but isn't it rather plain?

PILGRIM GIRL: It is the only one I have. May I touch your garment?

BONNIE: Oh, this old dress. I hate it.

PILGRIM GIRL: Why, it feels like a feather on my finger. It has the colors of the rainbow. Truly, it is the most beautiful dress I have ever seen.

PILGRIM BOY (*Fingering* EDDIE's *sweater*): Sister, look upon this overshirt. It is heavy of loom and has the color of fire.

PILGRIM GIRL: Aye, brother, it is a wondrous thing. Oh! See there! (*She points to the armchair.*) That object! (*She runs to it.*) Let me guess. It is for sleeping!

BONNIE (*Laughing*): No, it is a chair — for sitting! (*She helps* EDDIE *seat the* PILGRIM BOY *in the armchair.*)

PILGRIM GIRL: All chairs are of wood, hewn with an axe.

PILGRIM BOY (*Bouncing in chair*): Truly, it must be for sleeping. It is soft like a bed and would be easy to warm.

EDDIE: No, it's a chair. Our beds are in the bedroom.

PILGRIM GIRL: A separate room for beds?

EDDIE: Why, of course. Next to the bedroom is the bathroom. The kitchen is over there.

BONNIE: And this is the living and dining room.

PILGRIM GIRL: So many rooms! It is like a palace!

BONNIE: How many rooms do you have?

PILGRIM GIRL: Only one. All families have but one except the Squire, who is rich, and he has three.

PILGRIM BOY: But our cabin is warm, for I sealed the cracks between the logs with grass and clay to keep the cold wind out. Did I not, sister?

PILGRIM GIRL: Aye, brother. No grown man could have done the task better.

PILGRIM BOY (*Picking up doll*): Oh, look upon this rare little creature. Is it alive?

BONNIE: Alive? Of course not. That's my old doll. She's ugly and disgusting.

PILGRIM GIRL (*Taking doll*): No! Oh, no. Why, she is like a real, true child. Real arms. Real legs. Oh! She has real hair, golden as the ripened wheat.

PILGRIM BOY: Her eyes are the blue of a summer sky.

PILGRIM GIRL: She is truly an angel.

EDDIE: Do you have a doll, Pilgrim Girl?

PILGRIM GIRL: Aye, my doll is a length of wood with a corn husk for a dress, but I love her, for she is mine. (*She gives the doll to* BONNIE, *who cradles it in her arms.*)

EDDIE (*Pulling the ball from his pocket*): Have you seen one of these? (*He bounces it as the* PILGRIM BOY *and* GIRL *laugh and clap their hands.*)

PILGRIM BOY: It jumps! It jumps!

PILGRIM GIRL: It jumps like magic! Oh, let me make it jump.

PILGRIM BOY: Nay, me. Prithee, friend, take all I possess —these smooth round pebbles—but let me hold the ball.

EDDIE (*Exchanging the ball for the stones*): Sure. Here.

PILGRIM BOY: See, sister, see! I am making it jump!

PILGRIM GIRL: It is magic. It must all be magic. (*She walks to the table. Others follow.*) I cannot look for wonder. Brother, look upon this table. It is prepared for a feast.

PILGRIM BOY: It is prepared for a king.

EDDIE: Here, have a banana.

PILGRIM BOY: What is this?

EDDIE: A banana. Eat it. There are more.

PILGRIM BOY *and* GIRL (*Examining it*): A bah-nah-nah?

BONNIE (*Laughing*): You say it so funny.

PILGRIM GIRL: It is an odd name.

PILGRIM BOY: A bah-nah-nah. (BONNIE *and* EDDIE *laugh*.) Is that not right?

EDDIE: That's pretty close. Taste it. You'll like it.

PILGRIM BOY (*Tries to bite it*): This bah-nah-nah—its hide is thick! (*Bites again.*)

EDDIE: Wait! You have to peel it first! (*He does so.*) There. Now taste it.

PILGRIM GIRL: Stop, brother! Art thou not frightened of this bah-nah-nah? It may be more magic like the jumping ball.

PILGRIM BOY (*Eating*): Nay, sister. Its meat is soft and strangely sweet.

BONNIE: It's a fruit.

PILGRIM GIRL: A fruit? Nay. Apples and pears and peaches I have seen, but never this.

BONNIE: What about oranges? Do you have these? (*Hands an orange to* PILGRIM GIRL)

PILGRIM GIRL: It is the magic ball again! Now it will jump for me! Watch closely. (*She tries to bounce it.*) Oh! I have broken it.

BONNIE (*Picking up orange*): No, an orange won't bounce like a rubber ball. Here, squeeze the juice into your mouth.

PILGRIM GIRL: Ah, it is good. Sharp, but sweet.

PILGRIM BOY: You must be very rich to own such treasures: your shirt of fire, the magic ball, the sleeping chair—

PILGRIM GIRL: The angel doll, the rainbow dress and this strange fruit.

PILGRIM BOY: You must be richer than the Squire.

EDDIE: No, we're not rich at all. We're poor.

BONNIE: We don't even have a turkey for Thanksgiving. (*There is a knock on the door.*)

PILGRIM BOY *and* GIRL (*Running to painting*): Heaven protect us! We must fly! Home! Home!

BONNIE *and* EDDIE: Don't go! Don't go! (*The* PILGRIM

FATHER *and* MOTHER *enter. All four* PILGRIMS *sit, resuming their former positions, with heads bowed. There is another knock.* MR. BROWN *crosses from the kitchen to the door.*)

MRS. BROWN (*Calling from kitchen*): Bonnie! Eddie! See who is at the door.

MR. BROWN: I'll answer it, children. (*He opens the door.*)

MR. MARKS (*Enters jovially, carrying a package*): Well, well! Caught you at home. Happy Thanksgiving!

MR. BROWN: And a happy one to you, Mr. Marks.

MRS. BROWN (*Entering*): Oh, it's Mr. Marks, chairman of the school board. Come in, Mr. Marks. Let me take your coat.

MR. MARKS (*Putting down the package and removing his hat*): No, no. I can't stay. Just stopped by for a moment. Hello, Eddie, my boy. What a pretty dress, Bonnie.

MRS. BROWN: I'm afraid she doesn't think so.

BONNIE: Oh, but I do, Mother. It's my favorite dress. See, Mr. Marks, it's the colors of the rainbow. (*She twirls around.*)

MR. MARKS: Careful there. You'll make that doll dizzy spinning around like that.

BONNIE: I wouldn't do that. I take good care of my doll.

MRS. BROWN: Now, Bonnie.

BONNIE: Yes, Mother, I do. I mean, I'm going to. I'm going to make her a new dress and wash her face and comb her hair.

EDDIE: I'll fix her leg.

MRS. BROWN: Well, I declare! What's come over you all of a sudden? You said you hated that old doll.

BONNIE: No, I love her. She's like an angel to me.

MR. MARKS: What a pretty thing to say!

MRS. BROWN: I don't understand it at all. Why, next, Eddie will be telling us he likes his old red sweater.

EDDIE: Yes, Mother, I do.

MRS. BROWN: What!

EDDIE: It's still warm. It hasn't faded a bit—see, it's the color of fire.

MR. MARKS: Well, Mrs. Brown, I would say that you are very lucky. Two children who appreciate their clothing and who take care of their toys—a real blessing.

MRS. BROWN: Yes, this time I believe they really mean it.

MR. MARKS: Mr. Brown, to get down to my reason for coming here: I've come in person, because I bring you good news. I am happy to tell you that the school board has voted to buy your Pilgrim painting.

MR. BROWN: Mr. Marks!

MRS. BROWN: How wonderful!

MR. MARKS: Yes, they finally made up their minds. We will hang it in the lunchroom as planned. What is more, we want you to do a painting for each holiday in the year. That should keep you busy for some time.

MR. BROWN: Mr. Marks, it's wonderful.

MR. MARKS: Here is the check to pay for the Pilgrim painting. I'll have someone come tomorrow and take it away.

EDDIE: Oh, no!

BONNIE: You can't!

MR. MARKS: What? What's this?

MR. BROWN: What do you mean?

BONNIE: Oh, Daddy, don't sell it! Don't sell the Pilgrims.

MR. BROWN: Why not?

BONNIE: We want them to stay. Don't we, Eddie?

EDDIE: Yes, Dad. Please don't sell it.

MRS. BROWN: I don't understand. You've done nothing all day but complain about this very thing.

BONNIE: We like the painting now.

EDDIE: We want to keep it.

BONNIE: We like the Pilgrim boy and girl.

EDDIE: They started our country!

BONNIE: They taught us many things!

EDDIE: Bonnie's right. They did teach us many things.

MR. MARKS: That is true, of course. The Pilgrims did lay the foundation for our nation when they landed at Plymouth Rock. And they did give us our heritage of freedom, for they came to this new land seeking freedom of worship.

BONNIE: That is why we celebrate Thanksgiving.

MR. MARKS: Yes, but if the painting has taught you all this, don't you think the other boys and girls at school would want to see it?

BONNIE: Yes, that's true.

EDDIE: Bonnie, we would be able to see it every day if it's hanging in the lunchroom.

BONNIE: I know it, but what would happen to—you know who?

EDDIE: Sh-h-h.

MRS. BROWN: Whom do you mean?

BONNIE: Well, I mean—I mean—

EDDIE: She doesn't know what she means, Mother. She's just talking. Forget it.

MRS. BROWN: I wonder. Excuse us, Mr. Marks. Sometimes they do imagine things.

MR. MARKS: The privilege of youth. Well, I must be going. (*He starts to the door.*)

MR. BROWN: Mr. Marks, I don't know how to thank you for the check and the school board for buying my paintings. It makes today the happiest Thanksgiving we have ever had.

MR. MARKS: My pleasure. Oh, I almost forgot. That package there. The Pilgrims have sent you something else besides freedom. At least, they looked like Pilgrims.

EDDIE: Who?

BONNIE: What do you mean, Mr. Marks?

MR. MARKS: It was very strange. As I was coming here, a

man and woman stopped me just in front of your house and asked me to deliver this package to you. They were all dressed up like Pilgrims. On their way to a costume party, I suppose. (BONNIE *and* EDDIE *exchange looks.*)

MRS. BROWN: Thank you for bringing it, Mr. Marks. I hope it is something for the children.

MR. BROWN: Yes, thank you. Thank you for everything, sir.

MR. MARKS: Goodbye, Bonnie. Goodbye, Eddie. Happy Thanksgiving! (*He goes.*)

MR. BROWN (*Grabbing* MRS. BROWN *and dancing her around*): Oh, my dear, we've sold it! We've sold it! Look at this check!

MRS. BROWN: It is wonderful! Really wonderful!

EDDIE: Stop, Mother! Father! Have you forgotten the package? Let's open it.

BONNIE: Yes, the package! May we open it now? (MR. *and* MRS. BROWN *nod their heads.* BONNIE *and* EDDIE *quickly open the package and show the turkey.*)

MRS. BROWN: A turkey!

MR. BROWN: A real Thanksgiving turkey!

MRS. BROWN: Wherever did it come from?

MR. BROWN: Who would have sent a turkey to us?

MRS. BROWN: Mr. Marks said a man and woman in Pilgrim clothes gave it to him.

MR. BROWN: That's right, he did. Do you two know anything about this?

BONNIE: Well, we—we—

MRS. BROWN: Come, Bonnie, out with it!

BONNIE: You see—oh, Eddie! Help me!

MR. BROWN: What about it, Eddie?

EDDIE: Dad, we might be able to make a guess, but even if we told you, you wouldn't believe it.

BONNIE: We don't even know whether to believe it ourselves!

EDDIE: So can't we just say that it's a secret? A secret handed down by the Pilgrims?

MR. BROWN: That's good enough for me. You keep the secret and I'll keep the turkey. (*Starts to table*) Bring it along to the table, children, and let us sit down to eat. (BONNIE *and* EDDIE *follow their parents. As they pass the painting they hold the turkey high. The* PILGRIM FAMILY *waves and smiles. The* BROWN FAMILY *sits.*)

MR. BROWN: Bow your heads. We have more to be thankful for this Thanksgiving Day than we could ever have imagined. (*They all bow their heads, then* BONNIE *and* EDDIE *look up once more and wave to the* PILGRIM BOY *and* GIRL, *who wave back.*)

MRS. BROWN (*Almost catching them*): Bonnie! Eddie! (*They quickly duck their heads—as do the* PILGRIM CHILDREN—*and the lights fade.*)

THE END

In the Name of Miles Standish

by Helen Ramsey

Characters

CAPTAIN MILES STANDISH, *a soldier of Plymouth*
JOHN ALDEN, *a handsome young cooper*
PRISCILLA MULLENS ⎤
ELIZABETH ⎟
DESIRE ⎬ *girls of Plymouth*
MARY ⎦
WRESTLING BREWSTER ⎤ *boys of Plymouth*
FRANCIS BILLINGTON ⎦
SQUANTO, *the Pilgrims' Indian friend*
GOVERNOR BRADFORD
ELDER BREWSTER
CROWD, *Pilgrim men*

SCENE 1

TIME: *1622.*
SETTING: *A street in Plymouth.*
AT RISE: WRESTLING *enters alone. He turns and motions to someone.*

WRESTLING: Hurry along, Francis. Squanto will be here directly.

FRANCIS (*Entering hastily*): Did he say he would take us fishing?

WRESTLING: Of course. The herring have begun their spring run up the brook. Perhaps we can set a trap for them.

FRANCIS: I hope I catch a nice fat fish. I never have enough to eat any more, it seems to me.

WRESTLING: Nor does anyone else.

FRANCIS (*Greedily*): I wish we could have another harvest feast like the one last November. That was fun. All those huge platters of wild fowl, and the clams and oysters, and puddings and corn bread.

WRESTLING: Don't forget the roast deer meat. We couldn't have had that if Massasoit hadn't sent his braves out hunting.

FRANCIS: I shall never forget seeing Chief Massasoit arriving with his ninety Indian braves!

WRESTLING: They did, though. That feast lasted for three whole days.

FRANCIS (*Looks aside*): Someone is coming. Perhaps it is Squanto.

WRESTLING (*Looks*): No, it is John Alden. (ALDEN *enters carrying small barrel or box.*) Have you seen Squanto, John Alden?

ALDEN: Aye, he will be here directly with the others. Why do you want to see Squanto, lad?

WRESTLING: He has promised to take us fishing.

ALDEN (*Puts barrel down, sits on it*): I hope you have a good catch.

WRESTLING: Priscilla says she will cook a fish especially for me. And Priscilla is the best cook in Plymouth.

FRANCIS: Priscilla is the prettiest girl in Plymouth, 'tis said. Don't you agree, John Alden?

ALDEN: Aye, I do indeed. She is the prettiest in Plymouth or anywhere else. (*Breaks off*) I think I see Squanto coming now. It looks like Captain Miles Standish and the Governor with him. (STANDISH *enters, walking very erect, followed by* BRADFORD, BREWSTER *and other Pilgrim men.* SQUANTO *follows.*)

FRANCIS (*Goes to* SQUANTO): When do we go fishing, Squanto?

SQUANTO: Squanto stay here. While men parley. You lads go ahead. Squanto follow.

WRESTLING: All right. Come on, Francis. (*They go off.*)

BRADFORD: And you think we should start building a fort now, Captain Standish?

STANDISH: We shall need a fort very soon, Governor Bradford, if we are to remain safe from possible attack by the Narragansetts.

BREWSTER (*Wearily*): But how are we to perform a task so heavy, Captain Standish? Many of us are weak from hunger and sickness. We have had too little food this winter.

OTHERS (*Ad lib*): Aye. Certainly. That is so. (*Etc.*)

STANDISH (*Gruffly*): Hungry bellies will not serve as an excuse when we need to stave off enemy redskins, should they choose to attack.

BRADFORD: Gently, gently, Captain. Do not be angry. How like a little chimney you are, so quick to flare up. If we must build a fort for our protection, then it must be done. We Pilgrims have always found strength to do what is right.

BREWSTER: Aye. We know well enough that not all of the Indians are like our good friend, Squanto, here.

SQUANTO: Squanto help build fort. Squanto stay with white man. White man brave. Keeps his word.

BRADFORD: We know you will help us, Squanto. We should never have survived our hardships here at Plymouth without your help. (*To others*) Are we in accord, then? We will start work according to our Captain's orders.

OTHERS (*Ad lib*): Aye. It shall be done. Right away. (*Etc.*)

BRADFORD: Then I must be getting back to the Common House. There is much work to be done. Are you coming, Captain?

STANDISH: I will join you presently. First, I would speak to John Alden. (*Men exit as* ALDEN *turns to* STANDISH.)

ALDEN: You wish to speak to me?

STANDISH: Aye. I have a favor to ask of you. Harrumph! A rather unusual one, my friend. You are my friend, I take it.

ALDEN: Truly, I am your friend. Prithee, ask away. I shall do my best to grant any favor you ask. (ALDEN *seats himself unconcernedly on cask.*)

STANDISH (*Walking about nervously*): Perhaps you realize, John Alden, that my life has been lonely since the sad passing of my beloved wife.

ALDEN: I can quite understand that you have been lonely.

STANDISH: 'Tis so, indeed. And, since you understand my loneliness, you will not be surprised that I should give thought to—harrumph—marrying again.

ALDEN: Marrying, Captain?

STANDISH (*Offended*): You seem astounded. Am I then too old to wed again?

ALDEN: No, no! Of course not, sir. (*Hesitates*) Would you perhaps care to divulge the name of the—the lady in question? Have you decided who it is to be?

STANDISH: I have indeed. Harrumph! A very estimable young woman is the one of my choice. An orphan, too. Her parents died during the past sad year, and for that reason, she will be in need of a husband. Yes, I believe Miss Mullens will look with favor upon my suit.

ALDEN (*Rises, startled*): Miss Mullens! You don't—you can't mean Miss Priscilla Mullens?

STANDISH (*Nettled*): And what is so astounding, pray? Have you aught but favorable things to say of her?

ALDEN: No, no! Far from it, in fact. (*He sinks back, staring.*)

STANDISH (*Pleased with himself*): I consider Miss Mullens to be an excellent young woman! Industrious, modest, well favored, is she not?

ALDEN: Well favored? Yes, yes, sir. She is indeed. She is— beautiful. (*With an effort*) Will you tell me, sir, has she —has Miss Mullens agreed to become your wife?

STANDISH: Harrumph. Well, not exactly. In fact, that is what I wish to speak to you about, John.

ALDEN: To me, sir?

STANDISH: Yes, in truth I have not spoken to Miss Mullens, because—well, being somewhat awkward with the ladies, that is—harrumph! I am not sure that I would present my case in a manner that would be the most favorable to all concerned. Indeed, I am afraid—

ALDEN: I cannot imagine *you* afraid of anyone, sir.

STANDISH (*Bristling*): Nor am I. In matters of war, I am fearless. Have I not kept the redskins in subjection? The whole colony is safe with my men to guard them. But in matters of the heart—that is different. I am some-what shy. And that is why I have chosen you, John, to carry my proposal to Miss Mullens.

ALDEN (*Thunderstruck*): Nay, sir! I could never do that. Pray do not ask it of me.

STANDISH: Is not the name of friendship sacred to you? Did you not say you would act as my friend?

ALDEN: Yes, yes, of course. I will do what I can for you.

STANDISH: Good. I knew I could count on you. And I would like you to go at once to convey my message to Priscilla Mullens. I am an impatient man, and I would have my answer as soon as possible.

ALDEN (*Subdued*): Very well, sir. What shall I say?

STANDISH: You may say you have come in the name of Captain Miles Standish; that he sends Miss Mullens his respects; that he is aware of her exemplary character, and that he would like to have her hand in marriage. Can you remember that?

ALDEN (*In anguish*): I shall try, sir.

STANDISH: It will not be hard for you. You have a way with women and with words. And now, I must get to the Common House and give my directions for starting to build the fort. You will find Miss Mullens at the home of Elder Brewster where she is staying since the death of her parents. (*He goes off quickly as* WRESTLING *and* FRANCIS *enter from opposite direction.*)

WRESTLING: Is Squanto here, John Alden?

ALDEN: You will find him at the Common House with the others, Wrestling. Captain Standish is giving them directions for building a fort.

FRANCIS: Building a fort! (*Excitedly*) That will be a big undertaking. Come on, Wrestling. Let's go listen to the plans.

WRESTLING: And afterward, Squanto will take us fishing. (*The boys go out.* ALDEN *looks after them, dejectedly. Picks up barrel*)

ALDEN: Aye, a big undertaking. But one I would gladly accomplish single-handed if I could be spared the task awaiting me. How can I propose to Priscilla for another man, when I love her more than life itself? (*He goes off slowly.*)

CURTAIN

*   *   *

SCENE 2

TIME: A *little later.*

SETTING: *Interior of the Brewster home Plymouth.*

AT RISE: PRISCILLA, MARY, DESIRE *and* ELIZABETH *are seated on stage.* PRISCILLA *is spinning.*

DESIRE: Your busy hands quite put me to shame, Priscilla.

PRISCILLA: Nonsense. I like to keep busy, and Mistress Hopkins needs my help with the spinning. Besides, if I am busy I have less time to dwell on the sadness of the past year: the deaths of my parents and my brother. (*Cheerfully*) But tell me, what is the news?

MARY: What news can there be, pray? I vow, Plymouth is a dull place.

PRISCILLA: Not a single encounter with unfriendly Indians?

ELIZABETH: None that our esteemed Captain Standish is not capable of handling with one hand—or so he says.

PRISCILLA (*Laughing*): Are you jesting at our brave Captain Standish?

MARY: Captain Shrimp, you mean. (*She jumps up, does imitation of* STANDISH, *marching about pompously.*) Get into your places, men. Harrumph! (*All laugh.*)

DESIRE: Fie upon you, Mary, making sport of our brave Captain.

MARY: Well, I owe him naught of consideration, Desire. After all, it is not *I* that he looks upon with favor, but Priscilla here.

PRISCILLA (*Astonished*): I?

DESIRE: 'Tis true, Priscilla. I have seen him casting sheep's eyes in your direction more than once.

PRISCILLA: That cannot be.

ELIZABETH: Perhaps it is not Captain Standish's glances that interest Priscilla. If those glances came from a certain handsome young cooper now . . .

MARY: Look! Look! Priscilla is blushing.

PRISCILLA: Nay, it is not seemly to torment me so. Let us hear no more about the subject.

MARY: Very well, Priscilla, dear, we shall say no more. Not that I blame you for looking with favor upon John Al-

den. If I were not affianced to another handsomer young
man . . .

ELIZABETH (*Rising*): Come, girls, we are making Priscilla
uncomfortable with our chaffing. We had better leave.
(*Others rise.*)

MARY: Do forgive our teasing.

PRISCILLA: Of course I forgive you. Must you be going so
soon?

DESIRE: I fear so. There are many tasks awaiting me.
Goodbye, Priscilla dear.

MARY: We will leave you to your dreams— of Captain
Shrimp. (*All go out, laughing.* PRISCILLA *sits motionless
a moment. Door opens, and* WRESTLING *comes in. He
carries a fish on a string.*)

WRESTLING (*Excitedly*): Look! Look, Priscilla.

PRISCILLA: What is it, Wrestling?

WRESTLING: A fish. A lovely fish. (*He waves it before her.*)

PRISCILLA (*Shudders*): Ugh, please. Not so close to my
nose.

WRESTLING: But is it not a beauty?

PRISCILLA: I suppose so—as fish go.

WRESTLING: You said you would cook it for me.

PRISCILLA: And so I will. It is a beautiful fish, and you are
a valiant fisherman. Tell me, did you catch it all by
yourself?

WRESTLING: Well, not exactly. Squanto helped me a little.
And I am glad *you* are going to cook it, Priscilla. You're
the best cook in Plymouth.

PRISCILLA: Who says so?

WRESTLING: John Alden said so this morning. He also
said you are the prettiest girl.

PRISCILLA: Did John Alden say that?

WRESTLING: He did. And he's coming to see you, right
now. (*He looks out.*)

PRISCILLA (*Smoothing her hair*): Where? You mean he's here?

WRESTLING: He's right at the door. I'll let him in. (*Goes to door*) Come in, John Alden. Priscilla is here, waiting for you. (JOHN ALDEN *enters, carrying bouquet of flowers.*)

PRISCILLA (*Rises*): Do come in.

ALDEN: I—I brought you some mayflowers. They grow beside the brook.

PRISCILLA: Oh, thank you, John. I do love them so.

WRESTLING: Well, I guess I had better put my fish in the spring. (*He goes out.*)

PRISCILLA: Pray be seated, John.

ALDEN: I trust I am not disturbing you, calling at this unseemly hour.

PRISCILLA: You are very welcome. (*She returns to her work.*)

ALDEN (*Clears throat*): The weather is fine, is it not?

PRISCILLA: Yes, quite so, although there is a wind blowing off the harbor, I believe.

ALDEN: Quite so. (*He watches her work, then speaks suddenly, desperately.*) Miss Mullens—Priscilla—I have come on a very special mission. 'Tis my fervent hope that you will not find it too surprising, too shocking.

PRISCILLA: Surprising! Shocking!

ALDEN: I mean—that while the idea is not new—it is quite old, in fact—it may seem so to you.

PRISCILLA: I am puzzled. Pray continue. You have aroused my curiosity.

ALDEN (*Rises*): Miss Mullens—Priscilla—my mission is to bear you a proposal of marriage . . .

PRISCILLA (*Rises*): A proposal! Of marriage. Oh, John!

ALDEN: From Captain Miles Standish. I come as the emissary of our esteemed Captain. He sends his respects, and asks that you do him the honor of becoming his wife.

PRISCILLA: But if Captain Standish wishes to wed me, why did he not come and ask me? Is he afraid?

ALDEN: The Captain is the bravest man I know, Priscilla. But in affairs of the heart, he is somewhat shy.

PRISCILLA: And so you have come in his place, to propose marriage to me from Captain Standish.

ALDEN (*Stares straight ahead*): Such is my mission.

PRISCILLA (*Buries head in hands*): Oh, John, John!

ALDEN: It is apparent that I present a figure of fun.

PRISCILLA: Forgive me, John. I am not laughing, I assure you. 'Tis just that I had something different in mind.

ALDEN: And what message, pray, am I to give to Captain Standish when I return? Do you accept his proposal?

PRISCILLA (*Rises, speaks with dignity*): You may tell Captain Standish that Miss Mullens sends him her respects. That she is well aware of the great honor he is offering her, but it is one she cannot accept.

ALDEN (*Whirls around*): You—you cannot accept?

PRISCILLA (*Gently*): Nay, I cannot.

ALDEN (*Overcome, forgets himself a moment*): Oh, Priscilla!

PRISCILLA: Does my answer surprise you so much, John?

ALDEN: I hardly know. But—but can you give me some reason—something to take back to Captain Standish?

PRISCILLA: Tell him then, I cannot marry him because I love another.

ALDEN: You do? I mean—you do not love Captain Standish because there is someone else? Who is it, Priscilla?

PRISCILLA (*Turns away*): That I cannot say, but—(*Demurely*) why don't you speak for yourself, John?

ALDEN (*Clasps her hands*): Priscilla, do you mean—can it be! Nay, I must first go back and report to Captain

Standish. 'Tis only right that I should give him your message before I can speak for myself. But I will return, Priscilla. I will return. (*He rushes off.*)

PRISCILLA (*Stands motionless, smiling*): Yes, John. You will return. And I will be waiting. (*Curtain*)

THE END

Turkey, Anyone?

by Juliet Garver

Characters

MR. LONDON
MRS. LONDON
SALLY
DICK
PAM
LINDA, *Dick's girl friend*
MRS. PARKER, *a neighbor*
AUNT AUGUSTA

TIME: *Two days before Thanksgiving.*
SETTING: *The living room of the London family.*
AT RISE: MR. LONDON *is sitting at the coffee table, holding a carving knife and fork while reading a cookbook, muttering to himself.* MRS. LONDON *is sitting in an arm chair, knitting, but with one amused eye on her spouse.* SALLY, *completely oblivious, is sighing over the contents of her movie magazine.* PAM, *the little sister, is sitting in a chair, frowning at a big, heavy book in her lap.*

MR. LONDON: Now let me see. (*Picks up knife and waves it in air*) The best way to carve turkey, it says here . . .
PAM (*Looking up from her book*): Is to let Mom carve it ahead of time in the kitchen.

MR. LONDON (*Puts knife down and props up book so he can see it better*): No, no. This year I'm going to do it. After all, I'm head of this house.

PAM: But last time you tried carving turkey, you cut three fingers.

MR. LONDON: Two. Only two fingers. I don't know why you're always exaggerating.

SALLY (*Looking up from her magazine*): Brent Halliday sat at the head of the table last night in the movie I saw, and he carved a turkey like nothing—as if it was paper.

MR. LONDON: Probably was. You know how they fake things in the movies.

SALLY (*Indignant*): Father! How can you talk like that about a dreamboat like Brent Halliday? Why he's . . .

PAM (*Disgusted*): He's nauseating.

SALLY (*Scornfully*): Of course you're only a child. You wouldn't understand a man like Brent Halliday.

PAM: Psychologically he's a mess.

SALLY: What?

PAM: In plain English, a show-off . . .

SALLY: Well, I never.

MRS. LONDON: Let's get back to carving the turkey. Go on, dear, why don't you read what it says in the cookbook?

MR. LONDON (*Looking troubled*): Funny thing. I read it but I . . . well . . . say, maybe I could practice on something.

PAM: Don't look at me.

MRS. LONDON: I know. We have half a chicken left over from last night's dinner. You could try it.

MR. LONDON: I certainly will. (*Gets up, taking carving set and book with him.*) Thanksgiving's only two days off. I'd better get busy. (*He exits.*)

PAM: I hope you have enough bandaids in the house.

MRS. LONDON (*Smiling*): Oh, Pam.

PAM: Men! They're so clumsy.

SALLY: Look what's talking about men!

MRS. LONDON: Girls . . . please . . . stop fighting a minute. I want to tell you something. I didn't order a turkey this year.

PAM: You didn't? Well, what are we going to have instead? Peasant under glass?

SALLY: Pheasant, you dope.

MRS. LONDON: No, I . . . oh dear, I was just hoping I wouldn't have to cook Thanksgiving dinner for once. Every year on Thanksgiving, I spend hours in the kitchen.

SALLY: But, Dad. Look at him. He's practicing as if he's going to perform in front of an audience.

MRS. LONDON (*A bit sadly*): I know . . .

PAM: Why didn't you come right out and tell Dad you want to go out for dinner?

MRS. LONDON: I couldn't. He's been so excited about carving the turkey, and last night he talked about how he'd sit at the head of the table and look at his family. I just didn't have the heart to tell him.

SALLY: We'll have to think of something.

PAM: Maybe I'll send him an anonymous letter. Say, Mom, how many years have you been cooking Thanksgiving dinners?

MRS. LONDON: Why, ever since we were married.

PAM: I'll put that in the letter. Add up all the turkeys, sweet potatoes, pumpkin pies and how many hours you spent over a hot stove.

MRS. LONDON: Oh, no. I don't think that would be good. (*Phone rings.*)

PAM: It's the meat market, calling to tell you that you've won a free turkey.

MRS. LONDON: Oh no, it couldn't be! I did buy a ticket for a turkey raffle, but I never win anything. (*Phone rings again.*)

SALLY (*Gets up*): I'll answer it.

PAM: Maybe it's Brent Halliday calling you from Hollywood.

SALLY: You be quiet. (*Picks up phone*) Hello? Oh, hello, Miss Encrest. Yes. Why, yes, I could. I will. And thank you . . . thank you very much. Goodbye. (*Hangs up phone*)

PAM: I know. Miss Encrest wants you to play the turkey in the Thanksgiving play. (*Affectedly*) Gobble, gobble, said the turkey. Soon 'twill be Thanksgiving Day.

SALLY (*Annoyed*): Mother! Will you please tell this child to be quiet?

MRS. LONDON: Stop teasing, Pam . . . and Sally, why don't you tell us what Miss Encrest wanted?

SALLY: The girl who plays the grandmother in the Thanksgiving play has the flu, and Miss Encrest asked if I would step in and take the part. I said I would, and I have to run right over to her house now.

PAM: The grandmother? Ha! Brent Halliday should see you now!

SALLY: Oh, you be quiet. (*Getting dramatic*) Who knows? Maybe there'll be a talent scout in the audience, and he'll discover me.

PAM: Hiding behind your gray wig.

SALLY (*With an angry glance at* PAM): I'm leaving. (*She exits.*)

MRS. LONDON: I wish you and Sally didn't fight all the time.

PAM: It's perfectly normal for two sisters to fight. I read all about it in a psychology book.

MRS. LONDON: Oh, you and those books. I don't think you understand half the things you read. (*Doorbell rings*)

I wonder who that could be. (*She goes to door.* MRS. PARKER, *a neighbor, enters.*)

MRS. PARKER: Emily, I hate to bother you . . . I'm not bothering you, am I?

MRS. LONDON: No . . . no . . . not at all.

MRS. PARKER: I suppose this is a bad time, right before Thanksgiving . . .

MRS. LONDON: No, I'm not so busy.

MRS. PARKER: Not doing your Thanksgiving baking yet, are you?

MRS. LONDON: No . . . uh . . . not yet.

MRS. PARKER: I hate to ask my friends, but I have only a few left, a few raffle tickets for the Garden Club. We're raffling off two turkeys and three free memberships in the Garden Club.

PAM: Think of that.

MRS. LONDON (*Reprovingly*): Pam.

MRS. PARKER (*Still bubbling*): You will buy a ticket from me, Emily dear, won't you? Only fifty cents . . . and just think, you might win a twenty-five-pound turkey.

MRS. LONDON: Oh, dear.

MRS. PARKER: Now wouldn't that make you happy?

MRS. LONDON (*Weakly*): Oh, yes.

PAM: Delirious.

MRS. PARKER (*Tears ticket off booklet and gives it to her*): Here you are. Ticket 77. Two lucky numbers.

MRS. LONDON: They won't be lucky for me. (*Takes her purse off desk*) I never win anything. (*Gives her the money*)

MRS. PARKER: Don't be too sure. Beginner's luck, you know. Thanks, Emily. The drawing is this afternoon.

MRS. LONDON: This afternoon?

MRS. PARKER: Well I was supposed to have all my tickets sold by last night, but I . . . (*Laughs*) I'm just working overtime. I have to hurry. 'Bye. (*Exits.*)

PAM: Be just your luck to win that turkey.

MRS. LONDON: I never won anything in my whole life. (DICK LONDON *enters. He's wearing his band uniform.*)

PAM: Well here comes the General— General Nuisance, I mean.

DICK: Very funny. Hi, Mom.

MRS. LONDON: How are you, Dick?

DICK: Starved. What's there for me to eat.

MRS. LONDON: Your father's cutting up what's left from last night's dinner.

DICK: Cutting it up? What for?

PAM: You could just eat it whole like Henry the Eighth.

DICK: What's wrong with that?

MRS. LONDON: Your father's practicing so he can do a good job carving our Thanksgiving turkey.

DICK: Say, that reminds me, Mom. (*Fishes in his pocket*) I bought a raffle ticket for a turkey. The school band is going to raffle one off to raise money for our next trip. (*Looks closely at ticket.*) Hey, the drawing's this afternoon! I've had this ticket in my pocket for so long, I almost forgot about it.

MRS. LONDON: Uh . . . that's fine, son.

PAM: Fine and dandy.

DICK: Wouldn't it be swell if we won it?

PAM: Terrific!

DICK: Well, I'd better see if there's any of that poor old chicken left. (*Exits.*)

PAM (*Eagerly*): Mom, wouldn't it be awful if . . .

MRS. LONDON (*Protests*): No . . . don't say it!

PAM: Maybe something will happen . . .

MRS. LONDON: Too much has happened already. In fact, I have a terrible headache. I'm going upstairs to comfort myself with two big aspirin. (*She exits.*)

PAM (*Goes and picks up her book, sits down and starts to*

read it): Psycho—neu—rosis . . . (*Whistles*) must be a terrible disease. (MR. LONDON *enters.*)

MR. LONDON: Whew! That was really a workout I just had. I can hardly wait for the real event, when I have that nice browned turkey in front of me.

PAM: Uh . . . Dad.

MR. LONDON: Yes, Pam?

PAM: You know, sometimes I don't think you understand your wife.

MR. LONDON: What?

PAM: Have you ever stopped to think that maybe Mom doesn't want to make Thanksgiving dinner?

MR. LONDON: What? (*Brushing her aside*) Don't be silly. It's . . . why it's a family tradition in this house ever since you children were babies. I gave you a drumstick when you were still in your highchair.

PAM: Did you ever take her out for Thanksgiving dinner? Just think of all the dinners Mom has had to make.

MR. LONDON: Had to?

PAM: Did you ever take her out for dinner Thanksgiving?

MR. LONDON: No. You think I should?

PAM: I certainly do.

MR. LONDON: Maybe I have been selfish . . . thinking of myself.

PAM: At the head of the table.

MR. LONDON: I can still sit at the head of the table, even at a restaurant.

PAM: Of course.

MR. LONDON: You think Mom would like it if I made a reservation at the Blue Grotto?

PAM: She'd love it.

MR. LONDON: I'll do it right now. (*Goes to phone*) Hello, operator, give me the Blue Grotto Restaurant. Hello? Blue Grotto? This is Mr. London—Wallace London.

I'd like to make a reservation for five for Thanksgiving dinner. Five . . . Yes . . . around four-thirty . . . Yes, all right . . . Goodbye. (*Hangs up*) There. I'm not such a bad husband and father.

PAM: Of course not. (DICK *enters.*)

DICK: Think I'll go out for a couple hamburgers.

MR. LONDON: After all that chicken you ate and six slices of bread?

DICK: That was just a snack.

MR. LONDON (*Pointedly*): You see why we never go to restaurants?

DICK: Who wants to go to a restaurant? They never give you enough to eat.

PAM: If you don't watch yourself, you're going to outgrow that band uniform, and wouldn't that be terrible?

DICK: Well, maybe I won't eat those hamburgers after all.

PAM: Yeah, you can starve yourself till dinner time. After all, General, you can't afford to be fat.

DICK: Stop calling me General. *And* I don't want you calling me General Nuisance in front of Linda again. If anyone's a nuisance . . .

MR. LONDON: Dick . . . Pam . . . for heaven's sakes! There's always a battle going on in this house.

PAM (*To* DICK *again*): I know why you like Linda. After all, her father's a butcher. If you marry her, at least you'll know you'll always have plenty to eat.

DICK: Is that so? I suppose you think I think of nothing but eating?

PAM: That and playing your trumpet.

MR. LONDON (*Sighs, shakes his head*): I give up. This is the noisiest family I ever saw. Everybody has to get into the act.

DICK: Speaking of acting, where is our poor imitation of Sarah Bernhardt?

PAM: She's going to be in the Thanksgiving play. She's playing the part of the grandmother.

DICK: Grandmother? Wow! That's a good one! Sally, with her silver toenails. Now she's going to have silver hair. This I've got to see.

PAM: I wouldn't miss it for the world. (MRS. LONDON *enters.*)

MRS. LONDON: I tried to rest but you're all making so much noise.

MR. LONDON: Your exuberant family. Now, my family was different. Most of them were . . .

PAM: Here we go again. (*Doorbell rings*) Saved by the doorbell! (*She goes to door.* LINDA *enters.*) Oh, it's you.

LINDA: I have the most exciting news!

DICK (*Worried*): Linda . . . you're not going to the Thanksgiving Dance with . . . with someone else, are you?

LINDA: No . . . no . . . of course not.

DICK: You had me scared for a minute.

LINDA: I came over to tell you something else. You know, my father raffled off a turkey for Thanksgiving.

DICK: Oh sure. He does it every year.

LINDA: Well, we just had the drawing and guess what?

PAM: I can guess.

LINDA (*Ignoring her, rambling on*): Mrs. London, you won the raffle.

MRS. LONDON: Oh, dear! (*Sinks into a chair*)

LINDA: It's a twenty-three-pound turkey—a real beauty!

PAM: Mom's so excited she doesn't know what to say.

MRS. LONDON: Words fail me.

DICK: I can taste that turkey already.

LINDA: Oh, Dad said . . . (*Gets shy all of a sudden*) Would it be all right if Dick went back with me to pick up the turkey? I mean . . . Dad would give us a ride back when he closes the store.

MRS. LONDON: Of course, Linda. Go ahead . . . and thank your Dad for the turkey. First time I ever won anything. (DICK *and* LINDA *exit.*)

MR. LONDON: You don't seem very happy about that turkey, Emily.

MRS. LONDON: Frankly, I'm not. I wish it had happened to someone else.

MR. LONDON: Maybe we ought to go out for Thanksgiving dinner for a change.

MRS. LONDON (*Brightening*): Oh, Wally, you have such wonderful ideas!

MR. LONDON: Yes . . .

MRS. LONDON: How did you sense I wanted to go out for dinner?

MR. LONDON (*Feigning modesty*): Well . . .

MRS. LONDON: But what will we do with the turkey? I don't have room in the freezer.

MR. LONDON: We'll give it away. There's a new salesman down at the store, nice young fellow, has a wife and a baby, doesn't make much money. I'll drive over later and give him the turkey.

MRS. LONDON: Oh, Wally . . . you're wonderful!

PAM (*Looking from one to the other*): Sometimes I feel absolutely superfluous around here. (SALLY *enters.*)

SALLY: Anybody home? (*Walks towards center of stage*) Oh, Mother, something dreadful has happened . . . absolutely catastrophic.

PAM: They didn't give you the part.

SALLY: No . . . I got the part all right. It isn't that.

MRS. LONDON: Well, what is it, dear?

PAM: The suspense is killing us . . . inch by inch.

SALLY: The Drama Club had a raffle for a turkey . . .

PAM: Oh, no!

SALLY: Miss Encrest insisted I buy a ticket. She said the

money was for a good cause . . . to pay for our costumes. How could I say no?

MRS. LONDON: Of course you couldn't.

SALLY: But, Mom, you don't know what happened.

PAM: Oh, yes, we do.

MRS. LONDON: You won the turkey.

SALLY: Oh, Mom . . . I'm sorry.

MR. LONDON: Say, Emily, with your luck, you ought to play the horses.

SALLY: But, Dad, you don't understand.

MR. London: Oh, I'm a very understanding guy.

PAM: Dad wants to take us all out for Thanksgiving dinner.

MR. LONDON: I made reservations at the Blue Grotto.

SALLY: But what about the turkey?

MR. LONDON: You leave that to me. I'll give it away. I'll take it along with the other one.

SALLY: What other one?

PAM: Oh, Mom also won a turkey at the butcher shop.

SALLY (*Smiling*): Not really!

MRS. LONDON: First thing I've ever won in my whole life. (*Doorbell rings.*)

PAM: If that's someone else with a turkey, we're not home. (*She goes to door.* MRS. PARKER *enters.*) I have a sneaking hunch it is.

MRS. PARKER: Emily! I'm so excited I can hardly breathe!

MRS. LONDON: Oh, no, it can't be!

MRS. PARKER: But it is. You won first prize! A great big . . .

MRS. LONDON: Don't tell me.

MRS. PARKER: I don't blame you for being excited. I'm quite beside myself. And to think I sold you the ticket.

MRS. LONDON: Yes, just think.

MRS. PARKER: It's a twenty-two-pound turkey. Doesn't that thrill you?

Mrs. London: Oh, yes . . . to death!

Pam: It thrills all of us, through and through.

Mrs. Parker. You're so lucky, Emily. I wish it had happened to me.

Mrs. London: So do I. I wish you had my luck.

Mrs. Parker: Why, thank you, Emily, that's very sweet of you. I don't feel so bad though. After all, the proceeds went to the Garden Club, and where would I be without our wonderful Garden Club?

Mr. London: I don't know.

Mrs. Parker: Oh, Mr. London, you'd better practice your carving skills. The turkey will be delivered to you tomorrow. Goodbye, everybody. (*She exits.*)

Sally: Now what?

Mr. London: I guess I'll have to deliver another turkey.

Pam: We should have given it to Mrs. Parker.

Mrs. London: Why didn't *I* think of that?

Pam: Out of the goodness of your heart.

Mr. London: Pam, maybe you can catch her. Run out and call her back. (Pam *exits.*)

Mrs. London: I'm beginning to get awfully sick of the work "turkey."

Mr. London: I never saw such a winning streak.

Mrs. London: If they were raffling off a mink stole, I'd never get it. I guess I must be more the turkey type.

Sally: Oh, Mother.

Mr. London: To me, you're more the mink stole type. Of course, I haven't been able to see my way clear yet, but . . .

Mrs. London: I didn't mean anything, dear. I was just talking. (Pam *and* Mrs. Parker *enter.*)

Mrs. Parker: What is this dear child trying to tell me? That you don't want the turkey?

Sally: Oh, no . . . it isn't that at all.

Mrs. London: I think you deserve to have this turkey.

After all, who works harder for the Garden Club, year
in and year out?

MRS. PARKER (*Pretending modesty*): Well—I . . . I try
to do my bit.

MRS. LONDON: Everybody knows you do more than that.

SALLY: Everybody.

MRS. LONDON: I insist. I want you to have the turkey.

MRS. PARKER: Well, if you're sure . . .

MRS. LONDON: I insist. You can have my ticket (*Goes to
purse and gets ticket*), and I consider it a privilege to
give it to you. (*Gives her ticket*)

MRS. PARKER: I don't know how to thank you.

MRS. LONDON: You don't have to . . . just enjoy the
turkey.

MRS. PARKER: You're certainly generous, Emily. (*Starts
to exit*) Thanks, everybody. (*She exits.*)

MR. LONDON: Well . . . that's that.

MRS. LONDON: You know I don't think I'll even be able
to eat turkey this year.

SALLY: I think I'll order something like broiled whitefish
myself. (DICK *enters, carrying a turkey wrapped in a
large package.*)

DICK (*Putting package down on table*): Well, here it is.

PAM: Oh, no! Not another! I won't say it . . .

DICK: It's a nice turkey, but . . . I have some bad news,
too.

SALLY (*Eagerly*): Maybe Linda's father wants it back?

DICK: No . . . of course not.

MRS. LONDON: Then what is it?

DICK: Well, you know that ticket I bought for the school
band raffle? The first prize was two turkeys.

PAM: Oh, no!

DICK: I didn't win it.

SALLY: How wonderful!

MR. LONDON: Best news I've heard all day.

PAM: Hurray! Hurray! He didn't win the turkeys!

MRS. LONDON: Thank heavens for that.

DICK (*Looking from one to the other*): Hey, what's going on here? Has everyone in this family gone crazy?

SALLY: We've been winning turkeys like mad.

PAM: Yes, it's been raining turkeys!

DICK: What's so terrible about that?

SALLY: Dad's taking us all out to dinner Thanksgiving Day.

DICK (*Looks at package of turkey in his hands*): What'll I do with this?

MR. LONDON: I'll take it along with the other one. I'm going to give them away.

DICK: I hate the thought of giving away food.

PAM: I'll bet you do.

SALLY: It's time Mom had a vacation from the kitchen. Every holiday we have is no holiday for her. Cooking, cooking, and more cooking!

DICK: Now you're talking like a woman.

SALLY: What's wrong with that? (*Phone rings*)

PAM: Anyone buy any *more* raffle tickets?

SALLY: I'll get it. (*Goes to phone*) Hello? Oh, yes, Mr. Baumstead, he's here, just a moment, please. Dad, it's for you.

MR. LONDON: The boss? Calling me at this hour? (*Goes to phone*) Yes, Mr. Baumstead? Uh huh. Oh, yes, I see. Well, of course, I'm delighted.

PAM (*Half whispering*): He doesn't sound like it.

DICK: He looks sort of sick.

SALLY: Slightly pale green around the gills.

MR. LONDON (*Still on phone*): Well, thank you very much, Mr. Baumstead. I'll . . . I'll never forget it. 'Bye. (*Hangs up phone, looks around at everybody*)

MRS. LONDON: Bad news, dear?

MR. LONDON (*Groans*): You'll never guess.

PAM: I've got a hunch, but I hope I'm wrong.

MR. LONDON: Mr. Baumstead decided to give all his employees a free turkey this year, with his compliments.

PAM: I think we ought to open up a butcher shop.

SALLY: We'll just have to get rid of it, that's all.

MR. LONDON: But it's from my boss.

MRS. LONDON: He'll never know, dear.

SALLY: He won't be peeking over your shoulder watching you eat, Father.

MR. LONDON: You don't know Mr. Baumstead.

DICK (*Holding up his package*): What'll I do with this turkey?

MRS. LONDON: Go take it out to the kitchen and put it . . . wait a minute, I don't have room in the freezer or in the refrigerator for such a big bird. I know. Dick, take that turkey up to the corner and see if old Mr. Lansing would like to take it home to his daughter. He was just telling me the other day what a big family she has—how many mouths to feed. Maybe she'd like it.

DICK: All right, Mom. (*Exits*)

PAM: One more turkey disposed of . . .

SALLY: Maybe.

PAM: Pessimist.

SALLY: Who wouldn't be after what's happened?

MRS. LONDON: Oh, dear. I have a terrible feeling that we're going to have to eat at home after all.

MR. LONDON: You may be right.

SALLY: Oh why should it be so complicated for us to simply go out for dinner?

MR. LONDON: I don't know, why should it? (*Doorbell rings.*)

MRS. LONDON: That's probably Dick.

PAM: It couldn't be. He just left.

MR. LONDON (*Raising his voice*): Open the door and you'll find out.

PAM: Why is it I always have to go to the door? (*She goes.* AUNT AUGUSTA *enters.*)

AUNT AUGUSTA: Surprise, everybody! (*She comes towards center of stage carrying suitcase and umbrella.*) Emily dear, I hope you don't mind, but I just couldn't bear the thought of spending Thanksgiving alone.

MRS. LONDON (*Goes towards her, puts her arm on her shoulder affectionately*): Of course I don't mind, dear. I'm happy to have you with us.

AUNT AUGUSTA: And Emily, I hope you haven't ordered your turkey yet.

MRS. LONDON: No.

SALLY: Mother didn't order a turkey at all this year.

PAM: She didn't have to. They all fell in her lap.

AUNT AUGUSTA: What was that?

MR. LONDON: Nothing, Aunt Augusta. You know children, they just prattle.

AUNT AUGUSTA: The dears. Oh, yes, Emily, before I came here, I made the taxi stop, and I ordered you the nicest turkey.

MRS. LONDON: You did?

AUNT AUGUSTA: Yes.

MR. LONDON: You didn't have to do that.

MRS. LONDON: No, you shouldn't have.

AUNT AUGUSTA: But I wanted to. After all, look at me, barging in on your Thanksgiving dinner. But you're the only family I have, and I get so lonesome Thanksgiving Day. It's such a family day, don't you think?

MR. LONDON: Oh, sure!

SALLY: But, Aunt Augusta, we were going to . . .

MRS. LONDON (*Quickly*): Have a nice big Thanksgiving dinner.

PAM: It's a conspiracy, that's what it is. (*Phone rings. She answers.*) Hello? Oh, yes, Mr. Baumstead. One minute. (*Calling*) Dad.

MR. LONDON: I hear you, I'm not deaf. (*Goes to phone*) Uh, yes, sir. Oh, that's too bad, sir. Well, uh . . . why don't you come and spend Thanksgiving Day with us? We always make a big thing of it.

PAM: We sure do.

MRS. LONDON: Quiet, Pam.

MR. LONDON: Oh, no. No trouble at all. Mrs. London will be delighted. Goodbye. (*Hangs up*)

PAM: Don't tell us, we can guess.

SALLY: We're so intelligent.

AUNT AUGUSTA: What a funny way for children to talk. I just don't understand children these days.

MR. LONDON: Mr. Baumstead's wife was called out of town. Very sudden it was. Her sister's ill. She went to help, and Mr. Baumstead didn't want to have to spend Thanksgiving Day alone.

AUNT AUGUSTA: I don't blame him. Nothing more lonesome and dreary.

SALLY: So you invited him for Thanksgiving dinner.

MR. LONDON (*Throws up his hands, exasperated*): What else could I do?

MRS. LONDON: It's all right, dear.

MR. LONDON: I had the best of intentions.

MRS. LONDON: I know.

AUNT AUGUSTA: It was that letter you wrote me, Wally, that really made me come.

MRS. LONDON: What letter?

MR. LONDON: Oh, I . . . I just wrote Aunt Augusta a note.

AUNT AUGUSTA: He wrote me how he was practicing to carve the turkey like an expert, and then he wrote what it would be like for him to sit at the head of the table Thanksgiving . . . beaming at his family.

PAM: How mushy can you get?

MRS. LONDON: Pam, be quiet.

AUNT AUGUSTA: I just couldn't stay away when I read that.

MRS. LONDON (*Turns to her husband*): You . . . wrote that?

MR. LONDON: A . . . a weak moment.

MRS. LONDON: I didn't know it meant so much to you.

PAM: If I had a violin, I'd play hearts and flowers right now.

MR. LONDON: Pam, you can go to your room.

PAM: All right . . . banish me . . . see if I care! (*She exits.*)

MRS. LONDON: And Sally, will you take Aunt Augusta to the guest room? Help her unpack her things.

SALLY: Sure . . . be glad to. Come on, Aunt Augusta. (*They exit,* SALLY *carrying the suitcase.*)

MR. LONDON (*Fondly*): Emily, you're a peach!

MRS. LONDON: Now, now I've no time for compliments. What am I standing here for? I have work to do. There's baking and planning. We're going to have the best Thanksgiving dinner we've ever had, and I'm so happy.

MR. LONDON: Happy? But I thought you wanted to go out for dinner?

MRS. LONDON: I did at first, but then . . . oh, there's nothing like spending Thanksgiving at home with your family. (*Starts to exit, then turns back to wink*) And with such a nice head of the table. (*She exits.*)

MR. LONDON: What am I standing here for? I have to get my carving set and practice. Now where did I put that knife and fork? Oh, I remember. (*Faces audience*) I'm going to sit at the head of the table and carve that turkey just like you see in the movies. (*Quick curtain*)

THE END

The Thanksgiving Scarecrow

by Eleanor D. Leuser

Characters

SCARECROW
TWO VILLAGE GIRLS
TWO VILLAGE BOYS
FARMER
FARMER'S WIFE
TIM
JINNY

SETTING: *A road by a fence.*
TIME: *Thanksgiving Eve.*
AT RISE: *The stage is empty except for* SCARECROW, *who is talking to himself.*

SCARECROW: It's very sad. For ten Thanksgiving Eves have I stood here and not a soul has spoken to me. If they only knew what they were missing! Why, 'tis said if folks would chance to speak to a Scarecrow on Thanksgiving Eve, they could make a wish, and their wish would come true. Folks wish all right but as for giving me a word . . . not one of them does it. Oh, well, perhaps tonight will be different. (*Looking offstage*) Here come the first folk on their way to town. Maybe they'll stop and pass the time of day with me. (TWO GIRLS *come*

191

along the road and stop beside SCARECROW. *One leans against the fence. The other sits on a log by the big tree.*)

1ST GIRL (*Stretching wearily*): I'm tired, that I am, working hard in the dairy all day and having to walk home at night. I wish there were no long road to walk home. My feet hurt.

2ND GIRL: Never mind the road. It would be worse if we had none to walk on. Just think about the party tonight, and the Thanksgiving dance tomorrow. I wish I had a trunkful of new clothes to wear to both of them.

1ST GIRL (*Fixing her hair*): I wish the handsomest man would come along and ask me to dance. Oh, I can just see him.

2ND GIRL: Little good wishing will do for either of us. Come on, let's be stretching our legs if we want to get home tonight. (*They leave arm in arm.* SCARECROW *looks after them sadly.*)

SCARECROW: There, you see! Wouldn't they have been surprised if the road had vanished and a new trunkful of clothes had appeared! The pretty little girl could even have had her handsome man. What a pity they didn't know about talking to a Scarecrow and wishing on Thanksgiving Eve. . . . Hello, who's this? (*Two little* VILLAGE BOYS *appear, chasing each other. They see* SCARECROW *and stop to look at him.*)

1ST BOY: Goodness, what a funny-looking old Scarecrow! Let's throw things at him.

2ND BOY (*Picking up something and throwing*): I bet I can knock his hat off. Don't you wish you could hit him?

1ST BOY (*Throwing but missing*): I wish I could knock the pipe out of his mouth. Let's pick up lots of stones and try.

2ND BOY: Let's!

SCARECROW (*As* BOYS *are busy pretending to pick up stones*): I hope *they* don't speak to me. I'd lose my head.

Thank goodness, here come the Farmer and his Wife. I hope they hurry. (FARMER *and* FARMER'S WIFE *enter in a hurry.*)

FARMER (*Threateningly*). Stop that, you boys! Leave my Scarecrow alone. Hurry up and be off with you, now. (*He chases them off with a stick. He returns breathless.*) Boys sure are a nuisance, Mother! I wish the whole dratted lot of them were on a desert island.

WIFE: Oh, now, John, don't wish things like that. Remember our little John? He was a mischief, too. (*Sighing*) I wish he could have been with us this Thanksgiving.

FARMER: Now, now, Mother! Don't start that. For my part, I wish we had a new scarecrow. That one has been stuck out here in rain and storm for so many years he's falling apart. I'd better take him down, I reckon.

WIFE: Leave him a little while longer, John. He seems like one of the family, if he is a mite shabby.

FARMER: Well, I'll leave him up till after Thanksgiving. Then I think I'll make a new one.

WIFE (*Dreamily*): I wish . . .

FARMER: Come, now. Stop your wishing. What's that old saying . . . "If wishes were horses, beggars might ride." Come along. The boys are gone now. (FARMER *and* WIFE *exit.*)

SCARECROW: And that Farmer's Wife might have had her wish if she'd only spoken to me. Wouldn't they have been surprised if John had turned up? Too bad! Too bad! But that farmer . . . he really means it about getting a new Scarecrow. Then what will happen to me? And I won't have granted even a single wish. If only *someone* would speak to me. The next person who comes by surely will. (JINNY *and* TIM *enter together, bouncing a ball or playing catch. It goes over fence and* TIM *goes after it, climbing over fence.*)

JINNY (*Anxiously*): Did you find it, Timmy? It's my brand-new ball.

TIM: It went right by this scarecrow's feet. I'll find it in a minute.

JINNY (*Looking at* SCARECROW): What a nice old Scare-crow! I like him. Hello, Mr. Scarecrow, don't you mind it out here all alone?

SCARECROW (*Excitedly*): She spoke to me! At last! (*To* JINNY) Hello, little girl, how are you?

JINNY (*Astonished*): Good gracious! Can you talk?

TIM (*Coming back over fence*): Here's your ball, Jinny. Who were you talking to? I don't see anyone around.

JINNY: I was talking to that Scarecrow. You know, Tim, I'm almost sure he answered.

TIM (*Scornfully*): Don't be silly! Scarecrows can't talk. Come on. Hurry! (*He pulls her by the arm and they start away.*)

JINNY (*Almost crying*): I know he spoke. Don't hurry me so, Timmy. (*Looking back*) Goodbye, Mr. Scarecrow.

SCARECROW (*As he calls, the children start with amaze-ment*): Come back here, children. Of course scarecrows can talk . . . that is when they are spoken to. I want to tell you something. (*The two* CHILDREN *come back slowly—gazing at* SCARECROW.)

JINNY: I told you he could speak.

TIM (*In awe*): He can . . . can't he?

SCARECROW: Not only that . . . but if someone speaks to a scarecrow on Thanksgiving Eve, the Scarecrow may grant him a wish. I've been waiting here ten years to grant a wish so make it a good one, little girl. What do you want?

TIM (*Excitedly*): Go ahead, Jinny, wish!

JINNY: But I don't know anything to wish for.

SCARECROW: Oh, come now, think hard. I may not be here

another Thanksgiving Eve. The Farmer seemed to think I was about worn out. Let me grant one wish.

JINNY (*Slowly*): I don't know . . .

TIM: Think, Jinny, think! You must want something.

JINNY (*Thinking hard*): I have a nice warm house, and Daddy and Mother are in it. There'll be a good hot supper waiting for me. No, I have everything, thank you.

TIM (*Impatiently*): But don't you want clothes or money or anything? I could think of a thousand things.

SCARECROW: But it isn't your wish, young man. Think hard, Jinny. It must be something you would really like.

JINNY (*Slowly*): Mother just made me a brand-new dress because tomorrow is Thanksgiving, and Daddy gave me a shiny new dollar just this morning.

SCARECROW (*Anxiously*): But if you could just make a wish and I could grant it, I would be the happiest Scarecrow that ever lived, though I suppose Scarecrows don't really live.

JINNY (*Interrupting*): That's it! I know what to wish. I wish that you could come home with us and stay for Thanksgiving dinner.

SCARECROW (*Taken by surprise*): My stars! What an amazing wish! For goodness sakes . . . (*He almost falls from his pole and then straightens up*) I believe I'm turning into a man! (*He takes steps to the fence with much difficulty and leans against it.*)

TIM: Jinny, he's really alive. Let's help him over the fence.

JINNY: Of course he is. Isn't it wonderful? (JINNY *and* TIM *help the* SCARECROW *over the fence.*)

SCARECROW (*Still amazed*): You wished me alive and . . . here I am. (*Walks a few steps—almost falls*) It feels wonderful. Thank you, Jinny, thank you! (*He still staggers a little.*)

JINNY (*Anxiously*): You're coming home with us for Thanksgiving?

SCARECROW (*Testing each leg*): That's what you wished so I'll have to accept, though I'm certainly a bit shabby. (*Looks down at his clothes sorrowfully.*)

JINNY: Oh, Daddy will fix you up. Don't you mind a bit. Come along.

SCARECROW: I wish I could do something for you. Wait a moment. Jinny, you didn't wish for anything for yourself so I'm going to wish for you.

JINNY (*Delightedly*): Oh, Mr. Scarecrow, I'll like anything you wish.

SCARECROW (*Still slowly*): You won't understand this now, but you'll know what I mean as you get older. Jinny, I wish that you may always keep the same thankful heart that you have today. It will bless you and yours always. (*JINNY and TIM link arms with SCARECROW between them, and they start offstage as the curtain falls.*)

THE END

Governor Bradford's Scissors

by Graham DuBois

Characters

PRUDENCE, *a Pilgrim mother*
FAITH, *her daughter*
REBECCA
HOPE
GOVERNOR BRADFORD
JIM
TOM
CAPTAIN MILES STANDISH
SQUANTO

TIME: *Autumn, 1621.*

SETTING: *The living room in the home of Prudence, in Plymouth, Massachusetts.*

AT RISE: PRUDENCE *is sitting behind the table, paring a bowl of apples. Near her, at the table, sits* FAITH, *struggling to untie the string at one end of a bag of meal. A bowl and a small knife are before her on the table. On each end of the table are two pumpkins.*

FAITH: I wish I had Governor Bradford's scissors!

PRUDENCE (*Glancing at* FAITH): The Governor's scissors? For what?

FAITH: To cut this string.

PRUDENCE (*Laughing quietly*): There's not much chance of getting them for that purpose.

FAITH (*Tugging at the string*): I guess not. I hear that he always wears them fastened to his garments by a stout chain.

PRUDENCE: He really does.

FAITH (*Laughing merrily*): I suppose when he goes to bed he attaches them to his nightgown.

PRUDENCE: I shouldn't be surprised. But why do you want to untie that bag?

FAITH: I need more meal for Indian pudding. Governor Bradford asked especially that we have a large supply for the Thanksgiving feast this afternoon.

PRUDENCE: But, my dear, we probably have more already than we shall use. Put the bag aside and help me with these apples. (*Takes a few apples and puts them into* FAITH's *bowl*)

FAITH: Just as you say, Mother. (*Lays bag on table*) But I'm afraid you underestimate the taste of our young men for Indian pudding. (*Picks up an apple and begins paring it*)

REBECCA (*Entering front door breathlessly*): I suppose you have heard the news? (*Walks to chair*) I think the Governor has lost his mind. (*Sits*)

PRUDENCE: The Governor? Why, what has he done?

REBECCA: He has invited the Indians to the feast.

FAITH: How many of them?

REBECCA: All of them—the whole tribe.

PRUDENCE (*Stunned*): No! Why, we have prepared only enough food for ourselves.

FAITH: Why did the Governor do such a thing?

REBECCA: He says that the feast should be not only one of Thanksgiving for an abundant harvest, but a celebration of the peace that has existed between us and the Indians.

(*Rising*) Well, I must go around and tell the other house-wives. (*Walks to door*) I guess the men will have to go after game once more. (*Exits*)

FAITH: Oh, Mother, there's not enough food in the entire colony to feed all those Indians.

PRUDENCE (*Reassuringly*): Probably only a few will come. (*Knock at door*) Who in the world is that? (*Calling*) Come in!

HOPE (*Entering and looking around hastily*): Have you seen little Mercy?

PRUDENCE: Why, no! Is she lost again? Do sit down, Hope.

HOPE (*Sitting*): Just for a minute. Mistress Carver told me that she saw Mercy following Squanto. She was crying.

PRUDENCE: That's strange! I thought Squanto loved the child.

HOPE: Oh, he does. They're the best of friends. I think maybe she wanted him to take her to the Indian camp. (*Rises*)

PRUDENCE: How full of life that child is!

HOPE: Full of mischief you mean. No wonder her father nicknamed her the Imp. She is into everything. Yesterday he found her with his silk hat. She had filled it with mud and was planting an old weed. (*Exits*)

FAITH (*Looking at* PRUDENCE *in desperation*): Mother, how can we feed such a horde of Indians?

PRUDENCE: I don't know, but we'll find a way. Governor Bradford is eager to cultivate their friendship. He thinks they can be staunch allies, says they really have big hearts.

FAITH: And even bigger appetites. Jim says that one Indian can eat more than three white men.

PRUDENCE (*Impatiently*): Jim! Don't quote that boy to me. What he says is almost always an exaggeration.

FAITH: Be careful, Mother. (*Playfully*) I may go to the Thanksgiving feast with him.

PRUDENCE (*Earnestly*): James Taylor is just a ne'er-do-well.

FAITH: But I may go with him, Mother. He asked me yesterday, and Tom Edwards will probably invite me, too.

PRUDENCE: Surely you can't admire men like them, after all Captain Standish has said about them.

FAITH (*Indignantly*): Captain Standish has another reason for talking against them.

PRUDENCE (*Surprised*): What reason could Captain Standish possibly have?

FAITH: He wanted to take me to the feast himself.

PRUDENCE (*Proudly*): He has done you a great honor, my child.

FAITH (*Contemptuously*): Honor indeed!

PRUDENCE: Next to Governor Bradford, he is the most important man among us.

FAITH: What of it? Don't you think he shows a great deal of vanity in assuming that I would choose him over attractive young men like Jim Taylor or Tom Edwards?

PRUDENCE: Hush, child! You must show more respect for such an important person. Governor Bradford says he doesn't know what this colony would have done without Captain Standish. (*Knock at door*) There's somebody at the door.

FAITH (*Rising*): I'll go, Mother. (*Walks to door*) It may be Jim. He said that he— (*Opens door*) Why, Governor Bradford! Come in.

BRADFORD (*Entering*): Thank you, Faith. (*Walks to chair*) I see you are busy, Prudence. (*Sits*) Preparing for this afternoon's feast?

PRUDENCE: Yes, Governor, but with all those Indians coming, I don't know how we are going to feed everybody.

BRADFORD (*Suddenly serious*): I don't know how many Indians are coming. I'm afraid that none may come.

PRUDENCE (*Amazed*): None? You amaze me, Governor. Aren't we and the Indians on the most friendly terms?

BRADFORD: We *were* on friendly terms.

PRUDENCE: Why do you say *were*, Governor?

BRADFORD (*Shaking his head doubtfully*): Yesterday morning something happened to change things. In fact, it may threaten the peace that has existed between us and the Indians.

PRUDENCE: This sounds serious. Can you tell us what happened?

BRADFORD: Yes. My scissors disappeared.

FAITH (*Puzzled*): Your scissors?

BRADFORD (*Nodding*): My most priceless possession. I doubt that there is another pair on this side of the Atlantic.

PRUDENCE: You mean—they were stolen?

BRADFORD: I don't know. I wish I did. There is a possibility that I may have mislaid them or that somebody borrowed them.

PRUDENCE: You have always been so careful with them.

BRADFORD: I have indeed. I never lend them to anybody without requiring a receipt, and we have searched every nook and cranny in the house.

PRUDENCE: It looks like a case of theft, Governor.

BRADFORD (*Sadly*): I'm afraid so.

FAITH: Do you suspect anybody?

BRADFORD: A half dozen or more.

PRUDENCE: But how are the Indians involved? How does all this affect their coming to the feast?

BRADFORD: A number of people were at my house yesterday before I missed the scissors. Among them was Red Feather, one of the Indian braves. He has always admired the scissors, likes to see them sparkle in the light, is fascinated when he watches me cut things with them.

FAITH: Has he ever stolen from you before, Governor?

BRADFORD (*Emphatically*): Never. And, somehow, I can't believe he has done so now.

PRUDENCE: You have more faith in the Indians than I have, Governor.

BRADFORD: We all have cause to trust them and be grateful to them. They have taught us much about hunting and planting. And Squanto is one of the best friends the colony has.

PRUDENCE (*Grudgingly*): Yes—but Squanto is an exception. He has learned much from the white man.

BRADFORD: I think the white man has learned much from him—faith and generosity and courage. He is one of the reasons this colony has survived. He was among my callers yesterday.

PRUDENCE: I see. And he is among those under suspicion.

BRADFORD: I would as soon suspect my own mother. But he feels responsible for keeping the Indians from the feast.

PRUDENCE (*Surprised*): He does? In what way?

BRADFORD: Last evening he went to their camp and told them of the loss of the scissors. He asked Chief Massasoit if any of his men had seen them, and the Chief was indignant. He said if we thought his men were thieves, they were not fit to come to the feast. Unless I find the thief before this afternoon, we may have lost the friendship of the Indians. And that is a much greater loss than the scissors.

PRUDENCE: Who else went to your house yesterday, Governor?

BRADFORD: Let me see. (*Thinks for a moment*) James Taylor was there.

FAITH: Surely you can't suspect him.

BRADFORD (*Gently but firmly*): I have to suspect each person who was in my house yesterday. Tom Edwards was there, too.

FAITH (*Astonished*): He is one of the most respected young men in the colony. He plans to enter the ministry.

BRADFORD: I am aware of that, and I certainly hope he is innocent. And I can say the same of Kenneth Bacon.

FAITH: Kenneth? You mean he visited you, too?

BRADFORD: Yes—on perfectly plausible grounds.

FAITH: Why, even Captain Standish trusts him.

BRADFORD (*Chuckling*): Captain Standish trusts nobody this morning. He has vowed to find those scissors. He is visiting every house and asking questions. He will be here before long.

FAITH (*Perplexed*): But, Governor Bradford, I don't understand what a young man would want with a pair of scissors.

BRADFORD: My dear, there is hardly a more valuable article in the colony—especially since it is the only pair.

FAITH: But what could he do with them?

BRADFORD: Trade them to Massasoit or his men. There's not an Indian here who wouldn't give a dozen furs for them. And furs can be shipped to England and sold for fabulous sums.

FAITH (*Thoughtfully*): And Jim and Tom both trade with the Indians.

BRADFORD: Lately, the Indians have been sewing red ribbons on their garments, and Jim and Tom have never been so prosperous.

FAITH: It isn't fair to take advantage of the poor Indians.

BRADFORD: I quite agree with that statement, my dear. But I really believe these young men have no intention of taking advantage of the Indians. They look upon each other as merchants competing for trade, and lately competition has been strong. (*Rising*) Well, Prudence, let us go decorate the meeting house. I suppose these pumpkins are for that purpose. (*Takes a pumpkin under each arm*)

PRUDENCE: They are indeed. I'll bring the others. (*Takes a pumpkin under each arm. To* FAITH) While I'm gone, dear, be sure to see that the bread doesn't burn. (*Followed by* BRADFORD, *she walks to door, humming a harvest song.* FAITH *rises, runs to door, and holds it open.* PRUDENCE *and* BRADFORD *exit.* FAITH *closes the door, walks to table, humming the song, picks up the two bowls, and carries them to the kitchen. After a moment, she returns to the table and begins wiping it with a cloth. There is a knock at the door.*)

FAITH (*Startled*): Who is it? Come in! (*Walks to door and opens it*) Jim Taylor! You are all out of breath. You have been running! Why?

JIM (*Entering, breathing heavily*): I—I think Captain Standish—is after me.

FAITH: Why should he be after you? What have you done?

JIM: I—I took something.

FAITH (*Amazed, shrinking back from him*): You took something? Then Captain Standish was right, after all. You mean—you are a thief?

JIM: No! But I guess Captain Standish thinks so. I just borrowed it. I meant to put it back before Standish found out, but I haven't had the chance. He will throw me into the guardhouse, and I want to take you to the feast.

FAITH (*Calmly*): There are many things more important than feasts, Jim. Honor is one of them. I advise you to go to Captain Standish and tell him the truth.

JIM: He wouldn't believe me. He detests me.

FAITH: It is the only way. Governor Bradford will see that the punishment is just. (*Knock at door*) What was that? Somebody at the door!

JIM: Don't open it. It may be Standish.

FAITH: What do you expect me to do?

JIM: Hide me. (*Pleadingly*) Just for a little while.

FAITH: I—I don't know. (*Knock repeated*)

JIM: Just until Standish leaves.

FAITH (*Hesitating*): I—I don't know what to do. I like you, Jim—despite the dreadful thing you have done— but I have often heard Mother say that a person who protects a thief is as bad as the thief himself.

JIM: Protect a thief? What are you talking about? (*Knock repeated*) Please hide me.

FAITH: Very well. Come with me. (*Leads him to closet left and opens it*) Go in there. (JIM *enters closet and she closes it behind him. She walks to front door and opens it.*) Why, Tom Edwards! What are you doing here? Come in.

TOM (*Entering*): I came to ask you a question. Will you go to the Thanksgiving feast with me?

FAITH: I don't know. That depends.

TOM: Depends? On what?

FAITH: Somebody else has asked me, but he may not be in a position to take me. (*Knock at door*) Pardon me a moment. (*Turns toward door*)

TOM: Don't open that door. (*Puts his hand on her arm*)

FAITH (*Looking at him in amazement*): Why not?

TOM: It may be Captain Standish.

FAITH: Why shouldn't Captain Standish come in?

TOM: I have good reasons for not wanting to see him this morning. Call to him that you are busy.

FAITH: I can't do that. Mother thinks highly of him. She would never forgive me. (*Knock is repeated, and* FAITH *turns toward door.*)

TOM: Just a moment, I beg of you, Faith. Before you open that door, please do me just a little favor.

FAITH: And what is that?

Tom: Hide me.

Faith (*Looking at him in amazement*): You, too?

Tom: Only until Captain Standish is out of the way.

Faith (*Hesitating*): Oh, very well. Come with me. (*Leads him to closet right and opens it*) Go in there. (Tom *enters closet and she closes door. Knock at front door is repeated. Calling*) I'm coming. (*Insistent knocking*) Just a minute! (*Hurries to door*) Somebody's in a dreadful hurry. (*Opens door.* Standish *enters.*) Oh, it's you, Captain Standish!

Standish: Yes, my dear, it is I. But you don't seem especially happy to see me.

Faith (*Embarrassed*): I—I'm just as happy as I ever am to see you.

Standish (*Chuckling*): Well, that doesn't mean you are overjoyed. Aren't you going to ask me to sit down?

Faith (*Bowing low and motioning toward a chair with mock courtesy*): Won't you be seated, Captain Standish?

Standish (*Bowing low*): Thank you. (*Walks to chair and sits*) I have something of the utmost importance to discuss with you.

Faith (*In consternation*): Oh, no, Captain! Not this morning! I'm not— (*Sits down*)

Standish: Don't be alarmed, Faith. I'm not going to ask you again to go to the feast with me. What I have to say concerns the welfare of this whole colony. (*Holds out his clenched hand*) Do you know what I have in this hand?

Faith: I haven't the slightest idea. How could I know?

Standish: It was on your doorstep. I picked it up just before I came in.

Faith: Don't keep me in suspense, Captain. What is it? (Standish *opens his hand and extends it toward her*) A bit of ribbon!

Standish: Yes. A bit of ribbon—red ribbon, such as some

rascals sell to the Indians for a hundred times its value. (*Hands it to her*) The scoundrels carry pieces like this as samples to tempt the Indians.

FAITH (*On the defensive*): There is nothing wrong in trading with the Indians. Governor Bradford said so only this morning.

STANDISH: Ah, the Governor is far too kind and lenient to the rascals. I'd throw them into jail.

FAITH: You can't throw a man into jail without reason.

STANDISH: I may be close to a reason now for jailing at least one of them. (*Nods toward the ribbon in* FAITH's *hand*) That may be an important clue.

FAITH (*Examining ribbon*): This? Why, it's just like all other ribbon in the colony. The last ship from England brought a quantity of it.

STANDISH: Note the edge of that ribbon—how evenly it is cut.

FAITH (*Puzzled*): You mean—

STANDISH: There is only one instrument in Plymouth that can cut like that.

FAITH: You mean— a pair of scissors?

STANDISH: Yes—Governor Bradford's scissors. And they have been stolen.

FAITH (*Indicating the ribbon in her hand*): How did this come here?

STANDISH: That is a question I was about to ask you. To whom does this ribbon belong?

FAITH: I—I don't know, Captain. I—I really don't know.

STANDISH (*Suspiciously*): Wasn't James Taylor here within the past fifteen minutes?

FAITH: Yes, he—he was. But I don't know who—

STANDISH: You are not trying to shield him, are you? If he was here, isn't it likely that he dropped the ribbon?

FAITH: He isn't the only one who has been here, Captain.

STANDISH: Who else? (*Insistently*) Speak up, child!

FAITH: I—I can't tell you.

STANDISH: Why not? Don't you know that you are obstructing justice? Do you realize the Indians won't come to the feast until we have thrown the culprit into prison? You know that Governor Bradford believes that half the success of the celebration depends upon having them here.

FAITH: Yes. I heard the Governor say so.

STANDISH: The Governor insists that friendly relations with the Indians must be maintained. The peace of the colony may be at stake.

FAITH: I wish I could help the Governor.

STANDISH: You can help him. You are shielding either James Taylor or somebody else. Who is it?

FAITH (*Handing him the ribbon*): I'm sorry, Captain, but I will not answer that question.

STANDISH (*Taking the ribbon and rising indignantly*): You stubborn girl! (*Stalks to the door*) The Governor shall hear about this. (*Turns to face her*) I warn you that you are interfering with the law. (*Exits.* FAITH *runs to the window, watches him walk away, and then hurries to door left.*)

FAITH (*Opening door*): Come out, Jim.

JIM (*Entering*): Just in time! Another moment and I would have smothered.

FAITH (*Crossing to door right*): Perhaps that's what you deserve.

JIM (*Amazed*): What I deserve?

FAITH (*Opening door*): Captain Standish has gone, Tom.

TOM (*Entering*): It's good to breathe again. (*Taking a deep breath*) I was choking in there.

JIM (*Angrily*): Tom Edwards! What are you doing here? Hiding in that closet, were you? Afraid to face me like a man.

TOM (*Angrily*): I'm not afraid to face you or anybody else. It seems to me that you were hiding in a closet, too. Eavesdropping on Faith and me, were you?

JIM: Watch your words, Tom Edwards! (*Clenches his fists and advances menacingly toward* TOM) If you—

TOM (*Clenching his fists and standing in a belligerent attitude*): I have good reason for being here. Faith and I are going to the feast together.

JIM (*Laughing derisively*): You are a little late, my boy. She is going with me.

FAITH (*Stepping between them*): Enough of this! I may go with neither of you.

TOM: With neither of us?

JIM: You mean there is somebody else who—

FAITH: I mean one of you will probably be in jail before the feast begins. Come, let us talk things over calmly. (*Leads them downstage*) Jim, you will sit there. (*Indicates chair.* JIM *sits*) And, Tom, over there. (*Indicates chair.* TOM *sits. She takes a chair between them.*) And I will sit between you—just to prevent hostilities. (*Looking from one to the other*) Which of you will do something for me?

TOM: I will. Anything. Just name it.

JIM: There's nothing I wouldn't do for you.

FAITH: Good! I want you to go to Captain Standish, give yourself up, and confess your crime.

TOM (*Indignantly*): I'm no criminal!

JIM (*Amazed*): What crime?

FAITH: Theft—one of the most serious crimes.

JIM (*Stunned*): You mean you think that I—

TOM: Theft of what?

FAITH: Governor Bradford's scissors.

TOM (*Amazed*): Governor Bradford's scissors?

JIM: I haven't even seen them for a week.

FAITH (*Very seriously*): Jim, when you came here you said you had taken something and that Captain Standish was after you, and you wanted me to hide you.

JIM: But I didn't have time to explain, Faith, before there was a knock at that door. (*Points to front door*) I was going to say that yesterday Governor Bradford asked me to be one of the party to kill game for the feast. My gun was out of order. I went to the arsenal to borrow one. There was nobody there, and so I just took one. I planned to return it this morning before Standish got around, but he has been there since dawn.

FAITH: Why didn't you explain to Captain Standish?

JIM: Faith, have you ever tried to explain anything to that stubborn old bear? It's like talking to a stone wall.

FAITH (*Tearfully*): Oh, Jim, I do believe you. (*Turning to* TOM) What is your story, Tom?

TOM: It's something like Jim's. Kenneth told me that my name was on the list for guard duty this afternoon. I wanted to take you to the feast, Faith. I decided to keep out of Standish's way so that he wouldn't have a chance to notify me. I have been dodging him all morning.

FAITH: You foolish boys! I don't believe that the Captain wants you for borrowing a rifle or trying to avoid guard duty. The only thing the Captain is interested in this morning is Governor Bradford's scissors.

TOM (*Insistently*): But I tell you I didn't take them, Faith. I am innocent.

JIM: So am I.

FAITH: If you are innocent, surrender to Captain Standish and prove your innocence to him.

JIM: Fine chance I would have of proving anything to him! He would throw me into prison for taking a weapon without permission.

TOM: And I would get the same punishment for trying to avoid guard duty, even though I explained to him that

I only wanted to postpone it for a while. (PRUDENCE *enters, followed by* REBECCA *and* BRADFORD.)

PRUDENCE (*Eyeing* TOM *and* JIM *coolly*): How are you, Jim?

JIM: Very well, thank you. (*Rises*)

PRUDENCE: I hope your mother has recovered from her cold, Tom.

TOM (*Rising*): She is quite well now, thank you.

BRADFORD (*Slapping* TOM *and* JIM *warmly on the shoulder*): I am glad to see you boys. You are the very ones to help us with preparations for the feast. (*All sit.*)

JIM: I am at your service, Governor.

TOM: I'll be glad to do anything I can. (*A knock at the door is heard.*)

FAITH (*Rising and calling*): Just a moment! (*Goes to door and opens it.* STANDISH *enters.*)

STANDISH (*Sternly*): Young lady, you may be in a very serious position.

FAITH (*Alarmed*): In a serious position? For what reason?

STANDISH: For obstructing justice. I have every reason to believe that you were hiding these culprits (*Indicates* TOM *and* JIM) when I was here a while ago. One of my men saw them enter. He kept a steady watch. He did not see them leave.

JIM (*Stepping forward. To* STANDISH): It wasn't her fault. She didn't know I had borrowed the rifle.

STANDISH (*Surprised*): Borrowed the rifle? What rifle? I don't know anything about it.

JIM (*Crestfallen*): You don't? Oh, I thought—

TOM (*Rising*): When she hid me, she didn't know that I was trying to avoid you so that I wouldn't be on guard duty today.

STANDISH (*Perplexed*): On guard today? Why, your name is on my list for next month.

TOM (*Chagrined*): It is? Oh, I had been told—

STANDISH (*Chuckling mirthlessly*): How true the Scriptures are! "The wicked flee where no man pursueth." (*Walks to* JIM *and* TOM) I arrest you for the theft of Governor Bradford's scissors.

BRADFORD: Don't let's be too hasty, Captain. Have you sufficient evidence for an arrest?

STANDISH (*Peevishly*): Governor, I beg of you not to interfere with the operation of the law.

BRADFORD: But, Captain, a man is innocent until he is proved guilty. Can you offer any evidence against these men?

STANDISH: I have enough evidence to throw them into jail to await trial. They have been avoiding me all morning. And I found a bit of ribbon on the doorstep—the kind of ribbon these men trade in. It had obviously been cut with a pair of scissors. And the only pair in the colony is yours.

BRADFORD: Highly circumstantial. You will need much stronger—(*Shouting offstage*) What was that? (*Rises and walks to window, looks out*) It's the Indians over on that hill.

PRUDENCE: They may be planning an attack. (*Shouting gets nearer*)

REBECCA (*Terrified*): They have been camping there for the past week. That hill is not a quarter of a mile from the settlement. We shall all be slaughtered.

BRADFORD (*Turning from window*): Calm yourselves. Those Indians are not on the warpath. (*Returns to chair*) They are laughing and slapping one another on the back. (*Sits*) I can't make it out.

REBECCA: It may be a trick to throw us off our guard.

BRADFORD: I hardly think so. I rather believe those Indians are— (*Knock at door*)

FAITH (*Calling*): Come in. (SQUANTO *enters.*)

ALL (*Ad lib*): Squanto. Where have you been? What brings you here?

SQUANTO: I come from Indians. They very happy. (*Takes scissors from pocket and hands them to* BRADFORD) Governor, your scissors.

BRADFORD (*Amazed*): So Red Feather took them, after all?

SQUANTO: Red Feather no take.

STANDISH (*Suspiciously*): I suppose one of these young men traded them to the Indians? (*Indicates* JIM *and* TOM)

SQUANTO: No, Indians no have. Little Mercy Johnson, the Imp, she have.

BRADFORD (*Bewildered*): Little Mercy Johnson? How in the world could a child—

SQUANTO: I pass by. I see Imp dig in sand with scissors. I go to Indians, show scissors, tell about Imp. They very happy; they sing and dance. They coming to feast.

BRADFORD (*Fervently*): Thank God! (*Suddenly playful*) When the history of this colony is written, the Imp may have a place as one who almost wrecked its peace. (*Serious again. To* SQUANTO) And, Squanto, one of the highest places of all will be reserved for you for having saved our colony.

HOPE (*Entering*): Oh, Governor Bradford, I want to apologize. I had no idea the Imp had those scissors.

BRADFORD: There is no need for an apology, my dear. After all, little Mercy is hardly more than an infant.

HOPE: I think I know how she got them. Do you remember yesterday when you came to tell me about the feast? I was sewing a dress in the dining room, and you took off your scissors and cut the thread.

BRADFORD: I do indeed remember! And then you led me into the kitchen to show me the bench your husband had made, and I suppose I left the scissors on the dining room table.

HOPE: That is what I think must have happened. (*Turns toward door*) I'm going home to give the Imp the spanking of her life.

BRADFORD: Oh, no, my dear, this is no time for punishment. (*Glances playfully at* STANDISH) Unless our good Captain here wants to throw the Imp into prison.

STANDISH (*Frowning*): Anybody can make a mistake occasionally. (*Hands bit of ribbon to* HOPE) Maybe you can explain this bit of ribbon I found on the doorstep.

HOPE (*Examining ribbon*): This looks like one of those little pieces of ribbon that the Governor gave the Imp to play with yesterday. I guess it must have clung to my dress. (*Returns ribbon to* STANDISH)

BRADFORD: I hope this feast of Thanksgiving will be perpetuated. I like to think of future generations pausing from their many tasks to thank God for his numerous blessings, as we do today. How different the present is from our dreadful first winter, with its cold and sickness and hunger.

PRUDENCE: Yes. And the Indians not too friendly.

BRADFORD: Then think of today, with its abundance and its promise of a lasting peace. (*Quoting*) "It is a good thing to give thanks unto the Lord." (*The shouting and the laughter of the Indians seem nearer.*)

FAITH (*Walking to window and looking out*): They have come. (*Turns from window*) There are dozens of them. Massasoit and his whole tribe. (*Joins the others*) How can we feed them all?

BRADFORD: Don't worry, my child. After all the hardships this colony has faced, feeding them should be no problem. (*Rises*) Come, let us join our friends. (*Offers his arm to* PRUDENCE) May I have the honor? (PRUDENCE *takes his arm*)

STANDISH (*Offering his arm to* REBECCA): Permit me. (REBECCA *takes his arm*)

HOPE (*To* SQUANTO): It would be a privilege, Squanto, if you—

SQUANTO: I happy to. (*Offers arm, which she accepts*)

TOM (*To* FAITH, *offering his arm*): Am I to have the pleasure of escorting you?

JIM (*Protesting to* FAITH): I asked you yesterday to go to the feast with me.

FAITH (*In doubt for a moment, looking from one to the other*): I think I'll go with both of you. (*Takes the arm of each. They form a little procession,* BRADFORD *and* PRUDENCE *leading, followed by* STANDISH *and* REBECCA, *then* SQUANTO *and* HOPE, *with* JIM, FAITH, *and* TOM *bringing up the rear. They sing an old harvest song as they go out, and the curtain falls.*)

THE END

Hand-Me-Down Hildy

by Sara E. Sagoff

Characters

HILDY BROWN
SUE BROWN
JANE BROWN
PAT BROWN
JILL BROWN
MRS. BROWN
PEGGY PETERS
MOLLY PETERS
LADY, *from the Children's Home*
FIVE GIRLS, *from the Children's Home*

SCENE 1

TIME: *A few days before Christmas.*
BEFORE CURTAIN RISES: HILDY *is sitting cross-legged in front of curtain, with her chin in her hand, looking glum. She is wearing a shabby blue coat.*

HILDY: Hello. I really should say Merry Christmas, but I don't feel very merry. And I'll tell you why. (*Gets up and turns slowly once around*) Do you see my coat? (*Recites, with appropriate gestures*)

216

When this coat was bright and new
We bought it for my sister Sue.
We let it out for sister Pat
Because she was a little fat.
The hem was lowered quite a bit
So Jill could get some use from it.
Since sister Jane was very thin,
We bought a belt to pull it in.
And now that they have all outgrown it,
I'm the last of us to own it.
Hand-me-downs, hand-me-downs. I'm just Hand-me-down Hildy. It's the same with all my dresses and skirts, and sweaters and hats. It's just no fun being the youngest. Even my poor old doll wears hand-me-downs. How I wish I had something new to wear!

Sue (*Offstage*): Hildy, Hildy! (Sue, Pat, Jill *and* Jane *enter.*) There you are! Mother is waiting for you so we can go Christmas shopping. I'm going to get a new hat, with fur on it.

Pat: Then I can have Sue's hat with the bells on it, and jingle wherever I go.

Jill: And I'll get Pat's, with the big red pompons.

Jane: Your hat with the tassel goes to me, Jill. (*To* Hildy) And you can have this old thing. (*She pulls a shapeless, battered hat from her head and shoves it at* Hildy.)

Sue: Come on, Mother's waiting. (Sue, Pat, Jill *and* Jane *exit.* Hildy *turns to the audience, holding out the hat.*)

Hildy: There. You see what I mean? (*She slaps the hat comically on her head.*)

Mrs. Brown (*Offstage*): Hildy!

Hildy: I'm coming! (*She exits. After a pause the curtain opens.*)

* * *

TIME: *Immediately following Scene 1.*

SETTING: *The living room of the Brown home, decorated for Christmas.*

AT RISE: *Door opens at left and* MRS. BROWN *enters, followed by* PAT, JANE, JILL, *and* HILDY, *all carrying packages.*

MRS. BROWN: What a big day of Christmas shopping! So many presents. But now I've forgotten how we hide our presents for each other.

PAT: I remember! I always hide mine in the garage.

JILL: And I put mine in the attic.

JANE: My special places are in the bedrooms. Remember last year when I hid Sue's present right behind her own mirror, and she didn't know it?

HILDY (*Looking around*): But where is Sue?

JILL: Maybe she got lost in the store.

HILDY: No. She was at our meeting place at four o'clock, right near the store Santa Claus. Wasn't she, Mother?

MRS. BROWN: Yes, that's right. She'll be along any minute. She's just picking up something I forgot. Now all of you —go hide your gifts. And no peeking. (JILL, PAT, *and* JANE *exit.* HILDY *remains.*)

HILDY: Close your eyes, please, Mother. The living room is my place. (MRS. BROWN *closes her eyes and* HILDY *places packages behind furniture, under cushions, etc. As she finishes, the doorbell rings.* MRS. BROWN *opens door.*)

MRS. BROWN: Peggy and Molly Peters! Come in, children.

PEGGY *and* MOLLY (*Entering*): Hello, Mrs. Brown. Hello, Hildy.

PEGGY: We can't stay. We have to go to every house on the block before it gets dark.

MRS. BROWN: What are you doing?

MOLLY: We're going around to remind everyone that Christmas is the time for giving.

HILDY: We all know that. We've been saving up our money to give each other presents.

PEGGY: That's part of it, but it's not what we mean. This year in our family, we're sending gifts to the children in the Children's Home.

MOLLY: They don't have mothers and fathers to buy them things and take care of them, so we're going to share our presents with them.

MRS. BROWN: Good for you. I send a bagful of our used clothes to the Children's Home every year. (*Goes to closet and pulls out a plain shopping bag which is nearly full.*) There's room for a few more things in here. Hildy, run upstairs and see if you have anything to give to the Children's Home. And ask your sisters, too.

HILDY: All right, Mother. (*Has a sudden thought*) Yes. I think I *do* have some things. (*Exits quickly.*)

MRS. BROWN (*To* PEGGY *and* MOLLY): Thank you for coming, children. And Merry Christmas!

PEGGY *and* MOLLY: Merry Christmas, Mrs. Brown. (*They exit.*)

MRS. BROWN: I'll leave this bag out here in case we find some more clothing. And I must remember to call the Children's Home and have them pick the things up. (*There is a knock at the front door, and* SUE *peers in.*)

SUE: Psst. Is it all clear?

MRS. BROWN: Oh, Sue! Come in quickly. Hildy has just gone upstairs. (SUE *enters, carrying some packages and a large Christmas shopping bag. She puts the shopping bag down and pats it fondly.*)

SUE: Here they are, Mother. Fine new clothes for Hildy, for Christmas. Won't she be surprised?

MRS. BROWN: Did you have them gift-wrapped?

SUE: No. It was getting late, and the store was ready to close. I wrapped them up in brown paper and put them at the bottom of this bag.

MRS. BROWN: Leave it here for now. I'll wrap them in Christmas paper myself, later.

SUE (*Putting Christmas bag next to plain shopping bag*): What's in this bag, Mother?

MRS. BROWN: Used clothes for the Children's Home. Maybe you have something upstairs to add.

SUE: I'll look and see. Right now I'm going to hide my gifts.

MRS. BROWN: And I must get supper started. (SUE *exits with packages, as* MRS. BROWN *exits at other side of stage. The lights dim, then come up.* HILDY *peeks around the corner of the stage, then enters, wearing red flannel pajamas and carrying a sack. She puts her finger to her lips, and addresses the audience.*)

HILDY: Sh-h. Don't make a sound, please. Everyone is sleeping. Did you think I was Santa Claus? (*She imitates Santa's laugh.*) Ho, ho, ho! In a way I am. Here is my sack full of presents for the children in the Children's Home. All my old hand-me-downs! I'm giving them all away. Now I'll *have* to get something new. (*She sees shopping bags. Goes to plain one.*) This is nearly full. But there's room in this Christmas bag for my old clothes! (*She takes some clothes out of her sack and holds them up one by one.*) My hat, my mittens, my scarf, my muff—and my old coat. (*Shoves them into Christmas bag. Then she does another Santa laugh and puts the empty sack over her shoulder.*) Ho, ho, ho! No more Hand-me-down Hildy. (*Exits. The stage lights brighten.* MRS. BROWN *enters in her coat, hurriedly. She sees Christmas shopping bag.*)

MRS. BROWN: Oh, dear. I forgot to wrap Hildy's gifts. I guess they'll have to stay as they are. (*Raises voice*) Children! Children! (*Goes to front door as* PAT *enters*) I'm in a hurry, dear. I'm going to get my hair done. If the lady from the Children's Home comes, give her the plain shopping bag. Remember—the plain one, not the Christmas bag!

PAT: Yes, Mother. We're all upstairs taking our gifts out of their hiding places. We're going to put them under the tree. Tomorrow's Christmas!

MRS. BROWN: Fine. I'll be back soon. (MRS. BROWN *and* PAT *exit. After a pause,* HILDY *enters and begins to take her packages out from behind the furniture and set them under the tree. Doorbell rings.* HILDY *opens door.* LADY *enters.*)

LADY: Hello. I'm from the Children's Home. Is there a bag of clothing here for us?

HILDY: Yes. Two bags of clothing! (*She brings both shopping bags to the* LADY.)

LADY: Oh, my. When your mother called, she said there would be only one. What a nice surprise for the children.

HILDY: Yes. I . . . I found some things at the last minute.

LADY (*Looking around*): I see you are all ready for Christmas. You must have a large family, to have such a big tree and so many fine decorations.

HILDY: Yes, ma'am. I have four sisters. I'm the youngest.

LADY: How lucky you are. I suppose you are all giving each other nice, new gifts?

HILDY: Yes. I've just put mine under the tree.

LADY: I see. And the poor children in the Home get all these old clothes. But that's something, I suppose.

HILDY (*Slowly*): Do you mean that the children in the Home never ever get anything new?

LADY: Almost never, I'm afraid. Even the people who want to be kind only give us what they can't use any more. (*She indicates shopping bags.*) But, we are so pleased to have extra clothing this year, even if it is old. I have some other calls to make now. Be sure to look for us on Christmas morning. The children will be out caroling then. Merry Christmas!

HILDY (*Slowly and thoughtfully*): Merry Christmas. (LADY *exits with both bags.* HILDY *stands thoughtfully at the center of the stage, looking after her, as the curtains close.*)

*   *   *

SCENE 2

TIME: *Christmas morning.*

SETTING: *The same. The floor is strewn with papers, ribbons, etc.*

AT RISE: JILL, PAT, JANE, SUE *and* HILDY *are opening their presents around the tree.* MRS. BROWN *enters.*

MRS. BROWN: Have you opened all those gifts already?

ALL (*Ad lib*): Yes, Mother. Thank you for the bracelet, Mother. (*Etc.*)

MRS. BROWN: Then it's time for the big surprise—Hildy's special surprise.

HILDY: A surprise for me?

SUE: But, Mother, where is the Christmas shopping bag?

MRS. BROWN (*Looking around*): Why, I left it in the middle of the room. Girls, have you seen the Christmas bag?

HILDY (*Beginning to realize*): The Christmas bag? I . . . I gave it to the lady from the Children's Home. It was full of old clothes. (*Sound of "O Little Town of Bethlehem" is heard softly offstage.*)

JILL, PAT, JANE *and* SUE (*Ad lib*): But Hildy! Oh, no, you didn't! How awful! (*Etc.*)

MRS. BROWN: That's impossible. There were new clothes in

that bag. New clothes for you, Hildy. How did it ever get full of old ones? (HILDY *gives a sob and buries her face in her hands.*)

JILL: Poor Hildy. A new coat was just what she wanted.

MRS. BROWN: Wait a minute, girls. Pat, didn't I tell you to give only the plain shopping bag to the lady from the Children's Home, and save the Christmas bag?

PAT: Yes, Mother. But then I went upstairs to hide my gifts. I didn't hear the lady come in at all. What shall we do?

JANE: Hildy was the only one who heard her. Oh, all those lovely new things!

MOTHER: But why did you give her both bags, Hildy? Didn't you see the package in the Christmas bag?

HILDY: It had just a brown paper wrapping. I thought it was for the children. And then—I put all my old clothes in the Christmas bag, so that you'd *have* to get me new ones for Christmas. (*She sobs again.*)

MRS. BROWN: We can't ask for them back, now that we've given them to those poor children. And now you have no clothes at all, Hildy. (*The sound of singing grows louder, and the front doorbell rings.*)

SUE: There's the doorbell, Mother. I'll get it. Maybe it's the carolers.

MRS. BROWN: And I had such a nice surprise planned for little Hildy. (SUE *opens door for* LADY, *who enters with the Christmas shopping bag. She is followed by* FIVE GIRLS. *Each one is wearing an article of* HILDY's *old clothing.*)

LADY: Excuse me. I'm sorry to interrupt your Christmas Day, but—

SUE: The bag! The Christmas bag!

LADY: I think there has been some mistake. Underneath the old clothes in this bag, there were some brand-new ones wrapped in brown paper, with a card saying, "Merry Christmas to Hildy." Since there's no one named

Hildy at the Home, and since we never receive such bright new clothes—well, I decided there must have been a mistake.

MRS. BROWN: There certainly was a mistake. (*Takes bag from* LADY.) Here are Hildy's new clothes—safe and sound. Come here and try them on. (HILDY *comes slowly to* MRS. BROWN. MRS. BROWN *draws out one by one a muff, a scarf, a pair of mittens, a hat, and last, a bright blue coat, and puts them on* HILDY, *who stands very still. The* FIVE GIRLS *from the Home "oh" and "ah" at each item.*) Now, that's better. Merry Christmas, Hildy.

HILDY: No. There is still some mistake, Mother. (*She goes to* 1ST GIRL.) Please let me have my nice old hat. You may have this new one. (*Takes old hat off* 1ST GIRL's *head and puts new one on her. To* 2ND GIRL) I wish I could have my scarf back. This new one is for you. (*Exchanges scarves. To* 3RD GIRL) Those are my favorite mittens. Will you take these instead? (*Exchanges mittens. To* 4TH GIRL) I always liked that muff; it kept me warm. Won't you please trade it for this new one? (*Muffs are exchanged.* HILDY *pauses before* 5TH GIRL, *who is wearing her faded coat. She looks down at her new one and begins very slowly to unbutton it.* MRS. BROWN *steps forward, but* SUE *has already jumped up.*)

SUE: Wait, Hildy! Let me make the last gift.

PAT: I would like to give something, too.

JANE: And me. I have too many new toys.

JILL (*To* 5TH GIRL): Come and choose from all of our presents.

5TH GIRL: Oh, thank you! (*Joins sisters around tree, as they begin to hold things up for her to choose from.*)

GIRLS (*Crowding around* HILDY): Thank you, Hildy, thank you. (HILDY *turns to* MRS. BROWN.)

HILDY: Is it all right, Mother?

MRS. BROWN (*Putting arm around* HILDY): Of course it's

all right, Hildy. You have taught us all something important about the meaning of Christmas.

HILDY: I think I've learned something, too. Oh, Mother—thank you for my beautiful Christmas coat!

LADY: We know a Christmas song to go with it. (*Begins to sing "Deck the Halls," and all join in. At the line, "Don we now our gay apparel," everyone holds up or points to a new item of clothing. Song is repeated as the curtain falls.*)

THE END

One Night in Bethlehem

by Deborah Newman

Characters

SIMON, *the innkeeper*
LYDIA, *his wife*
SARA, *his niece*
ABNER, *a jewel merchant*
ABIGAIL ⎫
RACHEL ⎭ *wealthy guests*
SHEPHERDS
WIVES
MARY ⎫
JOSEPH ⎭ *in manger tableau*

TIME: *The evening of Jesus' birth.*
SETTING: *The innyard at Bethlehem.*
AT RISE: SARA *is sweeping. She stops for a moment, sighs wearily, and then sits on a bench.* LYDIA *enters, carrying a bowl of apples. She stops when she sees* SARA.

LYDIA (*Angrily*): Sara! What are you doing, you lazy girl? (SARA *jumps up.*)
SARA: I am sorry, Aunt Lydia. I am so tired. I have been working all day long.
LYDIA: You will be working all night long, too, if you

stop to dream like this. Get back to your sweeping at once. And then you must help me polish these apples. They have been ordered by one of Herod's soldiers. (*She sits on a bench and polishes the apples.*)

SARA: Yes, Aunt Lydia. (*She sweeps again.*)

LYDIA: Did you take fresh linen to the doctor's family?

SARA: I—I think so.

LYDIA: You *think* so! Don't tell me you have forgotten something else. I have had nothing but complaints about you all day, you ungrateful girl.

SARA: But we have never had so many guests before. The inn has been full since noon.

LYDIA (*Proudly*): Ah yes, every room is taken. When the decree went out from Caesar Augustus that all the world should be taxed, I never thought that Bethlehem would be so crowded. (ABNER *appears at the gate at right, carrying his jewel cases. He pulls a rope attached to a bell, and the bell rings.* LYDIA *sees him, rises, and goes to him.*)

ABNER (*Entering the innyard*): Good evening. I seek lodging for the night.

LYDIA: I am sorry, sir. There is no room at the inn.

ABNER: I have come to Bethlehem to pay my taxes. I seek a room just for the night. I am a jewel merchant, and must be off about my business in the morning.

LYDIA: You may rest yourself here, sir, and I can offer you food and drink. But we have no room.

ABNER (*Sitting on a bench*): I can pay you well. (*He opens a jewel case.*) Do you, perhaps, like rubies? (*He takes out a large ruby on a gold chain and holds it up.*) This necklace was made for a princess. (LYDIA *takes the necklace and holds it out admiringly.*) It shall be yours—for a room.

LYDIA: It is beautiful! (SARA *stops sweeping and comes over to look.* LYDIA *turns to her angrily.*) Get back to

your sweeping! You have wasted enough time already.
(SARA *sweeps.*)

ABNER (*Looking into case*): I might even have a trinket
for your daughter.

LYDIA: Daughter! She is no daughter of mine. She is my
husband's niece. When her parents died, she came to
stay with us. And I can tell you, she has given us nothing but trouble. (ABIGAIL *and* RACHEL *enter.*)

ABIGAIL (*To* LYDIA): Are you the wife of the innkeeper?

LYDIA (*Nodding*): I am. What can I do for you?

RACHEL: You can see that we get the fresh water we asked
for an hour ago.

ABIGAIL: You can see that we get the fresh linen we were
promised.

LYDIA: Sara! (SARA *stops sweeping and comes forward.*)
Ladies, it is just as I was telling this gentleman. This
stupid girl forgets everything. Sara, go to the well at
once. You will have no dinner tonight until you finish
your work. (SARA *takes a jug from the wall and exits.*)
I am sorry, ladies. The inn has never been so crowded.
We are known in Bethlehem for our excellent service.

ABNER (*Taking necklace from* LYDIA): If this necklace
does not interest you, I must be on my way.

ABIGAIL (*Touching necklace*): What a beautiful ruby.

RACHEL: I have never seen such a fine stone.

ABNER: It was made for a princess, but I offered it for a
room at the inn. And now, since there is no room, I will
be on my way. (*He starts to pack up his cases.*)

LYDIA: Wait! (ABNER *turns, still holding necklace.*) There
is a room—the room of that silly girl. Of course! Sara
can sleep in the stable tonight. (*To* ABNER) It is a
very small room, with one tiny window. But it is yours,
if you wish.

ABNER: I do not need a big room, and I will not be looking out of the window at night.

LYDIA: Then come! The room is yours.

ABNER (*Giving her necklace*): And the necklace is yours. (ABNER *picks up his cases and exits with* LYDIA.)

ABIGAIL: The innkeeper's wife is getting a good price for that child's room.

RACHEL: Poor little girl. She seems so tired.

ABIGAIL: I am sorry I complained. I did not realize the girl would be blamed. (SIMON *enters.*)

SIMON: Good evening, ladies. Do you have everything you wish?

RACHEL: Thank you, innkeeper. Everything is as we wish.

SIMON: Please be sure to tell me if you want something. We are very busy, but we will do our best. (SARA *comes running in.*)

SARA: Uncle Simon! I am so glad I found you here. I want to ask you something.

SIMON: What is it, little Sara?

SARA: Uncle Simon, there are some people from Galilee resting in the stable—a beautiful lady and her husband. The lady is very tired.

SIMON (*Shrugs*): All travelers are tired. (*To* ABIGAIL *and* RACHEL) Since morning, people have been arriving in Bethlehem. From Joppa, Cana, Nazareth—from all over they come here, these descendants of the House of David.

ABIGAIL: We know. We did not want to come—but we must obey the law.

RACHEL: Let us hope this is the last time we must be taxed. One such trip to Bethlehem is enough for me! (ABIGAIL *and* RACHEL *exit.*)

SIMON: Sara, I hope you told this couple from Galilee that we have no room.

SARA: That is what I want to ask you, Uncle Simon. I know all our guest rooms are taken, but could I give them my room? I could sleep in the stable.

SIMON: Little Sara, you are very tired. You should sleep in your own bed tonight.

SARA: Please let me give them my room. The lady cannot go on. She is resting on the straw in the stable, and she is so tired. Oh, please, Uncle Simon. I want to do something for her.

SIMON: All right—if that is what you really wish.

SARA (*Taking* SIMON's *hand*): Oh, thank you! I will do the sweeping and bring the water and polish the apples and everything. You will see how hard I can work. (LYDIA *enters. She is wearing the ruby*).

LYDIA: Ah, Sara. Have you brought the water? (*She sits on a bench and polishes the apples.* SIMON *sits near her and helps her.*)

SARA (*Shaking her head*): No. I shall bring it right away. But first I must go to the stable. A man and a lady are resting there, and Uncle Simon says I may bring them to the inn. I am going to give them my room.

LYDIA: *Your* room!

SARA: Yes. I want to give these people something. Uncle Simon says I may give them my room. I will sleep in the stable.

LYDIA: You are going to sleep in the stable, you lazy girl, but you may not give them your room.

SIMON: Let the child do it if she wishes, Lydia.

LYDIA: Sara may not give up her room because I have already rented it to Abner, the jewel merchant.

SARA: Oh, no! The lady is so tired. She cannot sleep by the road tonight. (*She sinks to the ground and cries.*)

LYDIA: I do not want to hear another word about it. Stop that crying at once and get back to your work. You still have not finished the sweeping, and it is almost dark. (LYDIA *picks up the bowl of apples and exits.*)

SIMON (*Patting* SARA's *shoulder*): I am sorry, Sara.

SARA: You would love these people if you saw them, Uncle

Simon. The lady smiles so gently and sweetly, even though she is tired. I—I cannot turn them away. (*Brightens*) Perhaps they could stay in the stable with me. Would that be all right?

SIMON: I do not think the lady would want to sleep in a stable.

SARA: Let me ask them, Uncle Simon. Oh, please!

SIMON: All right, Sara. If they want to stay in the stable, they may.

SARA: Thank you. (*She rises.*) You will see—I am right not to turn them away. (*She exits.* SIMON *picks up the broom and begins sweeping. A Christmas carol is heard from off-stage.* SIMON *stops sweeping to listen. The carol ends, and some* SHEPHERDS *and their* WIVES *appear at the gate. A* SHEPHERD *rings the bell, then the group enters.*)

1ST SHEPHERD (*To* SIMON): Are you the owner of this inn?

SIMON: I am.

2ND SHEPHERD: We seek a baby born this day. Can you help us?

SIMON: No. I have many guests, but no baby has been born in my inn.

1ST WIFE: We do not seek a baby born in your inn.

SIMON: I have been busy all day with my guests. I do not know about babies born in the countryside.

2ND WIFE: The baby we seek has been born in a stable.

SIMON: A stable? Why should you seek a baby born in a stable?

3RD SHEPHERD: The baby we seek is the Saviour.

SIMON (*Laughing*): Come, shepherd. I am a busy man and have no time for jokes. The Saviour would never be born in a stable.

3RD WIFE: We do not joke, innkeeper. Listen to their story.

4TH SHEPHERD: We were in the field, keeping watch over our flock, when suddenly an angel appeared before us. We were afraid.

5TH SHEPHERD: But the angel said, "Fear not: for behold, I bring you good tidings of great joy, which shall be to all people. For unto you is born this day, in the city of David, a Saviour."

SIMON: But then you must search all the houses in Bethlehem for the baby.

4TH WIFE: No. The angel said, "And this shall be a sign unto you: Ye shall find the babe wrapped in swaddling clothes, lying in a manger."

SIMON (*Thoughtfully*): The babe lying in the manger. (LYDIA *enters.*)

LYDIA (*To* SIMON): Our guests are complaining about the noise in the innyard. (*To* SHEPHERDS) I must ask you people to leave.

SIMON (*To* LYDIA): They seek the Saviour. An angel has told them the Saviour was born in a stable this day.

LYDIA: How can anyone believe that he would be born in a stable?

5TH WIFE: That is what the angel said.

LYDIA: Then believe what you will—but be off. No baby was born in our stable. The only person in our stable is the stable boy. (SHEPHERDS *and* WIVES *start to go.*)

SIMON: Wait! (*They turn back.*) There are some people in our stable. A man and his wife—from Galilee.

LYDIA (*Angrily, to* SIMON): In *our* stable! Simon, I won't have it. This must be Sara's doing. I will tell those people to leave at once. (*She exits to the stable.*)

1ST SHEPHERD: This lady from Galilee—was she about to have a baby?

SIMON: I do not know. My little niece wanted to let them stay in the stable because there was no room for them in the inn.

1ST WIFE: Long have we waited for the Saviour to appear. And tonight the angels sang, "Glory to God in the highest, and on earth peace, good will toward men."

SIMON: I will never forgive myself if he has been born in my stable. I could have given up my own room. (LYDIA *enters with* SARA.)

LYDIA: A baby *has* been born in our stable. I found him lying in the manger. (*She goes to a bench and sits, thoughtfully fingering her necklace.*)

SARA: Uncle Simon, you should see the baby. He is so sweet.

LYDIA: It is strange. When I looked at the baby, I felt so peaceful.

SARA: He is the most wonderful baby I have ever seen.

2ND SHEPHERD: Then this must be the baby we seek.

2ND WIFE: This baby is the Saviour.

SIMON (*Going to stand beside* LYDIA): Lydia—this baby should have been born in the inn.

LYDIA: I know. (*She hides her face.*)

SARA (*Running to* LYDIA): Do not cry, Aunt Lydia. (LYDIA *takes* SARA's *hand and pulls the girl gently down beside her on the bench.*)

LYDIA (*To* SARA): I took a room away from them. And all because I wanted this ruby.

SARA: But you could not know about the baby.

LYDIA (*Shaking her head*): I could have been kind, but I was not. You told me you wanted to give these people something, but I did not listen. (*She rises, and takes off her necklace.*) Sara, you must give this necklace to those people in the stable. (*She gives the necklace to* SARA.) They are poor people. They can sell the necklace, and use the money to buy food and clothing for the baby.

SIMON: That is a good gift, Lydia.

LYDIA: But I must do something more. I must show how sorry I am in my heart for the dreadful things I have done. (SARA *rises, and takes her hand.*) Sara, you would have given them your room—the only gift you had. I will give them a room now.

SIMON: I do not think they will want to leave the stable.

LYDIA: That is not what I meant. I will give away a room each night to someone who needs it. That will be my gift.

3RD WIFE: That is a gift the baby will like.

4TH WIFE: That is a true gift from your heart.

5TH WIFE: I would like to see the baby.

SIMON: I will open the stable so that we all may see him. (SIMON *and a* SHEPHERD *open the stable doors as* ABNER, ABIGAIL *and* RACHEL *enter.*)

ABIGAIL: What is it?

RACHEL: What has happened? (*All kneel and point to the manger tableau of* MARY, JOSEPH *and the baby.*)

1ST SHEPHERD: It is the Saviour.

1ST WIFE: It is the Prince of Peace.

2ND SHEPHERD: He has been born to us in Bethlehem. (*All continue to kneel as a Christmas carol is heard in background, coming up full as the curtains close.*)

THE END

Santa and the Efficiency Expert

by Frances B. Watts

Characters

SANTA CLAUS
SARAH CLAUS, *his wife*
HARVEY SPEEDWELL, *an efficiency expert*
ALICE SPEEDWELL, *his wife*
HOLLY ⎤
JOLLY ⎥
TINSEL ⎥
SPARKLE ⎬ *Santa's elves*
JINGLE ⎥
CHEERIE ⎦

TIME: *Early in the Christmas season.*
SETTING: *The living room of the Claus home.*
AT RISE: SANTA *is mending dolls at table down center.*
SARAH *is sitting in rocker right, sewing. As she sews,*
SARAH *sings "Santa Claus Is Coming to Town."*

SANTA: I wish you wouldn't sing that song, Sarah. It makes
me nervous.
SARAH: It always puts me in a jolly mood.
SANTA: It just reminds me of all the work we have to do be-
fore Christmas. We're running so far behind schedule!
SARAH: You fuss and fret like this every year, but we always

come through on time. (*Holds up doll dress*) I'm coming
along fine with the doll dresses.

SANTA: Yes, I can always depend on you. It's those scatterbrained elves that drive me frantic. (*Goes to her, holding
out doll*) Look at this. Jolly and Holly put this batch of
dolls' heads on backward. Now I have to straighten them
out!

SARAH: It's only natural for little elves to make mistakes
now and then. But you must admit they're hard workers.

SANTA: The only trouble is, they work just as hard making
mistakes as they do making things right. (TINSEL *and*
SPARKLE *enter, carrying Teddy bears.*)

TINSEL: Santa! Santa! We've run out of teddy bear sawdust!

SANTA: Oh, no! You both assured me that you had enough
on hand for the season.

SPARKLE: We thought we did. But Tinsel insisted on stuffing the bears very solidly.

TINSEL: They last longer that way, Sparkle.

SANTA (*Sighing*): Well, all right. I'll walk down to the
storehouse after a while and get more sawdust. In the
meantime, you can start painting wagons.

SPARKLE: The red paint can's empty.

SANTA: Open another can then!

TINSEL: Don't get excited, Santa. We will. (*Elves exit, giggling.*)

SANTA: Those giddy elves are so undependable, and so inefficient. (*Goes to window*) I wonder where the mailman
is. I'm expecting an important letter from Harvey Speedwell.

SARAH: Harvey Speedwell? Didn't you go to school with
him years ago in Alaska?

SANTA: That's right. Old Harvey has done very well for
himself. He's an efficiency expert at Zippy Motors in
Detroit now.

SARAH: Why would you be expecting a letter from him after all these years?

SANTA: Because I wrote to him last week. I thought he might give me some pointers on how to run my workshop more smoothly and efficiently. We don't use very modern methods around here.

SARAH: We may be old-fashioned, but we do have a jolly time.

SANTA: What's jolly about running around in a frenzy, trying to meet a deadline? By the time we get the toys sorted, the sack packed, and the reindeer hitched on Christmas Eve, we're all exhausted.

SARAH: It's fun, nonetheless. And the elves love their work and take pride in it.

SANTA: Love and pride, huh? Well, nowadays, *efficiency* is the most important word in the dictionary. (*Looks up*) Was that a helicopter I heard? (*Goes to window*) Looks like visitors to me.

SARAH (*Running to window*): Visitors! Dear me, I hope there's enough roast beef for supper. (SANTA *opens door.* HARVEY *and* ALICE SPEEDWELL *enter, carrying suitcase and briefcase.*)

HARVEY: Claus, old buddy! You haven't changed a bit! (*Pats* SANTA's *tummy*) Except for that bay window. We'll have to do something about that.

SANTA: Harvey Speedwell!

HARVEY: In the flesh, old boy. And this is Alice, the little woman.

SANTA: Come in! Come in! What a surprise. This is my wife, Sarah. (*All greet each other, remove coats, and sit.*) When I wrote to you for advice, Harvey, I never expected to see you in person.

HARVEY: Your letter indicated that there was a real job to do here, buddy. When there's a real job to do, I like to get things done in person. A real Johnny-on-the-spot, that's me.

ALICE: And Harvey certainly knows how to get things done. He has so many time-saving ideas. I don't know how I'd run our household without him.

HARVEY: We may as well get down to business right away, pal. (*Takes out notebook*) I have a list here that should improve your working efficiency by fifty per cent.

SANTA: Wonderful. (JOLLY *and* HOLLY *enter.*)

JOLLY: Excuse us, Santa. We have a problem.

HOLLY: We went out to feed the reindeer, and found no hay in the hay bin.

SANTA: Then go up in the mow and pitch some hay down!

HOLLY: We never thought of doing that!

SANTA: And don't stop to play in the haymow. Remember, you have toy wagons to paint.

JOLLY *and* HOLLY: O.K., Santa. (*They exit.*)

HARVEY (*Shaking head*): Reindeer! That's the first thing on the list, Claus, old pal. It's absurd that you still use reindeer for deliveries. I insist you get a helicopter.

ALICE: In fact, he's sending you one from Zippy Motors, in time for Chirstmas Eve.

SARAH: But the children always expect Santa to arrive by reindeer and sleigh.

HARVEY: Bah! What do children know about efficiency? Think of the time it takes to feed the reindeer, clean their stables, and brush their hides. And I guarantee that a helicopter will cut the delivery time by four hours. And you can start saving time right now by sending your deer off to the forest to forage for themselves.

SANTA (*Hesitating*): Yes, I suppose I could.

SARAH: But they'll miss us. They'll be lost without us.

HARVEY: Nonsense! Deer belong in the forest.

SANTA: It does seem the sensible thing to do. Sarah, will

you please tell Jolly and Holly to lead the deer into the forest, instead of pitching down more hay.

SARAH (*Sighing*): Very well. (*She exits*)

ALICE: You won't regret it, Mr. Claus. Helicopter travel is so fast and smooth, and it's much warmer than an open sleigh.

HARVEY: That brings up the next matter. You'll have to get rid of those ridiculous clothes. (SARAH *re-enters*.)

SANTA: What's the matter with my clothes?

HARVEY: They're old-fashioned. Besides that, they're heavy, and slow up the movements of the body. Now that you'll be flying in a heated helicopter, you won't need all that red wool and fur.

SARAH: But Santa can't wear anything else. It's part of his personality. The children's image of him is in a jolly red and white suit.

HARVEY: Children are romantic dreamers. If he is going to think and act modernly and efficiently, he has to dress more modernly and efficiently.

SANTA: I think Harvey is right, Sarah.

ALICE: Harvey is always right.

HARVEY (*Holding up suitcase*): I brought you a suit, old buddy. The latest thing in men's wear. Let's try it on.

SANTA: Good idea, Harvey. Right this way. (*They exit.*)

ALICE: You'll swoon with delight when you see how snappy your husband is going to look, Mrs. Claus.

SARAH: I doubt it. Would you like to come to the kitchen with me, while I check the roast? You're staying for supper, of course.

ALICE: Thank you, but we can't. Harvey is due in Chicago tonight.

SARAH: I'm sorry you can't join us.

ALICE: You know, you shouldn't have to spend time cooking.

SARAH: No cooking, no eating.

ALICE: Not any more, Mrs. Claus. (*Opens purse and holds up bottle of capsules*) Apparently you've never heard of Jiffy Gems.

SARAH: Jiffy Gems? What are they?

ALICE: Meals in a capsule. One capsule has all the nourishment of a full home-cooked meal. Harvey and I have Jiffy Gems most all the time. Why, dinner can be prepared and consumed in less than ten seconds.

SARAH: Amazing!

ALICE: Here, keep this bottle, my dear. We have more in our luggage. They save so much time. Be sure to use them.

SARAH (*Thoughtfully*): I just may do that. (*Puts them into pocket.* HARVEY *enters with* SANTA *who wears a business suit.*)

HARVEY: Doesn't he look snazzy, girls? The real executive type.

ALICE: What about his beard, Harvey?

HARVEY: Fortunately, beards are "in" right now. But Santa's beard will need a good trimming.

SANTA (*Parading about*): Well, what do you think of my suit, Sarah?

SARAH: The children won't even recognize you! (JINGLE *and* CHEERIE *enter with whistles.*)

CHEERIE: Where's Santa?

SANTA: Right here, Jingle and Cheerie.

JINGLE: What have you done to yourself, Santa?

CHEERIE: Where's your red suit?

SANTA: Never mind that. What do you want?

JINGLE: Listen to these toy train whistles. (*Blows whistle*)

CHEERIE: They tweet instead of toot. (*Blows whistle*) We can't have train whistles tweeting instead of tooting!

SANTA: I'll see to them later. Right now I'm busy with Mr. Speedwell. (*Other elves enter.*)

TINSEL: Santa! Are you Santa?

SPARKLE: It must be. He's the only one here with a white beard.

TINSEL: Santa, Jolly and Holly have led the reindeer away!

HOLLY: Santa told us to do it.

JOLLY: He did! He did!

SPARKLE (*Starting to cry*): But why, Santa?

TINSEL (*Sobbing*): We love the reindeer, Santa. We'll miss them. (*Other elves start to cry*)

SANTA: Please quiet down, all of you!

HARVEY: Your elves are next on the agenda, old boy. Elf labor is the most inefficient labor in the world. Elves are flighty, forgetful and entirely unreliable.

SANTA: But who else can I get to help me? Skilled laborers are practically nonexistent at the North Pole.

HARVEY: Buck up, buddy. We're going to change your whole method of production. From now on, no toy-making. You're going to close up shop.

ELVES: Not make toys?

SANTA: What will I bring to the children on Christmas?

HARVEY (*Taking papers from briefcase*): There's nothing more efficient and time-saving than a gift certificate. On Christmas Eve you will just slip a gift certificate under each child's door.

ALICE: It's so beautifully simple. All the children need do is go to a department store the next day and select what they want.

SARAH: But it's all so dull and businesslike. What child wants a piece of paper for Christmas? And what about filling the Christmas stockings?

HARVEY: Eliminate the stockings! You are running a non-profit business, Claus, so the children ought to be grateful for anything they get.

SANTA: I suppose you're right.

HARVEY: Of course I'm right. I have thousands of gift cer-

tificates here for you. All you need do is sign your name
at the bottom. Think of the time and overhead you'll
save.

ALICE: You'll have them all signed in a few days. Why,
you two could even squeeze in a vacation before Christmas.

HARVEY: As for your elves, you can tell them to fly home
to Elfland.

TINSEL *and* SPARKLE: We don't want to leave you, Santa!

HOLLY *and* JOLLY: We love to help you make toys!

SANTA: Please don't put up a fuss. If you want to help me,
you'll fly along home now.

JINGLE *and* CHEERIE: All right, Santa.

ELVES (*Tearfully*): Goodbye, Santa.

SANTA: Goodbye, chums. And thanks for all your help in
the past.

SARAH: Come, dears. I'll give you some cookies to nibble
on the way. (SARAH *leads elves out*)

HARVEY: Well, Claus, I think we have covered all the important points. Now, Alice and I must whiz off to Chicago.

SANTA: You've been a great help, Harvey. Thanks for coming. (SARAH *re-enters*)

HARVEY: Don't mention it. I'll send you my bill after
Christmas.

SANTA: Bill?

HARVEY: Yes, I always charge when I act as a personal con-
sultant. But don't worry. (*They put on coats.*) I'll give
you a special rate. Always give special rates to old school
chums. Well, goodbye, folks. (SPEEDWELLS *exit.*)

SANTA: Well, well. That was good of old Harvey to come
up. He sure has taken a load from my shoulders.

SARAH: No doubt his bill will take a load from your pocketbook, too.

SANTA: Now, now, Sarah. We can't expect a famous effi-

ciency expert to come clear to the North Pole without
pay. Say, why don't we start signing those gift certificates?

SARAH: Well, all right. We may as well get it over with.
(*They sit at table and write for a few moments.*)

SANTA: My, it's as quiet as midnight around here.

SARAH: Naturally. The reindeer and elves are gone. We're
all alone.

SANTA: It's lonesome. Those little elves are scatterbrained,
but they're good company. (*They write again.* SANTA
looks up.) Seems funny not to hear the reindeer stomping
about in the stable. I wonder how they are making out?

SARAH: No doubt they're hungry and cold.

SANTA: Oh, my, I hope not. Do you think I acted too hastily, setting them loose like that?

SARAH: I don't believe it matters what I think. (*They write
silently.*)

SANTA: Oh, blast it! My pen is leaking and my writing hand
is tired already. Signing certificates is a bore!

SARAH: It certainly isn't as jolly as making toys.

SANTA: I'm hungry, too. How about supper now?

SARAH (*Taking bottle out of pocket*): No sooner said than
done. Have a Jiffy Gem, my dear.

SANTA: What's a Jiffy Gem?

SARAH: A nourishing meal in a capsule. Mrs. Speedwell
gave them to me. They are so efficient that one can dine
in ten seconds.

SANTA (*Standing*): Jiffy Gems, my foot! I want rare roast
beef and browned potatoes!

SARAH: I thought you'd be delighted at the time we'd save.

SANTA: I won't have it! You can't substitute a pill for roast
beef. It takes all the joy out of eating!

SARAH (*Standing*): But, my dear, *you* are substituting a
dull piece of paper for toys and gifts. And that takes
all the joy out of Christmas.

SANTA: By George, you're right, Sarah! I was so determined

to be efficient that I almost forgot the purpose of our Christmas work.

SARAH: Yes, you did. Many years ago we decided that we wanted to bring joy to others at Christmas, no matter how much work it required. That is why we started the workshop, remember?

SANTA: Oh, Sarah, what came over me? Why did I listen to Harvey? Look at me. I look like "The Man in the Gray Flannel Suit" instead of Santa Claus. My poor reindeer are off starving in the forest. My elves are probably in Elfland by now. And there's nothing but capsules for supper!

SARAH: You just let the pressures of Christmas get the best of you. That is why you listened to Mr. Speedwell. But things aren't as bad as they seem. (*Goes to door*) You may come in now, dears. (*Elves enter, dancing*)

ELVES: Hi, Santa!

SANTA: You didn't go home after all!

TINSEL (*Giggling*): No. Mrs. Claus hid us in the broom closet.

HOLLY: We didn't take the reindeer to the forest either. We hid them, too.

JOLLY: Mrs. Claus told us to.

SARAH: Please don't scold me, Santa. I had a feeling that once you realized how dull and joyless Mr. Speedwell's ideas were, you'd have a change of heart.

SANTA: Scold? I'll hug you instead! (*Hugs her*) You've helped me see that there is more to life than efficiency. What is Christmas without my good reindeer, merry elves, and toy-making? (JINGLE *and* CHEERIE *exit.*)

SPARKLE: Are we really going to make toys, Santa?

SANTA: We sure are. I'll tear up those gift certificates. What's more, I'll wire Harvey to keep that newfangled helicopter. It's the good old reindeer and sleigh for us.

Children like it that way. (JINGLE *and* CHEERIE *enter with* SANTA'S *suit.*)

JINGLE: Slip on your old suit right now, Santa. The children like you in it, and so do we! (SANTA *chuckles as he slips suit over his clothes.*)

SANTA: My, my, it's good to feel like my old self again. (*Pats tummy*) Now all I need to make my happiness complete is a good piece of rare roast beef with browned potatoes.

SARAH: Then your happiness *is* complete. I'd say the beef was roasted to a turn by now. Come to the kitchen, everybody!

SANTA: Sarah, you're one in a million!

ELVES: Hooray for Mrs. Claus! (*All exit, singing "Jolly Old St. Nicholas", as curtains close.*)

THE END

That Christmas Feeling

by Mildred Hark and Noel McQueen

Characters

MR. HARRY JACKSON
MRS. GWEN JACKSON, *his wife*
DAVE ⎫
IRENE ⎪
LOUISE ⎬ *their children*
JOHNNIE ⎭
TOM BARRY ⎫
RUTHIE BARRY ⎬ *next-door neighbors*
1ST FIREMAN
2ND FIREMAN
VOICES OF CAROLERS

TIME: *Christmas Eve.*

SETTING: *The living room of the Jackson family, gaily decorated for Christmas. In one corner there is a large Christmas tree, with lights on it, but no other decorations. On a card table there are packages, wrapping paper, ribbon, and seals. Upstage center, there is a fireplace with a mirror over it.*

AT RISE: JOHNNIE, *age seven, sits in a chair looking at a picture book.* LOUISE, *ten, sits at card table wrapping a present.* MR. *and* MRS. JACKSON *are at stage center, getting ready to go to a party.* MRS. JACKSON *holds a small*

hat in her hand. IRENE, *thirteen, is fastening* MRS. JACK-
SON'S *dress in the back.* MR. JACKSON *holds his suit
jacket over his arm. His overcoat and hat are on a chair.*

JOHNNIE (*Reading solemnly*): " 'Twas the night before
Christmas and all through the house, not a creature was
stirring, not even a mouse."
LOUISE: It certainly isn't that way around this house! Try-
ing to get presents wrapped, and having Mother and
Dad rushing off to a Christmas party—
MR. JACKSON (*As he slips on suit jacket*): Are you ready,
Gwen?
MRS. JACKSON: You've asked me that a dozen times. Is my
dress zipped up, Irene?
IRENE (*Zipping it up*): There, Mom, you're all set.
MRS. JACKSON (*Putting hat on*): No, I'm not. I can't decide
whether or not to wear this hat. (*She turns and peers at
herself in mirror.*)
LOUISE: Do wear it, Mom. It's just right for a Christmas
open house. (DAVE, *about fourteen, enters carrying some
wrapped packages.*)
DAVE: I have some of my presents wrapped. (*He starts toward tree.*)
IRENE: You can't put them under the tree, Dave. Wait till
it's trimmed.
DAVE: O.K. (*He puts presents on a small table, then whistles as he notices his mother.*) That hat makes you look
like a glamour girl, Mom.
LOUISE: What did I tell you? It's Christmasy, too, with all
that sparkly stuff.
MR. JACKSON: Yes, my dear. You look wonderful. Now, if
we could just—
MRS. JACKSON (*Walking about a little. She takes her hat
off, then puts it on at a different angle*): I don't *feel*
wonderful. I've never heard of such a thing. Leaving our

family and having to go to a party on Christmas Eve!

MR. JACKSON: I don't like the idea much myself, but we've been over all that.

MRS. JACKSON: Your boss knows we have four children.

MR. JACKSON: He has this kind of party every year, and this year he seemed to feel very strongly that we should come. I somehow felt I couldn't refuse.

MRS. JACKSON: I wish you had. We're not ready for Christmas at all. The tree isn't trimmed, the turkey isn't stuffed, and there are presents still to be wrapped. We're always up till two A.M., anyway. This year it'll be six!

MR. JACKSON: If we'd just get started, we might get home some time. Then we can take care of the tree and the presents.

JOHNNIE: Won't Santa Claus bring some of them?

MRS. JACKSON (*Looking at* JOHNNIE): Yes, of course he will. But just the same, there's a lot to do, and I don't like leaving you children.

IRENE: Are Dave and I practically grown up or not? We can look after the kids.

JOHNNIE (*Putting down his book and rising*): Who needs looking after, anyway? (*He goes off left.*)

MRS. JACKSON: I'm worried about Johnnie. Someone at school told him there is no Santa Claus, and he doesn't know what to believe.

LOUISE: When he wakes up in the morning and sees all the presents, he'll believe in Santa all right.

MRS. JACKSON: It's a critical point in his life, and he needs his mother.

IRENE: Now, you just go off to your party and have a good time.

MRS. JACKSON (*Smiling*): All right, I'll stop fussing. (*Putting one hand to her ear*) Oh, my, I've forgotten my earrings.

IRENE: While you're at it, I'd put on just a touch more lipstick.

MRS. JACKSON: All right, I will. (*She goes off.*)

LOUISE (*Holding up present she has been wrapping*): Isn't this one pretty?

MR. JACKSON (*Sitting down*): Yes, it is, and that reminds me. (*Looking toward doorway left*) I have a present for your mother, and I don't know when I'll have time to get it wrapped.

LOUISE: Goody, I'll wrap it.

MR. JACKSON (*Glancing toward doorway again*): Sh-h-h, not so loud! This present is breakable, and I think Irene should take charge.

DAVE: Breakable? I'll bet I know. It's one of those new automatic electric coffee makers.

MR. JACKSON: No, it's not. Last year I gave your mother that electric frying pan, and she remarked that I always give her something practical. I felt she would like something impractical for a change.

IRENE: You're right.

MR. JACKSON: She's been talking and talking about a glass bowl to put flowers in for the dining room table.

IRENE: Yes, I know—one of those plain Swedish crystal bowls like the one the Barrys got for a wedding present.

MR. JACKSON: Exactly. Your mother even had the number of it. She was going to price it at Kramers, but I told her I thought it was foolish to spend money for a thing like that. (*Smiling*) Then she forgot all about it and left the piece of paper with the number on the table. I slipped it into my pocket, and the next day I went to Kramers and bought the bowl. It's fragile, so be very careful. It's on the top shelf in the hall closet. Sh-h-h, now, here she comes.

MRS. JACKSON (*Entering. She has coat on and is wearing*

earrings): Merry Christmas, everyone, we're off to the party. What are we waiting for?

MR. JACKSON (*Jumps to his feet, grinning*): What are we waiting for? I suppose I'm the one who had to find my earrings and put on more lipstick? I'm sure Mr. Santa Claus has less trouble getting started with all his reindeer. My dear, you look positively radiant.

IRENE (*Taking* MR. JACKSON's *hat and coat from chair and holding coat while he puts it on*): Sir, your hat and coat. (MR. JACKSON *slips into coat and with his hat in one hand offers an arm to* MRS. JACKSON.)

MR. JACKSON: My lady, allow me. We are off to the Christmas festivities.

MRS. JACKSON: I think I'm going to enjoy it after all. Irene, see that Johnnie gets to bed all right.

MR. JACKSON: If you should need any help, our young newly-wed neighbors are right next door.

IRENE: Yes, Mrs. Barry said they'd keep an eye on us.

MRS. JACKSON (*Laughing a little*): Ruthie Barry is a dear, but she's so young. She's been over almost every day to ask me how to cook something or other. She hardly knows how to boil water. This morning I gave her my recipe for turkey stuffing. I do hope it turns out all right.

MR. JACKSON: I'm not worrying about the Barrys' turkey. I'm worrying about ours. If we don't get to that party and back again, you'll never get ours stuffed at all.

MRS. JACKSON (*Starting for door right*): Yes, that's right.

JOHNNIE (*Enters left*): Mom, do you have to go?

MRS. JACKSON: Yes, Johnnie. Now be a good boy and go to bed. In the morning Santa will have everything ready for Christmas.

MR. JACKSON (*Opening door and leading* MRS. JACKSON *out*): Goodbye, all of you, for a little while. We'll be back before you know it, for a merry, merry Christmas!

OTHERS: Merry Christmas! Merry Christmas! (MR. *and* MRS. JACKSON *go out right and close the door.*)

IRENE: Johnnie, it's time for you to go to bed. Come on, and I'll read you a story.

JOHNNIE: I guess I'm big enough to read to myself. (*Picking up book he had been reading before*) I'll read "The Night Before Christmas" again.

IRENE: I'll come in later to see that you are tucked in.

LOUISE: In the morning, when you wake up, Santa will have been here with the presents.

JOHNNIE (*Going over to fireplace and peering in*): This chimney doesn't look big enough to me. Not for Santa Claus.

DAVE: He'll squeeze down somehow.

JOHNNIE: I've never seen him come.

IRENE: Of course you haven't. No one ever sees Santa come. He's like magic—like everything else about Christmas.

JOHNNIE: O.K. I guess I'll go to bed. (*He goes off left with his book.*)

DAVE: That's that. I thought we'd have more trouble.

IRENE: Poor kid. He's kind of confused. I wish I knew the right thing to say. Mom's the only one who could help him.

LOUISE: She isn't here, and neither is Dad. I don't feel Christmasy any more, either. I did when I started wrapping my presents. Now, it's lonesome, and not like Christmas Eve at all.

IRENE: Now, Louise, don't you start. It *is* Christmas Eve whether it feels like it or not—

DAVE: We have to wrap up the rest of our presents.

IRENE: Don't forget, we have to wrap Dad's present for Mom, too.

LOUISE (*Suddenly smiling*): Listen, I just had a wonderful idea! Why couldn't we do *everything*? Then it would seem like Christmas Eve.

DAVE: Say, that's a wonderful idea. We'll get everything all ready for Christmas!

IRENE (*Excited*): I don't see why we can't. What a surprise for Mom and Dad when they get back! Let's see, we'll have to get the tree decorations. Aren't they on the high shelf in the kitchen, Dave?

DAVE: They always were, but I thought Mom said she was going to store them somewhere else.

IRENE: Anyway, I'll find them.

DAVE: I'll get Dad's present.

IRENE: Do be careful of that, Dave.

LOUISE: We'll have to find Mom's recipe for turkey stuffing. It's probably in the recipe box in the kitchen.

IRENE: No, it isn't. The stuffing is like some of Mom's other good things to eat. The recipe is in her head.

LOUISE: Mom said she gave it to Ruthie Barry.

IRENE: That's right, so she must have written it down.

LOUISE: I'll call her up, right away. (*She goes to table and leafs through phone book.*)

DAVE: Good. I'm going after the glass bowl. (*He exits left.*)

LOUISE: I'll bet Mom left the number of the bowl on purpose where Dad would find it.

IRENE (*Smiling*): What if she did? This way she's getting something she really wants. I'm going to find those tree decorations. (*She exits.*)

LOUISE (*Reading from phone book*): Elm 214. (*The doorbell rings. She puts down book, goes to door and opens it.* RUTHIE BARRY *enters.*)

RUTHIE: Hello, Louise. Have your parents gone yet?

LOUISE: Yes, Mrs. Barry. I was just going to call you up.

RUTHIE: I came over to find out how to make turkey stuffing.

LOUISE: You did? That's just what I was going to ask you.

RUTHIE: Oh, dear me. What'll we do?

LOUISE: I don't know. We want to surprise Mom and get it done before she comes home. Mom gave you the recipe. She said so.

RUTHIE: Yes, she did, and I wrote it down as she talked. (*Taking paper from her jacket pocket*) Now I don't quite know what it means.

LOUISE (*Going and looking at paper*): Let me see. Sage, onion, melted butter, dry bread crumbs—doesn't it sound good?

RUTHIE: Yes, those are the ingredients—that part's all right, but it says *dry* bread crumbs, and all my bread is fresh. I don't know how to dry out the bread crumbs.

LOUISE: There must be some way. I know. Toast is dry. Why couldn't we put the slices of bread in the toaster?

RUTHIE: We'll need a lot. I should think at least a whole loaf of bread for mine and two loaves for yours. It'll take a long time to toast all that bread. Why couldn't we just put the loaves in the oven? That would dry them out fine.

LOUISE: I guess it would. Why don't you bring your bread over here, and we'll dry it all out together.

RUTHIE: That's a wonderful idea. (IRENE *enters left.*)

IRENE: Louise, I can't find the tree decorations anywhere. I've looked and looked. (*She sees* RUTHIE.) Hello, Mrs. Barry.

RUTHIE: Hello, Irene. Have you looked under all the beds? I often find things under the bed. (*There is a loud crash off left.*)

IRENE: What was that?

DAVE (*Off*): Oh, ouch! Oh, my gosh!

IRENE: Dave! I hope he's not hurt!

LOUISE: He was getting the bowl. What if it's broken? What'll we do? (DAVE *enters left, limping a little, carrying a white box.*)

IRENE: Dave, are you hurt?

DAVE: No, I'm not, but the bowl—I haven't looked at it, Irene, but listen. (*He rattles the box.*)

IRENE (*Taking lid off box and looking in, then closing it quickly*): It looks like cracked ice.

RUTHIE: I'm so sorry. It was a Christmas present, I suppose.

DAVE: Not just *a* Christmas present. It was Dad's present to Mom. I tried to be careful, but my foot slipped.

IRENE: It was so expensive, and now Dad won't have a present for Mom. Everything is going wrong—our whole Christmas!

RUTHIE: What kind of bowl was it?

LOUISE: One of those Swedish crystal bowls, just like yours, Ruthie. Mom admired it.

RUTHIE: Then everything's all right. I have two of them.

LOUISE: Two?

RUTHIE: Yes, I got two just alike for wedding presents. Now, you see, there's nothing to worry about. I'll go right home and get the bowl and the loaf of bread.

IRENE: Even if you do have two, I don't know what Dad and Mom will say.

DAVE: If we do take the bowl, I can start right after Christmas, and pay you from my allowance. I'm broke right now because of Christmas.

RUTHIE: Now, don't worry about it. Your mother's been so wonderful to me—all of you have—and this gives me a chance to do something for you.

IRENE: I don't know what to say.

RUTHIE: Don't say another word. Isn't Christmas the time for giving? I'll be right back, with the bowl and the bread. (*She exits right.*)

LOUISE: That certainly saves the day. Now, I ought to start on the turkey stuffing.

IRENE: All right. If you're going to the kitchen, why don't

you take this box with the broken bowl and put it in the trash can by the back door? It'll just upset Dad to see it.

LOUISE: O.K., Irene. (*Takes box and exits left.*)

DAVE: I still wonder what Dad will say about the bowl.

IRENE: Maybe we needn't tell him. (*She pauses.*) No, that would be wrong.

DAVE: I'm going to tell him. (*He sits in chair, rubbing his leg a little.*)

IRENE: Mom and Dad will understand, so quit worrying. Now, if I could only find the tree decorations.

DAVE: Did you look on all the closet shelves?

IRENE: All of them. What can we do? Getting the tree all trimmed was going to be the best surprise of all. (LOUISE *enters left.*)

LOUISE: Everything's ready to start the stuffing. I have two loaves of bread out, and as soon as Mrs. Barry gets here with hers, we can put them in the oven. (*The door opens right, and* RUTHIE *rushes in, carrying a loaf of bread and a box like the one* LOUISE *has just taken out.*)

RUTHIE (*Gaily*): Here I am again, and Tom's coming, too. Here's the bowl—(*She trips and the box and the loaf of bread go flying across the floor.*) Oh-h-h! Oh, my! Now, look what I've done.

DAVE: Another bowl gone!

LOUISE: Maybe it didn't break.

IRENE: I'm afraid to look. (TOM BARRY *enters, carrying glass bowl in one hand and three or four boxes under his arm.*)

TOM (*Grinning*): Hello, everyone. Here's your bowl.

RUTHIE: Bowl? But Tom, I stumbled, and the bowl was in that box.

TOM: It *was* in that box, but I took it out because I thought you might drop it on the way over. Here it is, safe and sound.

RUTHIE: Tom, you're so smart, you're wonderful! (*She*

reaches for bowl.) Now, we can put the bowl into the box.

TOM (*Holding it away*): No, you don't. Irene, you'd better take care of it. Now, put it in the box and wrap it up pretty. (IRENE *takes bowl and sets it on card table.* LOUISE *picks up box and bread. She hands box to* IRENE, *who puts bowl in box.*)

IRENE: I'll do it right away before anything else happens. (*She quickly puts a piece of Christmas paper around the box and sticks it down with two or three stickers.*)

LOUISE: I'll take your bread out to the kitchen, and start drying it with ours. I've turned on the oven. (*She goes off left with bread.*)

TOM: Dave, why don't you and I start trimming the Christmas tree?

DAVE: We haven't any decorations.

TOM (*Holding up boxes*): That's what you think. What do you suppose I have in these boxes? (*He puts boxes on table and takes lids off.*) Christmas tree balls, all shapes and sizes—not to mention tinsel.

IRENE (*Putting down package and coming to look*): They're beautiful! But where—did you get them?

TOM: Ruthie always buys enough, not to say too much.

RUTHIE: I wanted to be sure we had plenty.

TOM: We have enough decorations to trim two or three trees. Come on, let's get to work! (*He starts hanging balls on tree.*)

IRENE: They're such beautiful decorations. Mom and Dad will certainly be surprised. I can help trim now, too, but I'll have to go look at Johnnie first. (*She starts left as* LOUISE *enters.*)

LOUISE: Everything's all set. The bread's drying in the oven.

IRENE: Good, I'll be back in a minute. (*She goes out left.*)

LOUISE: Look at the tree! You found the decorations.

DAVE: No, we didn't. These are brand-new. The Barrys brought them.

LOUISE: Christmas Eve is turning out to be wonderful after all!

DAVE: Thanks to our neighbors.

TOM: This is fun for us, too.

LOUISE (*Glancing toward window*): Look, it's snowing.

TOM: A white Christmas!

RUTHIE: Our first one.

TOM (*Putting his arm around* RUTHIE): May all your Christmases be white!

IRENE (*Enters left, upset*): Johnnie is not in his bed.

DAVE (*Laughing*): He can't have gone far. Mom said she left some Christmas cookies in the kitchen for when the carolers come around.

IRENE: That's the first thing I thought of, but he's not in there.

RUTHIE: Maybe he went out the back door and over to a neighbor's.

LOUISE: He wouldn't do that at night. At least he never does.

TOM: Then he's in the house somewhere, and we'll look. (*He starts left as the phone rings.*)

RUTHIE: Maybe this is about Johnnie.

IRENE: I do hope it isn't Mom calling to find out if we're all right. (*She picks up phone.*) I'll have to tell her. (*Into phone*) Hello . . . Who? . . . You just looked out the window and saw a little boy on our roof? . . . (*Excitedly*) Oh, my! Thank you very much! (*She hangs up and turns to others.*) Mrs. Cole, from across the street, says there's a little boy up on our roof!

LOUISE: It must be Johnnie.

IRENE: How will we ever get him down? (*She starts right, and* DAVE *follows.*)

TOM: Wait a minute, let's take it easy. If we all rush out,

he may get excited and slip on the snow. Let me go out first and talk to him. (*He exits right.*)

RUTHIE: What made the child climb out there?

LOUISE: To look for Santa Claus, of course. He wants to make sure there is one.

IRENE: How did he ever get there?

DAVE: That's easy—up the side of the dormer. All you do is hold on to the gutter. I used to climb out when I had that room, but I never did it when it was snowing and slippery.

LOUISE (*Almost crying*): What if he falls? Just think if Mom and Dad come home and—

RUTHIE: Tom will get him down somehow. (TOM *re-enters right, stamping snow off feet.*)

TOM: He's up there all right. He has his snowsuit on, and he's right on the peak. He's afraid to start down.

IRENE: What'll we do?

TOM: I'll get my ladder. I told him just to sit tight.

DAVE: I doubt if we need a ladder. I think we can get him in the way he got out—through the window.

TOM: It's slippery.

DAVE: If you'll sit on the window sill and just hold onto my feet, I can reach him and pull him in.

TOM: That sounds all right. I think it's the best way to do it. Come on, Dave. (TOM *and* DAVE *go off left.*)

LOUISE: Maybe we can go out front and watch.

IRENE: No, it might make them nervous.

LOUISE: It's so hard—just waiting, wondering if Johnnie's going to fall—

RUTHIE: Try not to worry. Tom won't let him fall.

IRENE: I do hope they get him in before Mom and Dad get home. If they turn in the drive and see Johnnie sitting up on the roof, they'll be frantic.

LOUISE: Poor Johnnie, sitting up there all alone with the

wind blowing the snow around him—waiting for Santa Claus.

IRENE: I'll bet he won't climb out to watch for Santa Claus again. This should be a good lesson. (*Fire sirens are heard off right.*) What's that?

LOUISE: It sounds like fire sirens.

RUTHIE (*Running to window*): It *is* fire sirens—and a big red fire truck is just pulling in the driveway!

IRENE: Mrs. Cole must have called them to get Johnnie off the roof!

RUTHIE: I'll bet Tom has him in by now.

IRENE: Then we can just send the firemen away.

JOHNNIE (*Off left*): I wasn't scared. I could have stayed up there all night.

IRENE: It's Johnnie. He's all right. (TOM *and* DAVE *enter left with* JOHNNIE. *He wears snowsuit over pajamas, but during next few lines, he unzips jacket and removes it.*)

DAVE (*Laughing*): Scared or not, it's a good thing we got you in before Dad got home.

TOM: I guess it's still too early for Santa and his reindeer, but we did see a big red fire truck. (*There is a loud knock on door right.*)

IRENE: Here they are. They've come to get Johnnie off the roof.

DAVE (*Starting right*): I'll tell them we don't need them. (DAVE *opens door and* TWO FIREMEN *enter, carrying fire extinguishers.*) Merry Christmas, fellows. Thanks for coming, but we've already got my kid brother down from the roof.

1ST FIREMAN (*Crossing left*): We see you have. (*He continues off left.*)

DAVE: So I guess it was kind of a false alarm.

2ND FIREMAN: That's what you think. (2ND FIREMAN *starts left as* MRS. JACKSON *and* MR. JACKSON *enter excitedly right.*)

MRS. JACKSON: The house is on fire!

IRENE: No, it isn't, Mom.

2ND FIREMAN: There's smoke pouring out of your back window! (*He goes off left.*)

MR. JACKSON: Yes, we saw it, too.

MRS. JACKSON: Hurry, get your coats on.

TOM: You can come over to our house.

MRS. JACKSON: Why should all this happen on Christmas Eve? (*The* FIREMEN *re-enter, grinning.*)

1ST FIREMAN: Merry Christmas, folks. It's all over but the smoke.

MR. JACKSON: How did you get it out so fast?

1ST FIREMAN: I turned off the oven, took out a tray with three loaves of bread burned to a crisp, and chucked them into the snow in the back yard.

LOUISE: Our bread for the stuffing. I forgot all about it!

RUTHIE: So did I. Your recipe said dry bread crumbs so we were drying out the bread in the oven.

MRS. JACKSON: You needn't have done that. I have two jars of bread crumbs all ready. Now, why don't we fix our Christmas dinners together? You bring your turkey over, and I'll show you how to stuff it. And then we can make the sauce for the plum pudding.

TOM: It's a wonderful idea. We can learn how to get ready for Christmas from an expert.

RUTHIE: We'll be right back. (*She takes* TOM's *hand and they hurry out.*)

LOUISE: This will be fun, but we wanted to surprise you and have the turkey all stuffed.

1ST FIREMAN: You sure did surprise your mother.

LOUISE: We could have stuffed it all right, too, if Johnnie hadn't climbed out on the roof.

MRS. JACKSON (*Excitedly*): Johnnie on the roof! (*Rushing to* JOHNNIE) How awful!

MR. JACKSON: Gwen, don't get excited. He's not on the roof now. He's right here.

MRS. JACKSON: Johnnie, are you all right?

JOHNNIE: Sure. I was just waiting for Santa.

2ND FIREMAN: Guess lots of boys and girls are doing that tonight, but I think the best place to wait is in bed.

1ST FIREMAN: Yes, and we had better be getting back on duty to see that Santa gets here all right.

JOHNNIE: What do you mean?

1ST FIREMAN: You never can tell. We might get a call from Santa to help him down a chimney. He might get stuck.

JOHNNIE: Did he ever?

2ND FIREMAN: Nope, but there's always a first time for everything. We wouldn't want that to happen. (*Waving*) Merry Christmas to all.

MR. JACKSON: Thanks again, and a Merry Christmas to you! (FIREMEN *go out right, closing the door.*)

IRENE: Christmas Eve is always exciting but I think this has been the most exciting one we've ever had!

LOUISE: We've been so busy, Mom.

IRENE: The tree's almost trimmed.

MRS. JACKSON: So it is, and it's simply beautiful. Those can't be our decorations. They look so new and shiny.

IRENE: No, Mr. and Mrs. Barry brought them. We couldn't find ours.

DAVE: The Barrys helped us with everything, Dad.

JOHNNIE (*Sleepily*): But Christmas isn't here yet. We don't have the presents until tomorrow morning.

MR. JACKSON: So we don't, but your mother and I have had a fine Christmas present already.

MRS. JACKSON: We do have a Christmas surprise for all of you.

DAVE: What's happened?

MR. JACKSON: There was a good reason for my boss wanting

us at that party tonight. I have a new job. I've been promoted to be manager of the entire plant.

DAVE: What do you know? Congratulations, Dad.

IRENE: Dad's a VIP!

LOUISE: Another Christmas surprise.

MRS. JACKSON (*Going to* JOHNNIE): Johnnie dear, you're almost asleep. You must go straight to bed.

JOHNNIE: O.K., Mom. I guess I *am* sleepy. (*He gets up, and* MRS. JACKSON *takes his hand.*) Maybe I'll just go to bed.

DAVE: No more watching for Santa Claus.

JOHNNIE: Santa will come all right. The firemen said so. (JOHNNIE *and* MRS. JACKSON *go off left.*)

MR. JACKSON: Everything's all right with Johnnie. I feel just the way he does. I'm not sleepy, but suddenly that good old Christmas feeling is stealing over me. (*He sits down in easy chair, relaxing.* TOM *and* RUTHIE *enter right. He carries the turkey and* RUTHIE *has a basket.*)

TOM: Here we are again, all ready to learn how to fix Christmas dinner.

RUTHIE: I brought sweet potatoes, and everything we'll need—even some popcorn to make some popcorn balls! (*She and* TOM *put their things on the table.*) Christmas is so exciting!

MR. JACKSON: Yes, Christmas is exciting. The best part of all is that real Christmas feeling.

TOM: I think I know what you mean, Mr. Jackson. Of course, this is our first Christmas together. (*He takes* RUTHIE's *hand.*)

MR. JACKSON: We've had a great many Christmases together. But that special Christmas feeling always comes just as though it's something new that you're experiencing for the first time. A sense of peace steals over you. (CAROLERS *are heard off, singing a Christmas carol.*)

IRENE: Dad, listen, it's the carolers.

MR. JACKSON: Yes, they are a part of Christmas Eve. (MRS. JACKSON *enters, carrying a large plate of cookies.*)

MRS. JACKSON: Johnnie fell asleep the minute his head touched the pillow. Tom and Ruthie, I'm so glad you got back in time for the carolers. *(She passes cookies.)* Let's invite our singing friends in for refreshments. (LOUISE *rushes to door right and opens it as* CAROLERS *finish carol.*)

LOUISE: Merry Christmas! Merry Christmas! *(There are shouts of "Merry Christmas!" from* CAROLERS *offstage.* MR. JACKSON *goes to door smiling and motions with his arm.*)

MR. JACKSON: Come in, come in, all of you. And a Merry, Merry Christmas! *(Curtain)*

THE END

Two Strangers from Nazareth

by Graham DuBois

Characters

DAVID, *a shepherd*
EDNA, *his wife*
LEAH ⎱ *their children*
ANN ⎰
ADA, *a friend of the family*
HEROD'S MAN, *one of Herod's police*
ABNER, *a friend of David's*
WISE MAN
JOSEPH
MARY

TIME: *The night of Christ's birth.*
SETTING: *A shepherd's hut near Bethlehem.*
AT RISE: DAVID *sits dejectedly on a bench near fireplace, whittling a piece of wood, his face toward audience.* EDNA *is sweeping the floor.* LEAH *and* ANN *sit at the table,* LEAH *sewing and* ANN *washing cups.* EDNA *pauses.*

EDNA (*To* DAVID): It's about time you went to Bethlehem. There are only two days more for paying taxes.

DAVID (*Evasively*): There's no hurry. I can go tomorrow or the next day.

EDNA (*Impatiently*): That's just like you, always putting

things off. You've been idling all day, sitting there tinkering with that wood, when you weren't feeding beggars who come to that door. (*Indicates door downstage right*) The last two or three days you've seemed to have something on your mind. You have stayed in the house all day, and last night you hardly slept at all. What ails you?

DAVID (*Patiently*): Nothing ails me, Edna.

EDNA: Then why don't you talk to me? You have hardly spoken to me since morning. I have the feeling that you are keeping something from me.

DAVID (*Sighing resignedly*): I have been keeping something from you, but you will have to know sooner or later. I cannot pay my taxes.

EDNA (*Dumbfounded*): You cannot pay your taxes! Why not?

DAVID: I do not have the money.

EDNA: What happened to it? Less than a week ago you sold that lamb to Abner. You should have more than enough for taxes. (EDNA *comes to bench.*)

DAVID: Abner has not yet paid me.

EDNA: You simpleton! You mean that you let that rogue have the lamb without paying cash? (EDNA *sits.*)

DAVID: Well, he has had a hard time—sickness, poor crops. He said he would pay me today or tomorrow.

EDNA: And you believed him? How foolish of you!

DAVID (*Quietly*): Abner has never lied to me.

EDNA: You must be the only shepherd who can say that. Most of them don't trust him enough to leave their flocks near him. (*She rises.*)

LEAH (*Raising her hand*): Listen! I hear somebody coming up the path.

ANN (*Walking to window*): I'll see who it is. (*She looks out.*) There is. It's a man leading a donkey.

LEAH: Is there anybody on the donkey?

ANN (*Turning from window*): Yes, a woman.

EDNA (*Alarmed*): We must not let them in. They are just two vagabonds. There's no telling what may happen if they come in here.

DAVID (*Soothingly*): Nothing is going to happen, Edna. They are probably weary and want to rest. (*Knock at door is heard.*)

EDNA: Do not open that door, David; we may all be murdered.

ANN: It is just a poor old man and his wife. They both look worn out and in need of rest.

LEAH: We cannot turn them away in that condition. We would regret it all our lives if we did. (*Knock is repeated.*)

EDNA: We may never live to regret it if we do.

DAVID (*Rising*): Ann, unbar the door.

ANN (*Unbarring and opening door*): Come in. You are welcome. (JOSEPH *enters.*)

JOSEPH: May the good God bless you! (ANN *closes and bars door and returns to seat.*)

DAVID: Sit right here and rest. You look tired. (JOSEPH *approaches bench.*)

JOSEPH: Thank you. I am tired and my wife, too, is very weary. (*He sits.*) It is hard for her to get on and off the donkey.

DAVID: Where are you from?

JOSEPH: From Nazareth. We have had a long, hard journey.

EDNA (*Sitting in the background, eyeing* JOSEPH *suspiciously, to* DAVID): Did you hear that? From Nazareth. Doesn't that open your eyes? (*She covers her face with her hands.*)

ANN (*To* JOSEPH): You must be hungry. Can I get you something? A cup of milk and some bread perhaps?

JOSEPH: I would be very grateful for a little food for my

wife. She has had nothing since this morning and she is with child. (ANN *exits.*)

DAVID (*To* JOSEPH): You are very courageous to undertake such a journey with your wife in her condition.

JOSEPH: We had to. There were only a few days left to pay our taxes.

DAVID: Was there nowhere you could leave your wife?

JOSEPH (*Shaking his head sadly*): There was nobody to take her in. (ANN *enters, carrying a tray, on which there are two cups of milk and some bread.* EDNA *sits sullenly by herself.* ANN *offers tray to* JOSEPH, *who shakes his head.*)

JOSEPH: No, not for me. Besides my tax money, I have barely enough to pay for my wife's food.

DAVID: We want no money. (*Solicitously*) You must eat something. You will drop on the way to Bethlehem.

JOSEPH: If you will let me pay you later, I will send you the money.

DAVID: Have it your way, but take something.

JOSEPH (*Taking bread and milk*): We can never thank you enough. (*He eats and drinks.*)

ANN (*Walking to door*): I'll take something to your wife. (ANN *exits.*)

DAVID: Where will you stay in Bethlehem?

JOSEPH: We have no place to stay. (*Sadly*) We are strangers, and if they find out we are from Nazareth, they will make it hard for us.

DAVID: The inn is the most likely place. Everybody in Bethlehem knows me. I will go with you and show you the way.

EDNA (*Rising*): You must be mad! You would leave three defenseless women here alone while you go off with two strangers from Nazareth? (*She sits.*)

DAVID (*Soothingly*): There is no danger, Edna. It will take only a few minutes. Bethlehem is not more than a quarter mile.

EDNA: Time enough for the three of us to be murdered.

JOSEPH: If your wife is afraid, maybe you had better not go. The two of us can manage, sir.

DAVID (*Firmly*): I insist on going with you. You are an old man, and your wife is weary. I would never forgive myself if any harm came to you.

JOSEPH (*Rising and putting cup on table*): Well, then, we had better be on our way so that you can get back as soon as possible. We are very grateful for your kindness. May God reward you! Without this rest and food, we could not have gone on. (DAVID *opens door, and he and* JOSEPH *go out.*)

EDNA (*Rising and coming forward as* ANN *enters with empty tray and cup*): Your father does not care what becomes of us, but he would never forgive himself if any harm came to two worthless vagabonds. (*She sits on stool at end of table.*)

ANN: They are not worthless vagabonds, Mother.

LEAH: And Father saw that their need was greater than ours.

EDNA: But he didn't even know them, and neither do you. Who are they?

ANN: He called her Mary, and she called him Joseph.

EDNA: That means nothing: those are probably not their real names.

ANN (*Very seriously*): Mother, have you heard the strange story the shepherds are telling? (ANN *walks to table and sits.*)

EDNA: What? That wild yarn?

ANN: They say that a new king to rule over Israel will soon be born. Perhaps Mary and Joseph will be his parents.

EDNA (*Amazed*): So you really believe it!

LEAH: And I, too, I believe it with all my heart.

EDNA (*Turning to* LEAH *incredulously*): You, too? I'm surprised at you. I always thought you were level-headed.

ANN: I think Father believed.

EDNA: I don't doubt that; he trusts anything.

LEAH (*Meditatively*): Suppose that Mary should really be the mother of the promised Christ?

ANN: He would bring new hope to this troubled world.

LEAH: And there would be no more war, no more oppression and hatred.

ANN: All men would live as brothers, and—

EDNA (*Rising angrily*): Enough of this nonsense! I forbid you to waste your time in this silly talk. There's work to do. (*Knock at door is heard.*) Keep perfectly quiet. (EDNA *sits.*) Don't make a sound. It may be the police after your father.

ANN: After Father? Why? What has he done?

EDNA: He has probably been seen in the company of those suspicious-looking strangers from Nazareth.

LEAH: They are not suspicious-looking, Mother. The old man has a frank, open face.

ANN: And the woman is lovely. She has the face of an angel. There is about her something not of this world. She made me feel I was in the presence of some heavenly creature. I looked at her with wonder and awe. (*Knock is repeated.*)

EDNA: Make no sound. Don't move.

ADA (*Offstage*): Let me in. It's only Ada.

EDNA: Let her in, but don't keep that door unbarred long.

LEAH (*Walks to door*): Only a minute, Mother. (*She unbars door, admits* ADA, *bars door and returns to seat.*)

ADA (*Very much excited, crosses room and stands near table*): I had to come to see you. There is something strange and holy about this night. (*She sits on stool.*)

EDNA: It's no different from any other night to me.

ADA: I have the feeling that something wonderful is going to happen.

EDNA: Nothing wonderful ever happens in Bethlehem. It's just taxes, taxes, and more taxes.

ADA: Haven't you seen the star?

EDNA: What's so wonderful about a star? I see thousands of them every night.

ADA: But never one like this. (*To* LEAH *and* ANN) You girls ought to take a look at it. (LEAH *and* ANN *go to window and look at sky.*)

EDNA: Have you come all the way here just to tell us about a star? (*She rises, goes to window, and looks upward.*)

ANN: Isn't it beautiful, Mother?

EDNA: No more beautiful than stars I have seen all my life.

LEAH: It's moving toward Bethlehem.

EDNA (*Turns away and walks toward table*): I don't see any movement. (*She sits on chair. A Christmas song is heard in the distance.*) What's that?

ADA: That's the shepherds. They've been singing all evening. They say they are happier than they have ever been in their lives.

EDNA: What reason have they to be happy? Times are hard enough, heaven knows.

ADA: They say they have received news that the King will come tonight.

EDNA: What king?

ADA (*Solemnly*): The King of Kings—the Christ Child. (*Christmas song grows closer and closer.*)

EDNA (*Apprehensively*): It sounds as if they are coming here. We mustn't let them in. (*To* LEAH *and* ANN) Is Abner among them?

LEAH: We cannot recognize anybody; it's too dark.

ADA: I can tell you that Abner is not there. He left home an hour ago. He told my husband he was going to some foreign land.

EDNA: That rogue! Running away from his debts! We are in real trouble now. David will not be able to pay his taxes, and they will throw him in jail.

ANN: The shepherds are streaming into the road.

LEAH: They are going toward Bethlehem. (*Christmas song grows closer.*)

ADA (*Rising*): I must go, too.

EDNA: Go where?

ADA: To Bethlehem, to see the King. The shepherds must have learned that He has come.

ANN (*Turning from window*): I will go with Ada.

LEAH: So will I.

EDNA (*Harshly*): You will not go. You'll stay right here with me. Do you suppose I want to be here by myself with all that thieving horde on the highway?

LEAH: You will not go see the Christ Child?

ANN: Please, Mother, let us go.

EDNA: No! I don't waste my time on nonsense.

ADA (*Walking to door*): You will be sorry if you don't. There has been nothing as important as this in the history of the world. (ADA *unbars door.*) I'll come back as soon as I have seen Him. (ADA *exits.*)

EDNA: Quick, Ann. Bar that door.

ANN (*Crossing to door*): Isn't it time that Father was getting back? (*She bars door.*)

EDNA: Time means nothing to him. He may have fallen in with some old cronies, or else he probably stopped at the tavern. (*Knock at door startles* EDNA.) Who is that?

ANN: Maybe that's Father now.

EDNA: Don't touch that door. (*Knock is repeated.*)

LEAH: What can we do? We have to see who it is.

HEROD'S MAN (*Offstage, knocking violently on the door*): Open this door! It will go hard with you if you don't. In Herod's name!

EDNA (*Frantically*): Herod's men! They have come! I knew they would. I always said that your father would get us into trouble.

HEROD'S MAN (*Knocking*): Open this door! We'll batter it down if you don't.

EDNA: Quick, Ann! Open it.

ANN: What can they want? (*She unbars and opens door.*)

LEAH: We have done nothing.

HEROD'S MAN (*Entering*): What took you so long to open the door?

EDNA (*Perturbed*): We—we were busy and couldn't come right away. He's not here.

HEROD'S MAN (*Curtly*): Who is not here?

EDNA: My husband: He had an errand in Bethlehem.

HEROD'S MAN: We are not interested in your husband. We are looking for a couple with a donkey.

ANN: They are not here.

HEROD'S MAN: They were seen on the road to Bethlehem not ten minutes ago.

LEAH: What have they done?

HEROD'S MAN: They are troublemakers. Herod's orders are to get them, even if we have to raid the town.

EDNA: What trouble are they making for Herod?

HEROD'S MAN: They have upset the whole town by spreading some crazy story about a king being born in Bethlehem. It may lead to riot and rebellion. We must find them.

ANN: They are not here.

HEROD'S MAN (*Looking about, sternly*): Are you sure you are not hiding them?

EDNA (*Earnestly*): I assure you, sir, that we are not hiding them.

HEROD'S MAN (*Turning toward door*): I will take your word for it for the present. (*He opens door.*) But if we do not find them, we shall be back to search the place. (*He exits.*)

EDNA: You see the trouble your father got us into? What will Herod do to us if he finds that David conducted that couple to Bethlehem?

ANN: Father would never do anything to bring us harm, Mother. He is good and kind. He felt sorry for that poor couple. (*She walks to door.*) Besides, he thought that they might be the parents of the king. (*She bars door.*)

EDNA: Hush! For all you know, that man may be listening at the door. It is treason to talk of having any ruler but Herod. (*Knock is heard at door.*) There! What did I tell you? He has heard what you said.

ANN (*Turning to door*): I am not afraid. I'll let him in. (*Knock is repeated.*)

EDNA (*Frantically*): Don't dare open that door. We will all go to prison.

DAVID (*Offstage*): Let me in! (*Pounding on door*) It is David.

LEAH: It is Father's voice!

EDNA: It sounds like him. Open the door just a crack and peep out, Ann. (ANN *unbars door and* DAVID *enters.*) (*To* DAVID) What did you do with that miserable couple?

DAVID (*Walking to bench near fireplace*): You mean Joseph and Mary? (ANN *returns to table and sits.*) I took them to the inn at Bethlehem. The innkeeper was none too glad to see them. (DAVID *sits.*)

EDNA: I should think not; he does not cater to that kind of people.

DAVID: He told them so outright. He said there was no room at the inn.

EDNA (*Curious*): Well, what happened to them?

DAVID: Mary was suffering. I begged him to let them sleep in the straw of the stable and he finally consented.

LEAH: It is strange he would do even that, greedy as he is, without getting something in return.

DAVID: Well, he—he did not exactly do it for nothing. I made him an offer.

EDNA (*Amazed*): An offer? An offer of what? You have nothing.

DAVID: I promised him two days' labor.

EDNA (*Angrily*): You simpleton! You have all you can do to feed your family. (*Knock is heard at door.* DAVID *rises.*) Don't go near the door. That man again! (LEAH *and* ANN *rise.*)

DAVID: What man?

EDNA: Herod's man. He came while you were gone. He may have found out that you took that couple to Bethlehem, and if you let him in now we are lost. (*Knock is repeated.*) We may all be arrested.

DAVID (*Walking to door*): I must open the door. What else can we do?

EDNA: We can run out the back way and hide in the woods. I tell you not to open that door unless you want to die.

DAVID: We shall not run like cowards.

EDNA: We had better run like cowards than die like fools.

DAVID (*Opening door and calling*): Come in. (WISE MAN *and* ABNER *enter.*)

EDNA (*Staring at* ABNER): You here! After all you have done to us, Abner, you dare to come? (*Sneeringly*) I suppose you'll say you came to pay your debt?

ABNER: That is why I did come. For that and to say goodbye. I am going on a very important journey, and I may be gone a long time, maybe forever.

EDNA (*Still suspicious*): What important journey could you be taking?

WISE MAN: The most important journey a man ever took. He goes to guide the Christ Child and his parents into Egypt.

DAVID: Has the Christ Child arrived?

WISE MAN: Yes, shortly after you left. He was born in the manger of the stable.

LEAH: But why does He have to go to Egypt?

ANN: Isn't He comfortable in the stable?

WISE MAN: He is comfortable enough, but He is in serious danger.

LEAH: The Christ Child in danger?

WISE MAN: Yes. (WISE MAN *puts his hand on* ABNER'S *shoulder.*) And this good man, at the risk of his own life, has volunteered to take the Saviour and His parents to a place of safety.

EDNA: I daresay he demanded a small fortune for his services.

WISE MAN: He asked nothing for himself; he stipulated only that he be given enough to pay his debts.

ABNER (*Feeling in his pocket*): And I am sorry that I had to ask even that. (*He draws some silver coins from his pocket and hands them to* DAVID.) Many thanks, David.

DAVID (*Pocketing coins*): I always knew you would keep your word. (DAVID *sinks down on bench.*) To think that I have not seen the King!

WISE MAN: You have stood in His presence.

DAVID (*Amazed*): I? When have I?

WISE MAN: On innumerable occasions. Your neighbors have told me about you. You have given your help to those in illness and in trouble. Only today, you fed the hungry who came to your door. You gave food and found a place of rest for two strangers from Nazareth, not knowing who they were, recognizing in them only two people in distress. He who does these things shall always stand in the presence of the King. (*There is the sound of music, then a Christmas song, as part of the backdrop is drawn aside and the tableau of the manger, with* MARY *and* JOSEPH, *is revealed. All kneel in an attitude of adoration as the curtain falls.*)

THE END

Long Live Christmas

by Islay Benson

Characters

GRANDFATHER LORENZ
PETER
BARBARA
LORENZ, *as a boy*
LISELLA
HERMAN
GEORGE
J. CRISPIN HUMBOLDT
MRS. J. CRISPIN HUMBOLDT
AMBROSE
BERT
TEENA
KING'S CHAMBERLAIN
KING ULRIC
MR. JASON
MRS. JASON
TWO GUARDS
CHRISTMAS FAIRY

PEACE
LOVE
KINDNESS
FAITH   } *Spirits of Christmas*
CHILDHOOD
HOPE
FUN
SIX PAGES
OTHER TOWNSPEOPLE
CAROLERS

SETTING: *A public square. The stage is bare, except for an arch upstage center and a bench at left. On the apron of the stage, at right, is another bench.*

AT RISE: PETER, BARBARA, *and* GRANDFATHER LORENZ *enter left. As they talk, they stroll across the stage.*

GRANDFATHER: Hurry up, children; let's go home. It feels like snow.

PETER: Snow! Oh, I hope so. Snow means Christmas.

BARBARA: How long is it until Christmas, Grandfather?

GRANDFATHER: Let's see, this is December fifth, so it's twenty days until Christmas.

BARBARA: Twenty days! That's forever. What a long time to wait!

PETER: Yes, I feel as if Christmas will never come.

BARBARA (*Quickly*): Don't say that, Peter! It will come, won't it, Grandfather?

PETER: Don't be silly, Barbara. Of course it will. That was just a saying. Christmas always comes.

GRANDFATHER: I remember once when it almost didn't come.

PETER: Almost didn't come!

BARBARA: Grandfather! Whatever do you mean?

GRANDFATHER: Oh, it was a long, long time ago, when I was a little boy.

PETER: Tell us about it, Grandfather.

GRANDFATHER: Well, let me see if I can remember the story.

BARBARA: Try, Grandfather, try!

GRANDFATHER: Listen! I hear carolers coming.

PETER: Oh, yes! Let's listen. And while we're listening, Grandfather will have a chance to remember the story.

BARBARA: Think hard, Grandfather! Think hard. (*They have reached the bench on the right side of the apron, and they sit down.* CAROLERS *enter on the left side of the*

*apron and sing a Christmas carol. When they have fin-
ished,* CAROLERS *exit.*)

PETER: Now, Grandfather, have you remembered?

GRANDFATHER: Yes, my dear. It was long ago, long ago and
far away, miles across the sea, in the land where I was
born, the little kingdom of Camerovia. This is the way
it happened. (*They turn towards the stage, as* 1ST *and*
2ND PAGES *enter behind the arch, carrying a large scroll
wound on two sticks.* PAGES *come down front, side by
side, then walk in opposite directions, thus opening the
scroll and revealing the words, "This is the Kingdom of
Camerovia." Then they exit.*) It was getting close to
Christmas, and one day my sister and I walked through
the public square in the capital of our little kingdom.
(LORENZ, *as a boy, and* LISELLA *stroll on.*)

LISELLA: Just think, Lorenz, it's almost Christmas!

LORENZ: Yes, isn't it exciting!

LISELLA: I can feel it in the air, can't you?

LORENZ (*Putting out his hand, as though to see if it were
raining*): Well—er—maybe.

LISELLA: Oh, I can. I love Christmas! I love everything
about it—the way the shops look, and the Christmas
trees, and everyone smiling and laughing and dashing
around full of—full of—

LORENZ: Turkey?

LISELLA: No! Just full of—Christmas. Let's sit here and
watch it all. (*They sit on bench at left.* HERMAN, *the
town decorator, and* GEORGE, *his assistant, come on with
wreaths and other Christmas decorations, which they
hang up.*)

LORENZ: What are you doing?

HERMAN: We're getting the town ready for Christmas.

LISELLA: The wreaths are beautiful.

GEORGE: We should have a merry Christmas this year.

HERMAN: There! We're all finished. Merry Christmas, children.

LISELLA *and* LORENZ: Merry Christmas.

GEORGE (*As he and* HERMAN *exit*): Merry Christmas. (MRS. J. CRISPIN HUMBOLDT *comes slowly on, carrying one tiny, tiny parcel and absorbed in a Christmas list about three feet long. Behind her is* J. CRISPIN HUMBOLDT, *her husband, almost hidden under a tower of packages. They stop and* MRS. HUMBOLDT *hands her tiny, tiny parcel to her husband. He gropes for it and she hangs it on his thumb.*)

MRS. HUMBOLDT: Here, dear, you carry this. I need both hands for my list. (*As they start walking again,* AMBROSE, *a careless youth, runs on and bumps into* MR. HUMBOLDT, *causing the packages to fall.* MRS. HUMBOLDT *does not look up, but continues to be absorbed in her list.*)

AMBROSE: I'm sorry, sir.

MR. HUMBOLDT: Oh, that's all right.

AMBROSE: You mean you're not angry?

MR. HUMBOLDT: Why no, my boy. You didn't mean to do it, I know. And I just can't get angry around Christmastime.

AMBROSE: Well, at least I can help you pick them up.

MR. HUMBOLDT: Thank you. (*They pick packages up.*)

AMBROSE: Thank you, sir. And I'm awfully sorry.

MR. HUMBOLDT: Forget it. Merry Christmas!

AMBROSE: Merry Christmas! (MR. *and* MRS. HUMBOLDT *and* AMBROSE *exit.* BERT *comes on, wearing sandwich boards which read "Joe's Meats" on one side and "Christmas Turkeys" on the other. He walks all the way around the stage, then stands to one side, looking out at audience.*)

TEENA (*Rushing on*): Hello, Lisella. Hello, Lorenz.

LISELLA *and* LORENZ: Hello, Teena. Merry Christmas!

TEENA: Oh, what pretty decorations! (*She runs about looking, singing "Good King Wenceslas" in a loud voice. 3RD and 4TH PAGES enter under arch and blow trumpets.*)

PAGES: Make way for the King's Chamberlain! Make way for the King's Chamberlain. (*All the people who have already been on stage rush back on, plus as many other TOWNSPEOPLE as desired. CHAMBERLAIN enters under arch. 5TH and 6TH PAGES walk a little behind him, each carrying a small tray. On one tray is a large scroll; on the other is a pair of white gloves.*)

CHAMBERLAIN: Oyez! Oyez! By Order of His Majesty the King! (*He flicks a thumb and finger at 5TH PAGE as a sign to be handed his gloves.*)

TOWNSPEOPLE (*Loudly*): The King! The King! Long live the King!

CHAMBERLAIN: Proclamation issued by His Majesty the King. (*He puts on the gloves and then looks for 6TH PAGE, who has moved back a bit.*)

TOWNSPEOPLE: The King! The King! Long live the King!

CHAMBERLAIN: The Proclamation! Where is the Proclamation? How can I proclaim without a Proclamation? (*6TH PAGE quickly hands the scroll to the CHAMBERLAIN, who continues to grumble beneath his breath as he opens it.*) Ahem! "Whereas, His Majesty the King—"

TOWNSPEOPLE: The King! The King! Long live the King!

CHAMBERLAIN (*Annoyed*): "Whereas His Majesty the King wishes to state that it is drawing close to that season of the year popularly known as Christmas, and whereas he is dismayed by the amount of money being spent on Christmas, and upset because the people are paying more attention to Christmas than they are to him, he hereby decrees that there is to be no Christmas this year in the Kingdom of Camerovia."

TOWNSPEOPLE (*Ad lib*): What! No Christmas? That's terrible! (*Etc.*)

CHAMBERLAIN (*Still reading*): "There shall be no signs of Christmas—no trees, no decorations, no bell ringing, no carol singing."

TEENA: No carol singing?

CHAMBERLAIN: Silence! (*Continues to read*) "No Christmas presents, no feasting on turkey and plum pudding, mince pies or eggnog. Anyone not obeying this proclamation will be punished severely." (*He looks up from proclamation*) His Majesty hasn't decided how yet, but you can bet it will be good! (*Continues reading*) "And banished forever from the Kingdom of Camerovia. By Order of His Majesty the King." (TOWNSPEOPLE *are silent.*) I said: By order of His Majesty the King.

TOWNSPEOPLE (*Quietly, with no expression or enthusiasm*): The King. The King. Long live the King.

CHAMBERLAIN (*Smiling unpleasantly*): The King has spoken. (*He exits, followed by the* PAGES. *Immediately* TWO GUARDS *enter and grimly remove the Christmas decorations. They change the sign "Christmas Turkeys," on* BERT'S *sandwich board, to one that reads: "Hamburger." They take away* MR. HUMBOLDT'S *Christmas presents.* TOWNSPEOPLE *exit unhappily, except for* LISELLA *and* LORENZ, *who remain on bench.*)

LISELLA: No Christmas! No Christmas!

LORENZ: It's terrible, isn't it?

LISELLA: I can't believe it! (*She starts to cry and* LORENZ *comforts her as they exit.*)

BARBARA: Oh, Grandfather, that was awful! What a thing to do!

PETER: Go on, Grandfather, go on!

BARBARA: Yes, what happened next?

GRANDFATHER: Just a minute, just a minute now. Don't rush me. Let an old man have time to think. Hark! The carolers are here again. Listen! (CAROLERS *enter and sing a Christmas carol. They exit, still singing.*)

BARBARA: Do you remember now?

GRANDFATHER: Yes, this is the way it was. One day, soon after the proclamation, my sister and I were in the public square, and a strange thing happened. (LORENZ *and* LISELLA *enter, sadly.*)

LORENZ: Everyone has been so unhappy since the King's proclamation.

LISELLA: No one laughs or smiles any more. (CHRISTMAS FAIRY *enters and taps the children on the shoulder.*)

FAIRY: Hello, children. I'm the Christmas Fairy.

LORENZ: The Christmas Fairy? What's that?

FAIRY: A little more respect, young man. I am not a "what," I'm a "who."

LORENZ: I'm sure I beg your pardon. What I really meant was what are you doing here?

FAIRY: I'm starting my Christmas checkup. I always make my rounds at this time of the year. There's a lot to be done, you know.

LORENZ: What, for instance?

FAIRY: Oh, I have to make sure people are preparing for Christmas, getting the right spirit, warming their hearts up. I have to see that everything's going smoothly for the great season.

LISELLA: Well, you've certainly come to the wrong place for that.

LORENZ: Yes, you won't have to stay here long.

FAIRY: What do you mean?

LORENZ: There isn't going to be any Christmas here.

FAIRY: No Christmas!

LISELLA: None at all.

FAIRY: What on earth do you mean?

LORENZ: The King has decreed that there is to be no Christmas at all in Camerovia this year.

FAIRY: But he can't do that!

LORENZ: He has done it.

FAIRY: Oh, he has, has he? We'll see about that. (*A few bars of music are heard, as she runs lightly to the left and lifts up her arms.*) Spirits of Christmas! Come! (*She runs to right.*) Spirits of Christmas! Come! Your queen calls you! (*The* SPIRITS OF CHRISTMAS *enter quickly as music is heard offstage. Four enter from left and three from right. All run lightly and gracefully, except* FUN, *who does cartwheels as he enters.*)

LISELLA: Who are all these?

FAIRY: These are the Spirits of Christmas. Peace, Love, Kindness, Faith, Hope, Childhood, and Fun. (*As each one's name is called, he comes forward and bows, except for* FUN, *who turns another cartwheel, and* CHILDHOOD, *who throws the ball in the air and catches it.*) These seven make up Christmas. Put them together, and you have Christmas. Without them there would be no Christmas, and with them you cannot help but have Christmas.

PEACE: You called us, dear Queen.

LOVE: We came as quickly as we could.

KINDNESS: What is your bidding?

FAIRY: I have something important to tell you. The King of Camerovia has decreed that there is to be no Christmas in his kingdom. (SPIRITS *laugh.*)

LISELLA: Why do they laugh at such a shocking thing?

FAIRY: Tell them why you laugh, Faith.

FAITH: Because it's not as simple as that. If the King wants to get rid of Christmas, he'll have to get rid of us first.

HOPE: And that's pretty hard to do. Others have tried it.

CHILDHOOD: And sometimes they seem to succeed, but not for long.

FUN: No, we're a match for the King of Camerovia, or any other king.

LOVE: Or all kings put together.

FAIRY: Yes, but we must keep our wits and work hard.

(*She turns to* LISELLA *and* LORENZ.) Go home to bed now, children, and don't worry. Leave the matter in our hands. The next time you see these spirits—well, you won't *see* them, for they'll be invisible to mortal eyes then. But they'll be there, and you'll soon know it. (LISELLA *and* LORENZ *exit.*)

FAIRY: Now come with me, my spirits, and I will tell you what we must do. (FAIRY *and* SPIRITS OF CHRISTMAS *exit.*)

BARBARA: Oh, Grandfather! What a place to stop!

PETER: Yes, you can't stop there!

BARBARA: What happened next?

GRANDFATHER: Now, now, children. Don't be impatient with me. Let an old man collect his wits. I must think a little. And besides—

PETER: I know. You hear the carolers.

BARBARA: Those carol singers always pop up at the most exciting point! (CAROLERS *enter and sing, then exit, still singing.*)

GRANDFATHER: This is what happened next. On Christmas Eve, the King's Chamberlain called all the people together. (1ST *and* 2ND PAGES *enter with a scroll, as before. It reads* "Christmas Eve in Camerovia." 3RD *and* 4TH PAGES *enter and blow trumpets.*)

3RD *and* 4TH PAGES: Make way for the King's Chamberlain! Make way for the King's Chamberlain! (LORENZ, LISELLA, TEENA, *and* TOWNSPEOPLE *enter slowly, without interest, looking unhappy.* CHAMBERLAIN *enters under the arch, with* 5TH *and* 6TH PAGES.)

CHAMBERLAIN: Oyez! Oyez! Oyez! By Order of His Majesty the King. (TOWNSPEOPLE *remain silent.*) I said by Order of His Majesty the King.

TOWNSPEOPLE (*With no enthusiasm*): The King. The King. Long live the King.

CHAMBERLAIN: Herewith a proclamation by His Majesty the King. (TOWNSPEOPLE *remain silent.*) I said a proclamation by His Majesty the King.

TOWNSPEOPLE: The King. The King. Long live the King.

CHAMBERLAIN (*Reading*): "Whereas His Majesty wants to remind the people of the importance of his decree, he has caused the following to be read in the public square. Whereas this is the 24th of December, formerly known as Christmas Eve—"

TEENA (*Bursting out in song*): "Good King Wenceslas—"

CHAMBERLAIN (*With a roar*): Silence! (*Reading*) ". . . formerly known as Christmas Eve, His Majesty wishes to remind the people that this evening is to be like any other evening and tomorrow is to be like any other day." (TEENA *wails.* CHAMBERLAIN, *with a roar*) Silence! (*Resumes reading*) ". . . formerly known as Christmas Eve, His Majesty wishes to remind the people that this evening is to be like any other evening, and tomorrow is to be like any other day." (TEENA *wails.*) Will you be quiet! I'm proclaiming. (*Reading*) "There will be no show of Christmas whatsoever." (*He rolls up scroll.*) And now I have a surprise for you, a splendid, delightful surprise. Out of the great goodness of his heart, His Majesty is coming here to make sure his people understand his decrees.

AMBROSE (*Rushing on, waving his arms*): The King! The King's coming!

TOWNSPEOPLE (*Ad lib*): Oh! What shall we do? The King! Coming here! (*Etc.*)

CHAMBERLAIN: Down! Down! Everybody down on your knees! (*All kneel except* TEENA, *who remains standing.* 3RD *and* 4TH PAGES *sound the trumpets.*)

3RD *and* 4TH PAGES: His Royal Majesty, the King of Camerovia, Gracious Lord of the Hills, Mighty Ruler of the Seas, and Monarch of all the People. Ulric the

First. (KING *enters slowly, stands in the arch and looks his people over. Noticing that* TEENA *is not kneeling, he frowns and points this out to the* CHAMBERLAIN. *By a gesture, the* CHAMBERLAIN *orders her to kneel. She shakes her head in refusal.*)

TEENA: But then I won't be able to see anything.

CHAMBERLAIN: There's nothing to *see*, you silly child. (*With a loud gasp, he turns to the* KING.) Oh, Your Majesty! Your Majesty! Forgive me. I never meant—I'd no intention—I was only—

KING (*Interrupting him*): Stop bumbling, Oscar. Her point is well taken. (*He looks steadily at* TEENA *for a moment.*) She may stand. You have issued our proclamation?

CHAMBERLAIN: I have, Your Majesty.

KING: They understand, you think?

CHAMBERLAIN: Oh, yes, Your Majesty, I should think so.

KING (*To the people*): Have any of our people questions to ask?

TOWNSPEOPLE: No, Your Majesty.

TEENA (*Running to* KING): Yes, Your Majesty.

CHAMBERLAIN (*Seizing her and whisking her back into crowd*): Get away from the King, you little imp!

TEENA: I'm not a little imp, I'm a people. Didn't you hear what the King just said?

CHAMBERLAIN (*Beside himself*): He didn't mean you.

KING: Silence, Oscar. Come here, child. You may speak.

TEENA (*Curtsying*): Thank you, Your Majesty. Your Majesty, is it really true about no Christmas?

KING: Absolutely true. No Christmas.

TEENA: No presents?

KING: No presents.

TEENA: No turkey?

KING: No turkey.

TEENA: No carol singing?

KING: No carol singing.

TEENA (*In a wistful voice*): Not even "Good King Wenceslas"? (KING *looks at her a moment.*)

VOICE (*Offstage*): Merry Christmas, everybody. (KING *looks in the direction of the voice.*)

KING (*Snapping at* TEENA): Not even "Good King Wenceslas"! (*With a roar, to the* CHAMBERLAIN) Enough of this nonsense! I thought you said they understood. Arrest that miscreant! (*Pointing in the direction of the voice*) We go to prepare the dungeons. (*He kicks his train out of the way and exits quickly.* PAGES *and* CHAMBERLAIN *rush after him.* TEENA *wails and rushes offstage right.* LORENZ, LISELLA, *and* TOWNSPEOPLE *rise from their knees and go off sadly and quietly.*)

BARBARA: What a wicked, wicked king!

PETER: Did he really put people in the dungeons?

GRANDFATHER: Wait, wait, wait. If you'll give me a chance, I'll tell you.

BARBARA: Oh, hurry, Grandfather. Quick, before any more carolers come. It's too exciting to stop now.

GRANDFATHER: This is what happened. (LORENZ *and* LISELLA *enter and sit on the bench sadly.*)

LORENZ: So you see, it's true. No Christmas. In spite of what the Christmas Fairy said, there's no Christmas!

LISELLA: Yes, I know. It's terrible! (*She sobs.* FAITH *runs on. She dances round* LORENZ, *but he does not see her, for she is now invisible to him. She touches him with her wand and runs off.*)

LORENZ: No, wait a minute. There *is*. There *is* Christmas. There must be. There always has been, and there will be again. How could anyone, even a king, do away with it just by a lot of words? You don't make Christmas by words. He could say "I proclaim there is no sky," but the sky would still be there.

LISELLA: Oh, but Lorenz, that's different. He's taken away

all our Christmas decorations and celebrations, so what's left?

LORENZ: Christmas is left! Christmas itself. I have faith again that this is so. (*As he is speaking,* HOPE *runs on and touches* LISELLA, *then runs off.*)

LISELLA: Oh, Lorenz, do you think so? Truly? You almost make me believe it.

LORENZ: You must believe it. You *can* believe it. It's true.

LISELLA: Lorenz, you give me hope again. And I'll go on hoping.

LORENZ: Let's try to find the Christmas Fairy. Maybe she can do something about it, if we can find her again. (*They go off. In a moment, from the other direction,* MR. *and* MRS. JASON *walk slowly on and sit dolefully on the bench. They stare into space, not speaking. In another moment,* MR. HUMBOLDT *comes on. Once again his arms are full of packages, but this time they are dull things like a mop, a pail, bulky brown paper packages. From the opposite direction comes* AMBROSE. *He is walking slowly this time, his head deep in the newspaper. They collide and the parcels fall.*)

MR. HUMBOLDT: Why don't you look where you're going?

AMBROSE: Why don't you!

MR. HUMBOLDT: You clumsy lout.

AMBROSE: Clumsy yourself! (KINDNESS *runs quickly on, touches them both with her wand, and runs off.*)

MR. HUMBOLDT: Oh, what am I talking like an old grouch for? You didn't do it on purpose, I know.

AMBROSE: No, I didn't. But just the same, it was careless of me. I'm sorry.

MR. HUMBOLDT: That's all right. Accidents will happen.

AMBROSE: I can help you pick them up, at any rate. (*He does so, and they exit.*)

MRS. JASON: You're a fine companion, I must say.

MR. JASON (*Angrily*): What do you mean?

MRS. JASON: Never a smile, never a word, just sit there, as glum as a caterpillar with corns.

MR. JASON: Well, that's the way I feel. What about you, anyway? Think you're any better?

MRS. JASON: Oh, I know. This was supposed to be Christmas Eve, and we should be home trimming the tree and getting the children's surprises ready. (LOVE *tiptoes in and touches* MRS. JASON *with the wand.* MRS. JASON *straightens up and smiles.*) Still, I suppose that's no reason for us to be such crosspatches. Even without the tree and the presents, we *do* have a lot of things to be thankful for.

MR. JASON: What, for instance? (LOVE *touches him and runs off as* CHILDHOOD *enters, bouncing the ball.* CHILDHOOD *touches them both with the ball gently and goes off.*)

MRS. JASON: Well, we have each other and the children. That's a lot, isn't it? Even without anything else.

MR. JASON: Yes, I guess you're right. We still have the children. And we're all home together, that's another thing. You're right, we do have a lot to be thankful for. (FUN *enters, smiling impishly. He tiptoes over to* MRS. JASON *and touches her with his jester's stick.* MRS. JASON *starts to laugh out loud.*) What is it?

MRS. JASON: I was just thinking how funny that man looked when all his packages dropped.

MR. JASON: Yes, it was funny, when you stop to think about it, wasn't it?

MRS. JASON: As soon as he'd get one picked up another one would drop. (*They laugh together.*) I guess little things can still amuse us, Christmas or no Christmas.

MR. JASON: Christmas or Christmas, you should say, my dear. I suddenly feel as I used to on Christmas Eve. I don't know why. Merry Christmas, my dear! (MR. HUMBOLDT *enters.*)

MRS. JASON: Merry Christmas.

MR. HUMBOLDT: That's just the way I feel. Merry Christmas! (MRS. HUMBOLDT *and other* TOWNSPEOPLE *enter, obviously in good spirits.* LORENZ *and* LISELLA *enter right.*)

LISELLA: Lorenz, look at the people! They must feel as we do.

LORENZ: Yes, they have their Christmas spirit back, too.

LISELLA: Oh, how wonderful! (TEENA *runs on and stands by* LORENZ *and* LISELLA. CHAMBERLAIN *enters hastily, under arch.*)

CHAMBERLAIN: What's going on here? What's all this?

TOWNSPEOPLE: Merry Christmas, your honor!

CHAMBERLAIN: What! Do you defy the King?

LORENZ: Does it look as if we do?

CHAMBERLAIN: What does that impudent remark mean?

MRS. JASON: Do you see any Christmas trees or decorations?

LISELLA: Or any sign of feasting?

MRS. HUMBOLDT: Or present giving?

MR. JASON: Or bell ringing?

ALL: Well, do you?

CHAMBERLAIN: No, but you were all saying Merry Christmas.

LORENZ: Well, it *is* a merry Christmas. (KING *enters under the arch, in a rage.* TOWNSPEOPLE *do not kneel.*)

KING: What was that! Who dared to say Merry Christmas?

LORENZ: I did, Your Majesty.

MR. HUMBOLDT: We all did, Your Majesty.

KING (*Menacingly*): What! All of you? You dare to disobey me?

MR. HUMBOLDT: No, Your Majesty. We have obeyed you. There are no trees or decorations, Your Majesty.

MRS. HUMBOLDT: And no presents, Your Majesty.

MRS. JASON: And no feasting, Your Majesty.

TEENA: Not even any carol singing. But Good King Wenceslas would have had carol singing! He was *in* a carol. *You* won't ever get in a carol, because you don't believe in Christmas. He did—and everybody loves him for it. Nobody will ever love you. (CHAMBERLAIN *grabs for* TEENA, *but* LORENZ *dashes to her and holds her protectively.*)

LORENZ: Oh, Your Majesty, please forgive her! Don't hurt her. She's only a little girl. If you punish her, you'll have to punish every one of us.

MR. JASON: The boy's right, Your Majesty. We've obeyed you, but we still have Christmas. You see, Christmas is not feasting or decorations or presents.

MRS. JASON: No, Your Majesty. You can abolish all those things, and it will still be Christmas. Christmas isn't *any* kind of show.

MRS. HUMBOLDT: No, Christmas is a state of mind.

MR. HUMBOLDT: And a state of heart. (SPIRITS OF CHRISTMAS *enter.*)

PEACE: Christmas is peace.

LOVE: Christmas is love.

KINDNESS: Christmas is kindness.

FAITH: Christmas is faith.

CHILDHOOD: Christmas is childhood.

HOPE: Christmas is hope.

FUN: Christmas is fun. (CHRISTMAS FAIRY *enters.*)

FAIRY: Yes, all those things make up Christmas, and when you have them, you don't need decorations and feasting. You have Christmas, and you'll always have it. No king, nothing and no one can ever take it from you. (*She runs to* CHAMBERLAIN *and to the* KING *and touches them with her wand.*)

MR. HUMBOLDT (*Going to* KING *and dropping on one knee*): Forgive us, Your Majesty. We can do as you say and banish the outward show, but we *must* keep Christmas in our hearts.

KING: Rise, good man. It is your king who must ask his people's forgiveness. I will never again try to take Christmas from you.

ALL: The King! Long live the King! Long live good King Ulric! Christmas! Christmas! Long live Christmas! (*Curtain*)

THE END

The Brownie Who Found Christmas

by Adele Thane

Characters

MERRYTHOUGHT ⎫
NIMBLETOES ⎬ *Brownies*
SHARPEYES ⎭
SANTA CLAUS
BELINDA
DANNY
BILL
ANN MARY
MATILDA
TOM
POLLY
OTHER BROWNIES

SCENE 1

TIME: *Christmas Eve.*

SETTING: *The space in front of the curtain represents a hallway in Santa Claus' Snow Palace on top of the North Pole.*

BEFORE RISE: *Several* BROWNIES *enter, with bulging sacks of toys on their backs, and march across the stage, singing to the tune of "The Toy Shop"* (Listen and Sing, Enlarged Edition, Ginn and Co.).

294

BROWNIES:

Oh, we are the Brownies who make all the toys
For all of the girls and for all of the boys;
Some dolls that sleep and horses that rock,
And gay jumping jacks that go knockety-knock.
Our big bags are full of a number of things:
A white woolly lamb and a birdie that sings,
Some skates that glide, and sleds that slide,
You just can't imagine how much is inside. (*As they sing,
all the* BROWNIES, *except* MERRYTHOUGHT, NIMBLETOES
and SHARPEYES, *march off the stage, down through the
audience, and out at the rear of the auditorium. At the
conclusion of the song,* MERRYTHOUGHT *throws down his
sack.*)

MERRYTHOUGHT (*Angrily*): I'm sick and tired of Christmas!

NIMBLETOES (*Shocked*): What did you say?

MERRYTHOUGHT: I said, I'm *sick and tired* of Christmas.

NIMBLETOES: Why, I've never heard of such a thing!

SHARPEYES: Neither have I!

NIMBLETOES: What's happened to you, Merrythought? You
used to love Christmas.

MERRYTHOUGHT: Well, it's not the same as it used to be.
Nowadays children want too many toys, and I'm sick
and tired of toys—and presents and Christmas trees and
tinsel and ornaments! Why, the very thought of it makes
me shudder from head to foot.

SHARPEYES: What you need is a change. Why don't you
ask Santa Claus to let you ride with him tonight?

MERRYTHOUGHT (*Crankily*): I don't want to go. It would
be nothing but toys, toys, toys. That's all children think
about at Christmas—how many toys they're going to
get.

NIMBLETOES: I don't believe all children have so many
toys. I'll bet if you went with Santa tonight, you'd see
some children who had very few toys indeed.

MERRYTHOUGHT (*Snorting*): With that sleigh full of dolls and jumping jacks and what-have-you out there? (*He points to the rear of the auditorium.*) Rubbish! (*He sits cross-legged on the floor and scowls.* SANTA CLAUS *enters, rubbing his hands together with satisfaction and smiling broadly.*)

SANTA: Isn't this *fun?* There's nothing in the world quite like Christmas and plenty of toys for everyone. Eh, Merrythought? (MERRYTHOUGHT *responds with a grunt of disgust, and* SANTA CLAUS *turns to* NIMBLETOES *and* SHARPEYES.) What's the matter with *him?* He looks as if he'd lost his best friend.

NIMBLETOES: He has; he's lost Christmas.

SANTA: Lost *Christmas?*

SHARPEYES: Yes, he doesn't like Christmas any more.

SANTA: Merrythought, is this true?

MERRYTHOUGHT (*A little shamefacedly*): Yes, Santa.

SANTA: But I don't understand. You always liked Christmas best of all my helpers.

MERRYTHOUGHT: I know I did, but I guess I've had too much of it.

SANTA: Good gracious, that's dreadful! You'd better come along with me on my rounds and see if you can get back some of your Christmas spirit.

NIMBLETOES (*Pulling* MERRYTHOUGHT *to his feet*): Go ahead, it will do you good.

MERRYTHOUGHT (*Glumly*): Well, all right, but I don't expect much. (*He picks up his sack and, accompanied by* NIMBLETOES *and* SHARPEYES, *he follows* SANTA *offstage and out the rear of the auditorium. From behind the curtain, children's voices are heard singing a lively Christmas carol.*)

*   *   *

SCENE 2

TIME: *Later that night.*

SETTING: *The interior of a poor cottage. The room is bare of Christmas decorations.*

AT RISE: *Six children in night clothes are seated on benches near the table, facing the stove. They are singing a carol. Pieces of torn blankets are pulled around their shoulders to keep them warm. The seventh child,* BELINDA, *apparently the eldest, is standing center, fully dressed. She is leading the singing, and beats time with a wooden mixing spoon.* SANTA *and* MERRYTHOUGHT *enter at the rear of the auditorium and walk up the aisle to the stage. The children continue to sing, but softly, so that the following dialogue can be heard.*

MERRYTHOUGHT (*Looking about*): Where are we? At the end of the world?

SANTA: Go and look in that window, and if I'm not mistaken, there will be something for you to see.

MERRYTHOUGHT: Somebody trimming a tree, I suppose, and filling stockings. More tinsel and toys! (*He goes up on stage, grumbling, then turns to* SANTA.) Aren't you coming?

SANTA: No, I still have quite a few places to visit. I'll be back for you later. (*He goes out at the rear of the auditorium.*)

MERRYTHOUGHT (*Pantomimes looking through a window left stage on the apron*): Just some children singing. (*Voices increase in volume, then soften again.*) That's funny! There aren't any Christmas decorations in the room. (*The carol ends, and the younger children start sniffing the air with gusto.*)

CHILDREN: I smell them! I smell them! I know I do! (*They*

jump up and down excitedly and lose their coverings.
BELINDA *goes around wrapping them up again.*)

BELINDA: Sit still and keep covered, or you'll catch cold.

MERRYTHOUGHT: They must have a turkey in the oven, but what a strange time to cook it. And where are their father and mother? (*He sniffs the air vigorously.*) I *have* to find out what's in that oven. It doesn't smell like turkey exactly. I wonder when they'll take it out, whatever it is. (*He continues watching.*)

DANNY: Belinda, come over here and *sniff!*

MATILDA: It smells *heavenly,* Belinda!

BILL: Belinda, *don't* you think they're done?

TOM: *Do* look in the oven, Belinda!

POLLY: Please, *please,* Belinda!

ANN MARY: Oh, Belinda, we can't wait a minute longer!

BELINDA (*Laughs and shakes her finger at them*): Very well, stand back, and I'll take a look. (*But they don't stand back; they crowd around and peek as* BELINDA *gently opens the oven door.*)

MERRYTHOUGHT (*Wild with curiosity*): *What* can it be? (*The children start clapping their hands rhythmically and sing to the tune of the chorus of "John Brown Had a Little Indian."*)

CHILDREN:
What's in the oven, baking, baking?
What's in the oven, baking, baking,
What's in the oven, baking, baking,
For our Christmas dinner?

BELINDA: They're done! (MERRYTHOUGHT *strains forward eagerly as* BELINDA *takes seven little saucer-pies from the oven and carefully sets them on the table in a row. The children sing and prance around the room.*)

CHILDREN:
Pies in the oven, baking, baking,

Pies in the oven, baking, baking,
Pies in the oven, baking, baking,
For our Christmas dinner.

MERRYTHOUGHT (*Surprised*): My goodness! Pies!

DANNY: There's someone at the window! (*They all rush downstage to see who is there, and* BELINDA *pantomimes opening the door.*)

BELINDA (*Calling to* MERRYTHOUGHT): Come in, come in, little boy! (MERRYTHOUGHT *pantomimes stamping snow from his feet and steps upstage into the room. He stands shyly for a moment while the children stare at him.* BELINDA *reprimands them.*) Don't stare, children, it's not polite.

POLLY (*Coming forward*): Are you Santa Claus?

MERRYTHOUGHT (*Kindly*): No, little one, my name is Merrythought. (*He inhales the aroma of the pies with an expression of bliss.*)

TOM (*Proudly*): Those are our pies you smell.

DANNY *and* BILL (*Simultaneously*): One apiece.

ANN MARY: Belinda made them.

MATILDA: For our Christmas.

POLLY (*Slipping her hand into* MERRYTHOUGHT'S): Merry Christmas, Merrythought!

BELINDA (*Laughing*): It isn't Christmas Day yet, darling— not for another (*She glances at the clock on the table.*) quarter-hour.

MERRYTHOUGHT: But why aren't you all in bed? And where's your tree? And stockings?

BELINDA (*Explaining*): Well, you see, Father and Mother went to town almost a week ago. Father went to help build a house; he's a carpenter, you know. Mother went to do some sewing for the minister's wife, and they left me to take care of the children. They meant to be home tonight, but the snow is so deep, I guess they couldn't get here. Mother was going to bring each of the children an orange, so I made the pies to cheer them up. The children will like them just as well as toys.

CHILDREN (*Hopping about the table*): Smell mine! Smell mine!

MERRYTHOUGHT (*Remorsefully to himself*): And I said children thought of nothing but toys!

ANN MARY (*Holding out her pie to him*): Here, take it, it's yours. I want to give it to you, because you haven't any pie or anything for Christmas. (*Pleadingly, as he shakes his head in refusal.*) *Please* take it. The other children will give me bites of theirs; they said they would.

MERRYTHOUGHT (*Takes the pie*): Thank you, my dear. (*He tastes it.*) Delicious! It's the best pie I ever ate. What's in it?

POLLY: Belinda wouldn't tell us. (*The children bite into their pies and sing "Our Christmas Pie": Our Songs, New Edition, C. C. Birchard and Co. The following words may also be sung to the tune of "Lazy Mary."*)

CHILDREN:

What can be in our Christmas pie,
    Christmas pie, Christmas pie,
What can be in our Christmas pie,
    On Christmas Eve in the nighttime?
Meat and apples and spice, say I,
    Spice, say I, spice, say I,
Meat and apples and spice, say I,
    On Christmas Eve in the nighttime.
We are jolly as we can be,
    We can be, we can be,
We are jolly as we can be,
    On Christmas Eve in the nighttime.

MERRYTHOUGHT (*Suddenly snaps his fingers as he gets an idea*): Wait a minute! *Don't stir.* (*He runs downstage and pantomimes opening the door. He looks out and listens, then listens again. In the distance he hears sleigh bells, faint and clear.*) Just as I thought! Santa Claus is coming back for me. (*The sleigh bells grow louder and then come to a jangling stop.* MERRYTHOUGHT *calls out front.*) Hold on, Santa! I'll be right with you! (*He turns back into the room and speaks to the watching, wondering children.*) Quick, think fast, each one of you! Think just as fast as you can, and then tell me what toy you would like most of all for Christmas.

DANNY: A sled!

BILL: A pair of skates!

TOM: A jumping jack!

MATILDA: A doll, a sleepy doll!

ANN MARY: A singing bird!

POLLY: A woolly lamb on wheels.

MERRYTHOUGHT: And what do you want, Belinda? Everyone has told but you.

BELINDA: I want a sewing box, a sewing box with a lock and key, so that the children can never touch what's inside.

MERRYTHOUGHT (*Nods, starts toward the door, then turns back again*): But you mustn't look, not one little peek! Promise me that you won't look until I say you can.

CHILDREN: We promise! (*They kneel down in a row by the side of the bed, their backs to the room, and cover their eyes.* MERRYTHOUGHT *goes downstage and beckons to* SANTA, *who enters from the rear of the auditorium with both arms and pockets full of gifts.*)

SANTA: Yes, yes, I know all about it. Here, help me with these things, will you? This is Danny's sled. Pile these blankets on top.

MERRYTHOUGHT: Blankets? Nobody wants blankets.

SANTA: Oh, yes, somebody does—their mother. Didn't you see how thin their blankets were? And a new saw for their father. (*The gifts are placed center stage just inside the imaginary door.*) Here are Bill's skates and Belinda's sewing box with a lock and key. Put them on top of the blankets. (*He reaches down first into one capacious pocket and then into the other.*) Here's Matilda's sleepy doll. You made her, Merrythought, and she's one of your prettiest. This is Tom's jumping jack. How it can jump! (*He tries it out.*) What's this? Oh, Ann Mary's singing bird. And here's Polly's woolly lamb on green wheels with a bell round its neck. (*He shakes the bell softly.*) Now, just a little candy. (*He packs seven boxes neatly on the edge of the sled.*) There! Have I forgotten anything?

MERRYTHOUGHT: No. We'd better be off. (*He glances over at the children.*) I doubt if they can stand the suspense much longer.

SANTA (*Chuckling*): Do you think there are too many toys here, Merrythought?

MERRYTHOUGHT (*Shaking his head earnestly*): No, not enough toys. The moment we get home, I'm going to begin making toys for those seven children for next year. (*Seriously*) I owe them a great deal, Santa. They helped me to find Christmas again. (SANTA CLAUS *throws an arm affectionately about* MERRYTHOUGHT'S *shoulders, and they move downstage to the right, where* MERRYTHOUGHT *calls back to the children.*) All right, youngsters, you can look now! Merry Christmas! (*The children leap to their feet and run to the pile of gifts.*)

DANNY: My sled!

BILL: My skates!

MATILDA: My doll! She really sleeps!

ANN MARY: Look, look, a bird that sings when you wind it up!

TOM: See my jumping jack! See how high he jumps!

BELINDA (*Admiring her sewing box*): A real little key, and it locks as tight as tight can be!

POLLY: Listen! *Listen! (She stamps her foot, and they all stop their chatter while she shakes the bell of her woolly lamb.)* Tinkle, tinkle, tinkle! (SANTA *and* MERRY-THOUGHT *have been watching this happy scene as they walk slowly down the aisle through the audience. They reach the rear of the auditorium just as everyone on stage is listening to the bell on* POLLY's *lamb.*)

SANTA (*In a booming voice*): Merry Christmas to all, and to all a good night! (*The children face front and wave to him as he and* MERRYTHOUGHT *exit, waving back.*)

CHILDREN: Good night! Thank you, Santa! Thank you, Merrythought! Merry Christmas! (*Curtain*)

THE END

Looking for Lincoln

by Deborah Newman

Characters

ABE LINCOLN
SAM HILL, *the storekeeper*
MRS. GREENE
MRS. ALLEN
MRS. LUKINS
BILL
JACK
CALEB
SUSAN
JANE
MARY
NANCY
MENTOR GRAHAM, *the schoolmaster*
JOHN STUART, *a lawyer*

TIME: *April, 1834.*
SETTING: *A store in New Salem, Illinois.*
AT RISE: ABE LINCOLN *is standing at the counter at right, reading a book. He makes a note on a piece of paper, then turns a page.* MRS. GREENE *enters.*

MRS. GREENE: Good morning, Abe. That's a big book you're reading.

ABE: Morning, Sally. (*He closes book.*) I'm not reading, I'm studying.

MRS. GREENE: What are you studying now, Abe?

ABE: Law. I kind of figure on being a lawyer some day.

MRS. GREENE: Law! Lands sakes, Abe, you're going to wear yourself out with all this studying.

ABE: Oh, I reckon I won't do that. Well, Sally, what can I do for you?

MRS. GREENE (*Holding up letter*): I want to send a letter to my cousin in Boston.

ABE (*Bowing*): Postmaster Lincoln, at your service. (*Takes letter*) Boston? That's quite a ways from New Salem— maybe a thousand miles from here to Boston. I reckon your cousin will have to pay twenty-five cents to get this letter. (*Marks on letter*) Postage: twenty-five cents. Some day soon we'll have postage stamps in this country. (*Puts letter under counter*) I'll see your letter goes out on the next mail stage.

MRS. GREENE: Thank you, Abe. (*She starts to go out.*)

ABE: Hold on a minute, Sally. (*He gets a letter from under the counter, picks up his hat from counter, puts the letter in the hat and then puts the hat on his head.*) I'll walk with you a way. A letter came for Mrs. Short, and I know she's been looking for word from her brother. I might as well take the letter out to her.

MRS. GREENE: That's right nice of you, Abe. (ABE *and* MRS. GREENE *exit left.* SAM HILL *enters, goes to counter at right and starts to arrange bolts of material.* BILL, JACK *and* CALEB *enter, carrying poles with fish hanging from the ends.*)

JACK: Fishing time, Abe!

CALEB (*Looking around*): Abe isn't here.

SAM: Howdy, boys. What's all the noise about?

BILL: Howdy, Mr. Hill. We're looking for Abe.

JACK: It's good fishing weather. Look what we've caught—catfish and sunfish.

CALEB: The river's full of them.

BILL: We want Abe to come fishing with us. Where is he?

SAM: It's hard to tell where Abe is. Maybe he's out surveying, or delivering some letters. Abe always likes to see folks get their mail right away—even if he has to deliver the letters himself.

JACK: We'll never find Abe if he's out delivering mail.

SAM: Sounds like you boys have spring fever. Why, it won't take you any time at all to walk around New Salem and find Abe. (*Shakes his head*) New Salem's one of the smallest towns in Illinois now. Used to be lots bigger. (*Yawns and stretches*) Guess I have a touch of spring fever myself.

BILL: Come on, let's go look for Abe. It's more fun to fish when he goes with us—he always tells us jokes.

JACK: If Abe comes in, tell him we're looking for him, Mr. Hill.

SAM (*Nodding*): I'll do that. (*The boys exit.* SAM *goes back to the counter and cuts himself a slice of cheese as* MRS. ALLEN *and* MRS. LUKINS *enter.*)

MRS. ALLEN: Good morning, Sam.

SAM: Morning, ladies. I have some fine bacon, and dandy calico for a new summer dress. (*He hands each woman a bolt of material.*) Just think how pretty you'd look in a dress made from this.

MRS. ALLEN (*Fingering material*): I always did fancy lots of flowers on a dress. But we didn't come in to buy anything today, Sam.

MRS. LUKINS: We're looking for Abe Lincoln.

SAM (*Shaking his head*): Looking for Abe Lincoln! Everyone's always looking for Lincoln. You'd think I was his pappy, instead of a storekeeper, the way everyone keeps asking me, "Where's Abe? Where's Abe?" Well, I don't know where Abe is. (*He takes a gun from the wall and polishes it as they talk.*)

MRS. LUKINS: Sam, this is important. John Allen just came back from Springfield, and he says they're going to stop having a post office at New Salem.

MRS. ALLEN: John heard we don't need a post office because so many people are moving away from New Salem.

SAM: That's right. New Salem isn't as big as it used to be.

MRS. LUKINS: But what's Abe going to do? He needs his job as postmaster.

MRS. ALLEN: Poor Abe. (*She counts on her fingers as she speaks.*) First he loses his job because Offutt's store goes out of business. Then he tries to be elected to the legislature—and loses. Then his own store winks out, and he owes money to everyone. And now, just when he's doing nicely as postmaster, maybe the government's going to take that away from him, too.

SAM: Say, you're right. This would be bad for Abe.

MRS. LUKINS: We want to find Abe to tell him we'll all help him. Goodness knows, he helps all of us. (SUSAN, JANE, MARY *and* NANCY *enter.* SUSAN *carries a man's shirt, and* JANE *has a jug of maple syrup.*)

SUSAN: Good morning, Mr. Hill. We're looking for Abe Lincoln.

SAM (*Shaking his head*): Everyone's looking for Lincoln.

JANE: Mammy sent us over with some maple syrup and a new shirt for Abe. She made the shirt to thank him for cutting all our firewood when Pappy was sick.

MRS. ALLEN: Isn't that just like Abe!

MARY: Abe's the best wood chopper I ever saw.

MRS. LUKINS: I reckon Abe's the strongest man in New Salem. Why, when he's chopping wood, you'd say three men were working, he goes so fast.

NANCY (*Taking shirt from* SUSAN *and holding it up*): Mammy made the shirt sleeves extra long for Abe. She says Abe's arms are longer than most.

MRS. ALLEN (*Smiling*): Abe's clothes always do seem a mite small for him. Sam, we'd better go find Abe. If he comes in, tell him we're looking for him.

SAM: I'll do that. Girls, why don't you leave your presents here? I'll see Abe gets them. (*The girls leave the shirt and jug on the counter and then go out with* MRS. ALLEN *and* MRS. LUKINS. SAM *sits down in the rocking chair, yawns, and then falls asleep, snoring loudly.* MENTOR GRAHAM *enters with* JOHN STUART. GRAHAM *goes to* SAM.)

GRAHAM: Ahem! Ahem! Sam—could you wake up for just a minute?

SAM (*Opening his eyes*): Hm-m? Oh, howdy, Mentor. How's the school teaching going this spring? Do all your pupils have spring fever?

GRAHAM: Oh, I reckon some of the boys do. (*Shakes his head*) Not Abe, though. He's my prize pupil. Sam, I've taught maybe six thousand pupils—and Abe Lincoln is the smartest one I've ever had. I'm glad to help Abe study at night.

SAM (*Getting up*): What can I do for you? We just got in some seed.

GRAHAM: No, thank you, Sam, I don't need any seed right now. As a matter of fact—

SAM (*Nodding*): I know. You're looking for Abe.

GRAHAM: That's right. This is John Stuart from Springfield, a friend of Abe's.

STUART: Hello, Mr. Hill.

SAM: Pleased to meet you, Mr. Stuart.

GRAHAM: Sam, do you have any idea where Abe is?

SAM: Mentor, I'll tell you something. I need to come to your schoolroom to get some learning. Nine **people** have come to my store this morning, and all of them asked me the same question. One simple question. But I don't know the answer.

GRAHAM: Sounds like a hard question.

SAM: Oh, it is, it is. The question is, where is Abe Lincoln? That's what everyone wants to know. Everyone's looking for Lincoln.

STUART: So am I. I came all the way from Springfield to talk to Abe. I want to make sure he runs as a candidate for assemblyman this time. He has a good chance of winning, and Illinois needs men like him. He's a fine man.

SAM: You'll never find a better man than Abe Lincoln, Mr. Stuart. I can tell you that. (*Screams are heard from offstage, and the four girls run in, shouting excitedly.*)

SUSAN: Wolf! Wolf!

JANE: There's a wolf running around New Salem. (*Wolf howls are heard from offstage.*)

MARY: Oh, listen to the wolf! I'm afraid.

NANCY: Please shoot the wolf. (*The girls huddle together down right as another wolf howl is heard.* GRAHAM *and* STUART *go to them.*)

SAM (*Grabbing gun*): I'll get the wolf. I'll shoot the critter. (*He goes out. A moment later,* ABE *enters, holding on to the three boys and pulling them into the store.*)

ABE (*Calling*): Sam, put your gun down. (SAM *enters.*) Here's your wolf. (*As* JACK *starts to pull away,* ABE *grabs him.*) Tell us about the wolf in New Salem, Jack.

JACK: Aw, Abe, it was just a joke.

BILL: We wanted to scare the girls.

CALEB: We didn't think anyone would believe us. (MRS. ALLEN, MRS. LUKINS *and* MRS. GREENE *enter.*)

MRS. ALLEN: What's all the noise about a wolf?

ABE: Just a joke, Nancy. These young turkeys have a funny sense of humor. (*He slaps* CALEB *on the shoulder.*) They won't play that joke again.

CALEB: No, Abe. We promise.

STUART (*Stepping forward and holding out his hand*): Hello, Abe. I've come to talk to you.

ABE: John Stuart! (*He shakes* STUART's *hand.*) Well, howdy. I didn't see you here. What are you up to now?

STUART: Abe, I want you to run as a candidate for assemblyman.

ABE (*Shaking his head*): I'm afraid you have the wrong man, John. I lost the last time I ran.

STUART: Almost everyone in New Salem voted for you.

SAM: We sure did. And now—why, Abe, I reckon you're the most popular man in New Salem. All morning long folks have been coming in here asking for you.

ABE: I'd like to be an assemblyman. But I don't know. I'm happy here, being postmaster, and doing surveying, and studying. I like New Salem.

MRS. ALLEN: Listen, Abe, you may not be postmaster much longer. The government's going to stop having a post office in New Salem.

ABE: Is that true, John?

STUART (*Nodding*): I've heard talk about it. Abe, New Salem's a small town, and getting smaller. You can do bigger things than being postmaster. You can go to the state capital—and then maybe Washington.

SUSAN: Washington! That's where the President lives.

NANCY: Wouldn't it be wonderful if Abe got to be President some day?

JACK: President! That's all girls know! President!

MRS. ALLEN: I just wouldn't be surprised if Abe were President of the whole United States some day.

ABE: Whoa! Hold on, everyone. This talk's running faster than a prairie hen. I'm still trying to make up my mind about an election right here. (*Shakes his head*) John, I don't know. Maybe folks want to vote for an educated man. I'd have to tell them I've had less than one year of regular schooling in my life.

GRAHAM: Abe, if you keep on studying the way you have, you'll know more than any Harvard man.

SUSAN: If I could vote, I'd vote for you, Abe.

ABE: Thank you, Susan.

CALEB: Women can't vote. But when I'm a man, I'll vote for you, Abe.

ABE: Thank you, Caleb.

GRAHAM: Abe, you have to run. We're all behind you.

ABE (*Thoughtfully*): Well, it looks as though I'm going to run for election, doesn't it? (*Shrugs*) If I'm elected, I shall be thankful. If not—it will be all the same. (SUSAN *whispers to her sisters.*)

BILL: Hurrah for Abe!

SUSAN: Listen, everyone. We have a new song for Abe. You can sing it with us. (SUSAN *leads the girls in singing a variation of "Old Abe Lincoln," a Lincoln campaign song sung to the tune of "The Old Gray Mare.")*

GIRLS (*Singing*):
Abe Lincoln came out of the wilderness,
Out of the wilderness, out of the wilderness,
Abe Lincoln came out of the wilderness,
Down in Illinois.
Down in Illinois, down in Illinois,
Come join the crowd that's mighty proud of him
Down in Illinois.
(*All join in singing the song as they march around* ABE *and the curtains close.*)

THE END

Visitor to Gettysburg

by Earl J. Dias

Characters

PATIENCE HOLMES, *19*
JOHNNY HOLMES, *her brother, 14*
MR. HOLMES
MRS. HOLMES
MAGGIE, *the maid*
ABRAHAM LINCOLN
UNCLE ALEC, *Mrs. Holmes' brother*

SCENE 1

TIME: *Late afternoon, November 19, 1863.*

SETTING: *The living room of the Holmes household in Gettysburg, Pennsylvania.*

AT RISE: JOHNNY *is seated on the sofa before the fireplace, warming his hands.* PATIENCE *is busily dusting the chairs and table, and tidying up.*

PATIENCE: Where all the dust comes from, I'll never know. Maggie went over the room this morning, but look at it now. (JOHNNY *continues to stare unhappily at the fire.* PATIENCE *goes to the window at left and looks out.*) No sign of them yet. (*She returns to table, picks up Bible and dusts it carefully.* MAGGIE *enters from right.*)

312

MAGGIE: Now, Patience, why are you soilin' those pretty hands? That job's for me. It's what your folks pay me for. (*She takes cloth from* PATIENCE *and begins to dust.*)

PATIENCE: I don't mind, Maggie. After all, it isn't every day that the President of the United States comes to spend the night in our home.

MAGGIE: I caught a glimpse of him when his carriage passed by the house this mornin'. Ah, there's a sad-eyed man.

PATIENCE: He has reason to be sad.

MAGGIE: Sure, and he's so tired lookin', too. And well he might be what with him bearin' half the burdens of the world on his shoulders.

PATIENCE: Father says Mr. Lincoln wasn't always so serious. When he and Father were young lawyers in Springfield, Mr. Lincoln was always one for joking.

MAGGIE: I believe it. Sure, the crinkly lines about his eyes must have come from laughin'. (*She glances toward the silent* JOHNNY *and points a thumb at him.*) His honor is still sulkin', I see.

PATIENCE (*Sitting in easy chair left*): He hasn't uttered a word for ten minutes.

MAGGIE: Still wants to become a young hero, I suppose. Wants to enlist—enlist at the age of fourteen, may all the saints be praised! It's no wonder your mother and father have refused him. He's still a babe in the woods for all his size! (JOHNNY *remains silent. He lies on the sofa now, hands locked behind his head, eyes closed.*) Well, he might as well be holdin' his tongue. Goodness knows, there's enough speech-makin' around these parts today. All of Adams County seems to be in Gettysburg. (*To* PATIENCE) How is it you're home so early? I should think you'd be wantin' to hear all the speeches.

PATIENCE: I heard part of Mr. Hale's speech. He's a wonderful orator, I know, but he goes on and on—

MAGGIE: I know the type. And yet it's the men who always are sayin' that it's women who like to exercise their vocal cords.

PATIENCE: It was chilly there, too. And a cemetery isn't exactly the most cheerful place in the world. Then I began thinking of Robert—somewhere with the Union Army, but heaven knows where. I haven't heard from him for weeks. I grew so depressed that I came home. I think I would have cried if I'd stayed there much longer.

MAGGIE (*Coming to* PATIENCE *and patting her arm affectionately*): There, now—sure, and the war can't last forever. And your handsome broth of a man, Captain Robert Brent, will be comin' home to you.

PATIENCE: Sometimes I almost give up hoping. This war has gone on so long.

MAGGIE: That's been the lot of women since time began —waitin' and hopin' while their men go out to fight their wars. (MAGGIE *returns to her dusting.*) You didn't hear the President speak, then?

PATIENCE: No, Mr. Hale was still orating when I left.

MAGGIE (*Pointing thumb at* JOHNNY): His imperial majesty come home with you?

PATIENCE: Yes, he—

JOHNNY (*Eyes still closed*): Why should I stay to hear about a war that I should be fighting in?

MAGGIE: Listen to the boy! The place for you is school, and you know it!

JOHNNY: It's a man's duty to help preserve the Union.

MAGGIE: A man, is it! Excuse me while I be enjoyin' a good laugh! A man at fourteen! Why it was only yesterday you were spinnin' tops around the house.

PATIENCE: You know you ought to finish your schooling at the Academy. Father's always dreamed of sending you to Harvard.

JOHNNY (*Contemptuously*): Harvard!

MAGGIE: Sure, and there's many a lad would give his right arm for a chance to go to Harvard. Sometimes I think there's rocks in your head where your brains should be.

JOHNNY: There are plenty of fellows my age in the army. They serve as drummers and flag-bearers, and—

MAGGIE: And since when have you been able to play a drum?

JOHNNY: I could learn. (*The sound of voices is heard outside*)

MAGGIE: Here they come! I'll get back to the kitchen! I've got a roast in the oven that would bring a smile to the spiteful face of the devil himself. (MAGGIE *exits right.* JOHNNY *rises hurriedly from sofa and walks toward door left.*)

PATIENCE: Where are you going? Don't you want to meet the President?

JOHNNY: No.

PATIENCE: Johnny, what's come over you, anyway?

JOHNNY: I couldn't stand meeting him. He'll wonder why an able-bodied fellow like me isn't doing his bit for the nation. I'm going to my room.

PATIENCE: You're impossible. What shall I tell Mother and Father?

JOHNNY: Tell them I don't feel well. Tell them anything —I don't care. (JOHNNY *exits left.* PATIENCE *shakes her head in exasperation. The upstage center door is opened by* MR. HOLMES. *He holds the door open to admit his wife and* ABRAHAM LINCOLN. UNCLE ALEC *follows.*)

MR. HOLMES: Come in, Abe. Come in, and make yourself comfortable. You must be very tired. This room looks like a tomb. Let's have some light. (*He goes to table, lights oil lamp*) There—that's a bit more cheerful.

MRS. HOLMES: Now, let me take your coat and hat, Abe, and just seat yourself on the sofa where you'll get the benefit of the fire. (*She helps him to remove his coat and exits right with coat and hat.* LINCOLN *crosses to sofa and sits down with a sigh.* MR. HOLMES *seats himself on one side of table,* UNCLE ALEC *at other.* PATIENCE *remains standing at center.*)

MR. HOLMES: Well, I almost forgot. Abe, this is my daughter, Patience. (LINCOLN *rises from sofa;* PATIENCE *goes to him and extends her hand.*)

PATIENCE: How do you do, Mr. President?

LINCOLN: Hello, child. (*He stands off and looks at her.*) You're the image of your mother when she was your age.

PATIENCE (*Smiling*): I consider that a very pretty compliment, Mr. President.

UNCLE ALEC: Now don't go filling her with too much praise, Abe. She's the belle of Gettysburg now.

LINCOLN: I can understand that, Alec. Sit here beside me, child. (PATIENCE *sits beside him.*)

UNCLE ALEC: But she's a belle who's given her heart already.

LINCOLN: If I were a young bachelor I'd be sorry to hear that. Who is the lucky man, Patience?

PATIENCE (*Somewhat embarrassed*): Captain Robert Brent.

LINCOLN: Brent? (*He seems somewhat startled but recovers his composure quickly.*)

PATIENCE (*Eagerly*): Do you know him, Mr. President?

LINCOLN: No, child, but I should like to know a young man with such excellent taste in fiancées.

PATIENCE (*Lightly*): Another compliment—but it's I who have shown the good taste.

LINCOLN: I'm sure of it. With what division is your Captain Brent serving?

PATIENCE: I haven't heard from him for weeks, but he was with General Grant at Vicksburg.

MR. HOLMES: He's a fine young fellow, Abe. Salt of the earth.

UNCLE ALEC (*Gloomily*): That's the trouble. All our fine young fellows have become so much cannon fodder.

LINCOLN: I share your sorrow, Alec. War is a terrible thing.

UNCLE ALEC: It's a wasteful thing —and no good ever came of it.

LINCOLN: God knows I tried to prevent it.

MR. HOLMES: Of course you did, Abe. Don't mind Alec. He always looks on the dark side of things.

UNCLE ALEC (*In sepulchral tones*): It's a dark world.

MRS. HOLMES (*Entering from right*): The dinner is coming along nicely. I hope you like a good roast of beef, Abe.

LINCOLN: Myra, there's nothing I like better.

MR. HOLMES: Back in the old days in Springfield, I remember you used to like it rare.

LINCOLN: I still do. Mary, though, likes it well done. We're rather like Jack Spratt and his wife. You remember he could eat no fat; she could eat no lean.

UNCLE ALEC: I'm not surprised. When two human beings agree on anything, it's a sort of minor miracle.

MRS. HOLMES: My, you're gloomier than ever today, Alec.

UNCLE ALEC: It's a gloomy world we live in.

PATIENCE (*Laughing*): But Uncle Alec, why try to make it gloomier?

MRS. HOLMES: Where's Johnny?

PATIENCE: He's not feeling well, Mother—so he went to his room.

MR. HOLMES: He's getting to be a real problem.

MRS. HOLMES: Things certainly are serious when he's willing to miss a meal. He has always eaten everything that wasn't nailed down.

UNCLE ALEC: My advice is to let the boy alone.

LINCOLN: How old is your Johnny?

MRS. HOLMES: Fourteen—but quite grown up for his age.

MR. HOLMES: Too grown up. He wants to enlist.

UNCLE ALEC: You see what your war does to the young, Abe. Gives them all the wrong ideas and foolish notions that blood and battle are heroic things.

LINCOLN (*Gently*): It isn't *my* war, Alec. It's everybody's.

UNCLE ALEC: Well, it certainly isn't a war that belongs to a boy of fourteen.

LINCOLN: I agree with you there.

MRS. HOLMES: Johnny will be all right. (*Attempting to change the subject*) I enjoyed your speech, Abe.

LINCOLN: It was short, anyway—and that's always a blessing for the listeners.

UNCLE ALEC: By the time that Hale was finished, there wasn't much time left. Why, that man spoke for two hours!

LINCOLN: Hale is a great orator. I suspect his speech will go down in history.

MR. HOLMES: You said a lot in a few words, though. That's always more difficult to do than to say nothing in a long speech.

LINCOLN: Well, you remember what Franklin said once in one of his letters. He apologized for its length, but said he didn't have time to write a brief one.

MRS. HOLMES: Yours was the better speech, Abe. There was something almost Biblical about it.

LINCOLN: Thank you, Myra. I wrote it on the train coming to Gettysburg. I'm so busy these days that I have to squeeze in all my extra duties whenever I can.

PATIENCE: I wish I'd heard you, Mr. President. I came home, though, while Mr. Hale was speaking.

LINCOLN (*Laughing*): You showed good sense, child. Listening to speeches can be mighty tedious.

MRS. HOLMES: Sam, you ought to go in to begin carving the roast. And don't forget—the rarest piece is for Abe.

LINCOLN: I see I have a powerful friend in this household.

MR. HOLMES: Powerful is right, Abe. (*Rising*) You can see who runs this family. We'll call you when things are ready. (*He and* MRS. HOLMES *exit right.*)

LINCOLN (*Sighing*): What a pleasure it is to be able to relax with good friends—even if only for a little while.

UNCLE ALEC: Nobody can relax much these days. There's too much blood in the air.

PATIENCE: Will the war last much longer, Mr. President?

LINCOLN: I don't think so, child. The South's back was broken here at Gettysburg. Their soldiers are brave and their leaders able, but they can't hold on much longer. No, it's not the war I'm worried about—it's what will come after. All the bitterness and the ruin—

UNCLE ALEC: And what bitterness and what ruin!

PATIENCE: Personally, I think the country will be in good hands.

LINCOLN: Thank you, my dear. I hope you're right. But I'll need help—so much help. (MAGGIE *appears.*)

MAGGIE: Dinner is served, Mr. President. (MAGGIE *drops a curtsy and exits, flustered.*)

PATIENCE (*Laughing*): Maggie is very excited today.

LINCOLN: Sam says she's the best cook in Pennsylvania.

PATIENCE: And she is.

UNCLE ALEC (*Rising*): Let's hope the excitement hasn't made her lose her skill.

PATIENCE: Always the pessimist, Uncle Alec.

UNCLE ALEC: It's a pessimistic world.

LINCOLN: Go in, my dear, with your uncle. I'll join you in a moment. I have a dispatch here in my pocket. It was handed to me at the cemetery, and I haven't had a chance to read it. I won't be long.

PATIENCE: Your arm, then, Uncle Alec. (UNCLE ALEC *offers her his arm, and they go toward right.*) You promise to hurry, Mr. President?

LINCOLN (*Smiling*): I promise. (UNCLE ALEC *and* PA-
TIENCE *exit.* LINCOLN *walks slowly to center, takes paper
from his pocket, and begins to read it*). I'm sure I've
heard that name. Let's see now. (*Reading from paper*)
"Missing in action—Addison, Harold M.; Ayers, Daniel
B.; Bell, Raymond C.; Brent, Robert D.—" (*He places
his hands over his eyes and shakes his head.*) Poor child.
(*He straightens his shoulders and walks toward right.*)
I'm ready for that roast beef! (*He exits right as the cur-
tains close.*)

*　　*　　*

SCENE 2

TIME: *Around midnight, the same day.*
SETTING: *Same as Scene 1.*
AT RISE: *The stage is in semidarkness.* LINCOLN *is seated on
the sofa, a shawl around his shoulders. He is dressed, but
is wearing carpet slippers.* JOHNNY *enters stealthily from
left. He is dressed for outdoors and carries a valise in one
hand, a piece of paper in the other. He comes to the table
at center and lights the oil lamp. He sets valise on floor
and begins to write on the paper.* LINCOLN *has turned
and is watching* JOHNNY. JOHNNY *finishes writing, props
the paper up against the Bible and is about to put out the
lamp, when* LINCOLN *speaks.*

LINCOLN: You must be Johnny.
JOHNNY (*Very startled and jumping back in surprise*): Mr.
President!
LINCOLN (*Smiling reassuringly*): I see I'm not the only
fellow in the house who's bothered by insomnia. I often
get up at night and wander around. I've been sitting
here for half an hour—just thinking.

JOHNNY (*Gulping, but speaking firmly*): It's not that I couldn't sleep. I'm leaving home.

LINCOLN (*Rising and coming to center*): Leaving home?

JOHNNY: Yes, Mr. President. (*Proudly*) I'm going to enlist in the Union Army.

LINCOLN (*Gravely*): Aren't you a little young for soldiering? I heard today that you're fourteen.

JOHNNY (*Very seriously*): But you'll notice, Mr. President, that I'm big for my age. I can pass for sixteen, or seventeen—or even eighteen.

LINCOLN: Yes, I expect you could. (*Pausing*) So you've decided you want to do your bit for the cause?

JOHNNY (*Proudly*): Yes, sir!

LINCOLN (*Sitting at right of table*): Well, Johnny, it's a noble idea. I did some soldiering myself once. Sit down for a moment. (JOHNNY *sits at left of table*) That was more than thirty years ago—in the Black Hawk War.

JOHNNY: Did you enjoy it, sir?

LINCOLN: Can't say that I did. I had five weeks of it, and do you know what it is that I remember best about the entire campaign?

JOHNNY (*Eagerly*): What?

LINCOLN (*Smiling*): The mosquitoes.

JOHNNY (*Grinning in spite of himself*): Mosquitoes?

LINCOLN: Yes, sir. They'd descend on us in droves when we were camped for the night. I still have some of the scars of combat. They were far peskier than the Indians.

JOHNNY: That couldn't have been very pleasant.

LINCOLN: Pleasant! Why those infernal creatures seemed to know instinctively the most sensitive parts of a man's skin. They were highly-educated mosquitoes. No, Johnny, soldiering has its defects.

JOHNNY: But a man ought to fight for his country, Mr. President.

LINCOLN: Of course.

JOHNNY: So you see why I just have to enlist. It's my duty.

LINCOLN: But there are many ways of fighting for one's nation, and they're not all in the actual battle line.

JOHNNY (*Puzzled*): Many ways?

LINCOLN: Yes, a great many.

JOHNNY: I don't think I understand.

LINCOLN: It's very simple, really. Just think, for example, of what war has done to our country for the past two years. We've seen brother fighting against brother; we've reaped a harvest of bitterness and ruin and lack of trust. (*Looking intently at* JOHNNY) I'm going to reveal something important to you, Johnny. Can you keep a secret?

JOHNNY (*Firmly*): Yes, sir!

LINCOLN: The war won't go on much longer. The South is on the brink of defeat, and I thank God that the slaughter and savagery will soon be over. But the most important task lies ahead; it's to unite the nation and to restore it to good health and prosperity. That is the most difficult and most significant task before us. You see that, don't you, Johnny?

JOHNNY: Yes, I do.

LINCOLN: In other words, the nation is going to need men of honor, intelligence, and integrity, men of unselfish patriotism—men of education, Johnny. (JOHNNY *nods, intent on every word.* LINCOLN *rises.*) Do you know the Book of Ecclesiastes, Johnny?

JOHNNY: Of course. It's in the Bible. I studied it in Sunday school.

LINCOLN (*Picks up Bible from table, opens it, and searches for the passage he wants*): Listen, Johnny. "To every thing there is a season, and a time to every purpose under the heavens. A time to be born, and a time to die; a time to plant, and a time to pluck up that which is planted; a time to kill, and a time to heal; a time to break down, and a time to build up; a time to weep, and a time to laugh; a time to mourn, and a time to dance; . . . a time to love, and a time to hate; a time of war, and a time of peace." (*Looking up*) Do you know what those wise words mean, Johnny?

JOHNNY: I think so. (*Slowly*) I suppose they say there's a time and place for everything. (*Pauses*) And that a man's duty is to recognize what needs to be done and do it.

LINCOLN: That's it exactly. And you noted, "A time to break down, and a time to build up." We're coming to the building-up time, Johnny—and we'll need builders.

JOHNNY: But how does all this—

LINCOLN (*Seating himself*): I want you to be one of the builders. (*Smiling*) You know I have a right to give you orders.

JOHNNY: Of course you have, sir.

LINCOLN: After all, I am Commander-in-Chief of the armed forces that you want so much to enlist in. My orders are these—keep on with your education. Go to Harvard as your father desires. We'll need men of your type, Johnny, in the great rebuilding that lies ahead. Will you take those orders from your Commander-in-Chief?

JOHNNY (*Rising and smiling happily*): Of course I will! (*He salutes briskly.* LINCOLN *returns the salute gravely.*)

LINCOLN: From now on, consider yourself under my personal orders.

JOHNNY (*Very happily*): Yes, Mr. President.

LINCOLN: There's one other matter in which you can perform a great service.

JOHNNY (*Expectantly*): Yes, sir?

LINCOLN: I received a dispatch at the cemetery this afternoon. It's the latest list of those missing in action. One of the names on that list is known to you—Captain Robert Brent.

JOHNNY (*Startled*): Bob!

LINCOLN: Yes, your sister's fiancé.

JOHNNY: Oh, golly, he was such a wonderful fellow! We were great friends.

LINCOLN (*Rising and coming over to pat* JOHNNY's *shoulder sympathetically*): Don't lose hope though, Johnny. I haven't informed your sister or your family. Heaven knows they'll hear soon enough through regular channels. Remember, too, that many of those who are listed as missing often turn up hale and hearty. I've known it to happen many times.

JOHNNY (*Sadly*): But sometimes no one ever hears again from them.

LINCOLN: That's true. And all this gives you a task that will require your best efforts. When your sister hears about Captain Brent, she'll need all the help and hope and encouragement she can possibly get. That will be a man-sized job. Are you still willing to accept orders from your Commander-in-Chief?

JOHNNY: Yes, sir.

LINCOLN: Then I want you to do what you can for her. Be with her a great deal. Try to keep her from brooding. Try to make her hopeful that Captain Brent may be found. Do all you can to ease her sorrow. It won't be easy.

JOHNNY: No, it won't.

LINCOLN: It will require courage and tact and unselfishness. (*Smiling gently*) But I think you're equal to it.

JOHNNY: Thank you, Mr. President.

LINCOLN: And don't forget your other orders. They're important, too. Educate yourself. Make yourself worthy of and capable of helping in the task of reconstruction that lies before us. I said something this afternoon at the cemetery that expresses fairly clearly what I mean. (*Pauses*) Let's see if I can remember the words. "It is for us, the living, rather to be dedicated here to the unfinished work which they who fought here have thus far so nobly advanced. It is rather for us to be here dedicated to the great task remaining before us—that from these honored dead we take increased devotion to that cause for which they gave the last full measure of devotion; that we here highly resolve that these dead shall not have died in vain; that this nation, under God, shall have a new birth of freedom; and that government of the people, by the people, for the people, shall not perish from the earth."

JOHNNY (*Earnestly*): I won't forget, sir.

LINCOLN: You see, your time has come. The tasks and the season in which you must perform them are here—as the Good Book said. (*There is the sound of voices from upstairs.*)

JOHNNY: Gosh, that sounds like Mother and Father! What will they say when they see me?

LINCOLN: Let me help you, in return for the help you're giving me. Let's have that coat. (*He helps* JOHNNY *to remove his coat*) And that valise. (*He picks up valise from floor*) And this note. (*Takes note from table and slips it into his pocket. He then goes to sofa and puts valise and coat behind it.*) Now come over here, and sit beside me. (LINCOLN *seats himself on sofa.* JOHNNY *crosses to sofa and also sits.* MR. *and* MRS. HOLMES *enter hurriedly at left. They are wearing dressing gowns over their night clothes.*)

MRS. HOLMES: Oh, it's you, Abe.

MR. HOLMES: We heard voices down here, and we wondered who it could be.

LINCOLN: Nothing to worry about. I couldn't sleep, so I came down to sit for a while, Johnny dressed and came down to keep me company—a very neighborly gesture on his part.

MRS. HOLMES: I think it's about time that both of you got to bed. You always were a night owl, Abe.

MR. HOLMES (*Chuckling*): You see, Abe, I told you who runs this family.

LINCOLN: And we couldn't be in better hands, Sam. Myra's right. Johnny and I both need sleep. To bed, Johnny— (*Smiling*)—and that's an order.

JOHNNY (*Rising and returning the smile*): Yes, Mr. President. (*He walks toward left, then looks back at the place where the coat and valise are concealed.*)

LINCOLN: And don't worry, Johnny. I'll take care of everything.

JOHNNY (*At left door, saluting briskly*): Yes, sir. (*He exits as* LINCOLN *returns the salute.*)

MRS. HOLMES: I haven't seen him look so happy for days.

LINCOLN: He's a fine boy, Myra—with good stuff in him. We had a splendid talk.

MR. HOLMES: Since no highwaymen have invaded our home, we may as well get to bed.

MRS. HOLMES: Right, Sam. (MR. *and* MRS. HOLMES *move toward left.*) Coming, Abe?

LINCOLN: I'll be up in just a minute. I think I can really sleep now. Good night.

MR. *and* MRS. HOLMES: Good night, Abe. (*They exit left.* LINCOLN *rises from sofa, gets coat and valise from their hiding place, and goes toward left. He pauses at the table at center, pats the Bible affectionately, and turns off the oil lamp. He goes to the door at left, pauses, and smiles thoughtfully.*)

LINCOLN: "A time to break down and a time to build up." Wise words. (*He exits left as the curtains close.*)

THE END

Young Abe Lincoln

by Aileen Fisher

Characters

MRS. SARAH BUSH LINCOLN, *stepmother of Abraham Lincoln, as an old woman*
HARRIET CHAPMAN, *her granddaughter, about 35*
AUGUSTUS CHAPMAN, *Harriet's husband*
MRS. LINCOLN, *as a young woman*
ELIZABETH (BETSY) ⎫
MATILDA (TILDA) ⎬ *her daughters, as children*
JOHN, *her young son*
ABRAHAM LINCOLN, *11*
SARAH (SAIRY), *his sister, 13*
JOHN ROMINE
HANNAH GENTRY
WILLIAM JONES
DAVE TURNHAM
BETSY, *as Mrs. Dennis Hanks*
ELIZABETH CRAWFORD
SHERIFF
ABRAHAM LINCOLN, *at 20*
CROWD, *partly offstage*

TIME: *February 1, 1861.*
SETTING: *Sitting room in the home of Augustus and Harriet Chapman in Charleston, Illinois.*

AT RISE: *A dimly lit stage. In a rocking chair near the window at one side sits* MRS. LINCOLN, *stepmother of Abraham Lincoln, rocking quietly. She is 73 years old. There is a candle on the table.* HARRIET *comes in carrying a candle.*

HARRIET: Aren't you going back to bed, Grandma? Uncle Abe wouldn't have wanted you to get up so early to say goodbye unless he thought you'd go back to bed.

MRS. LINCOLN: Don't you worry about me, Harriet. I fancy sitting here quiet, thinking about Abe. (*Rocks slowly*) Seems like just the day before yesterday I laid eyes on him for the first time . . . lanky, hungry-looking ten-year-old, with such a shock of black hair you'd think the crows nested in it. (*Chuckles*) Had a time getting Abe to let me tidy him up, I did!

HARRIET: The house is cold, Grandma, and it's a long time till sunup . . .

MRS. LINCOLN: I'll keep warm, wrapped in the black wool shawl Abe gave me . . . (*Dreamily*) My, but he was a forlorn tyke when first I saw him, Harriet, all those years ago. He'd not had a mother for more than a year, and his sister Sairy, bless her heart, could not take her mother's place; she was only twelve. Now Sairy's long been dead and buried . . . and Abe's to be President of a nation that's splitting from one end to the other over the slavery question. Queer, how things work out.

HARRIET: He is probably at the station by now, after stopping to pick up Mr. Marshall.

MRS. LINCOLN: I regret Abe having to catch such an early train. He had such a full day yesterday . . . driving out to Tilda's to get me and all. And then talking to the crowd at the Town Hall last night. He must be all tuckered out.

HARRIET: Not Uncle Abe. He's used to crowds and making speeches.

MRS. LINCOLN: Everybody's so bound and determined to shake hands with the President-elect of the United States! Think of him coming all the way from Springfield just to say goodbye to his folks before going to Washington.

HARRIET: He came mostly to say goodbye to you, Grandma. You've always had a foremost place in his heart. His own mother couldn't have meant more to him after the mothering you have given him all the years.

MRS. LINCOLN (*Slowly*): Abe's never forgotten me . . . even though his pappy's been dead for ten years now. He was ever a good boy, Abe was. I can say what scarcely one mother in a thousand can say—he never gave me a cross word or look. And I never gave him a cross word in all my life. He seemed like my own flesh and blood, every bit as much as my own son, your Uncle Johnny. Maybe more.

HARRIET: I know.

MRS. LINCOLN: Be seven years this spring since Johnny died. And here's Abe elected President of the United States. They grew up together, those two boys, but how differently their lives worked out. Just seems Abe was born with character, somehow, and a destiny.

HARRIET: There never was anybody like Uncle Abe. I know, after living that year with him and his family in Springfield when I was eighteen.

MRS. LINCOLN: Can't help wondering sometimes how it all happened, Abe getting so famous and all. He'll ever be a lad to me, though . . . for that's how I knew him best, back there at Pigeon Creek in Spencer County, Indiana. Those were good days we had in Tom Lincoln's cabin . . . eight of us in the one big room and loft . . .

Tom and me, and my two girls and my boy John D., and Abe and Sairy, and cousin Dennis Hanks . . . your pappy, he turned out to be. Those were hard-working days, but we had our good times along the way.

HARRIET: Gus ought to be back from the station before long. (*Steps to window*) It's still so dark out I can't see a thing.

MRS. LINCOLN: I reckon the train's late more often than not. And he'll have the horse to put away.

HARRIET: You sure you're all right, Grandma? Sitting up so long?

MRS. LINCOLN: Fit as a fiddle . . . though a few of the strings are beginning to sag a bit, now I'm along in years.

HARRIET: Oh, I have been meaning to ask you . . . what do you think of Uncle Abe's new whiskers?

MRS. LINCOLN: To my mind they become him, though I had to get used to them at first. They make him look more distinguished, don't you think? Though I always did say Abe had a fine strong face.

HARRIET: You should hear the unflattering things some of the newspapers have to say about Uncle Abe's looks.

MRS. LINCOLN: Sometimes I reckon it's just as well I never learned how to read. (HARRIET *gets another shawl, covers* MRS. LINCOLN'*s legs.*) What's there about a lad makes him timber for the Presidency, I wonder? What set Abe apart even when he was a boy? (*Pauses*)

Partly his hunger and thirst for learning. I never saw anything like it. How he pounced on the few books I brought along from E-town, Kentucky, when his pappy fetched me to be his second wife! You would think I'd brought bricks of solid gold. And I was as bad as the young 'uns, wanting to hear Abe tell about what he read. We never got work done so fast as when Abe was set to tell us a story at the end of it . . . (*Candle out, spot on other side of stage.* MRS. LINCOLN, *at 32, comes in with her daughter* BETSY, *14. Their arms are full of blankets and pillows.*)

MRS. LINCOLN: There, Betsy, that's done. I always say there's nothing fresher than getting bedding aired and pillows out in the sun. You can put the boys' bedding there by the peg ladder. Abe can hand it up to Johnny when they come in.

BETSY: Abe can almost reach it up to the loft himself, he has such long arms.

MRS. LINCOLN: He's stretching out, Abe is. Here, give me a hand folding these blankets. (*They work around.*) Reckon the young 'uns will be rounding up soon to hear that story Abe promised. I'm good and ready to listen myself.

BETSY: Nobody can tell a story the way Abe can.

MRS. LINCOLN: Sairy says there's not a book for miles around he's not borrowed and read and been careful to return . . . and him only eleven. Reckon he'll turn out to be a schoolmaster or a preacher man.

BETSY: If he's heard a sermon once, he's heard it for all time, Mama. He comes home and speaks it word for word to Johnny and us girls.

SAIRY (*Hurrying in*): Butter's churned and worked down as much as I can without some more spring water. The bucket's plumb empty.

MRS. LINCOLN: Abe and Johnny should fetch some more. (JOHN *appears at door in time to hear.*)

JOHN: Fetch more water? (*Flops down*) I'm tireder than a dog chasing a rabbit. Been dragging and piling brush all afternoon at the new field. Why don't we get a well at the house like the Grigsbys and Gordons?

SAIRY: Pappy's tried several holes but the water petered out.

MRS. LINCOLN: We'll get a well in good time. Meanwhile the spring water's smart tasty and cool.

JOHN: And nearly a mile away!

SAIRY: Reckon I could use rain water from the barrel to finish working down the butter?

MRS. LINCOLN: Best not, Sairy. The boys will go to the spring in a bit.

TILDA (*Entering, with basket*): Here's enough greens to last a week.

MRS. LINCOLN: Wait till you see how they cook down, Tilda. Where's Abe?

TILDA: Still chopping. Just about finished, though. (*Giggles*) I notice every time he rests he's got a book handy to rest his eyes on! Maybe that's why he's not here yet.

ABE (*At door*): Who says I'm not here?

JOHN: We feared you'd get so taken up with your work, you'd forget about telling us a story!

ABE (*Grinning*): When it comes to working, I'm a good match for you, Johnny! Well, does anybody have any idea what's the smartest bird?

SAIRY: The smartest bird? I'd say it was one that could *sing*.

TILDA: Uncle Chris in E-town always said a goose was the smartest bird, though most people say "silly as a goose."

BETSY: Your cousin Dennis thinks a crow is smart, Abe. Remember him saying how the crows sit around watching where every kernel of corn is planted? Then they peck them out without wasting time, when nobody's looking.

TILDA: Betsy's always quoting Dennis.

ABE: Seems Mr. Aesop rates crows both dumb and smart. (*Sits on stool.* MRS. LINCOLN *and girls take out knitting or sewing.* JOHN *sprawls on floor.*) Take the time a sly old fox saw a crow fly off with a piece of cheese.

JOHNNY: Where would a crow get a piece of cheese?

ABE: Reckon he snitched it from the table when the window was open.

SAIRY: I'm glad Pappy cut out a window in the cabin before he heard *that* story.

ABE: Anyway, the crow flew off to a tree with the cheese. The fox was hungry and he wanted that cheese, but foxes aren't noted for climbing trees, as you know. So the fox had to think of something else. He sat there at the foot of the tree and said, "Good morning, crow. How fine you look up there! How glossy your feathers are, how bright your eye. I don't know when I have seen a finer bird. Surely your voice must surpass other birds', too. Let me hear you sing. Then I will know for certain that you are the queen of birds." So the crow began to caw . . .

SAIRY: Oh! When it opened its mouth, it dropped the cheese!

ABE: That's right. Dropped the cheese in front of the fox, at which the fox gave a sly smile and said, "In exchange for your cheese, here is a piece of advice: Never trust flatterers."

MRS. LINCOLN: Goodness, I should think not.

ABE: So, you see, Betsy, in spite of what Dennis says, all crows are not smart. But some of them are, right enough. Like the one that was half-dead from thirst . . .

JOHN: Why didn't he take a drink?

ABE: He was away from home, the weather had been hot and dry, and he didn't know where to find water. He looked this way and that, and finally he found an old pitcher with a little water in the bottom. He could perch on the rim of the pitcher and see the water, but he couldn't reach it. Time and again he tried and failed. Then he got an idea. He began to gather pebbles . . .

JOHN: Pebbles?

ABE: One by one he dropped them in the pitcher. The more pebbles he put in, the higher up the water came . . . until finally it was high enough for him to drink. It all goes to show that "little by little does the trick." (*Blackout. Spotlight moves back to* MRS. LINCOLN *and* HARRIET *sitting near window by candlelight.*)

MRS. LINCOLN: Abe was like that crow, Harriet. Pigeon Creek was like that pitcher with a little water in the bottom. Abe walked his legs off looking for pebbles, you might say . . . borrowing a book here, a book there, slowly and surely filling himself up with learning. If there was ever a boy set on finding things out, it was Abe.

HARRIET: And never forgetting what he read. That's the surprising thing to me. After all these years Uncle Abe remembers those old stories. He's ever using bits of them to illustrate a point.

MRS. LINCOLN: Always spilling over, he was . . . telling us what he read, explaining things, asking questions, thinking out loud, you might say. Many's the time he'd come in and sit around talking things over with me . . . till I had to remind him his pappy had a calculating eye for the work done in a day. You've heard it all many times from your mammy and pappy, of course.

HARRIET: They never get over talking about Uncle Abe, recalling things, especially now he's famous.

MRS. LINCOLN: Learning and pondering, that's how Abe grew up. And there was another trait always struck me about him. He had a streak of kindness unusual for a boy . . . compassion, I reckon you'd call it. I don't mean he wasn't full of mischief on occasion, poking fun and playing for a laugh. But he'd not do mean things like most young 'uns . . . thoughtless, hurtful things. Abe had respect for life wherever he found it. He'd never go hunting with his pappy or his cousin Dennis or the other boys . . . not after the first wild turkey he shot and saw quivering in the grass. He'd not lift a hand against a critter to harm it. I recall Sairy coming home from school one day ahead of the others . . . (*Candle out. Spotlight on side of stage.* Mrs. Lincoln, *as a young woman, and* Betsy, *about 14, are working around when* Sairy *bursts in, half-crying.*)

Sairy: They'll hurt him! I'm feared they'll hurt him!

Mrs. Lincoln: Hurt who, honey?

Betsy: What's happened?

Sairy: It's Abe. He's the only one standing up for the turtle.

Mrs. Lincoln: Catch your breath, Sairy, and tell us what's happened. Where're Johnny and the others?

Sairy: They're watching. I couldn't stand it. "Don't give in, Abe Lincoln," I told him, and came on home. But if he won't give in, the boys'll pile on him and pummel him hard.

Betsy: Whatever for?

Sairy: Nat Grigsby found a turtle just before school started again at noon. He built a little pen around it out of stove wood, so it couldn't get away. Then after school Billy Grigsby said why not put live coals on the turtle's back to see what it would do. All the boys were for doing it except Abe.

Mrs. Lincoln: Johnny, too?

Sairy: Johnny said he'd bet the turtle would jump around like mad.

Betsy: What'd Abe say?

Sairy: Said the turtle had a right to live, like anyone else. Said to leave it alone, it wasn't harming anything. Said life was something nobody could explain and nobody on earth could create.

Mrs. Lincoln: He's right.

Sairy: Abe tried to keep the boys from starting a fire to get the coals, but they went ahead, anyway. He just stood there in front of the turtle, his legs spread apart, protecting it. I could not bear to watch . . .

MRS. LINCOLN: Abe's big and strong for his age. And he's more than that, Sairy. He's persuasive. He has a way of talking . . . so I count on him trying words before fists. He'll win one way or the other.

BETSY: Put coals on a turtle's back! I'm glad I quit going to school if that's all they have in their heads.

SAIRY: Seven or eight boys against just Abe and the turtle . . . (*She takes the broom and begins to sweep.*) Reckon I'd best keep busy so my fears won't run away with me.

MRS. LINCOLN: Don't fret yourself, Sairy. Abe always stands up for what he believes in, and he's not been hurt yet that I recollect.

BETSY: Dennis says Abe's going to get somewhere some day if he just keeps on the way he's started.

MRS. LINCOLN: He's got a knack of winning folks over, Abe has. You ask me, after today nobody's going to think again of putting coals on a turtle's back.

SAIRY: Oh, I hope you are right, Mama. But you didn't see how set and stubborn Billy and the others were. (*Goes to door and looks out*) I'll be glad when I see Abe coming home alive and whole. (*They work around in silence. Soon voices are heard offstage.*)

BETSY: That must be them now. (*Runs to look*) Abe's a-striding along lively as ever, Sairy. (SAIRY *hurries to look. In a moment* ABE, JOHN, *and* TILDA *come in talking.*)

TILDA: Wasn't he scared stiff when he saw the tracks in the sand, Abe?

JOHN: What'd he do then, after he found the man Friday?

ABE: That's as far as I've got. You'll have to wait till I get a chance to read some more.

JOHN: Wish there was a place to get shipwrecked around *here.*

SAIRY: You all right, Abe?

ABE: Me?

SAIRY: They didn't pummel you?

ABE: Pummel me?

SAIRY: Where's the turtle?

ABE: Oh, the turtle. Wandering 'round happy as a clam, I reckon. It got a good start when I took the boys down to the creek to look for tracks.

JOHN (*Laughing*): The turtle! We clean forgot all about that old turtle, Sairy, when Abe started us off on Robinson Crusoe. (*Spot out, scene back to* MRS. LINCOLN *and* HARRIET *by candlelight.*)

HARRIET (*Going to window*): I'd think Gus would be back by now.

MRS. LINCOLN: Not if the train is late. They'll be standing around the station talking law and politics, law and politics. Abe's been interested in the both of them for a good long time. Ran for the State Legislature of Illinois when he was only twenty-three, Harriet.

HARRIET: I thought he was twenty-five when he went to the Legislature!

MRS. LINCOLN: He was . . . when he *went*. He lost the first election, though his own precinct was practically unanimous for him. Wasn't till two, three years after he went to the Legislature that he was admitted to the bar. But he knew a lot about the law long before that.

HARRIET: Pappy says he read the Statutes of Indiana inside out and upside down whilst you still lived at Pigeon Creek . . . practically learned the book by heart, including the Constitution and the Declaration of Independence.

MRS. LINCOLN: Used to declaim the Preamble to me, I recollect. Can't put my finger on when Abe first got interested in the law, though. His pappy always took it for granted' Abe would follow in his footsteps and be a carpenter and farmer. Abe's interests were different, though. But what chance had he of doing anything else? All in all, his schooling didn't amount to more than a year. He used to write verses, and essays on the American form of government and the need for preserving the Constitution, and he'd read them out to me when we were alone. But nobody in Spencer County, Indiana, could make a living that-a-way.

HARRIET: Or in Coles County, Illinois, either. Or Springfield.

MRS. LINCOLN: Even as a lad, Abe had a legal mind, you might say. Sairy used to tell how boys at school would come up to Abe to patch up their quarrels. He'd listen carefully to both sides, sort of peering around the problem, and come out with an answer agreeable to both.

HARRIET: And when he was getting on in his teens, he used to walk over to Rockport and borrow books from a lawyer there, didn't he? And listen to cases in court?

MRS. LINCOLN (*Nodding*): And when he was sixteen, seventeen he had a bit of firsthand experience with the law that must have given him food for thought. He was summoned to court.

HARRIET: Uncle Abe was? I didn't know that. Why, that's the next thing to being arrested, isn't it?

MRS. LINCOLN: Yes, he was summoned to court. He'd gone down to work at a place near Troy, where the Anderson River flows into the Ohio. First time he'd been away from home . . . and he was gone nigh to six months. Seems Abe built himself a scow, and in his spare time he'd row passengers out to packet boats on the Ohio River. He made pretty good money for those days. But two brothers who ran a ferry nearby claimed that under the law they had the ferry rights across the river. So they had Abe brought before a justice of the peace . . . for toting passengers. Abe tried his own case, knowing he faced a heavy fine if he lost. Seems he pointed out to the judge he only took passengers to the middle of the river, not *across* the river . . . so he wasn't infringing on anybody's right. And the judge held with Abe and dismissed the charge.

HARRIET: Sounds just like Uncle Abe even now.

MRS. LINCOLN: But I reckon the first really big case Abe settled was the case of the old gray goose.

HARRIET: When was that, Grandma?

MRS. LINCOLN: Back at Pigeon Creek, the year before we moved to Illinois.

HARRIET: The year before Uncle Abe came of age?

MRS. LINCOLN: Round about then. A body'd never suppose a silly old goose could make so much trouble.

HARRIET: I don't see how a goose *could* make any trouble.

MRS. LINCOLN: It happened two of our neighbors each had a flock of geese. We had all lived as neighbors a good many years, peaceful-like, sharing each other's pleasures and trials, the way country folk do. Then one day John Carter missed a fat old goose. When he passed Tom Barrett's the next day, he swore he saw his goose in Barrett's flock. The two men got to disputing . . . and you know how such things go. Hot words . . . ugly charges . . .

Well, it got so the whole neighborhood began taking sides. Got so bad the case finally went to court, to be settled the first time a justice of the peace came around.

Abe had been away when the fracas started, taking a flatboat of produce down to New Orleans with Allen Gentry. Didn't get back till just before the old gray goose case was to come up. 'Course, everybody turned out to hear the case. (*Candle out, spot on other side of stage. Noise of people talking offstage.* JOHN ROMINE *and* HANNAH GENTRY *come in.*)

JOHN: I'm betting on Carter. Though how he's going to

prove it's *his* goose is a mystery to me. One goose is the same as the next one, any way you look at it.

HANNAH: That's where you're wrong, John. I've heard geese are different, just like folks. Wait till we're married and have a flock, and you'll see.

JOHN: We'll not have a flock of geese, Hannah. Not if they're going to make trouble. Where's that justice of the peace, anyway? He's long past due.

HANNAH: Must have been delayed along the way. (*Takes* JOHN's *arm*) Look, John, there's Abe . . . with all those men around him, laughing. He looks taller than ever, doesn't he though?

JOHN: His pappy always seemed like a big man to me . . . till Abe grew up. Let's mosey over. (*They go out as* WILLIAM JONES *and* DAVE TURNHAM *come in.*)

WILLIAM: What would Tom Barrett want with Carter's cantankerous old goose, anyway? It doesn't make sense. Besides, a man ought to be able to keep count of his own flock. If Tom says there's not an extry, he ought to know.

DAVE: But Carter is missing one, and he ought to know, too. Reckon it's not going to be an easy case to settle. Where's the judge?

WILLIAM: That's what everybody's asking. Feeling is running so high; if he doesn't turn up soon we're apt to see some fists flying. What's the commotion over there? Maybe the fighting's started already.

DAVE (*Craning his neck offstage to see*): No . . . it's Abe, Billy. Telling one of his stories.

WILLIAM: Abe! I heard he was back. Good old Abe! Say . . . that gives me an idea. Come along, I want to have a word with the sheriff . . . (*As they go out,* BETSY—*now Mrs. Dennis Hanks*—*and* ELIZABETH CRAWFORD *enter.*)

BETSY: Isn't it exciting? And all over a silly goose.

ELIZABETH: Not exciting, Betsy. I'd call it positively distressing. I fear something terrible will happen if the judge doesn't come soon.

BETSY: I can't help wondering what Abe thinks. Just home from his trip and caught in the midst of so much hard feeling!

ELIZABETH: I can imagine what he thinks. Look, Betsy, here comes the sheriff. Reckon he's going to get up on that box and say something? (SHERIFF, *followed by some of the* CROWD, *enters.* BETSY *and* ELIZABETH *draw back.* SHERIFF *mounts box, calls out.*)

SHERIFF: Ladies and gentlemen. We have been waiting here a good long time for the judge to come to settle a certain dispute. (CROWD *titters.*) And I say it's high time the dispute was settled. (CROWD *agrees.*) While we're waiting . . . it's been brought to my attention that one of our good neighbors has just returned from a flatboat trip to New Orleans . . . Abe Lincoln. (CROWD *applauds.*) Maybe Abe will have a few words to say to us whilst we're waiting. How about it, Abe? (CROWD *shouts as* ABE, *now 20, enters, nods to friends.* SHERIFF *gets down from box.* ABE *takes his place.*)

ABE (*Looking around*): Friends . . . I hope I can call you that . . . though it seems to be a word that's in dispute around here at the moment. (CROWD *titters.*) I gather that whilst I was away all the geese haven't been confined to barnyards. (*More titters*) I've heard of only one that's actually purported to have gone astray, but judging from the cackling roundabout I can't help thinking my information is incorrect.

Allen Gentry and I spent considerable time thinking about home whilst we were down south. Floating along on a slow-moving flatboat, a man has plenty of time to think. When we passed plantations with slaves working in the fields, and when we stopped at the slave market in New Orleans, we kept thinking how Spencer County,

Indiana, was a sensible, civilized place to live. Then, coming home, what'd I get into but the whole district with its feathers up and its neck stretched out . . . a-crackling and a-hissing. All on account of an old gray goose. Folks who were good friends when I left weren't speaking to each other any more. Neighbor was set against neighbor . . . like one of the feuds of old. And all on account of a silly old goose.

Now you're waiting for the judge to come and settle it all. Leastwise that's what you think you're waiting for. But how's the law a-going to settle anything in a case like this? If the judge rules for one side, is the other side going to give up its hard feelings? Is anything going to be settled?

Folks, I've read a few books and papers in my time (CROWD *titters.*), and I'm grateful to more than one of you for lending them to me. I recollect reading once in one of the books I borrowed that the winner in a lawsuit is often the real loser. Ponder that and you'll see it's true. Whichever side wins in this case gets an old gray goose. But what's a goose compared to the time that's been wasted a-bickering and arguing, and the hard feelings that have been scattered about like tares? What's an old gray goose compared to friends? I submit, folks, that "a pennyweight of love is worth a pound of law," as the maxim goes, and "he who goes to law for a sheep loses his cow."

There's another thing strikes me, looking at the case as an outsider. I recollect when I was a boy, we'd have occasional picnics here at the meetinghouse to celebrate some event like the Fourth of July or a wedding or a new preacher. Seems with more settlers coming into the district, those gatherings have been fewer and farther between.

Now what I'm thinking is this: Why don't we cook

the goose that's been causing all this trouble? Why don't we have ourselves a good old-fashioned picnic, with Tom Barrett and John Carter contributing the goose and the rest of us bringing something appropriate . . . like the sauce for the goose and the gander? (CROWD *applauds.*)

SHERIFF (*Interrupting*): I recommend we settle the goose case Abe's way . . . out of court! All those in favor say "Aye."

CROWD: Aye!

SHERIFF: Those opposed? (CROWD *is silent.*) The motion is carried for a community picnic, to cook the goose along with all the hard feelings flying back and forth. And I recommend we ask the judge to partake in the celebration when he puts in an appearance. (CROWD *shouts approval. Everyone wants to shake* ABE'S *hand. Spot out as candle is lighted again on other side of stage. Noise down.*)

HARRIET: Good for Uncle Abe! Who else would have thought of it? Oh, Grandma, if he could settle a case like that the first time he tried, surely he can settle the troubles facing our country today . . . with all the experience he's had in the meantime.

MRS. LINCOLN: Now he's faced with the biggest case of his life, Harriet. He'll need all his learning and all his compassion and strength and understanding to save the Union.

HARRIET: He can do it!

MRS. LINCOLN: But the states in the south have already started to break away. How many have seceded from the Union by now, Harriet?

HARRIET: Six . . . with Louisiana pulling out last week and Georgia the week before.

MRS. LINCOLN: And the trouble's only just started. Oh, how simple the old gray goose looks compared to this. But in a way it helped prepare Abe, I reckon. Everything helps prepare a man for the bigger things ahead. (*Door opens.* AUGUSTUS CHAPMAN *comes in.*)

AUGUSTUS: Still up, you two? You shouldn't have waited . . . the train was late.

HARRIET: We had a lot to talk about, Gus. Let me take your coat.

MRS. LINCOLN: Abe get off all right?

AUGUSTUS: He was in good spirits, Grandma Lincoln, talking to Tom Marshall and me and a few others gathered at the station. For all the problems on his mind, he still has some good stories up his sleeve.

MRS. LINCOLN: The next train he takes will be carrying him east, to Washington, D.C.

AUGUSTUS: Yes . . . he plans to leave Springfield on the eleventh, he said.

MRS. LINCOLN: The day before his birthday.

HARRIET: Come, Grandma. Now you know Uncle Abe's safe on the train, you'd best go back to bed. There's still a good while before sunup.

MRS. LINCOLN: You go, Harriet. You had a full and busy evening with all the family here for supper, and Abe leaving so early. I'm all right. Don't you worry about me.

HARRIET: Coming, Gus?

AUGUSTUS: In a bit. Want to warm my feet at the stove first. (HARRIET *goes out.*)

MRS. LINCOLN: Do you think he can do what's uppermost in his heart, Augustus?

AUGUSTUS: What do you mean, Grandma Lincoln?

MRS. LINCOLN: Preserve the Union.

AUGUSTUS: He can if anyone can. He'll make a great President. You'll be proud of him.

MRS. LINCOLN: He doesn't have to be President for me to be proud of him. I've been proud of Abe from the first, when he was just a gangly boy. (*A catch comes into her voice.*) Oh, I wish he hadn't been elected . . .

AUGUSTUS: You what?

MRS. LINCOLN: I've a feeling in my heart that something terrible will happen to him. I've a feeling I'll never see him again.

AUGUSTUS: Oh, come, Grandma. There are great days ahead for him. Not that the way will be easy . . . but Uncle Abe will bring us through. You're tired. You've been sitting up too long. Why don't you go back to bed for a while?

MRS. LINCOLN: No. You go, Augustus. I fancy sitting here thinking.

AUGUSTUS: Sure you're all right?

MRS. LINCOLN: Fit as a fiddle. (AUGUSTUS *goes out.* MRS. LINCOLN *rocks quietly, speaks slowly*) Where'd the years go? Seems like just the day before yesterday I laid eyes on Abe for the first time . . . lanky, hungry-looking ten-year-old, with such a shock of black hair you'd think the crows nested in it. . . . Can't help wondering sometimes how it all happened, Abe getting so famous and all. (*Curtain*)

THE END

The Valentine Tree

by Marjorie Barrows

Characters

JIGGERS, *the king's fool*
MADAM SNAP, *the fairy dressmaker*
SNIP, *her husband, the king's private secretary*
KING TWINKEM, *the fairy king*
TWINK ⎫
SQUINK ⎬ *elf Twinklets*
BLINK ⎭
JOAN, *a little girl*
FAIRIES

TIME: *Valentine Eve.*
SETTING: *The edge of a fairy wood. Gold hearts are blossoming on the Valentine Tree at the left and on the bushes in front of the screen at right. Two stools or tree stumps are on the green ground.*
AT RISE: *No one is on stage, but* FAIRIES *are heard singing in the distance.* JIGGERS' *head pops out from behind the screen, but pops back again when the* FAIRIES *come dancing in.*

FAIRIES (*Singing to the tune of "Maryland, My Maryland,"
and dancing joyously around the wood*):
Oh, come ye fairies, dance and sing,

Near the Tree of Valentines,
Dance and prance while bluebells ring,
By the Tree of Valentines;
Hearts that catch a rainbow gleam,
Sunset rose and gold will seem,
Twinkling in a fairy dream
On the Tree of Valentines! (*The* FAIRIES *dance off again.* JIGGERS *creeps stealthily out, on all fours, from behind the screen. He stops every now and then, holding a hand to his ear, and then begins searching the ground very excitedly.*)

JIGGERS: The silver penny! The silver penny! It must be here! I heard it tinkle as it fell. If I can only find it—I'll spoil the fairies' fun and ruin the Ball! Ah, here it is. The silver penny! The silver penny! (*He darts forward, clutches a silvery coin in his hand, holds it up before him and laughs softly. Then he creeps back behind the screen again, muttering to himself. Soon* MADAM SNAP *appears, sewing some tinsel on a white cheesecloth scarf, as she walks.*)

MADAM SNAP: Oh, dear, oh-dear-oh-dear-oh-dear! Oh, dear! (*She sits down, still sewing.*) It's all very well to have "heartistic" costumes for the Valentine Ball. Fairies *will* be fairies, I know. But what about *me?* Beeswings and butterflies! *I* have to make every single one of them, myself. Oh, dear, oh-dear-oh-dear-oh-dear, oh! (*She pricks her finger and puts it into her mouth. Then she blows a whistle that is hanging from a cord around her neck.* SNIP *saunters in holding a large book marked "Rhyming Dictionary" on the cover. He has several watches pinned to his clothes and strapped to his wrists.*)

SNIP (*Yawning elaborately*): Yes, my love?

MADAM SNAP (*Sewing as fast as she can*): Snip, what time is it?

SNIP (*Peering first at one watch and then at another*):

Seventy-three, no, sixty-nine, no, fifty-five, no, ninety-one blinks to sunset, my dear.

MADAM SNAP: Toadstools and tinklebells! Why *don't* you wind your watches? Here I am, Madam Snap, the fairy dressmaker who creates chic costumes for fastidious fairies—here *I* am sewing and sewing and sewing on all these "heartistic" gowns for the Valentine Ball, while *you,* my husband and the king's very private secretary, can't even give me the right time. Do you call that kind? Do you call that helpful?

SNIP (*Searching on the ground for something*): There, there, my love. Calm yourself. I have to write "heartistic" songs for the Ball, don't I? If there's going to be any Valentine Ball.

MADAM SNAP (*Dropping her jaw and her sewing*): Going to *be* any! Why, what do you mean?

SNIP (*Still searching on the ground*): Just what I say. If they can't find a Queen of Hearts, there won't be any Valentine Ball tonight.

MADAM SNAP: But Princess Pussywillow is beautiful and brave and loving. And she can compose a "heartistic" poem! Why won't she be chosen Queen of Hearts?

SNIP (*Scratching his left wing*): Haven't you heard? She's gone off to visit King Twinkem's mother-in-law, and she won't be back here in time.

MADAM SNAP: Don't scratch your wing, Snip. It's not polite. Well, with the silver penny, you and King Twinkem can summon another Queen of Hearts, can't you?

SNIP: Ye-es, if we can find the silver penny!

MADAM SNAP: Snip! You haven't— you haven't *lost* it?

SNIP (*Nodding in a bored fashion*): I suppose so. It must have slipped from my pocket. I only hope Jiggers won't find it.

MADAM SNAP (*Joining the search*): If that foolish Jiggers

finds it, he'll do something dreadfully silly with it, and
then there won't be a Valentine Ball tonight. Have you
looked in our shop for it? Don't scratch your wing!
(*They exit, and distant fairy music is heard.* JIGGERS
*creeps out from the screen, tossing the silver penny up
in the air and catching it again. He chuckles, then, and
dances and turns a somersault.*)

JIGGERS (*To a little homemade, singsong tune*):
Jiggers found
The silver penny;
Other fairies
Haven't any.
Now that they are
Through with it,
What shall Jiggers
Do with it?
What shall Jiggers
Do with it?
What—shall—Jiggers
Do—with—it? (*He throws himself down on the ground,
and tosses the penny from one hand to the other.*)
Shall he wish for
Bluebell tarts?
No, he'll try a
Queen of Hearts! (*He holds the penny up to his eye.*)
Queen of Hearts!
Queen—of—Hearts! (JOAN *enters, walking dreamily.*)

JOAN (*Sitting down and looking dreamily about her*):
First I came through the windless wood and over the
brook that whispers. Now I am here, and I feel so
fairylandish. It must be a dream.

JIGGERS: Fairylandish! Ho! Ho! Ho! Of course you do!

JOAN (*Whirling around and seeing him for the first time*):
Why, who are you?

JIGGERS (*Kicking his heels together as he rolls on the*

ground, laughing): Ho! Ho! Ho! This *is* a fairy wood. I'm Jiggers, the king's fool. Who are you?

JOAN: I'm just Joan.

JIGGERS: Well, now you're going to be the Queen of Hearts at the fairies' Valentine Ball. How'll you like that? Here, put this silver penny in your pocket—that way. (*He hands her the coin.*)

JOAN (*Dreamily*): The—Queen—of—Hearts—I'd love that. I'd—love— (*She closes her eyes.*)

JIGGERS: They'll find her when she wakes up. But they won't know she has the silver penny in her pocket *upside down!* Oh, what a joke! Ho! Ho! Ho! (*He prances out, laughing. Soon the* FAIRIES *enter and start to join hands for a dance. Then they discover* JOAN, *and draw back.*)

1ST FAIRY: Look! A little girl!

2ND FAIRY: She looks brave and beautiful!

3RD FAIRY: And kind!

1ST FAIRY: Perhaps she'll be our Queen of Hearts.

ALL: Our Queen of Hearts! (*They join hands and dance, singing the same fairy song that they sang before. Towards the end,* JOAN *wakes up and watches them.*)

1ST FAIRY: She's awake now. See?

2ND FAIRY: Sh! Here come King Twinkem and his Twinklets!

3RD FAIRY: And Snip and Madam Snap. (KING TWINKEM, *the* TWINKLETS, SNIP, *and* MADAM SNAP *enter.*)

KING TWINKEM: You can't find the silver penny, Snip? How careless of you! Oh, dear me!

TWINK: Oh—

SQUINK: Dear—

BLINK: Me!

KING TWINKEM: The Twinkems never lose their silver pennies. They're always careful. (*He sees* JOAN.) Hello! What's all that?

TWINK: What's—

SQUINK: All—

BLINK: That?

SNIP (*Scratching his wing and yawning*): The creature seems to be a little girl, Your Majesty.

MADAM SNAP (*Frowning and pulling* SNIP's *arm*): Oh, Your Majesty, won't she do for the Queen of Hearts?

KING TWINKEM: She might. But it's all most irregular. The Twinkems never have little girls in their woods. Let's investigate.

TWINK: Let's—

SQUINK: Inves—

BLINK: —Tigate!

KING TWINKEM: Come here, little girl. Who are you? How did you get here?

JOAN (*Shyly*): Please, Your Majesty, I'm Joan. I got lost in a windless wood while chasing a wild dog away from some little bunnies.

1ST FAIRY: She's beautiful.

2ND FAIRY: She's brave.

3RD FAIRY: She's kind.

SNIP (*Pulling* KING TWINKEM's *sleeve and whispering loudly in his ear*): Why don't you ask her to make up a valentine rhyme? She must do that, you know, if she's to be Queen of Hearts.

KING TWINKEM: Stop tickling my ear!

MADAM SNAP: She must be Queen of Hearts, Your Majesty. We can't have all my "heartistic" costumes go to waste.

KING TWINKEM: Oh, all right. See here, little girl, we'll make you our Queen of Hearts tonight, before you go home, if you can make up a nice valentine about me. Think you can?

TWINK: Think—

SQUINK: You—

BLINK: Can?

SNIP (*Handing her a book*): This rhyming dictionary ought to help you.

JOAN (*Looking through the book*): My thoughts feel tangled, but I'll try. (*They all stand waiting.* JIGGERS' *grinning face pops out from behind the screen to show he's waiting, too.*) How's this? (*Recites*)
Twinkem, be my valentine,
Fat old pumpkin, please be mine!

FAIRIES (*Hiding their smiles*): Goodness!

SNIP *and* MADAM SNAP: Gracious!

KING TWINKEM: That—a valentine? Girl, how dare you? Most insulting!

TWINK: Most—

SQUINK: In—

BLINK:—Sulting!

JOAN: The words don't seem to come right. I'll try again. (*Recites*)
Twinkem, you're a scarecrow king;
Be my valentine, old thing!

ALL: Terrible! Dreadful!

3RD FAIRY: She won't do.

JOAN: How's this? (*Recites*)
Twinkem, hear me ere we part,
To you I'll never give my heart!

ALL: Chase her away!

JOAN (*Hopefully*): How's this? (*Recites*)
The rose is red, the violet's blue,
Butter's fat and so are you!

KING TWINKEM (*Taking a tape measure out of his pocket and measuring his waistline*): I'm not. Put her out!

ALL: Put her out!

JIGGERS: Ho! Ho! Ho! Put her out!

3RD FAIRY: Jiggers! I'm sure he's had something to do with this!

2ND FAIRY: It's one of his jokes.

1ST FAIRY: She's bewitched!

MADAM SNAP: If she's bewitched, then she's wearing the silver penny upside down. Search her!

FAIRIES (*Taking penny from her pocket*): Here is the penny!

KING TWINKEM: Well! Now let's see if you can make up a proper valentine to me!

JOAN (*Reciting, happily*):
The poppy's red, the bluebell's blue,
Oh, King Twinkem, I love you!

KING TWINKEM: That's better. That's much better. (*He touches her with his wand.*) Now you're the Queen of Hearts!

TWINK: Queen—

SQUINK: Of—

BLINK: Hearts! (*As the FAIRIES run off the stage for a moment, JIGGERS disappears, and MADAM SNAP throws a sparkling valentine cape around JOAN and puts a crown of hearts upon her head.*)

KING TWINKEM: Very becoming, eh, Snip? Now let's begin the party!

TWINK: Let's—

SQUINK: Begin—

BLINK: The party! (*FAIRIES now run back on the stage, wearing strings of hearts around their necks, and hearts pinned on their wings. They carry balloons and throw confetti into the air as they dance with JOAN around the Valentine Tree.*)

FAIRIES (*Singing*):
Oh, come, ye fairies, dance and sing,
Near the Tree of Valentines,

Dance and prance while bluebells ring,
By the Tree of Valentines;
Hearts that catch a rainbow gleam,
Sunset rose and gold will seem,
Twinkling in a fairy dream
On the Tree of Valentines! (*Curtain*)

THE END

Valentine Stardust

by Jessie Nicholson

Characters

ROWENA CLACK
ALBERT CLACK, *her husband, better known as Mr. Moon-man*
BOOTSIE
BIBS } *orphan twins*
MRS. NIBBLE
MILDRED, *her daughter*
HORATIO TRUET
POLLY PRIM
SUGAR BUN
PIE CRUST
CREAM PUFF

TIME: *The day before Valentine's Day.*
SETTING: *The Sugar and Spice Pastry Shop, owned by the Clacks. The shop is decorated for Valentine's Day.*
AT RISE: ALBERT CLACK *is busily rolling out dough on a table at left, upstage, and cutting same with a large heart-shaped pastry cutter.*

MR. CLACK (*In sing-song fashion, going through the motions called for*):
Roll out your pastry and pat it into place,
Trim around the edges to make it look like lace,

Sprinkle on some stardust, sprinkle on some spice,
And you'll have Cupid's cookies all fashioned in a trice.
(*Enter* Bootsie *and* Bibs)

Bootsie *and* Bibs: Good morning, Mr. Moonman.

Mr. Clack: Well, bless my stars and call me Moonman, if it isn't Bootsie and Bibs. Good morning, Bootsie—good morning, Bibs. And what a very fine morning it is. Just about the very finest morning before Valentine's Day morning that I have ever seen. Or smelled. (*Sniffing ecstatically. The twins follow suit.*)

Bibs: It surely does smell good in here all right, Mr. Moonman.

Bootsie: Um-m—yum, yum!

Mr. Clack: Do try some cookies, children. Samples on that plate for my special customers. (*Pointing to plate on counter*)

Bootsie *and* Bibs: Oh, thank you, Mr. Moonman. (*They help themselves.*)

Bibs: Have you made any more trips to the moon lately, Mr. Moonman?

Mr. Clack: Oh, yes, indeedy. Just last night. I always need an extra supply of stardust for Valentine's Day. Cupid's cookies without it wouldn't do at all. Stardust is what dreams are made of, you know. What a happy place this poor world would be if we all partook of enough stardust!

Bootsie (*Timidly*): Perhaps some would be good for—for your wife, Mr. Moonman.

Mr. Clack: Well, that is what I thought, Bootsie. I even took her along with me, but alas! (*Shaking his head woefully*) I am afraid the journey to the moon upset her equilibrium entirely. She's not feeling at all pleasant today. In fact, if I don't finish these cookies soon (*Beginning to roll out the dough furiously*) I fear she will take the rolling pin to me!

BOOTSIE: Oh, dear, that would be dreadful! Don't you think she might have a change of heart?

MR. CLACK (*Dreamily*): A change of heart—now, that's a thought. If I could just make her a new one that had all the proper ingredients—the sweetness of a sugar bun, the tenderness of a flaky pie crust, the softness of a whipped cream puff—a confection that would simply melt in her mouth as she ate it. . . . But no. (*Sighing*) I am afraid it would be of no use. I could never get her even to try it. All she likes to do is suck on lemons, which sours her disposition most frightfully.

BOOTSIE: It's a very discouraging situation, isn't it, Mr. Moonman? That's what Miss Prim says when she's talking about Mr. Truet.

MR. CLACK: And who, pray tell, are Mr. Truet and Miss Prim?

BIBS: Why, Mr. Truet is the janitor of our school.

BOOTSIE: And Miss Prim is the seamstress who helps Auntie with her sewing business.

BIBS: Mr. Truet has been in love with Miss Prim for ever so long but he simply can't think of the right way to pop the question.

BOOTSIE: And Miss Prim has her answer all ready—it's "yes" of course—but if you don't ever get asked a question you can't very well answer it, can you?

MR. CLACK: Bless my boots, no, Bootsie, I'm afraid you can't. Now, I might make a very special heart-shaped Valentine cake for Mr. Truet to give to Miss Prim, well sprinkled with stardust and with the key to his heart inside. Do you think Miss Prim would understand?

BOOTSIE: Oh, I'm sure she would, Mr. Moonman.

MR. CLACK: That way she could say "yes," without having to be asked.

BIBS: Let's run and tell Mr. Truet now.

BOOTSIE (*Excitedly*): Oh, yes, let's. (*They exit.* MR. CLACK *starts busily stirring in a big bowl.*)

MR. CLACK: A heart full of love has Mr. Truet,
He'd like to propose but cannot do it,
It's up to Cupid to help him along
With this fine gold key he can't go wrong. (*He takes down a large gold key that hangs on the wall behind the counter, drops it into the bowl and pretends to pour the mixture into a heart-shaped pan. He sprinkles the top lavishly from a large shaker container labelled "Stardust."* MRS. NIBBLE *and her daughter* MILDRED *enter.* MRS. NIBBLE *is large, portly, and important-looking.* MILDRED *is thin and sharp-faced and cross-looking.* MRS. NIBBLE *samples freely from the trays, dropping back unfinished cookies disdainfully as she moves along.* MILDRED *follows her mother's example.*)

MRS. NIBBLE: I want the largest, finest cake you have in the shop. Mildred is having a party. (MR. CLACK *bustles about looking on all the shelves and under the counter. At last he takes out a small, burnt, lopsided cake and holds it up, gazing at it in mock admiration.*)

MR. CLACK:
This cake is made out of odds and ends,
Let Mildred share it with her little friends.

MRS. NIBBLE (*Indignantly*): I have never been so insulted in all my life!

MILDRED: Me either! (*Sticking out her tongue at* MR. CLACK) Yah!

MR. CLACK (*Shrugging*): It is the last cake I have left in the shop. (MRS. NIBBLE *sees the cake* MR. CLACK *has just finished mixing and points to it commandingly.*)

MRS. NIBBLE: What about that one? (*Then without waiting for an answer*) We will take it as soon as it comes out of the oven.

MR. CLACK (*Raising his eyes upward*): Hold my temper

and count my blessings—that cake is already spoken for
by a very special customer, Mrs. Nibble. (*He sets burned
cake down on the counter.*)

MRS. NIBBLE: Indeed—and who is more special than Mrs.
Justinius Nibble, may I ask? (ROWENA CLACK *enters.
She is tall and thin and disagreeable looking. Her hair is
drawn into a tight knot on the back of her head and the
corners of her mouth turn down sourly.*)

MRS. CLACK: AL-BERT! What do you mean, refusing Mrs.
Nibble a cake?

MR. CLACK (*Apologetically*): But Rowena, my love, this is
a special order.

MRS. CLACK: There is nobody more special than Mrs. Nibble—and dear little Mildred, of course. (*Smirking*)

MILDRED (*Sticking out her tongue at* MRS. CLACK): Yah!

MRS. NIBBLE (*Laughing*): Isn't she amusing?

MILDRED (*Sticking out her tongue at her mother*): Yah!

MRS. NIBBLE (*Angrily*): Mildred! How dare you? I don't
know whether I shall let you have a party or not. (*Gives
her a good shaking.* MR. CLACK *has picked up the cake
with the key in it and is trying to sneak out unnoticed
but is spotted by* MRS. CLACK, *who leads him back by the
ear.*)

MRS. CLACK (*Taking the cake from him forcibly*): I will
take charge of this cake. It goes into the oven at once,
dear Mrs. Nibble. It will be ready in half an hour, I
promise you. (MRS. NIBBLE *sails out of the shop, giving*
MRS. CLACK *a withering glance.* MILDRED *sticks out her
tongue as a parting gesture and exits.*)

MR. CLACK (*Shaking his head*): Ah me, I hate to think
what you're doing, my love. I shouldn't want to be held
responsible.

MRS. CLACK (*Sharply*): What *are* you talking about, Albert
Clack? What did you put in this cake? (*Sniffing it suspiciously*)

MR. CLACK: If the little dears choke on stardust, don't blame me, that's all.

MRS. CLACK: Fiddlesticks—you and your stardust! Into the oven it goes this minute, and if you don't finish rolling out those cookies promptly I—I shall—

MR. CLACK: Take the rolling pin to me—I know, my love. It is just fortunate I have such a thick skull or I would not have lasted this long.

MRS. CLACK (*Bitingly*): Numbskull is a better word, Albert Clack. What I ever did to deserve such a worthless husband, I am sure I don't know. (*She flounces out of the room through door at upstage left.*)

MR. CLACK: Bless the dear little woman! If I could only give her a change of heart, all would be well. (*He seats himself on bench against the wall at downstage left and gazes mournfully out towards the audience.*)

Like a trolley off its track,

Beats the heart of Mrs. Clack,

A Valentine I'd like to send her,

A new heart, soft and sweet and tender. (*His head nods and he murmurs drowsily.*) The sweetness of a sugar bun, the tenderness of a flaky pie crust, the softness of a whipped cream puff—ah, what a heart that would make. (*His head drops completely on his chest and he dozes. Enter* SUGAR BUN, PIE CRUST *and* CREAM PUFF, *running in hand in hand.*)

SUGAR BUN: Poor Mr. Moonman, his troubles are many, his joys are few.

PIE CRUST: Surely it's up to us to lighten his load.

CREAM PUFF (*Boastfully*): That should be easy for me. I'm feeling very light this morning—light and puffy.

PIE CRUST: Pooh, pooh, that's nothing. Cream puffs are always light and puffy—at least Mr. Moonman's are.

CREAM PUFF: I'm as soft as thistledown too. Stroke me and see.

SUGAR BUN: And I'm feeling extra sweet. Just what Mr. Moonman is looking for. Take a nibble if you don't believe it.

PIE CRUST: Don't mention the word nibble around here. It reminds me of that dreadful woman and her daughter, Mildred. (*He shudders.*) As for myself, I'm so tender I'd melt in your mouth. Just feel of my crust. (SUGAR BUN *pinches him and* PIE CRUST *squeals.*)

PIE CRUST: I didn't say to pinch me, stupid!

CREAM PUFF: I think we fill the bill all right. A bit of each of us rolled into one would make something better than pie crust or bun.

PIE CRUST (*Huffily*): Or cream puff, which personally I think we could do without.

SUGAR BUN: Come, come, don't let's waste time quarreling. Let's get busy. We'll do our mixing behind the counter where there's no fear of being seen. (*They huddle down behind the counter and at that moment* MR. TRUET *enters. He is small and timid-looking and at the sight of* MR. CLACK *asleep, he tiptoes over to the counter and looks all about hesitantly.*)

MR. TRUET: Dear, dear, I wonder where my Valentine cake for Miss Prim is. Bibs and Bootsie said it would be ready for me. (*Finally, he picks up the burned, lopsided one that* MR. CLACK *had offered* MILDRED, *and regards it unhappily.*) I suppose this must be it. I don't see any other. Somehow it isn't quite what I expected but I suppose one can't look a gift horse in the mouth; after all it does have the key to my heart in it. I wonder if I should wake Mr. Clack and thank him for it? (*He sets the cake down on the counter and tiptoes over to peer down at the sleeping figure. Behind his back* SUGAR BUN *pops up and appearing to poke a hole in the center of the cake, drops something inside and then disappears from sight again.*) No-o—I guess not. (MR. TRUET *straightens up.*) He looks so sort of peaceful and from what I hear that doesn't happen very often. I'll just drop by tomorrow and let him know how things worked out. (*He exits, taking cake with him and* PIE CRUST, SUGAR BUN *and* CREAM PUFF *pop up from behind the counter.*)

PIE CRUST (*Accusingly*): What did you put in that cake, Sugar Bun?

SUGAR BUN (*In an off-hand manner*): Only an old key. I didn't want Mr. Truet to be disappointed.

PIE CRUST (*Persistently*): What key, stupid?

SUGAR BUN (*Guiltily*): Well—er—that is—

PIE CRUST (*Ominously*): Go on—what key?

SUGAR BUN: Only the key to the—(*Swallowing hard*) to the city, that Mayor Trundle left for Mr. Clack this morning when he invited him to be mayor for a day.

PIE CRUST (*Groaning*): Ah, me, this fellow has more crust than I have!

CREAM PUFF: How perfectly odious of you, Sugar Bun—now what will poor Miss Prim do when she bites into the key of the city instead of the key to Mr. Truet's heart?

SUGAR BUN (*Impudently*): Be mayor for a day of course—what else?

PIE CRUST: A lady mayor! What a dreadful thought. If it wasn't that we were here to help Mr. Moonman, I declare, I'd roll you out as thin as a piece of pie crust and fill you with swiss cheese!

CREAM PUFF: Do stop quarreling and help me lift this confection up onto the counter. It's so soft and sweet and tender I'm fearful of its melting before our very eyes. (*Cautiously, they lift a cake onto counter. The top of the cake is decorated with slices of lemon.*)

SUGAR BUN (*Crossly*): I don't see why we had to spoil anything so sweet with anything as sour as lemon slices.

PIE CRUST: That's just to tempt Mrs. Clack into eating it,

silly, don't you see? Come on now, let's get away from here before we get caught. We'll sneak out behind the ovens and Mrs. Clack won't see us. (*They exit through kitchen door. Enter* Mrs. Nibble, *carrying a large black umbrella, followed by her daughter,* Mildred.)

Mrs. Nibble: Look at that lazy, good-for-nothing Clack— sound asleep. It is dreadful what his poor wife has to put up with. If our cake isn't ready, I'll rap him over the noggin with my umbrella. (*Waving the umbrella over his head threateningly*)

Mildred (*Jumping up and down excitedly*): Hit him, Ma, hit him on the noggin!

Mrs. Nibble (*Spying lemon cake on the counter*): It won't be necessary. This must be it. (*Poking at it with the tip of her umbrella*)

Mildred (*Beginning to howl*): Who wants old, sour lemons on a cake? Hit him on the noggin, Ma, hit him hard. He did it for spite.

Mrs. Nibble (*Nibbling at a bit of the cake*): Hush now, Mildred, my love. That must have been Mrs. Clack's idea. She's very fond of lemons (*Taking another nibble*) Um—not bad. I'm sure the cake Mr. Clack showed you first would be good enough for your little friends. I'm taking quite a fancy to this one myself.

Mildred (*Howling more loudly*): It's *my* cake. You promised. I don't want that other horrid old thing. Hit him on the noggin, Ma. (Mrs. Nibble *absent-mindedly raps her daughter on the head instead and sails majestically out of the shop carrying the cake which she is still nibbling.* Mildred *follows sniveling, sticking out her tongue at* Mr. Clack *in parting. Enter* Mrs. Clack, *bearing the freshly baked cake at which she is sniffing with obvious curiosity and suspicion. She fails to notice* Mr. Clack, *who has awakened abruptly and sneaks out to the kitchen behind her back.*)

MRS. CLACK: If I only *did* know what he put into this cake. Now that it's baked it smells more than ever like—like —oh, dear, what does it smell like? *Albert*—wherever has that man gone to? (*Setting down the cake and peering behind the counter and under the table and bench*) If that isn't just like him, going off and leaving the shop untended. What if Mrs. Nibble and her daughter had come back? (*She leans over and sniffs at the cake again.*) Stardust—fiddlesticks—but what *would* the stuff taste like,· I wonder. I guess I'll just take a little bite off the bottom and see what he's been up to myself. Mrs. Nibble will never suspect. (*She tips cake up and breaks off little piece from the bottom at which she nibbles reflectively.*) Um-m—not bad. (*Breaks off another piece*) In fact, quite delicious. (*Goes on consuming the cake from the bottom, her expression becoming happier all the time, the downward corners of her mouth turning upward into a smile. Suddenly, she discovers the gold key and draws it out in surprise.*) My goodness, so that's what was inside the cake! And it says, "The Key to My Heart," on it. How sweet. Dear Albert must have made it especially for me for Valentine's Day. No wonder he didn't want me to sell it to that nasty woman and her hateful daughter! (*At that moment* BOOTSIE *and* BIBS *come bursting into the shop, the bells on the door jangling furiously. At sight of* MRS. CLACK, *however, they fall back, bumping into each other in their confusion.*)

MRS. CLACK: Why, Bootsie dear, and Bibs, do come in. How are you both?

BOOTSIE (*Stammering*): W-why, we're just f-fine, aren't we Bibs? (BIBS, *his mouth open in surprise, first shakes his head and then being nudged by his sister, nods it vigorously.*)

MRS. CLACK: Is something wrong, children? You look quite flustered.

BOOTSIE (*Falteringly*): It's—it's Miss Prim. She's gone on a rampage.

MRS. CLACK (*Making a clucking sound of sympathy*): Dear, dear, how sad. We women are such fragile creatures. (BOOTSIE *and* BIBS *exchange startled glances.*)

BIBS: She's going about saying she's the mayor and everybody has to do as she says, especially Mr. Truet.

MRS. CLACK: How shocking—doesn't she know it's a woman's place to take orders, not give them? (MR. CLACK *appears in the kitchen door as she utters these words and he stares at her unbelievingly, his mouth open.*)

MR. CLACK: Pull up the shutters and let in the light—I must be dreaming!

MRS. CLACK: Oh, there you are, my love. Do come in and sit down. You look all tired out. (MR. CLACK, *completely bewildered, obeys. At that moment* MR. TRUET *rushes in looking very dismayed.*)

MR. TRUET (*Gasping*): Oh, Mr. C-C-Clack, whatever did you put in that cake for Miss Prim? It has quite gone to her head. She has been chasing me all over town.

MR. CLACK (*Dazedly*): But—but—but I don't understand. (*At that moment* MISS PRIM *enters looking very determined. She is wearing a placard around her neck on which is printed in large letters, "Mayor For A Day." When she turns about another placard is revealed hanging down her back which reads, "Why Not For Always? Prim For Mayor." The key to the city hangs at her waist.*)

BOOTSIE *and* BIBS: You see what we mean.

MR. TRUET (*Helplessly*): You see what *I* mean. She has that g-g-gleam in her eye. (*He runs and cowers behind* MR. CLACK *on the bench.*)

MISS PRIM (*Firmly*): Horatio Truet, I've caught up with you at last. (*Leading him out triumphantly from behind the bench by the ear*) No more shilly-shallying. It is high time woman asserted herself in this man's world. Will you or will you not, Horatio Truet?

MR. TRUET (*Fearfully*): Will I or will I not w-w-what, Miss Prim?

MISS PRIM (*Sharply*): Polly, if you please. And will you marry me, of course—what else? I am at least giving *you* the opportunity of saying yes or no.

MR. TRUET (*Sighing with relief*): Is that all you wanted of me?

MISS PRIM (*Tapping her foot on the floor*): Isn't it enough? What is your answer, Horatio?

MR. TRUET (*Beaming*): Why, it's yes, of course, Polly, my —(*Timidly*) my dear. What a weight you've taken off my shoulders! (MISS PRIM *discards her placards happily and drops the key to the city disdainfully on the counter. Arm in arm, she and* MR. TRUET *leave the shop.* MR. CLACK *jumps up to inspect the key.*)

MR. CLACK (*In surprise*): Why, this is the key to the city the mayor left with me this morning! How did she ever come by that?

BOOTSIE (*Reproachfully*): You promised it was going to be the key to Mr. Truet's heart, Mr. Moonman.

BIBS (*Accusingly*): Yes, Mr. Moonman—how about that? (MR. CLACK *stands scratching his head in bewilderment.*)

MRS. CLACK (*Coyly*): You can't fool me, my dear. You and your keys. I haven't a doubt this was just another one of your Valentine surprises. You're so thoughtful, Albert. It was sweet of you to bake that cake for me and I enjoyed every bite of it.

MR. CLACK: The—the cake *I* baked for *you*, my love?

MRS. CLACK: Why, yes (*Twisting her apron around her finger*), the one with the key to your heart in it.

MR. CLACK: Oh, ho, ho—so that's how things are. Stardust and dreams—um-m—(*Winking at* BOOTSIE *and* BIBS) I must say these little mix-ups have a pleasant way of turning out, even if I don't quite know how they came about. (*Enter* Mrs. Nibble *looking unusually benevolent,* Mildred *sidling along behind her docilely.*)

Mrs. Nibble (*Who has overheard the last remark*): Yes, don't they? Why, look at Mildred and me—as frisky as a pair of colts. (*Shedding her dignity completely as she jigs about the shop with* Mildred.) And all from eating a cake that wasn't meant for us. Why, we feel as though we'd had a complete change of heart, don't we, Mildred, my pet?

Mildred (*Sweetly*): Yes, Mother dear.

Mrs. Nibble: And we've come to apologize to Mr. Clack for being so rude, haven't we, Mildred, my love?

Mildred: Yes, Mother dear.

Mr. Clack (*Looking slightly puzzled and counting on his fingers*): Somehow, that seems to make one more cake than I can rightly account for. Oh, well, no matter— have a cookie, everybody, do. (*All help themselves and exit one by one, each wishing the* Clacks *a happy Valentine's Day as they depart.*)

Mr. Clack (*Going back to work table*): I'll just shake a little more stardust on these cookies before I pop them in the oven.

Mrs. Clack: Do, my love. The more, the merrier. (Mr. Clack *shakes from the big shaker vigorously but nothing comes out.*)

Mr. Clack: Bless my buttons—I'm very much afraid I'm fresh out of stardust again and tomorrow's Valentine's Day!

Mrs. Clack (*Holding up her hands in horror*): Dear, dear, what a catastrophe! Why don't we take a trip to the moon tonight and pick up some more on our way?

Mr. Clack: An excellent idea, my love. We had better go and get ready at once so that we can get an early start.

(They exit through kitchen door hand in hand. Enter PIE CRUST, CREAM PUFF *and* SUGAR BUN.)

CREAM PUFF *(Crossly)*: What a shame—wasting our talents on Mrs. Nibble! I'm sure the mix-up was all your fault, Pie Crust.

PIE CRUST: No such thing. Besides, Mrs. Nibble certainly needed sweetening up as well as Mrs. Clack. And as for her sour-puss daughter—

CREAM PUFF: Who cares about sweetening up Mrs. Nibble and her daughter anyway?

SUGAR BUN: Oh, do stop quarreling, you two. I say—all's well that ends well. *(They dance about friskily in a circle as curtain falls.)*

THE END

The Tiniest Heart

by Frances B. Watts

Characters

KING OF HEARTS
QUEEN OF HEARTS
TINY, *their youngest son*
JACK
TEN
NINE
EIGHT
SEVEN
SIX ⟩ *their other children*
FIVE
FOUR
THREE
TWO
UNCLE DIAMOND, *the King of Diamonds*
MESSENGER

SETTING: *A room in the shabby castle of the Royal Heart Family.*

AT RISE: TINY *enters and looks around. When he finds that he is alone, he speaks to audience.*

TINY:

I'm the youngest Heart, the tiniest Heart,
Of the Royal Heart Family.

Most of the time, yes, most of the time,
I'm as happy as I can be.
But I've one little worry, a worrisome worry,
For which I am not to blame.
I'm almost seven, though not quite seven,
Yet I don't have a proper name!
My folks call me Tiny, though I'm not very tiny,
I am growing so wonderfully fast.
Oh, I do hope today, yes, I pray that today,
I'll be given a real name at last!
(KING *and* QUEEN OF HEARTS *enter.*)

QUEEN (*Kisses* TINY): Good morning, Tiny. Where are your brothers and sisters?

TINY: Good morning, Mother. Good morning, Father. The others are still out walking. I ran on ahead, because I want to speak to you about a very important matter.

KING (*He helps the* QUEEN *to her throne, then sits down on his own throne*): I do hope the children won't be late for the Royal Family Hour. We have a serious problem to discuss today.

TINY: Father, won't you please listen to me before the others come?

KING: All right, all right, Tiny, my boy. What is it?

TINY: My name. When are you and Mother going to give me a proper name? Now that I'm growing up, Tiny hardly suits at all.

QUEEN (*She takes out her knitting*): We have tried to find a name for you, dear. We have read through whole dictionaries full of names, but we can't find one that we like. They all seem so ordinary.

KING: We need a very special name for the youngest child of the King and Queen of Hearts. (CHILDREN *enter. They are the ten remaining Hearts. They seem breathless from their walk. Some of the girls are carrying wild flowers.*) Well, it's about time that you children made an appearance! You're ten minutes late.

JACK: We're sorry, Father. It was so pleasant walking in the woods that we lost track of the time. (CHILDREN *line up in front of* QUEEN, *who kisses each child.* CHILDREN *sit on floor around thrones.*)

QUEEN (*Pointing to children in turn and calling their names*): Jack . . . Ten . . . Nine . . . Eight . . . Seven . . . Six . . . Five . . . Four . . . Three . . . Two. (*Smiles lovingly*) You're all such dear children. But I do wish that you had thought to wash your faces before coming to the Royal Family Hour. (CHILDREN *start to rise.*)

KING: No, no! There isn't time for face-washing now. We must get on with our discussion.

TINY: What about my name, Father?

TEN: Hush, Tiny. Father doesn't want to talk about your name.

NINE: That's right, Tiny. Father wants to talk about something important, don't you, Father?

KING: Yes, and, as usual, our trouble today is a most annoying one.

EIGHT: I'll bet I know what it's about!

SEVEN: I'll bet I know, too. It's about money.

SIX: What's the money problem today, Father?

KING (*Sighs*): Well, frankly, we've just about run out of it.

QUEEN (*Smiling brightly*): Why, I think that's lovely! If we've run out of money, we won't have any more problems, will we?

TWO, THREE, FOUR, FIVE (*Join hands and dance in a circle. They sing to the tune of "Here We Go 'Round the Mulberry Bush"*):
We've no more money to worry about,
Worry about, worry about.
We've no more money to worry about,

So all our problems are over! (*They fall down on the floor, laughing.*)

KING: Hush! All of you! This is a most uncomfortable situation. Since we have run out of money, we shall have to close down the castle and move to some ramshackle cottage. We may even go hungry!

QUEEN: Oh dear, I would hate to close down the castle. I'm quite fond of it, even if it is crumbling a bit.

TWO (*Crying*): I'd hate to go hungry. Imagine what it would be like if we couldn't have plum pudding anymore!

KING: If only I could borrow a large sum of money, I could build flour mills throughout the kingdom. Then the people would have more work and would earn more money.

NINE: And then the Royal Heart Family would have more money.

EIGHT: Everyone would be better off!

KING: Exactly. But alas, I have no idea where I can borrow a large sum of money! Until I can find a way, we all shall have to cut down on family expenses.

THREE: Oh dear, I did so want to buy a singing top.

FIVE: A singing top! Why, I don't even have a decent pair of shoes! (*Holds up a foot to exhibit his shabby shoe. MESSENGER enters, holding a letter.*)

MESSENGER: A letter for you, Your Majesty. (*He hands letter to the KING, then bows and exits.*)

KING (*Reads letter, then claps forehead in distress*): Good heavens! It's from my uncle, the King of Diamonds! Uncle Diamond is passing through our kingdom on his way to Westwind, and he wants to spend the night with us. He'll be here at any moment!

QUEEN (*Dropping her knitting*): Mercy, the castle is a sight! I haven't finished my spring castle-cleaning yet!

JACK: Isn't the King of Diamonds your rich uncle, Father?

SIX: Isn't he the one who owns all that land, but still allows his people to go hungry?

TEN: Isn't he the mean and stingy uncle?

KING: Yes, children, that's Uncle Diamond. I'm so ashamed to admit it, but there you have it. One can't choose one's relatives, unfortunately.

TINY: Perhaps Uncle Diamond isn't as bad as everyone thinks he is. Maybe he just doesn't know how to be a good king.

SEVEN: No, he's quite horrid. Why, he's the one who never allows his people to have any holidays.

QUEEN: Oh, how awful! He really must be a frightfully wicked man. (*Pauses thoughtfully*) How does one treat a frightfully wicked man?

JACK (*Grins slyly*): I think we ought to treat him with the utmost care. Give him a very royal welcome. Roll out the royal red carpet!

SIX: But Jack, our royal red carpet is threadbare.

JACK: Well, we can skip the carpet then. But we must be pleasant to Uncle Diamond. After all, he is rich. If we butter him up a bit, we might be able to borrow that money.

KING: By Jove! Jack is right! If we're all extremely nice to Uncle Diamond, he just may give us a loan!

TINY: Wouldn't we be nice to him anyway, even if he weren't rich?

KING: Of course, my boy. But today we must be so nice to Uncle Diamond that we fairly burst with niceness!

QUEEN: Perhaps I shall give the wicked man some of those cherry tarts I was saving for Sunday tea.

KING: I'll tell Uncle Diamond some of my favorite riddles.

JACK: I'll let him borrow my best fishing rod, if he should want to go fishing.

TEN: Nine, Eight, Seven, Six and I will entertain him royally. We'll sing for him!

FIVE: Four, Three, Two and I will dance for Uncle Diamond!

QUEEN: And what will you do, Tiny, my sweet?

TINY (*Sighs*): I don't do anything very well. I shall just ask him how he is feeling, and how he is getting along.

TWO: That's not much.

TEN: We can't expect little Tiny to do very much. (MESSENGER *rushes in.*)

MESSENGER (*With excitement*): His Majesty, the King of Diamonds, has arrived, Your Majesty! (*He bows and exits.*)

QUEEN: Go wash your faces, children! Hurry! (CHILDREN *run offstage.*)

KING (*To* QUEEN): Remember, be very, very nice to him, my love.

QUEEN (*Indignantly*): Well really, dear, I do think I'm rather a jolly sort, most of the time! (UNCLE DIAMOND *enters. There is a scowl on his face.*)

KING (*Pumping* UNCLE DIAMOND'S *hand*): Welcome, Uncle Diamond. Welcome to our lowly castle!

UNCLE DIAMOND (*He looks about the room*): Lowly castle is right! One good puff of wind would lay it low.

KING: Ha, ha, ha! What a keen sense of humor you have, Uncle. (*He turns to* QUEEN) Dear, haven't I always said that Uncle Diamond was screamingly funny?

QUEEN (*Nervously twisting her hand*): Oh, yes, dear Heart. You have always said that Uncle Diamond makes you want to scream. (*She hurries off.*)

KING (*Glares at the retreating* QUEEN. *He leads* UNCLE DIAMOND *to the easy chair*): With your jolly sense of humor, Uncle, perhaps you would appreciate one of my choice riddles. Tell me, what makes more noise than a pig in a pen?

UNCLE DIAMOND: I haven't the least idea, and I couldn't care less. Riddles bore me.

KING: Too bad, sir. It's such a dandy riddle, too. The answer, of course, is—two pigs in a pen. (QUEEN *enters. She is carrying a tray of tarts.*)

QUEEN (*Very sweetly*): Here are some lovely, lovely tarts, Uncle Diamond. Wouldn't you care for one of my lovely tarts?

UNCLE DIAMOND: I can't abide tarts. They give me dyspepsia. (CHILDREN *enter. All except* TINY *look uneasy.*)

KING: Ah, here are our dear children, Uncle Diamond. They have simply been aching to meet you. My eldest is Jack. Then Ten . . . then Nine . . . Eight . . . Seven . . . Six . . . Five . . . Four . . . Three . . . Two . . . And this is our tiniest Heart, Tiny. (*As each name is called, the child steps forward, smiles, and bows to* UNCLE DIAMOND.)

UNCLE DIAMOND: Tiny! That's a ridiculous name for a child!

TINY: But that's not my real name, sir. Everyone calls me Tiny because Mother and Father can't think of a suitable name to name me.

UNCLE DIAMOND: That's outrageous! Every child should have a proper name! If the next to the youngest child is named Two, why don't you call the youngest child One?

KING: We thought of that. But somehow the name One sounds so lonely.

QUEEN: Besides, if we named Tiny One, we would almost feel obliged to name any future child Zero. And Zero sounds like nothing at all. Don't you agree?

JACK: I don't think that we should waste Uncle Diamond's time, talking about Tiny's name. (*He hands* UNCLE DIAMOND *a fishing rod.*) Isn't this a fine rod, Uncle? What say if we spend a few hours fishing in the brook?

UNCLE DIAMOND (*Pushes rod aside*): Bah! Fishing is a waste of time. One thinks too much while fishing, and thinking is a most unpleasant occupation.

TINY: Why? Why do you find thinking unpleasant, Uncle?

UNCLE DIAMOND (*Looks at* TINY *with interest*): Because one is eventually forced to think of unpleasant things, my boy. The world is full of unpleasantness.

TEN (*Eagerly*): Nine, Eight, Seven, Six and I can give you a pleasant moment, Uncle. We'll sing for you!

TEN, NINE, EIGHT, SEVEN, SIX (*Standing in a row and singing to the tune of "Three Blind Mice"*):
Five black cats, five black cats,
Hear how they mew. Hear how they mew.
They all robbed milk from a milking pail.
The milkmaid caught them and took them to jail.
Did you ever hear such a comical tale?
Five black cats. (*They bow.*)

NINE: Did you like our song, dear Uncle Diamond?

EIGHT: Would you like to hear another?

UNCLE DIAMOND (*Dryly*): That song was quite enough, thank you.

FIVE: Then allow us to do a little dance for you, Uncle Diamond! (FIVE, FOUR, THREE, *and* TWO *do a clumsy little clog, humming "Oh Where, Oh Where Has My Little Dog Gone?" Then* FOUR *accidentally steps on* UNCLE DIAMOND's *toe.*)

UNCLE DIAMOND (*Rubbing toe*): Ouch! Ouch! You little rascal, you stepped on my corn!

FOUR (*Aghast*): I'm sorry, Uncle.

THREE: Four didn't mean to do it, sir. She's just a bit clumsier than the rest of us. Shall we begin our dance over again?

UNCLE DIAMOND (*He jumps to his feet and shouts at the entire family*): No! I don't want any more dancing, singing, cherry tarts, riddles, or any more of your foolish flattery. You don't fool me for a moment. All of you are trying to please me because you hope that I'll give you some money!

KING: You're wrong, sir! We don't want you to give—

UNCLE DIAMOND: Quiet! I know that you need money. By the looks of this crumbling castle, you must be as poor as a pauper's donkey. (*He shakes his fist.*) Well, I'm not going to give you a penny! Never! So please stop fawning over me and leave me in peace for awhile! (*All Hearts, except* TINY, *tiptoe off.* TINY *hides behind a throne.* UNCLE DIAMOND *sits down. He signs heavily. Then* TINY *walks slowly over to* UNCLE DIAMOND's *chair.*)

TINY: How are you feeling, sir?

UNCLE DIAMOND (*With a startled jump*): Wretched, thank you. My head is throbbing. My stomach is rumbling. My heart aches. Oh, I'm simply miserable! (*He looks closely at* TINY.) I believe that you truly *care* how I feel, lad.

TINY: Of course, I do. (*Pauses*) You're very unhappy, aren't you, Uncle Diamond?

UNCLE DIAMOND: I'm always unhappy. I'm a king, you see. It seems that most kings are destined to be unhappy. All a king ever gets are complaints and criticism from his chronically complaining subjects.

TINY: If I were the King of Diamonds, I would be ever so happy!

UNCLE DIAMOND (*Laughs scornfully*): Just why do you think you'd be happy, if you were the King of Diamonds?

TINY (*He capers merrily as he recites*):
If I were the King of Diamonds,
Instead of the tiniest Heart,
Oh, I would do such wonderful things,
I wouldn't know where to start!

UNCLE DIAMOND: What would you do?

TINY:
If only I weren't the tiniest Heart,
But the rich King of Diamonds instead,

I would plant barren fields with sweet golden wheat,
Then no one would hunger for bread.

UNCLE DIAMOND (*Sounding excited*): Yes, yes. Go on, lad.

TINY:

I'd declare a nice holiday once every month,
Provided, of course, I were king.
And I'd send through my kingdom this royal command,
"Everyone dance and sing!"

UNCLE DIAMOND (*Claps with delight*): You may have something there, my boy. Tell me more!

TINY:

If I were the King of Diamonds,
I would rule with a velvet glove,
For the happiest king has one special thing,
It's love, love, LOVE! (UNCLE DIAMOND *laughs aloud. He grabs* TINY *by the hands and dances him around the stage. The two recite the last verse as they dance.*)

UNCLE DIAMOND (*Laughing, he flops down in his chair. Then claps his forehead in surprise*): What am I saying? I *am* the King of Diamonds! So I can start doing all those nice things for my people right away! By Jove, lad, I do believe that you have shown me the way to happiness!

TINY: I hope so, sir!

UNCLE DIAMOND: Bless me, you're such a gem of a boy! So wise and loving. It's hard for me to understand how the other members of your family can be such deceitful cads!

TINY: You mustn't judge them harshly, Uncle. My father doesn't wish you to give him money. He only wishes that you might lend him some, so that he can build flour mills throughout the kingdom. The mills, you see, will help our people become more prosperous, and the Royal Heart Family will prosper, too.

UNCLE DIAMOND: Then why didn't your father speak right up and ask me for a loan, instead of encouraging his family to purr at me like pussy cats?

TINY (*Sighs*): I don't know, sir. They all thought it a brilliant idea at the time. They wanted the loan so very badly, you see. But I'm sure that they must realize now that nothing is ever gained by insincerity.

UNCLE DIAMOND (*Strokes chin, thoughtfully*): Perhaps I shall reconsider my ultimatum. Call your family back, my boy.

TINY (*Rushes to door*): Mother! Father! Come, everyone! Uncle Diamond wishes to see you! (*Family enters. They look sheepish.*)

UNCLE DIAMOND: Please be seated, everybody. (*They sit down.*)

QUEEN (*Nervously*): Did you decide that you would like some of those lovely, lovely tarts, after all, Uncle Diamond?

UNCLE DIAMOND: No tarts, thank you. (*To* KING) Nephew, I have decided to lend you some money to start flour mills flourishing in your kingdom.

KING: Why, thank you, Uncle Diamond! But how did— who told you—

UNCLE DIAMOND: Patience, Nephew. I will explain. Tiny here—and by the way, I still think it's dreadful that the boy doesn't have a decent name—anyway, this fine boy here told me all about your financial problems.

QUEEN: Dear Tiny, what a courageous boy you are! I would have been terrified to speak to Uncle Diamond so intimately!

UNCLE DIAMOND: Not only is he courageous, he's wise and loving as well. He is the only one in this family who cared enough to ask how I was feeling. All the rest of you simply flattered me, in hopes that you could flatten my purse.

KING (*Hangs his head*): It was a very shameful thing for us to do.

QUEEN: And most inconsiderate of us! How *are* you feeling, Uncle Diamond?

UNCLE DIAMOND: Fine, thanks to your youngest son. I do believe that he has taught me how to be a good and happy king.

KING: Why, that's fine! Perhaps Tiny can teach me a few things, too.

JACK: Our tiniest Heart seems to be growing up! Imagine our Tiny being smart enough to teach kings!

UNCLE DIAMOND (*Impatiently*): Tiny, Tiny, Tiny! I'm sick of the sound of it! Why don't you give the little chap a decent name? After due consideration, I believe that I have come up with a splendid name for him. Why don't you name him *Ace?*

TEN: Ace? What kind of name is that?

NINE: Ace? Is it a very special sort of name, Uncle Diamond?

UNCLE DIAMOND: Indeed! It's a name with meat and meaning to it. An ace, you see, is someone who excels in something. To put it precisely, an ace is tops!

EIGHT: Really? What does Tiny excel in?

SEVEN: Tiny can't sing.

FIVE: Tiny can't dance.

TWO: Tiny can't do much of anything.

UNCLE DIAMOND: Ah, but your tiniest Heart excels in wisdom and love!

QUEEN (*Smiling brightly*): Why, of course he does! Our tiniest Heart always has been the wisest and most loving Heart of us all! Strange that we never realized it before!

KING: Yes, Ace is the perfect name for him. Tiny, we hereby name you Ace. The Ace of Hearts.

TINY: Thank you, Father! Oh, it's wonderful to have a proper name at last!

CHILDREN: Hurrah for the Ace of Hearts!

TINY (*Dancing about the stage, he speaks to the audience*):

I'm the Ace of Hearts, the Ace of Hearts
Of the Royal Heart Family!
It's a jolly good name, a wonderful name!
Don't you agree with me?
(*Curtain*)

THE END

The Handwriting on the Wall

by Jessie Nicholson

Characters

SUE
DON, *her brother*
TAD, *a younger brother*
BONNIE MAE, *his twin*
HELEN, *the children's mother*
JUDGE HENDRICKS, *a family friend*
GEORGE WASHINGTON
MARTHA WASHINGTON

BEFORE RISE: GEORGE *and* MARTHA WASHINGTON *enter.*

GEORGE (*As they stroll slowly back and forth in front of the curtain*): You know sometimes, Martha, I get bored reading all the very dull books that have been written about me.

MARTHA (*Shocked*): Good gracious, George, how can you say such a thing? Why, you're the father of your country!

GEORGE: That's just the trouble. The father of my country —what a responsibility! Who would ever suspect to look at my picture that I was once quite a dashing fellow, with young ladies struggling for the honor of waiting upon me.

MARTHA (*Coquettishly*): Ah, but remember, George, it was but a lone widow who won you in the end.

GEORGE: A very beautiful young widow. Alas, your pic-

382

tures do not do you justice either, my love. If they could
have known you as I knew you with a red rose in your
hair, dancing a minuet by my side—(*They exit slowly
as curtain rises.*)

*   *   *

SCENE 1

SETTING: *The parlor of a country inn.*

AT RISE: SUE, *about sixteen years old, dressed in colonial
costume, is bustling about, plumping up sofa cushions,
straightening up chairs and humming softly.* DON, *a year
younger, can be seen at registry desk in hall, also in
colonial costume and powdered wig, writing busily.*

SUE: Oh, Don, isn't it wonderful the way our plan is working out?

DON (*Enthusiastically, coming into parlor*): It sure is.
We've certainly put the old inn right back on its feet.
Wait till Mother comes home and sees the guest book.

SUE (*Doubtfully*): That's the only thing that's worrying
me. She may decide we've been luring guests in under—
under false pretenses. Letting them think George Washington slept here, and wearing these colonial costumes
from the attic.

DON (*Disgustedly*): You sound like one of those mystery
melodramas on the radio—luring guests in under false
pretenses! Besides, maybe good old George did sleep
here.

SUE: And maybe he didn't!

DON: How can you be so certain? He could have. This
house was built in 1702. It's on the route George Washington passed over a good many times. That's history. It
used to be an inn, probably the only one for miles
around.

SUE: That's not proof.

Don: Shucks, there's no one to disprove it, is there?

Sue (*Flatly*): Mother!

Don (*Eagerly*): Not when she sees what a good start we've made. Besides, it was you who gave me the idea in the first place—remember?

Sue: I just said *if* George Washington had slept here, we'd really have something to attract sightseers. He'd probably be turning over in his grave right now if he could see the sign you've painted outside.

Don: I think it's pretty good myself. George, astride his white horse, brandishing his sword. As for the name I chose—that was really the perfect touch. (*Rolling the words over his tongue resonantly*) Independence Inn! The old boy should be proud to admit he slept here.

Sue: If only Mother would be proud, that's all I'd ask.

Don: We had to do something, you know, with the number of guests at a new low. Even Della threatened to leave if any more of her good cooking had to go to waste.

Sue (*Sighing*): Yes, I know. It *would* be dreadful to have to give it all up and go back to the city now. The whole trouble has been Grandmother being sick so much of the time and Mother having to make one trip after another to take care of her.

Don: And then Judge Hendricks keeping her worried. Making her feel she hasn't done the right thing by her children.

Sue: I guess it was up to us all right. This week with no school gave us just the chance we needed.

Don: And boy, what we've done with that chance! Why, folks have grabbed at the "George Washington Slept Here," line, like fish to bait.

Sue: Wait till you see Della in the kitchen all dressed up. She has what she calls George Washington's favorite soup recipe cooking in the kettle in the fireplace. The twins take turns stirring it for the benefit of the guests.

I do think it was a good idea letting visitors go through the old kitchen.

DON (*Dreamily*): It must look pretty much as it did when George Washington stopped here.

SUE: To hear you talk you'd think he actually had stopped here.

DON (*Hopefully*): Well, why not? Tomorrow's his birthday. Maybe the old boy will give us a sign. After all, we *are* having a ball in his honor!

SUE (*Anxiously*): If only Mother doesn't put a stop to it.

DON: Just remember, Mother doesn't want to go back to the city any more than we do. You haven't forgotten all the plans she and Father used to make for buying a country inn?

SUE (*Unhappily*): Yes, but we don't have Father to manage the place now. I heard Judge Hendricks tell Mother she wasn't cut out to be a country innkeeper. He said she should have stayed in the city after Father died where she could have had a job in his office instead of sinking her money into this—this moth-eaten old relic! (*The twins, who had popped their heads in at the kitchen door during this speech, now enter. They too are dressed in colonial costumes.*)

BONNIE MAE (*Indignantly*): It is *not* a moth-eaten old relic! It's a lovely, beautiful, old house and it probably has a secret room somewhere if Tad and I could only find it. Tad says old houses always have a secret room.

TAD: Aw, shucks, do you have to tell everything you know?

SUE: What are you children doing here? You're supposed to be helping Della in the kitchen.

TAD: We got tired of helping Della. Besides, she won't give us anything to eat and we're hungry.

SUE: She has a whole dining room full of people to feed. And after all, it's Mother you're really helping. Come along, I'll go with you and we'll all give Della a hand.

Don (*Eagerly*): I'll just come along too. Those girls who are waiting on table need a little—er—supervision now and then.

Sue (*Sweetly*): And I suppose *you* can give them the kind of supervision they need. Who, may I ask, will take care of the desk while you are exerting your authority?

Don (*Off-handedly*): Oh, I've already prepared for such an emergency. (*Going to desk*) You see this card? It says —Please ring for clerk. I place it in front of the bell— so—

Sue: And your conscience is quite at ease—thus! You slay me, you really do. (*Laughing affectedly*)

Bonnie Mae: Me too! (*Imitating her sister's laugh*)

Tad (*To* Bonnie Mae): Aw, keep still—what do girls know about running an inn anyway? (*They all exit, the twins jostling each other through the kitchen doorway.* George *and* Martha Washington *enter from the hall.*)

George (*Excitedly*): Did you hear them say they were giving a ball in my honor?

Martha: You were eavesdropping and you know it.

George (*Defensively*): Well, I just couldn't help over-hearing. Now I'm glad we dropped in here. I thought this house looked like a friendly place.

Martha (*Dreamily*): They said something about cooking in the fireplace in the kitchen. It sounded like the good old days.

George (*Gleefully*): Ah-ha—you heard them too. Now, who's been eavesdropping?

Martha (*Ignoring this remark*): They are such nice young people, George. They remind me of my own youth.

George (*Aggrievedly*): About the time you were chasing after young Custis and hadn't a thought in your head for me, I suppose.

Martha (*Laughing*): George, you can't still be jealous after nearly two hundred years!

GEORGE (*Ruefully*): Was it that long ago? My, how time does fly!

MARTHA: Yes, indeed—it makes me a little tired even to think about it. Let us sit down and enjoy the firelight. (*They seat themselves on sofa.*)

GEORGE: My, this is a pleasant room, even if the place did used to be run by a scalawag of a landlord.

MARTHA: Did you ever stop here, George?

GEORGE (*Emphatically*): Not I! The innkeeper was rumored to have Redcoat tendencies! I always avoided the place. The rascal finally fled the country. They say he made good his escape from this very room!

MARTHA: You mean there may be a secret passage behind the wall?

GEORGE: Very likely. In our day one was often compelled to disappear as quickly and quietly as the snuffing out of a candle.

MARTHA (*Looking all around*): I wonder where it can be?

GEORGE: Often they were near the fireplace. Between chimney and wall. Let's see— (*He presses on each brick carefully, working on right side from top down. Suddenly a section of paneling beside fireplace swings open revealing a dark passage.*)

MARTHA: My goodness gracious!

GEORGE: By all the guns at Bunker Hill, I was right. (*He stoops down and starts to enter the passageway.*)

MARTHA (*Sharply*): George, where are you going?

GEORGE: To explore, of course. You don't think I could rest well in my grave without knowing where this leads, do you?

MARTHA (*Shaking her head*): I declare, you'll never grow up. Well, do look where you're going and come back soon. (GEORGE *exits through passageway.* MARTHA *shivers a little.*) My, it's sort of spooky here all by myself! I'm glad only George can see me. (*She dozes.* BONNIE

MAE *enters with* TAD, *who is carrying a flashlight in his hand.*)

TAD (*In a loud stage whisper*): Now's a good time to look for the secret room when everybody's out in the kitchen.

BONNIE MAE (*Rapping excitedly up and down left wall*): It doesn't sound very hollow to me.

TAD: Sh-sh—not so loud!

BONNIE MAE: But you *said* that was the way to tell if there was a secret room behind the wall. Besides, who can hear us, silly? (MARTHA WASHINGTON *has wakened with a start. Being a ghost, she cannot of course be seen.*)

TAD: Well, you never can tell. (*In mysterious voice*) There may be other people sneaking around who'd like to find the secret room too. It might be full of hidden treasure or—or something.

BONNIE MAE (*In hushed tone*): Do you really think so, Tad?

TAD: 'Course I do. (*Looking all about cautiously, he suddenly spies open panel and gives a start of surprise.*) Look B-Bonnie Mae. (*Pointing with trembling finger.* BONNIE MAE *gives a little shriek and claps her hand over her mouth.* MARTHA WASHINGTON *shrinks back apprehensively as* BONNIE MAE *backs up against sofa.*)

TAD: Keep still, can't you? Do you want Sue to come and catch us?

BONNIE MAE (*Fearfully*): I don't care if she does. I'm scared!

TAD (*With bravado*): There's nothing to be scared of—(*With less assurance*) I—I don't think. Come on, you can hold the flashlight while I explore. (TAD *finally succeeds in pushing* BONNIE MAE *ahead of him into the passageway as* MARTHA *dodges.*)

MARTHA (*Breathing a sigh of relief*): My stars and stripes, as George would say, what a fright they gave me. I can never quite get used to the idea that it won't hurt if I get stepped on. (*A moment later* George Washington *comes bounding out of the passageway, somewhat disheveled, his wig at a rakish angle, his coat half-buttoned.*) Mercy on us, are you all right, George? I've been as nervous as a witch at the stake!

George: Well, I was having a simply ripping old time, when suddenly two children came charging into the room I'd discovered and spoiled my fun. They had a horrid sort of light that seemed to shine right through me—positively uncanny. I blew out my taper and retreated in a hurry. Did I say "retreat"? Dreadful sort of thing for George Washington to do, eh?

Martha: You *are* in a state. Do straighten your wig and fasten your coat. Why, you've lost one of your buttons. I declare, you are careless.

George: What's one button more or less? Only you and I will know about it.

Martha (*Proudly*): Once a general always a general. (*Then eagerly*) What did you find, George?

George: A room with a door opening into a tunnel that undoubtedly led to the sea. No wonder that scalawag of a landlord escaped. If I had him now— (*Brandishing his sword*)

Martha (*Soothingly*): The Revolutionary War is over, George. No need for fighting it again. Tell me about the secret room.

George: It had everything for the rascal's comfort. A chair, a cot, a desk, and a cupboard holding supplies—a bottle of wine and biscuits. I was going to sample the wine— it should be at its prime by now. The biscuits I feared might be a trifle moldy. But then those children put in an appearance and I had to make good my retreat.

Martha: Well, thank goodness for that. Maybe now we can get a little sleep. Sitting here by the fire has made me drowsy. Do you know that we haven't slept in a real bed for over one hundred and fifty years?

GEORGE: Then it's high time we did something about it, don't you think?

MARTHA: What would you suggest?

GEORGE: Nice comfortable quarters for the night, of course. There's a very charming bedroom just off the parlor here. (*Pointing to bedroom door*) I looked through the window before we came in.

MARTHA (*Shocked*): You've developed some very bad habits, George! Just because people can't see you—

GEORGE: Oh, tush, woman, come along. You know you enjoy being a ghost just as much as I do. (*He gives her his hand and they exit through bedroom door. A moment later, GEORGE sneaks back into the room again, looks all about slyly, and then, grinning mischievously, he darts to desk, rings bell noisily and flees back to his chamber, hardly able to contain his mirth. TAD and BONNIE MAE come plunging out of the passageway, TAD hastily closing panel.*)

TAD: Quick, Bonnie Mae, we have to go back to the kitchen right away before Don comes to answer that bell and we get caught. (*They exit hastily through kitchen door as DON and SUE enter through hall, looking very bewildered when they find no one about.*)

DON (*Puzzled*): That's strange. I'm sure I heard the bell ring, didn't you? (*Shrugging, with hands outstretched*) Guess there must be spooks around here or something!

SUE (*Shivering*): I hope the place isn't haunted.

DON (*Cheerfully*): Perhaps it's good old George making a return visit.

SUE: He's probably turning over in his grave this very minute at all the liberties we're taking with his name.

DON: He ought to be pleased, if you ask me.

SUE: All right, dear brother, have it your own way. However, it was you who raised this ghost in our midst—now I'll leave you to get rid of it. (*She exits to kitchen, and while* Don *is looking all about him a bit nervously, the curtain falls.*)

*   *   *

SCENE 2

TIME: *The next day, early evening.*
SETTING: *The same, with lamps lighted.*
AT RISE: GEORGE *and* MARTHA WASHINGTON *are seated on the sofa conversing.*

GEORGE: That Sue girl must think I spend all my time in my grave. She's always expecting me to turn over in it. Have you noticed, my love?

MARTHA: It's quite possible that she does. That's where most well-behaved, respectable ghosts do spend their time.

GEORGE: I had to be well-behaved and respectable for too long. Now, I want some fun. The peace and quiet of Mount Vernon no longer appeal to me. I'm a restless soul, so to speak, my dear.

MARTHA: I'm restless too, what with those sightseers parading through our bedroom at all hours.

GEORGE: I know, my dear, it has been a little trying. Really, the only reason I'm staying is because I would like to help these poor children out. Now that their mother has returned I know they are going to be in hot water.

MARTHA: But how do you think you can help them anyway? After all, you're only a ghost!

GEORGE: I slept here last night, didn't I? That's what they want, isn't it?

MARTHA: Yes, but there's no proof of it. Why, your head didn't even make a dent in the pillow!

GEORGE: I know. Just think—George Washington—unable to make an impression!

MARTHA: This is no joking matter. After all, these young people had no business taking liberties with your name. No wonder that Sue girl expects you to turn over in your grave.

GEORGE: Whatever they did was to help their mother. Besides, I might have slept here and now I have.

MARTHA (*Shaking her head*): And you were always such a stickler for the truth, George.

GEORGE (*Testily*): I suppose you're referring to that cherry tree business. Well, even if I owned up to it, I *did* cut the tree down first, you know.

MARTHA: You mean these children will be sorry and confess to their mother now that she's home?

GEORGE: Poor Don did that as soon as his mother came in the door. He's just been hoping a miracle would happen today.

MARTHA: Why today?

GEORGE: Well, I don't like to mention it (*Looking at her accusingly*), but it's my birthday!

MARTHA: Land o' Goshen, George, you aren't still expecting me to wish you many happy returns. You know I do that only once every century!

GEORGE: True, I'd forgotten. But nevertheless, I don't want anything to happen to spoil the ball that is being held in my honor. I am looking forward to dancing the minuet again with you, my dear.

MARTHA: You mean you and I are going to attend the ball? Oh, how I wish I had a new frock!

GEORGE (*Gallantly*): Just put a red rose in your hair, my love—and you will be as beautiful to me as ever.

MARTHA (*Excitedly*): Oh, George, I can hardly wait.

GEORGE (*Determinedly*): All the more reason to think of a way to help these children out. We mustn't have their mother put a damper on the ball before—before the ball even gets rolling—ha, ha!

MARTHA: That wasn't very funny, George. It didn't sound quite dignified. Sometimes I fear you're losing all your dignity!

GEORGE (*Chuckling*): I hope so. Whoever heard of a dignified ghost?

MARTHA (*Sighing*): I declare, I think you enjoy being a ghost more than you did being President!

GEORGE: I'd enjoy it still more if you'd help me figure out some way to solve the problem before us. You always were a great help to me, Martha.

MARTHA: Not in matters of strategy, George. At such times only you can see the handwriting on the wall.

GEORGE: A prophetic expression, my dear. It gives me an idea. (*Going into hall, he returns with a red rose which he presents to* MARTHA *with a deep bow.*) Go and make yourself ready for the ball. I will join you shortly. (*She exits.*) The handwriting on the wall—ah! (*He then proceeds to open the secret panel and enters passageway, drawing panel shut behind him. Enter* DON *and* SUE *with their mother from the kitchen, the young people looking very crestfallen.*)

MOTHER: It's no use, children. We cannot continue with this deception. I know you meant well but no sound business was ever built on lies. The sign must come down and we must explain to our guests immediately.

SUE (*Falteringly*): But Mother, what about the ball? It's almost time for it to start.

DON: Yeah, Mom, how about the ball? (*Pleadingly*) I hired the high school orchestra—cheap!

MOTHER (*Sadly*): I'm afraid there won't be any ball. When this gets around we'll be the laughing stock of the town.

DON (*Groaning*): I guess I did more harm than good. And it's all my fault. Sue was against it from the start.

SUE (*Contritely*): It was I who thought of the costumes.

MOTHER: Never mind, children. We'll just have to hold up our heads and be honest about it now. I want you both to go and change into your regular clothes and then we shall have to make a clean breast of it to our guests. In the meantime, I'll go talk to Della. (MOTHER *exits through kitchen door*, DON *and* SUE *through hall. A moment later* GEORGE WASHINGTON *emerges from passageway, sword in hand, just as the twins sneak into room from hallway.* TAD *points excitedly to open panel and tries unsuccessfully to drag* BONNIE MAE *towards it. In exasperation* GEORGE WASHINGTON *gives them a seemingly sly push into the passage, achieving this effect however without his hands ever quite touching them. He then closes the panel with a flip of his sword and strolls jauntily into his own chamber, as* JUDGE HENDRICKS *enters. He is a very pompous, self-righteous looking gentleman, dressed in dark, dignified apparel. He rings the bell on the desk demandingly and enters living room.* DON *and* SUE *and their mother come hurrying in.* DON *has only had time to remove his wig and* SUE *her cap and kerchief.*)

JUDGE (*Sternly*): What is the meaning of this? I am surprised you would stoop to such trickery.

DON (*Hastily*): It's my fault, Judge Hendricks. Mother had nothing to do with it.

JUDGE: Silence, young man. I—(*He is interrupted by a loud thud from offstage behind secret panel.*) My word, what was that?

MOTHER (*Nervously*): Maybe a falling brick. The chimney isn't in very good condition, I fear. (*Just then there is a hollow-sounding cry behind panel.*)

JUDGE (*Darkly*): If this is any more of your nonsense, Donald—

DON: Don't look at me, sir. I'm as much in the dark as you are.

SUE: Maybe the h-house *is* really haunted!

JUDGE: Nonsense, it must be the wind. (*Muffled voices are suddenly heard calling, "Sue—Don!"*)

MOTHER: Why, it's the twins! Where can they be?

JUDGE HENDRICKS (*In amazement*): The voices seem to come from behind the wall!

DON (*Shouting*): Tad—Bonnie Mae—where are you?

TAD (*From behind panel*): We're in the secret passage and we can't get out.

SUE: How did you get in?

BONNIE MAE (*Off*): We were pushed!

SUE: Now, that makes a lot of sense.

JUDGE HENDRICKS: There must be some way of opening that panel from this room. A great many of these old houses had concealed chambers. (*Looking all around and running his hand up and down the panel*)

DON: That's what they were looking for—a secret room. They probably stumbled on it.

BONNIE MAE (*Off*): Hurry up and get us out. Tad broke his flashlight and it's awfully dark in here.

JUDGE HENDRICKS: I told you, Helen, this was no place to bring up children. Now see what they've gotten themselves into. (*Crossly*) And I can't seem to find out how to get this confounded panel open.

MOTHER (*Forlornly*): I guess you're right, Phillip. You're *always* right. (*As DON and SUE glare at the JUDGE, she bursts out stormily*) But oh, why couldn't George Washington really have slept here. I think it was most inconsiderate of him not to!

JUDGE HENDRICKS (*Testily*): You talk like a child, Helen. I fear there's nothing for it but to get an axe and break down the paneling. (*At these words, while JUDGE is*

trying to locate the elusive spot, GEORGE WASHINGTON
*glides out of his bedroom looking very much annoyed
and with one swift blow of his sword, knocks out the
brick controlling the panel, which promptly flies open.*
TAD *and* BONNIE MAE *rush into their mother's arms and*
WASHINGTON, *after a couple of feints with sword at* JUDGE
HENDRICKS, *retreats to his bedchamber.*)

DON: Holy smokes—a real secret passage!

JUDGE HENDRICKS (*Smugly*): Very neatly done if I did do it
myself.

DON (*Politely*): Yes, but could you do it again, sir?

JUDGE HENDRICKS (*Still pleased with his unexpected
achievement*): Once was all that was necessary, Donald,
my boy. Come, let us investigate this passageway. I will
very likely be able to give you children a lesson in history.

MOTHER: Don, get the big flashlight in the kitchen for the
Judge. (DON *exits.*)

BONNIE MAE: We don't want to go in there again. We've
been twice. It's dark and—and smelly.

JUDGE HENDRICKS (*In annoyance*): You mean you children
discovered the secret of opening the panel?

TAD: We-ll—not exactly. It just seemed to open up all by
itself!

JUDGE HENDRICKS: Nonsense—stuff and nonsense!

SUE: The house *must* be haunted.

DON (*Who has returned with the flashlight, winking at*
SUE): Probably by George Washington's ghost!

JUDGE HENDRICKS: You see, Helen, their imaginations are
completely overwrought. I hope this will be a lesson to
you. Donald, give me the flashlight. Tad, you may lead
the way. Come, children. (*They all troop through the
opening,* JUDGE HENDRICKS *peering back suspiciously
over each shoulder, as if fearing he too might be pushed*

from behind. Enter GEORGE *and* MARTHA WASHINGTON, MARTHA *with a red rose in her hair.*)

GEORGE: Ah, my dear, you look very lovely tonight, just as you did in the days of old.

MARTHA: Do I really, George? I can hardly wait for the ball to begin. (*Dreamily*) Can't you just hear the fiddlers tuning up?

GEORGE (*As band is heard faintly, warming up offstage*): I believe I can and it certainly sounds very strange. I thought I heard Don say something about the musicians being—ah—academy youths, I believe. I had expected a Mozart quartet.

MARTHA (*Indignantly, as noise increases in volume*): It sounds more like the downbeat of Indian war drums to me!

GEORGE: I agree. (*Ruefully*) We could scarce dance the minuet to that fearful din.

MARTHA (*Holding her hands to her ears*): It quite gives me a headache just to listen. I declare, I'll be glad to get back to the peace and quiet of Mount Vernon. How soon do you think we may go?

GEORGE: It would hardly be polite to leave until the ball in my honor is over. Come, let us sit down before the fire, my love, and enjoy the charm of this old room while we may. (*They seat themselves on the sofa.*)

MARTHA: Tell me, George, just what have you been up to? The way you pushed those two poor children into the passage and closed the panel on them was quite disgraceful. Don't think I didn't see you.

GEORGE: Simply a part of my strategy, Martha. The discovery by the family of the secret chamber was necessary to the future prosperity of Independence Inn. After all, it was only a very little push, hardly more than a breath of cold air, you might say. (*Just then sounds are heard from passageway.*)

MARTHA: Sh—George. I think I hear someone coming! (*They rise hastily and back into corner, as* JUDGE HENDRICKS *comes stamping out of the passage, his face like a thundercloud.* MOTHER *and children follow, obviously triumphant.* DON, *holding small object in his hand, examines it closely under the light, surrounded by* SUE *and the twins, exclaiming excitedly over his find.*)

SUE: See how it shines!

BONNIE MAE (*Wonderingly*): Is it real gold?

TAD: 'Course it is. Girls ask such silly questions.

DON (*Grinning*): Good old George, I knew he'd come through.

JUDGE (*Testily*): Well I suppose you all think you've proved your point.

MOTHER (*Laughing*): I don't believe even you can deny that, Phillip.

JUDGE (*In great annoyance*): I suppose not. Of course that button alone, (*Pointing to object in* DON'S *hand*) would never have convinced me, even if Don does profess to know so much about it.

DON (*Looking the* JUDGE *straight in the eye*): I've made a very close study of the Washington mementoes in our museum, sir, and I can assure you that an identical button is missing from a coat of the General's on display there.

JUDGE: Indeed! I still maintain it could be mere coincidence—the button might even have been planted there. (*Glaring at* DON) But along with the other evidence that we—ah—unearthed, I cannot deny that you have proved your case. A little belatedly, I might add. (*Bitingly*)

MOTHER: You should be very happy for us, Phillip.

JUDGE (*Clearing his throat*): I should have been happier if you had stayed in the city where you would have been under my—er—protection. But if you are still determined to go on with this foolhardy adventure (*In an injured tone*), I suppose there is nothing more I can say. (*Picking up his hat*) I bid you all good evening.

MOTHER (*Coaxingly*): Oh, do stay for the dance, Phillip. It's being held in honor of George Washington, you know.

JUDGE (*Stiffly*): Then I will leave the General in full command. Certainly I would never attempt to compete with such a brilliant strategist! *Good* evening. (*He exits*)

MOTHER (*Laughing helplessly*): Poor, old Phillip. It was hard for him to accept defeat.

DON: He'll be around again or I miss my guess.

MOTHER (*Gayly*): Well, come on, children, what are we waiting for? On with the dance!

BONNIE MAE (*Excitedly*): You mean we may come too, Tad and I?

MOTHER (*Hesitantly*): Well—just for this once you may stay up, I guess. Run and get dressed quickly. (*They scamper off, shouting happily. Rhumba music comes in loudly now and* DON *exits through hall, followed by* SUE *and* MOTHER, *all doing the rhumba step. During this time,* GEORGE *and* MARTHA *have listened to the conversation with obvious interest and now* GEORGE *strides to the middle of the stage looking very pleased with himself.*)

GEORGE: Did you hear that, my love? That scalawag of a judge has left me in full command. He even admitted I was a brilliant strategist.

MARTHA: Everyone knows that, George. History has recorded it. (*Reprovingly*) I am sure the poor Judge meant well.

GEORGE: His strategy, Martha, left much to be desired. (*Chuckling*) I certainly had him cornered down there in the secret chamber!

MARTHA (*Curiously*): Just what *did* they find, George, that so convinced the Judge?

GEORGE: The handwriting on the wall, so to speak, my dear. You remember your own prophetic words?

MARTHA (*In exasperation*): Will you please stop beating around the bush and come to the point?

GEORGE (*Contritely*): Pardon me, my dear. I am afraid my dealings with the Continental Congress have made me a long-winded speaker. You remember my mentioning the desk in the secret chamber?

MARTHA: Yes, George, I remember.

GEORGE (*Reminiscently*): It is very like my old one where I did all my studying on the family plantation. The first time I laid eyes on it, I was beset with an irresistible longing— (*He pauses dreamily.*)

MARTHA (*Trying to be patient*): An irresistible longing to do what, George?

GEORGE (*Apologetically*): To carve my name on the lid with my sword—an old military trick, my dear. Your own words were what gave me the inspiration to return and do just that.

MARTHA (*Indulgently*): You're still just a boy at heart. Imagine—carving your name on a school desk!

GEORGE: Quite as telltale as handwriting on the wall, you must admit! I fear though that the tip of my sword was a trifle blunt. The letters did not have the nice, fresh, clean-cut look that they did in my youth. You might almost say that they were aged in the wood like old wine in a bottle!

MARTHA: Um-m, I am beginning to understand. Aged in the wood—what further proof could anyone ask that George Washington had once stopped here two hundred years ago, more or less?

GEORGE: Ah, but don't forget there was the button, too, even if the Judge did try to discredit it. A most amazing coincidence that there should be an identical one missing from a uniform of mine in the museum, wouldn't you say, my love?

MARTHA: Truly amazing, if I didn't know how many buttons you were in the habit of losing. I still can't help feeling a bit sorry for poor Judge Hendricks, though. I have a notion he aspired to the lady's hand and wanted to get her where he could keep an eye on her.

GEORGE: A bad loser. You know, Martha, there is something about him that reminds me of that rascally landlord. If the Judge had designs on the charming widow, I am glad he met a just defeat at my hands.

MARTHA (*Coquettishly*): You once had designs on a charming widow yourself George.

GEORGE (*Wagging his finger at her*): Ah, but I was an excellent strategist. I never accepted defeat. (*Pausing*) But listen—I do believe I hear the strains of a Mozart minuet. (*The music comes in clearly from offstage when he is not speaking.*) Those musicians must have come to their senses at last. (*Bowing to* MARTHA) Will you honor me with this dance, my love. You are much too beautiful to remain a wallflower tonight! (MARTHA *curtsies low and they dance a few steps of the minuet before the curtains close.*)

THE END

Martha Washington's Spy

by Earl J. Dias

Characters

GENERAL GEORGE WASHINGTON
MARTHA WASHINGTON
SILAS WEGG ⎫
CALEB JENKINS ⎭ *young soldiers*
BETSY, *a young girl*
BENJAMIN JAEKEL
SAM HOWARD

TIME: *A cold night in January, 1777.*
SETTING: *A sentry outpost at Valley Forge.*
AT RISE: SILAS *is pacing back and forth, a musket on his shoulder. He stops occasionally to stamp his feet and rub his arms. Footsteps are heard from off left. SILAS points his musket in the direction of the sounds.*

SILAS: Halt! Who goes there?
CALEB (*Offstage*): It's Caleb Jenkins, Silas.
SILAS: Come out here where I can see you. (CALEB *enters from left.*)
CALEB: Nervous, Silas?
SILAS: Cold more than anything. (*He shivers.*) Br-r—I could do with a big mug of hot tea.
CALEB: All of us could, I'll wager.

SILAS: Why are you traipsin' about on a night like this? If I could, I'd be back in the barracks with the covers over my head to keep out the cold.

CALEB: Orders from General Washington himself. Ever since Tom Weeks fell asleep at his post a week ago, the General has seen to it that someone inspects the sentry posts every night.

SILAS: As if anyone could sleep in this cold. And anyway, why all the care and caution? Who would want to come to this forsaken place?

CALEB: A spy, for one.

SILAS (*Sarcastically*): A spy! What old wives' tales have you been hearing?

CALEB: This is no old wives' tale. I heard the General say that the countryside is swarming with them.

SILAS (*Laughing*): With what? Old wives?

CALEB (*Blowing on his hands*): With spies.

SILAS: Spies, indeed! If the lobsterbacks want this miserable place, they're welcome to it as far as I'm concerned.

CALEB: Oh, you can laugh—but the British want to know our strength here, how many men we have.

SILAS (*Bitterly, as he begins his pacing once more*): I can tell them that easily enough. We've fewer men today than we had yesterday; and tomorrow, we'll have fewer men than we have today. They're certainly deserting fast enough.

CALEB: You sound as though you'd like to join the deserters.

SILAS (*Stopping his pacing and speaking angrily*): Let me make one thing clear, Caleb Jenkins—I'll not desert. Wars aren't won by the fainthearted, and liberty isn't gained by cowards. (*Pauses*) I keep thinking about Sam Howard. He comes from a farm near here, and, before I came on duty tonight, he told me he's decided to leave the army. "I can freeze at home as well as here," he said. "And at home, at least, I can be of help to my wife and baby." He has probably left by now.

CALEB: I never would have expected such an action from Sam.

SILAS: Nor would I. He always seemed a strong and honest enough fellow and devoted to the cause.

CALEB (*Sighing*): As Scripture says, "The spirit is willing, but the flesh is weak." Well, I'll be off about my duties. I have four more posts to inspect—if I don't freeze as stiff as a tree before I get to them. Good night, Silas.

SILAS: Good night, Caleb. (CALEB *exits right.* SILAS *begins pacing up and down once again. There is a sudden noise offstage left, a sort of thump followed by an exclamation.* SILAS, *pointing his musket in the direction of the noise, advances cautiously toward exit. He exits. In a moment,* SILAS *returns holding* BETSY *by the collar. She is dressed in a man's coat, a muffler about the neck, and a cocked hat.* SILAS *stands back and points his musket at his captive, who huddles shivering and afraid.*) Now, my sly fellow, just what is your business here?

BETSY (*In a high, shrill voice*): Don't shoot, sir. (SILAS *advances toward his captive, examines the face closely, and then whistles in surprise.*)

SILAS: Why! You're a girl!

BETSY: Y-yes. My name is Betsy.

SILAS (*Still covering her with his musket*): Betsy, is it? So the British are using females now to do their nasty work!

BETSY (*With a little more spirit*): What do you mean?

SILAS: My meaning should be clear. Here you are, creeping about the camp on a night as cold as King George's heart, and here you are, too, dressed as a man. It's as plain as a dish of beans that you're bent on mischief of some kind.

BETSY: That's not true.

SILAS: Well, it will do until a better explanation comes

along—and I doubt if a better one will. At least, my
duty is plain. (*He whistles loudly—two long whistles
and one short one.*) There. That will bring somebody
here who'll take you to General Washington.
BETSY (*Cringing*): Oh, no—please let me go! I swear to
you that I'm not a spy!
SILAS (*Laughing*): You're a splendid actress, miss.
BETSY: Please believe me.
SILAS (*Impatiently*): Then just what are you doing here?
BETSY: I can't tell you. It's something I must keep to myself. But I'm not a spy. (CALEB *enters hurriedly from
right.*)
CALEB: What's wrong, Silas? I heard your signal. (*Looking at* BETSY) And who is this?
SILAS: A female dressed as a man, Caleb.
CALEB (*Going to* BETSY *and examining her closely*): I
told you the countryside was swarming with spies.
BETSY (*Spiritedly*): Oh, you two are blockheads!
SILAS: Blockheads, indeed! Listen to her, Caleb. "I'm not
a spy," she says, "but I can't tell you what I'm doing
here. It's something I must keep to myself." Take her
to the General.
CALEB (*Grinning*): That won't be necessary. I'll bring
the General to her. He's not far from here now—inspecting posts himself tonight. And his wife is with him.
SILAS: His wife?
CALEB: She's visiting him for a spell. Brought him some
warm stockings for one thing. She's a pleasant-enough
lady—and about the only warmth I've seen around here
for a month. (*Going to* BETSY *and chucking her under
the chin*) My, you're a pretty lass. Too bad you're on
the wrong side.
BETSY: Mind your manners! (CALEB *exits, right. A noise
is heard offstage.*)

SILAS: Halt! Who goes there? (BENJAMIN JAEKEL *enters at left.*)

BENJAMIN: I am Benjamin Jaekel, sir, a friend to the cause. (*He goes to center and looks at* BETSY.) Aha! There you are! Caught, are you? I hoped you would be.

BETSY (*Surprised*): Who are you?

SILAS: This place is as crowded tonight as a Philadelphia street. Just what is your business here?

BENJAMIN (*Bowing with a flourish*): Benjamin Jaekel, as I told you, sir. A friend of the cause and sworn enemy to the British. I own a farm a few miles from here.

SILAS: Then why aren't you at home in your warm kitchen?

BENJAMIN (*Bowing again*): I'm in the service of liberty, young sir. I came out of my barn tonight and saw this person here (*Nodding toward* BETSY) sneaking across my fields. At first, I thought she was a man. Then I noticed the way she walked, rather mincing-like. I said to myself, "Benjamin Jaekel, there is something peculiar and sinister about all this." Oh, I've heard talk a-plenty about spies in these parts. So I said to myself, "Benjamin Jaekel, follow that woman. She's up to no good. And if she's a spy, why, perhaps there'll be a small reward for unmasking her." (*He grins*) I've heard that General Washington is a generous man.

SILAS (*Scratching his head*): Your story sounds reasonable.

BENJAMIN: Young sir, surely no one will doubt the word of Benjamin Jaekel. Honest Ben, they call me, all over the countryside.

BETSY: I tell you again. I am not a spy.

BENJAMIN (*Bowing to her*): Ah, young lady, never let it be said that honest Ben Jaekel ever argued with a woman — (*He winks at* SILAS) and a fetching one at that. But, at the risk of violating the politeness for which I am famous, I must contradict you. (*He places his hand over his heart*) But it wounds me here to do so.

BETSY (*Spiritedly*): Nonsense!

SILAS: We have a spitfire on our hands, Mr. Jaekel.

BENJAMIN: Ah, well, I'm sure that you and the rest of General Washington's men will be a match for her. Your lines seem well guarded enough. How many sentry posts do you have?

SILAS: That's a military secret.

BENJAMIN (*Bowing to him*): Of course. It was foolish of me to ask. I apologize, young sir, for my lack of discretion.

BETSY (*Impatiently*): Do we have to stand here in the cold like addle-headed idiots?

SILAS: Hold your tongue.

BENJAMIN (*Coughing politely*): Er—I believe, young sir, that our pretty and mysterious companion has a point. This cold tonight is as piercing as a dagger. (*He rubs his arms*) Could we not take our fetching spy to the proper authorities, where (*Winking at* SILAS) I might be rewarded for recognizing her evil errand?

SILAS: General Washington himself will be here at any moment.

BENJAMIN: Ah, what an opportunity! A chance to shake the hand of a man whose name is a byword among lovers of liberty everywhere. I am honored, honored.

BETSY: I wish he'd hurry, then.

SILAS: There'll be bad news for you when he does get here.

BENJAMIN: Right, young sir—bad news, indeed. What do you do with spies, sir? Hang them or shoot them? (*He shakes his head in mock sadness*) Such a lovely neck to have a noose around it. (*Placing his hand over his heart*) It wounds me here.

BETSY: Save your unwanted sympathy for those who can use it. I'm not a spy, and there won't be any hanging.

BENJAMIN (*Sadly*): Ah, poor child. You little know what you say. (CALEB *enters, followed by* GENERAL WASHING-

TON *and* MARTHA WASHINGTON, *his wife. Both are bundled in warm clothing.* SILAS *lowers his musket and salutes.* WASHINGTON *returns the salute.*)

WASHINGTON (*Looking at* BETSY): And who is this? Is this war now being fought by women?

SILAS: She's a spy, sir. I apprehended her attempting to get through the lines.

BENJAMIN (*Coughing politely*): With my help, General. I followed this young woman for several miles when I saw that her appearance was somewhat unusual.

WASHINGTON (*Looking at* BENJAMIN): And who are you?

BENJAMIN (*Bowing*): Benjamin Jaekel, sir, at your service and at the service of all true patriots. A farmer, sir, a poor but honest tiller of the soil, who counts it the privilege of a lifetime to meet the great General Washington face to face.

WASHINGTON: Hm-m. And what have you to say for yourself, young woman?

BETSY: I am not a spy, sir.

MARTHA (*Looking closely at* BETSY): Why, George, she's just a child!

BETSY (*Firmly*): I'm a woman, ma'am. I'm eighteen.

MARTHA: You certainly don't look like a spy.

CALEB: She says she isn't, but she's a pert thing.

WASHINGTON: If you're not a spy, what are you? And what are you doing here?

BETSY: I can't say, sir.

WASHINGTON (*A bit impatiently*): What do you mean, you can't say? Surely, if your presence here is entirely innocent, you can tell us about it. (*More gently*) I don't bite, child.

BETSY (*Beginning to cry*): I—I can't say.

MARTHA: Don't bully the child, George. Can't you see that she's upset and close to tears?

WASHINGTON: My dear Martha, I'm not attempting to

bully her. But surely it's my duty to discover just what errand she is on.

BENJAMIN: And mark my words—it's an errand that bodes no good to the Colonies.

MARTHA: You men are all alike—jumping to conclusions before the issues are clear.

WASHINGTON: But, Martha, this young woman seems to be making no attempt to clarify the issues for us.

MARTHA (*Gently*): Why can't you tell us why you are here, child?

BETSY: Because—well, because someone would get into trouble if I did.

MARTHA: But can't you see that you're in even greater trouble yourself?

BETSY (*Uncertainly*): But I—

MARTHA: Isn't it something you can tell me—just as one woman to another?

WASHINGTON: Martha, really—there's nothing to do but to take her to headquarters and to question her until she reveals the truth.

BENJAMIN: Wise words, sir, wise words. She'll confess with the proper treatment, I'm sure.

MARTHA (*Angrily to* BENJAMIN): No one has asked for your opinion!

BENJAMIN (*Bowing*): My deepest apologies, ma'am. (*Placing hand on heart*) I am wounded here—but no matter.

BETSY (*Angrily*): You're always being wounded! I think you're perfectly horrible!

WASHINGTON: Please—let's get to the business at hand. You had better come with us, young woman.

MARTHA: Wait, George. (*She places her arm around* BETSY's *shoulders*.) Surely, child, your secret cannot be so terrible that it is worth being regarded as a spy for. (*Very gently*) Again I ask you—isn't it something you can tell me?

BETSY: B-but if I tell you, you'll tell the General, and I know that he'll be very angry.

MARTHA: Not necessarily. Please believe me, the General is a reasonable and a kindly man. I ought to know, after nearly twenty years of marriage to him. (*She looks affectionately at* WASHINGTON)

WASHINGTON (*Smiling*): Thank you, Martha.

MARTHA (*Leading* BETSY *to right*): Let's get over here, and you can whisper your secret to me.

BETSY: Oh, I wish I could. (*Uncertainly*) I want to—you seem so understanding, but—

MARTHA: Of course you want to. And I know that everything will be all right. Very often problems that seem earth-shaking turn out to be very small ones really. Come.

BETSY: Well—

MARTHA: Please, it's for the best.

BETSY (*With obvious relief*): I will! (*She begins to whisper in* MARTHA's *ear.* MARTHA *nods occasionally and smiles, her smile becoming broader as* BETSY's *story progresses.*)

SILAS (*While* BETSY *and* MARTHA *are conferring*): This is a strange case, sir.

WASHINGTON: It's a strange war. You seem frozen to the bone.

SILAS (*Shivering*): It's a cold night, sir.

WASHINGTON: Do you know anything of a soldier named Sam Howard? He's missing from quarters.

SILAS: W-well, sir—

WASHINGTON: I see. He has deserted, and you don't want to give him away. Well, I suppose one must be loyal to one's friends, and heaven only knows there are enough deserters.

CALEB: Sam has gone back to his farm, sir. It's only a few miles from here.

WASHINGTON (*Shaking his head*): If only we can get

through this bitter winter. It does things to a man, weakens the very moral fiber of him.

BENJAMIN: No true patriot would desert his cause.

WASHINGTON: That may be true, but, after all, men are only human beings, compounded of strength and weakness. The conditions here try even the stoutest hearts. (*Grimly*) But we will survive.

CALEB: Amen to that, sir. (MARTHA *and* BETSY *come to center.*)

MARTHA: One thing is certain, George—this young woman —her name, by the way, is Betsy—is no spy.

WASHINGTON: Indeed—then what is she?

MARTHA: I'll tell you privately, George. There is no reason for her secret to be shared by the entire army.

WASHINGTON (*Dubiously*): But, surely—

MARTHA: George, certainly you don't doubt the word of your own wife. I'll take my oath that this young woman is as innocent of any sinister designs as a babe in arms.

WASHINGTON (*Shrugging his shoulders*): Very well, Martha. Of course I do not doubt you. (*To* SILAS *and* CALEB) You men had better take this young woman—Betsy, isn't it? (BETSY *nods*)—to my headquarters. Otherwise, she's certain to catch her death of cold. Give her something warm to drink. (*To* BETSY) Stay there until I return. I shall want to talk with you.

BETSY (*Happily*): Yes, General.

WASHINGTON: As soon as you two men have done your errand, return here. (*To* SILAS) I'll man your post until you get back. And have something hot to drink yourselves.

SILAS (*Saluting*): Thank you, sir. (SILAS, CALEB *and* BETSY *go toward right. Before they exit,* BETSY *turns and speaks.*)

BETSY: And thank you, ma'am. Thank you with all my heart. (MARTHA *nods and smiles as the three exit.*)

BENJAMIN: I could have sworn that girl was up to no good.

MARTHA (*Acidly*): I'm sure that you, like all of us, have made your share of mistakes in your time.

BENJAMIN (*Bowing*): Naturally.

WASHINGTON: When we return to our quarters, Mr. Jaekel, you might join us for a drink of something hot before you go back to your farm.

BENJAMIN: Ah, thank you, General. You are generous beyond measure, and the night is indeed cold. (SAM HOWARD *enters timidly*.)

WASHINGTON (*Noticing* SAM): Who goes there? Come forth to be recognized. (SAM *goes to center, visibly surprised at the sight of* WASHINGTON.) Your face is familiar. Who are you?

SAM (*Saluting*): Sam Howard, sir.

BENJAMIN: Aha, the deserter! The traitor to the noble cause of the Colonies!

WASHINGTON: Why are you prowling around the lines at this time of night? I heard you had gone back to your farm.

SAM: I started back, sir.

WASHINGTON: And what happened?

SAM: I found I couldn't do it, sir.

MARTHA: Good lad!

SAM: You see, sir, I have been worried about Betsy—that's my wife. She hasn't been well, and then there is the baby to care for. I decided I *had* to get home—that I could do more good there than I could here. So I left.

MARTHA: Your Betsy is here.

SAM (*Astounded*): Here? Betsy here?

MARTHA (*Smiling*): Indeed she is—and she came near to being taken as a spy.

SAM: But I don't understand. What is she doing so far from home?

WASHINGTON: You're not the only one who would like to solve that mystery.

MARTHA: You may as well know the story now, George. When Betsy received your last letter, Sam—

SAM (*Ruefully*): I said a lot of foolish things in that letter.

MARTHA: When Betsy received it, she could read between the lines. She had a suspicion you might be planning to desert the army because you were worried about her. So she walked a good eight or ten miles to see you tonight.

SAM: Poor Betsy—in all this cold.

MARTHA: She wanted to persuade you to stay. Betsy is all right. She says that things are now going well, that she is over her sickness, and that she can manage things on the farm. Her mother and father have come to stay with her.

SAM: But this is wonderful news! Now she won't be alone.

WASHINGTON (*Thoughtfully*): So that is why young Betsy attempted to break through the lines tonight. I see now why she was reluctant to discuss her mission.

SAM: And to think that I almost deserted. (*To* WASHINGTON) But do you know, sir, that after I had gone a few miles, my conscience began to plague me. That's why I turned back. I suddenly realized that freedom and liberty are worth fighting and being uncomfortable for. And I said to myself, "If all the army looked to their own comfort first, how could we win the war?"

WASHINGTON: How, indeed.

BENJAMIN: A very pleasing sentiment.

SAM (*Eying* BENJAMIN *closely*): General, who is this man?

BENJAMIN: Farmer Benjamin Jaekel, sir, at your service and devoted to the fight against tyranny.

SAM: Jaekel? (*He gazes intently at* BENJAMIN) That wasn't your name a year ago.

BENJAMIN (*Nervously*): I was born Benjamin Jaekel, and I shall die the same. Explain yourself, young man.

SAM (*Excitedly*): General Washington, when we were stationed at Trenton, months ago, I saw this man at a tavern there. He made several attempts to bribe a group of us soldiers—offering money for information about troop movements. Some of us set on him, but he escaped. I'll take my oath this is the same man. His name was Langdon then.

BENJAMIN: Young sir, you're mistaken—mistaken, indeed. Ben Jaekel is the name—honest Ben to all who know me. My farm is but a few miles from here.

SAM: So is mine. I know all the farms for miles around, and there's no Jaekel on any of them.

WASHINGTON: Well, honest Ben. What have you to say for yourself?

BENJAMIN: This is all a terrible error, General.

SAM (*To* BENJAMIN): Take off your hat.

BENJAMIN: Be reasonable, young sir. This joke, or this case of mistaken identity—call it what you will—has gone far enough. And to ask a man to remove his hat in this cold is an insult to his intelligence.

MARTHA: Why do you make such a request, Sam?

SAM: Because the Langdon I knew had a long scar on his scalp—a deep, red one.

WASHINGTON (*Sternly*): Remove your hat.

BENJAMIN: Sir, I will not be bullied! I—(*Together,* WASHINGTON *and* SAM *grasp* BENJAMIN *and pull off his hat.*)

MARTHA (*Inspecting* BENJAMIN'S *head as the others hold him*): You're right, Sam. Here's the scar, as big as life.

BENJAMIN: This is an outrage! The Continental Congress shall hear of this!

WASHINGTON: It will—though not in a manner favorable to you, Mr. Langdon. (*To* SAM) Sam, take this fellow to my headquarters. I'll be there as soon as the sentry returns. (*Sternly*) I'll want a few words with you, too.

SAM (*Saluting*): Yes, sir. Come along, Langdon.

MARTHA: And there's someone there whom I'm sure you will enjoy seeing.

SAM: You mean Betsy, ma'am?

MARTHA (*Smiling*): Find out for yourself.

SAM (*Grasping* BENJAMIN *roughly by the arm*): Come on.

BENJAMIN: Heads will roll for this!

SAM: Yours among them! (*They exit right,* BENJAMIN *still protesting violently.*)

WASHINGTON (*Sighing*): Well, my dear, you see now that anything can happen in the military life. The question now, I suppose, is what to do about Sam. After all, he did try to desert, so he should be court-martialed.

MARTHA: George, you wouldn't do such a thing to so nice a young man!

WASHINGTON: Military regulations are severe.

MARTHA: Well, they may be, but *you're* not, thank heaven. And I know you wouldn't want to make that courageous young woman unhappier than she is.

WASHINGTON: Now, about that young woman—wives of enlisted men aren't supposed to visit their husbands here, you know.

MARTHA: But it's perfectly clear why she did. She's a brave child. (*Smiling and very softly*) And, George, I came to you, after all, because I missed you so.

WASHINGTON (*Somewhat appeased*): And it's good to have you—but this is no place for a woman.

MARTHA: But about Sam?

WASHINGTON: Well—

MARTHA: Please, George.

WASHINGTON: It's against regulations—

MARTHA: You won't have him court-martialed, will you? After all, he unmasked that horrible Langdon.

WASHINGTON: That's true. He did. (*He looks at her affectionately*) Martha, you could charm a robin from a tree. No, I won't court-martial him.

MARTHA: Thank you. (*She kisses him lightly on the cheek.*)

WASHINGTON (*Chuckling*): You know, I believe I'll resign from the army.

MARTHA (*Surprised*): George, what are you saying?

WASHINGTON: And I'll recommend my wife as Commander-in-Chief. She seems to know more about human nature than I do.

MARTHA: I was worried for a moment. No, George, you're the man for the position. (*Archly*) Only sometimes an army can use a woman's touch.

WASHINGTON: Can it, indeed? Well, as your first duty, I command you to walk this post with me. (*He places an arm about her shoulders*) Come, now—and with true military posture, mind you. (*They begin pacing up and down, very straight and precise, and both laugh affectionately at each other as the curtains close.*)

THE END

George Slept Here, Too

by Anne Coulter Martens

Characters

MRS. DALE	FRANK, *a friend*
JIM ⎫	MISS HASTINGS, *a visitor*
NADINE ⎬ *her children*	LARRY
BABSY ⎭	MOIRA

TIME: *The present.*

SETTING: *The living room of the Dale home in Eastern Pennsylvania.*

AT RISE: NADINE *is sitting at a card table putting finishing touches on a poster.* JIM *stands on a footstool. He is declaiming as* MRS. DALE *enters, carrying a warm coat over her arm and also a handbag and a blue suitcase, which she sets down.*

JIM: Board members, faculty, friends and students— (BABSY *enters with a cooking pan suspended from her neck. She is beating it with two wooden spoons and singing loudly "Yankee Doodle."*)

MRS. DALE: Quiet, please! (JIM *and* BABSY *stop.*) Finished with your poster, Nadine?

NADINE: Almost.

JIM: I'm practicing my speech for the pageant. (*Declaims*) Board members, faculty—

417

MRS. DALE: Fine, just fine. I'm sure Fairfield School will put on a wonderful Washington's Birthday pageant, and we'll all be proud of you.

BABSY: Can I be a drummer boy?

JIM: Negative.

NADINE: You can sit in the audience and clap.

BABSY: (*Dolefully, sitting on sofa, clapping as she speaks*): Clap, clap.

MRS. DALE (*Looking at her watch*): I have to leave to meet that train. Make sure this place is tidy when Miss Hastings gets here.

BABSY: (*Taking pan from around her neck*): Mother, are you really going to ask her if she'd sell this house to us?

MRS. DALE: I am. Now, it has to be neat and tidy.

NADINE: I wish we could have bought it long ago. (*Puts paint jars and brushes on desk and picks up poster*)

JIM: I guess Miss Hastings hates to part with her family homestead. (*Folds up card table*)

MRS. DALE: Not any more. She's coming east to settle things.

NADINE: Pretty soon it will be *our* old homestead.

JIM: I'll be glad when we can take the FOR SALE sign down from the front lawn.

MRS. DALE (*Using compact and putting on powder*): When your friend Frank comes over, tell him I put a couple of Washington-type costumes in that suitcase, and he's to see which one fits him better.

BABSY: O.K.

MRS. DALE: I found them in that old trunk in the attic. Miss Hastings and her brother George must have done a lot of dressing up when they were young, and she saved everything. (*Telephone rings.*) I'll get it. (*On phone*) Yes, this is Mrs. Dale. . . . Oh, Mrs. Powell? I don't believe we've met. . . . Really? . . . It's quite an old house, yes. I don't know the exact age. . . . (*Children look worried.*) Certainly, Mrs. Powell, do come over and look around for yourself. . . . Goodbye. (*Hangs up*)

BABSY (*Worried*): Oh, Mother. . . .

MRS. DALE (*Ignoring her*): If this Mrs. Powell comes before I get back from the station, ask her to wait. (NADINE *and* JIM *look at each other, sigh deeply, and go out taking the poster and card table.*)

BABSY: She's interested in old houses?

MRS. DALE: Very much. (*Puts on her coat*)

BABSY: Just how old *is* this place?

MRS. DALE: Quite old. (*Checks her handbag*) Car keys, yes. I'll have to hurry.

BABSY: Did George sleep here?

MRS. DALE: Oh, yes, of course. (*Goes to door left*) Be nice to Mrs. Powell. (*Goes out left, as* NADINE *and* JIM *come in right.*)

BABSY: Mother just told me that George Washington once slept here! (*Dashes out left*)

NADINE: Where is *she* going? And what is she talking about?

JIM: Kids! She has George Washington on the brain. (*They sit down, chins in hands, looking discouraged.*)

NADINE: Just when we're ready to buy—another buyer comes along.

JIM: With scads of money, most likely. (BABSY *hurries in left holding a large sign on a lawn post.*)

BABSY (*Displaying sign which says* FOR SALE *and gives a phone number*): Maybe Mrs. Powell doesn't know the house is for sale.

JIM: She must, or why would she be so interested?

BABSY (*Unhappily*): I thought I'd hide the sign. (*Puts it behind the desk*)

NADINE: Much good that will do.

JIM: Button-brain.

BABSY: My brain's just as good as yours. I have an idea! Let's tell her this house is haunted!

JIM: Crazy. Who would haunt it?

BABSY: George Washington might, because he once slept here. Mother told me so, just now. We can pretend his ghost is around.

NADINE (*To* JIM, *eagerly*): You could come in dressed as George, Jim! (*Goes to suitcase, opens it*) There are two costumes in here.

JIM (*Hesitating*): Mother would be furious.

BABSY: We'll scare Mrs. Powell away before Mother comes back. She'll never know.

NADINE: Do it, Jim, do it! (BABSY, *at suitcase, takes out a white wig and puts it crookedly on her head.*)

JIM: What would I say?

BABSY: Just call (*In a ghostly voice*) "Martha! Martha!"

NADINE: And walk around.

JIM: What can I lose by trying? (*Takes a George Washington outfit from suitcase and removes wig from* BABSY'S *head*) There's still a complete outfit here for Frank.

BABSY: When you hear the signal, come in.

JIM: What signal?

BABSY: I'll beat on my drum and whistle "Yankee Doodle." She'll think it's one of his soldiers. (*Puts pan and spoons beside chair.*)

JIM (*Practicing a ghostly voice*): Martha! Martha! (*Goes out right*)

NADINE: I'll help. (*Goes out after him. There is a knock on the door and* FRANK *enters*)

BABSY: Hi, Frank. Your costume's in the suitcase. (*Hurries out*)

FRANK: What's the big rush? (*Calling*) I'll try it on. (*Half to himself*) As soon as I put my coat in the closet. (*Goes out right. A knock on the door left is heard.* MISS HAST-INGS *enters, followed by* MOIRA *and* LARRY, *who is carry-ing a blue suitcase, similar to the one with costumes in it.*)

MISS HASTINGS: They must have left the door ajar so I could walk in.

MOIRA: You're sure this is the right house, Miss Hastings?

MISS HASTINGS: I ought to know my own property. (*Looks around*) In spite of different furniture, it still looks familiar.

LARRY: Where shall I put your suitcase, Miss Hastings?

MISS HASTINGS: Just set it down anywhere, Larry. And thank your father again for the ride from the station.

LARRY (*Setting suitcase down at right*): I'm glad you and Moira got acquainted on the train, so Dad could give you a ride.

MOIRA: There doesn't seem to be anyone home, does there?

MISS HASTINGS: Not at the moment. (*Suddenly*) Oh, I forgot to bring in my small bag from your father's car.

LARRY: I'll get it.

MISS HASTINGS: And my other coat . . .

MOIRA: I'll get it.

MISS HASTINGS: And my shoe tote bag. What a memory! Let's all go! (*Laughs. They all exit left. As soon as they have gone,* FRANK *enters right.*)

FRANK: Suitcase. (*Sees* MISS HASTINGS' *suitcase, picks it up and exits right, as* MISS HASTINGS *enters left, carrying a tote bag which she sets down beside the sofa. As she un-buttons her coat,* BABSY *enters.*)

BABSY: Oh, hello. I'm Babsy Dale. Mother will be back soon. May I take your coat?

MISS HASTINGS (*Handing her coat to* BABSY): Thank you. The house looks fine.

BABSY: Let me tell you something about this house. George Washington once slept here.

MISS HASTINGS (*Surprised*): Oh, come, now.

BABSY: It's a fact. (*In a half whisper*) And around this time of year *he walks!*

MISS HASTINGS (*Amused*): You mean . . . his ghost?

BABSY: Of course. Maybe you'll even *see* him! (*Goes out right with the coat*)

MISS HASTINGS: Well! (MOIRA *and* LARRY *enter left, she carrying a coat, and he a small bag.*)

LARRY: I told Dad we'd wait with you till the family comes home. Our house is just around the corner. (*Sets the bag down beside the sofa, and* MOIRA *folds the coat, and puts it on top of small bag.*)

MISS HASTINGS: That's nice of you. I've already met one member of the family—Babsy. She told me the weirdest story about how George Washington haunts this house!

LARRY: Is she nuts, or something? Is the whole family like that?

MISS HASTINGS: Well, I liked Mrs. Dale years ago when I first rented to them. In fact, I even brought along a little family gift. (*Goes over to what she thinks is her suitcase, opens it and gives an exclamation of surprise.*) This isn't my suitcase! Look. There's an old-time costume in this.

MOIRA (*Enumerating items as* MISS HASTINGS *takes them from bag*): A white wig . . . knee breeches . . . buckled shoes . . .

MISS HASTINGS: The kind of outfit that George Washington used to wear!

LARRY: Very odd.

MISS HASTINGS: My guess is that while we were all out just now, someone in this house picked up my bag by mistake.

MOIRA: I don't understand.

MISS HASTINGS: All that talk about haunting. . . . They had *this* costume ready because they want to scare me away with a ghost! (*They move downstage center, their backs turned so they do not see* FRANK *enter quietly right, carrying suitcase. He sets it down, picks up the one with the costumes, and exits.*)

LARRY: A strange kind of welcome.

MISS HASTINGS: It must be a plot to make me come down in my price. (*Turns to look upstage*) Eventually, someone will come for that suitcase. But maybe we can pull a little trick of our own first.

MOIRA: What do you mean?

MISS HASTINGS: Are you game to help me a little more?

LARRY: Anything you say.

MISS HASTINGS: My brother and I were great for dressing up. (*Remembering*) There was an old trunk with costumes in the attic. I'm quite sure it's still there. Come on! (MISS HASTINGS, LARRY *and* MOIRA *exit left, and almost at once,* BABSY *and* NADINE *enter right.*)

BABSY: She was right here when I left.

NADINE: Maybe she's upstairs looking around.

BABSY: As if she already owned the place!

NADINE: I feel sort of guilty about doing this.

BABSY: We have to keep Mrs. Powell from buying the house. How's Jim doing?

NADINE: Great! Do you think she'll fall for it? What did she say when you told her about the ghost?

BABSY: She seemed kind of . . . stunned. (*Goes to desk and takes flashlight from drawer and puts it on floor beside chair.*)

NADINE: I see Frank didn't get the suitcase yet.

BABSY: He's probably raiding the refrigerator first. (MISS HASTINGS *enters, and* BABSY *turns to introduce her.*) This is my sister, Nadine.

GEORGE SLEPT HERE, TOO

MISS HASTINGS: It's nice to meet you.

NADINE: I'm glad to meet you. Please sit down. (*Indicates sofa, and* MISS HASTINGS *sits down*)

MISS HASTINGS: A very attractive house.

NADINE: Yes, isn't it? But frankly, we'd like to move as soon as we can.

MISS HASTINGS: Really?

BABSY: It's hard to heat in winter. If you're cool I can get you a sweater.

MISS HASTINGS: No, thank you. I hate overheated rooms.

NADINE: The original wing is most interesting, with beautiful wide floorboards.

BABSY: But walk carefully so they don't give way under you.

NADINE: And the rats in the cellar!

MISS HASTINGS: Oh, dear.

NADINE: Nice wide windowsills, too, but the windows aren't watertight and things get pretty sloppy in a bad rain.

BABSY: We worry about the ceilings. How awful if you got beaned on the head with a hunk of plaster!

NADINE: When you're in that part of the house, don't even sneeze!

MISS HASTINGS: I'll remember that.

BABSY: But don't get the wrong impression. I'm sure someone will buy the house, someone who doesn't mind that George comes snooping now and then.

MISS HASTINGS: The ghost of George Washington, you said? I find that hard to believe.

BABSY: So did we, at first.

NADINE: I get the feeling he doesn't like us.

MISS HASTINGS: Does he ever say anything?

BABSY: Sometimes he calls for Martha. His wife, you know.

MISS HASTINGS: She traveled with him often. Even stayed with him that terrible winter at Valley Forge.

NADINE: Really?

BABSY: Always, before we see him, we hear one of his men whistling "Yankee Doodle." And sometimes we hear a drum beating. (*Stands close to lamp beside chair at left.*)

NADINE: It gives me the creeps that any minute George may be looking over my shoulder. (*As* MISS HASTINGS *looks toward* NADINE, BABSY *turns off the lamp.*)

BABSY: Oh, dear, trouble with the lights again. (*She whistles "Yankee Doodle" and, stooping down behind the chair, beats time on her "drum."*)

NADINE: He's coming!

JIM (*Offstage, in a ghostly voice*): Martha, Martha!

BABSY: That gives me goose pimples all over. (*She reaches for the flashlight and shines it on the entrance at right. At the same time a small spotlight hits the center area.* JIM, *dressed as George Washington, enters from doorway right.*)

NADINE: He's here!

BABSY (*As if awed*): George!

JIM (*Standing still*): Who called? (FRANK, *dressed in an almost identical costume and wearing a white wig, enters left.*)

FRANK: Here I am! (*There are gasps of dismay from* NADINE *and* BABSY. JIM *turns toward right and takes a few steps.* FRANK *turns to left and takes a few steps. They turn, staring at each other, doing a double take.*)

JIM *and* FRANK: You!

MOIRA (*Calling from offstage*): George! George Washington! (*She enters center, wearing a long nightgown and robe, a little cap on her head, and carrying a candle.*) Where are you? (LARRY *comes in the same entrance, a candle in his hand and wearing a long-sleeved nightshirt and a sleeping cap over a white wig.*)

LARRY: Right here, Martha. (*There are shrieks from*

NADINE *and* BABSY. JIM *and* FRANK *get out of the spotlight quickly and one goes to right and the other, left.*)

BABSY: George Washington's ghost *does* walk here!

LARRY (*In ghostly tones*): I just can't sleep, Martha. I keep coming back to the houses where I used to have such a good rest, and I can't sleep a wink.

MOIRA: I declare, George, you worry me. Why can't you sleep?

LARRY: Because things have changed so much.

MOIRA: Don't let that concern you now.

GEORGE: But I'm the *father* of this country!

MOIRA: Please go back to bed, dear, and try to get a little rest.

LARRY: I don't like the way some of the young ones behave. Dropping out of school . . .

MOIRA: You did, too, George.

LARRY: But I kept on learning.

MOIRA: Oh, yes.

LARRY: I don't like the way they dress . . . sloppy clothes, long hair . . .

MOIRA: Your own hair is long, George.

LARRY: But it's too thin to make a good showing, so I have to wear this wig.

MOIRA: Very becoming, too.

LARRY: Their popular songs drive me crazy. In my day we had fine songs with good words.

MOIRA (*Reciting*): "Yankee Doodle went to town, a-riding on a pony; Stuck a feather in his hat and called it macaroni." Isn't that good, George?

LARRY: A good tune, anyway. They do such silly things, like cutting classes at school . . .

MOIRA: Cutting down your father's cherry tree wasn't very sensible, George.

LARRY: I was very young at the time.

MOIRA: So are they very young.

LARRY: They have no respect for order, always rebelling against it.

MOIRA: You did quite a bit of rebelling yourself.

LARRY (*Striking a pose, holding candle high*): For our country's independence!

MOIRA: I'm very proud of you.

LARRY: But is anyone else? Am I even remembered? To the young people today am I anything more than just a holiday?

BABSY (*Breaking in timidly*): Excuse me, but you *are* remembered. In our school they're giving a pageant about all you did for our country.

LARRY: They really are?

BABSY: In schools all over the country they're doing things in your honor.

MOIRA: Does that make you feel better, George?

BABSY: Even though this country is so much different now, it's still in good hands.

LARRY: Maybe I *can* sleep, now. (MRS. DALE *enters left.*)

MRS. DALE: Why no lights? (*Turns on lamp beside chair, revealing* JIM *standing behind the sofa.* BABSY *cries out and stoops down behind chair.*) What's going on here?

JIM (*Quickly*): I have to be going.

FRANK: Excuse me! (*They dash toward opposite exits, but* MRS. DALE *and* MISS HASTINGS *move quickly and block doorways.*)

MRS. DALE: Oh, no, you don't!

MISS HASTINGS: Not this way, either. (*To* LARRY *and* MOIRA) You put on a fine performance.

BABSY (*In a small voice, putting her head up*): Performance? (*Ducks down again*)

MRS. DALE (*To* MISS HASTINGS): Why, hello! I see you got here ahead of me. I was held up in a traffic jam. I hope the children entertained you.

MISS HASTINGS: These young ones tried to make me think the house is haunted.

MRS. DALE: Haunted?

FRANK (*Now himself*): I was just trying on a costume for the pageant.

JIM: That's true. I'm the one to blame.

NADINE: And me.

BABSY (*Coming from behind chair on her hands and knees*): And me, mostly.

MISS HASTINGS: I caught on to the plan and arranged a little haunting, myself. By my two young friends, Moira and Larry.

MRS. DALE: What a way to treat our guest!

BABSY (*Getting up; to* MISS HASTINGS): We did it to keep you from buying the house.

MISS HASTINGS: But I'm the owner!

NADINE, JIM *and* BABSY: Miss Hastings!

NADINE: We thought you were a Mrs. Powell.

MISS HASTINGS (*Coldly*): A most unlikely story.

JIM: But it's true!

MISS HASTINGS: It's obvious that you wanted me to reduce the selling price.

BABSY: Oh, please believe us!

NADINE: Our only excuse is that we like this house so much, we didn't want Mrs. Powell to buy it.

MRS. DALE (*To* MISS HASTINGS): There *is* a Mrs. Powell. She's president of the local historical society, and she called to ask if she could include this house in a tour of old houses.

JIM: Oh-oh.

BABSY: Because George Washington slept here?

MISS HASTINGS: But he didn't. This house isn't old enough.

BABSY: Mother, you said . . . I asked if George had slept here, and you said . . .

MRS. DALE: I meant Miss Hastings' brother George, of course.

JIM: We sure goofed, didn't we? (*They all sigh deeply.*)

LARRY: Will someone help me off with this nightshirt? Just pull. (*He pulls it up, showing his slacks rolled up under it, and his sweater.* BABSY *takes hold of the bottom edge of nightshirt, pulling it up over his head and tugs hard. It gets stuck at his head.*) Ouch! (*She pulls harder, and he pulls. The nightshirt comes off over his head with such force that he falls down.*)

MOIRA (*Going to him*): Larry, are you hurt?

LARRY: Only where the first George Washington got hurt when he chopped down that cherry tree! (*Gets up as everyone laughs.*)

MISS HASTINGS (*Now joining in laughter*): But he told the truth, remember, and he *didn't* get spanked.

MRS. DALE: I must apologize for my family, Miss Hastings.

NADINE: We're very much ashamed of ourselves.

MISS HASTINGS: I'll never find young people who appreciate this old house so much, even if Washington never slept here. Maybe they acted foolishly . . . but so did I. If you and your husband will make me a fair offer . . .

MRS. DALE: We will, we will!

MISS HASTINGS: Then we can consider the house sold to the Dale family! (*The young people cheer. Telephone rings.* MRS. DALE *answers the phone.* BABSY *takes the* FOR SALE *sign from behind the desk and works on the reverse side with* NADINE's *paint and brush.*)

MRS. DALE (*On phone*): Hello. . . . Oh, Mrs. Powell. . . . Sorry you were delayed, but do come right over. We'd be delighted to have our home included in your historical tour. . . . 'Bye. (*Hangs up.* BABSY *goes to center, holding the sign behind her back.*)

BABSY: Thank you, Martha. And thank you, Georges, one

and all. (*The two "Georges" and "Martha" bow.* BABSY *holds the sign up in front of her, showing the new printing on the reverse side, reading,* SOLD. *All cheer as the curtain falls.*)

THE END

The Other Side of the Wall

by Patricia Clapp

Characters

PRINCESS PRIMROSE
PRINCE NICHOLAS
QUEEN HILDEGARDE
KING ETHELBERT
JOHN
BOYS
GIRLS

SETTING: *The courtyard of King Ethelbert's castle, surrounded by a wall too high to see over. There is an opening leading into the castle on one side and a pair of gates with a heavy bar running across on the other. Two benches, one on each side of the stage, face each other; a small basket is on the ground upstage.*

AT RISE: PRINCESS PRIMROSE *is sitting on one bench, playing with a doll.* PRINCE NICHOLAS *is sitting on the other bench, carving a small piece of wood and whistling softly. Each has a book beside him.*

PRIMROSE (*After a moment*): Where did you learn that tune? I never heard it before.

NICHOLAS: Someone outside the wall was singing it the other day. A boy, I think, but of course I couldn't see.

PRIMROSE: I wonder what he was like.

NICHOLAS: Frightening, I expect.

PRIMROSE (*With a shiver*): I'm glad we don't have to see them.

NICHOLAS (*Bravely*): *I* should like to! Sometimes I climb to the top of the castle, way up in the tower—

PRIMROSE: You know you're not supposed to go up there! There are holes in the stairs! Father has told us over and over.

NICHOLAS (*Leaps up onto the bench*): I know. But I like to climb up anyway. And I look out of the highest windows.

PRIMROSE (*Eagerly*): What do you see?

NICHOLAS: Trees, mostly. But through the trees I can see blue water and a tiny glimpse of houses far off.

PRIMROSE (*Half frightened*): Do you see—*them*, too?

NICHOLAS (*Stepping down, speaking sadly*): No. Never.

PRIMROSE: But the one you heard yesterday, the one who was singing that song, he must have been close enough for you to see.

NICHOLAS: I know. And I ran to the top of the tower as fast as I could. But by the time I got there, he was gone.

QUEEN (*Offstage*): Children? Where are you? Primrose? Nicholas? (PRIMROSE *hastily puts her doll aside, picks up the book and pretends to read with great concentration.* NICHOLAS *swivels around on the bench, landing flat on his stomach; he opens the book and reads it, chin propped on his hands.* QUEEN *enters, with an apron over her royal robes.*) There you are! Studying hard, I see. What good children you are!

PRIMROSE (*Demurely*): Thank you, Mama.

QUEEN: And now it's time for lessons. Primrose, have you studied the chapter about turning around without tripping over your train?

PRIMROSE (*Rising*): Yes, Mama.

QUEEN (*Seating herself next to* PRIMROSE): You may show me. (PRIMROSE *walks upstage. Arranging her dress carefully, she walks downstage a few paces, turns and becomes wound in her train.*)

PRIMROSE: Oh, dear! It worked beautifully this morning.

QUEEN: You have to give it a little swish, my dear. See— like this. (QUEEN *rises, walks with dignity upstage a few steps, turns, swishing the train gracefully out of the way, and comes downstage.*) Now, try again.

PRIMROSE (*As she tries, more successfully this time*): I don't see why we have to wear trains all the time, anyway. They keep getting in the way.

QUEEN (*Calmly*): The royal family always wears trains, my dear.

NICHOLAS: It's awfully hard to climb trees in them, though.

QUEEN: You are not supposed to climb trees, Nicholas. No wonder the ermine on your sleeves gets so dirty! What were you doing up a tree?

NICHOLAS: Trying to see over the wall. And my crown came off and got caught on a branch, and I had to borrow Father's scepter to poke it down.

QUEEN: So *that's* where it went! You know you shouldn't look outside the wall. And your father was looking everywhere for that scepter last night! He needed it to hammer a leg on the throne. It's coming loose again. You must give the scepter back to him at once.

NICHOLAS: Yes, Mama.

QUEEN: And don't forget! (*Sits*) Now, Nicholas, let me see whether you have learned the lesson on knighting people. Stand by the bench. (NICHOLAS *rises.*) Now draw your sword. (*He draws sword.*) That's right. Primrose, you be the person who is being knighted. Kneel before your brother.

PRIMROSE: I'll get my robes dirty.

QUEEN: Here, spread my apron on the ground and kneel

on that. (*Removes her apron and hands it to* PRIMROSE, *who places it on the ground.*) There you are. Now, Nicholas, keep your chin up.

NICHOLAS: Then I can't see where her shoulder is.

QUEEN: Yes, you can. The royal family always keeps its chin up. That's right. Now, first one shoulder— (NICHOLAS *taps* PRIMROSE's *head.*)

PRIMROSE: Ouch!

QUEEN: Gently, Nicholas. Now the other shoulder.

PRIMROSE: Mother, he keeps hitting me on the head! On purpose!

NICHOLAS: I *told* you I couldn't see with my chin way up in the air. Anyway, what good is it to know how to knight somebody if I haven't anyone to knight? (PRIMROSE *rises, picks up apron, brushes it off and places it on bench beside the* QUEEN.)

QUEEN (*Patiently*): Every prince and every king must know how to knight people.

NICHOLAS (*Replacing his sword at his side*): Mother, you know very well there is absolutely no one in our whole kingdom except us!

QUEEN (*Rather helplessly*): Well, but there may be—someday. Perhaps our subjects will come back someday.

NICHOLAS: It has been years and years and years since they all left, a few at a time, climbing over the wall, until there was no one here at all. No one except us! And if they haven't come back in all these years, I don't think they're ever going to!

QUEEN: Oh dear, why must you be so difficult, Nicholas?

NICHOLAS: Because I think we should open the castle gates and let people come and go as they please! I hate being shut up here all by ourselves! I want friends, and other boys to talk to, and Primrose needs girls!

QUEEN: But you wouldn't want those monsters from out there.

NICHOLAS: How do you know they are monsters, Mama?

QUEEN: Why, your father says so. And the King is always right!

KING (*Offstage*): Hildegarde, my dear?

QUEEN (*Calling*): Yes, Ethelbert. We are here, in the courtyard. (*The* KING *enters.*)

KING: Isn't it almost time for lunch, my dear? I'm beginning to feel a little empty.

QUEEN (*Rising*): Yes, Ethelbert. I'll get it right away. Primrose, take that basket and run down to the henhouse. See if you can find any eggs.

PRIMROSE (*Getting basket*): Yes, Mama.

QUEEN: And put your train over your shoulder, dear. I simply will not wash it again this week! (*Ties apron around her waist.*)

PRIMROSE (*Putting train over her shoulder and starting off*): Yes, Mama. (*Exits*)

QUEEN: Ethelbert, I think you should have a little talk with Nicholas. He has some *very* peculiar ideas! (QUEEN *exits.*)

KING (*Sitting on bench*): Peculiar ideas, Nicholas? About what?

NICHOLAS (*Sitting on other bench and starting to whittle again*): I don't think they are peculiar, Father. I just wish we didn't always have to be shut up here alone. What's the good of learning to be a ruler if I haven't anyone to rule?

KING: It *is* unfortunate, I agree, that all our subjects chose to leave the kingdom. But that doesn't change the fact that you are the Prince, and someday you will be the King, and you must learn how to behave like one.

NICHOLAS: Father, why can't we open the castle gates?

KING: Good heavens, boy! And let those monsters in?

NICHOLAS: Were all our subjects monsters?

KING: No, of course not. All those within these walls were

wonderful people. But the others, those who have always lived outside, were monsters. And since our subjects have lived with them so long, by now they must be the same. Horrible! That great staring eye—

NICHOLAS: Did you ever see one?

KING: No, thank heaven!

NICHOLAS: Then how do you *know?*

KING: Because my father told me. And the King is always right!

NICHOLAS: But if we could only see for ourselves!

KING: There is no need to see. We *know!*

NICHOLAS (*Softly*): They sound happy.

KING: Happy? How do you know they sound happy?

NICHOLAS: One of them walked near the wall yesterday. I heard him singing a happy song.

KING: If they are getting that close, they might break in.

NICHOLAS: Why should they want to break in here? I should think they would be glad to be outside, where they are free.

KING (*Shaking his head*): Your mother was right, Nicholas. You have some very peculiar ideas. They would want to get in here, of course, because this is the best place to be. *We* are the royal family! *We* have the best of everything!

NICHOLAS: Like what?

KING (*Rising, waving his hand toward the castle*): Why, all this! This beautiful castle—

NICHOLAS: You know perfectly well it's falling apart.

KING: Well, it just needs a few shingles, and a nail here and there, and those holes in the tower stairs need fixing. Besides, think of the other things we have! This lovely courtyard—

NICHOLAS: That we can't see out of.

KING (*Gesturing widely*): Miles and miles of beautiful countryside—

NICHOLAS: That no one walks in.

KING: Farms and gardens—

NICHOLAS: That no one cares for, and so they have all gone to weeds.

KING: Charming little houses—

NICHOLAS: Where no one lives, and so they are all falling apart. No, Father. I'm sorry, but I don't agree. *I* think we have nothing! Nothing at all! And when I am King, I am going to open those gates! (*A gong sounds.*)

KING: There's the gong for lunch, Nicholas. Come in now, and have something to eat. You'll feel much better.

NICHOLAS: I'm not hungry, Father.

KING: Nicholas—

NICHOLAS: Please, Father. I'd really rather not.

KING (*With a little shrug*): Very well. But you are a great trial to me, Nicholas. I can't imagine how you'll ever manage as King! (KING *exits.* NICHOLAS *examines the wooden whistle he has been carving. He blows it experimentally, looking pleased with the result. A voice outside the wall is heard singing.* NICHOLAS *hears it and looks up; then he rises, faces the wall and blows the whistle again. The singing stops. He blows again. After a moment* JOHN'S *head appears above the wall among the branches.*)

JOHN: Hello, down there. (NICHOLAS *shields his face with his arm, and then slowly lowers it enough to peer over. After a moment, he lowers the arm entirely, and stares at* JOHN.) I said *hello!*

NICHOLAS: Hello. (*He stares a moment more, then bows*) How are you?

JOHN: I'm just fine.

NICHOLAS: I'm glad. What's your name?

JOHN: John. What's yours?

NICHOLAS: Nicholas.

JOHN: Hi, Nick. Why are you wearing all that stuff?

NICHOLAS: What stuff?

JOHN: That crown, and sword, and that fur on your suit.

NICHOLAS: I'm a prince. Princes always dress like this.

JOHN: Oh. Isn't it a nuisance when you play baseball? Or football? Or things like that?

NICHOLAS: I don't play those things. There is no one to play with.

JOHN: Oh.

NICHOLAS: You must be very tall to be able to see over the wall like that.

JOHN (*Laughing*): I'm up in the tree.

NICHOLAS: How come your head is so small? And why do you have two eyes?

JOHN: I don't know what you're talking about! My head's no smaller than yours, and *you* have two eyes.

NICHOLAS: And there are no flames coming from your mouth!

JOHN: I hope not! Why should there be flames?

NICHOLAS: Aren't you one of the monsters who lives outside the wall?

JOHN: Monsters? There aren't any monsters out here. Just people. *I* always thought there were monsters on your side of the wall!

NICHOLAS: You thought *we* were monsters? Why, *we're* the royal family!

JOHN (*Sympathetically*): I'm sorry.

NICHOLAS: *Sorry?* But being the royal family is the best thing of all! Why—we're famous! We have everything!

JOHN: What makes you think so?

NICHOLAS: My father says so. And the King is always right!

JOHN: Well, I'm glad I'm not in your royal family! I wouldn't want to live behind walls all my life.

PRIMROSE (*Offstage*): Nicholas? Mother says you must come in to lunch.

NICHOLAS (*Moving toward castle and calling excitedly*): Primrose! Come here! I'm talking to one of the mon-

sters! (PRIMROSE *enters fearfully and stands at one side.
She screens her eyes with her fingers, but peeks through.
She gives a little shriek.*)

PRIMROSE: Nicholas! Are you safe?

JOHN (*Annoyed*): I told you we are *not* monsters. Who's
that?

NICHOLAS: My sister. Primrose, come here. He says he's
not a monster.

PRIMROSE (*Approaching cautiously*): Where is it?

NICHOLAS (*Pointing to* JOHN): There. Over the wall. See?
(PRIMROSE *peeks at him, and after a moment takes her
fingers away from her eyes slowly.*)

PRIMROSE: Why—he's just a boy!

JOHN: Hi.

PRIMROSE: Hello. (*To* NICHOLAS) He's not frightening
at all! In fact, he looks rather nice!

JOHN. Why shouldn't I?

PRIMROSE: Well, we thought—that is, our father told us—

JOHN: I know. "The King is always right."

NICHOLAS: Would you like to come in here? I could open
the gate—

PRIMROSE (*Shocked*): Nicholas! You wouldn't! Why, the
monsters would all rush in and eat us up!

JOHN: Look. I wish you'd get this straight. In the first
place, nobody out here wants to hurt you; in the second
place, we are *not* monsters; and in the third place, I
don't think I *want* to come in there. I might never get
out again.

NICHOLAS: Primrose, keep on talking to him! I'm going to
get Father and Mother and let them see. (*He runs into
castle, calling back.*) Don't go away, John!

JOHN: It seems so quiet in there. Where is everybody? I
thought kings and queens had lots of subjects and serv-
ants and things.

PRIMROSE: We used to, long, long ago. But they all went away.

JOHN: I don't think I want to see the King. He might behead me!

PRIMROSE: Behead you? Whatever for?

JOHN: For looking over the wall. My father says it's forbidden.

PRIMROSE: Is *your* father always right, too?

JOHN: Oh, no. But he just might be this time. Goodbye, Primrose. (*He disappears behind the wall.*)

PRIMROSE: John! John, don't go! Will you come back?

JOHN (*Offstage*): Perhaps.

PRIMROSE: Please come back, John. Come back and bring your friends!

JOHN (*More faintly*): Perhaps. Goodbye, Primrose.

PRIMROSE (*Sadly*): Goodbye. (*She gazes at the spot where* JOHN *was.* NICHOLAS *runs in, talking over his shoulder to the* KING *and* QUEEN, *who follow.*)

NICHOLAS: You'll see, Father. He's no more a monster than I am!

KING: I don't believe it! Everyone knows—

NICHOLAS: Everyone is wrong! (*Stops short*) Primrose! Where is he? Where did he go?

PRIMROSE: He went away. He was afraid Father would behead him.

KING: Behead him? Why should I behead anyone? In any event, my sword has become extremely dull.

QUEEN: Where is this—monster, Nicholas? Interrupting our lunch, all for nothing. Your stomach is empty, Nicholas, and you've been seeing things!

NICHOLAS: Oh, Mother, why don't you believe me? He was a boy, just like me! He had a regular-size head, and two eyes, and not a single flame came out of his mouth when he talked. And his name was John.

PRIMROSE: I asked him to come back and bring his friends.

NICHOLAS: What did he say?

PRIMROSE: He said perhaps.

QUEEN (*Distressed*): Dear me! The gates will never stand up against a mob of the creatures! We'll be invaded and eaten alive!

NICHOLAS: Father, if you saw him, and if you found that he wasn't a monster at all, that he was just a—a person like me, then would you let me open the gates?

KING: Certainly not! There may be *one* out there who isn't ferocious, but there can't be more than that.

PRIMROSE (*Sitting on bench*): Besides, he said he didn't think he wanted to come in.

QUEEN: Why not?

PRIMROSE: He doesn't think he'd ever get out again, and he says he wouldn't want to live inside the gates all his life.

KING: Well! That's ridiculous! What better place could there be?

NICHOLAS: A place where people could come and go as they chose, Father, without ever being afraid of what might be on the other side of the wall. That would be a better place.

QUEEN: Well, he's not here, and I rather doubt that he ever was. Now come in, children, and have your lunch. All this racing around and excitement—you'll probably get indigestion! (*The* QUEEN *starts to exit when suddenly many voices singing outside the walls are heard. She stops and turns fearfully.*)

NICHOLAS (*Joyfully*): He's back!

PRIMROSE (*Rising quickly*): And he has brought his friends!

QUEEN (*Rushing to the* KING): Heaven save us! They'll beat the gates in! We'll all perish!

KING: *I will defend you!* (*Tries to pull sword from its sheath, but it sticks*) Oh, drat this thing! I knew I should have oiled it! (*Tugs on sword*)

NICHOLAS: Father, put your sword away! There's no need to defend us. (*Calls*) John? John, are you out there?

JOHN (*Offstage*): I'm here, Nick. Some of my friends are with me.

NICHOLAS: I'm going to open the gates and let you in.

JOHN: No, Nick! Don't! My friends are afraid! They're frightened of the King.

KING: Frightened of me? Why should anyone be frightened of me?

QUEEN (*Clutching* KING'S *arm*): Oh, Ethelbert, what will they do to us?

NICHOLAS (*To his sister*): Primrose! Help me open the gates!

KING: Nicholas, I forbid—(NICHOLAS *and* PRIMROSE *lift down the iron bar and slowly push open the gates, which are stiff from disuse.* JOHN *is revealed, standing surrounded by* BOYS *and* GIRLS *who look frightened but curious.*)

NICHOLAS: Come in, John. Come in and bring your friends.

QUEEN (*Hiding her face, but peeking out*): Ethelbert!

KING (*Retreating a little, but patting the* QUEEN'S *arm reassuringly*): There, there, my dear. Be brave.

JOHN (*To* NICHOLAS): You're sure it's all right?

NICHOLAS: I am the Prince. You have my word. (JOHN *approaches warily, followed by the* BOYS *and* GIRLS, *who gaze about. The* KING *and* QUEEN *are huddled together, watching them. Slowly, all seem to regain confidence. There are a few smiles and murmurs among the* BOYS *and* GIRLS.) You see, John? There is nothing here to hurt you.

JOHN: And all my life I've been so frightened—of nothing! Why, you're just like us!

NICHOLAS: Of course! And you are just like us! (*A* GIRL *picks up the doll and touches it gently.* PRIMROSE *goes to her.*)

PRIMROSE: That's my doll. You may play with her if you like.

GIRL: She's pretty. I have a doll at home. We could play together.

PRIMROSE: Will you bring her the next time you come?

GIRL: Of course. Perhaps tomorrow. (*A* BOY *has been gazing in the direction of the castle.*)

BOY (*To the* KING): My father is a builder. You should ask him to fix the castle for you. It needs repairing.

KING: I know. I'm not very good with tools myself. I'm afraid it is rather shabby.

QUEEN (*Smoothing her apron*): I—I made a cake this morning. I think there would be enough. Would you fetch it, Primrose?

PRIMROSE (*To* GIRL): Come with me while I get the cake for Mama.

GIRL: May I really see the inside of the castle?

PRIMROSE: Of course. Come along. (PRIMROSE *and* GIRL *exit.*)

NICHOLAS: Father, now do you believe me?

KING: Yes, my son. Now I believe you.

NICHOLAS: And may we keep the castle gates open?

KING: We will keep them open. People may come and go as they like.

NICHOLAS (*Turning to* JOHN): Do you hear, John? Father says the gates will stay open!

JOHN (*Joining them*): But, sir, you said we were all monsters, that we could never come inside the castle wall. And you said the King was always right.

KING: The King is only a man, my boy, and men are often wrong. Now, come in, all of you! Make yourselves at home! Look around. (*He takes* BOY *gently by the arm, draws him slightly aside, pointing to castle.*) Now, my boy, you see up there? The tower? The stairs are very bad. If your father would come and look at them with me—

BOY: I'll ask him as soon as I get home, sir.

KING (*Wistfully*): And perhaps I could knight him for his services. I haven't knighted anyone for years.

JOHN (*To* NICHOLAS): To think that we have been afraid of each other all these years, Nick! Why, we could have been having a dandy time together!

NICHOLAS: I know. It seems so silly. But maybe when you get to know people you're not afraid of them any more.

JOHN: And the gate is going to stay open?

NICHOLAS: The gate will stay wide open, John. Every single day! You have my word, and a Prince (*Grins widely*) is always right! (*Curtain*)

THE END

The Last Snake in Ireland

by Mary Malone

Characters

PATRICK	MICHAEL
BENNAN	SHEILA
CONNAL	FINN, *a child*
SNAKE	TOWNSPEOPLE
FERGUS	

TIME: *A long time ago in the days of St. Patrick.*
SETTING: *A hillside outside a cave in Ireland.*
AT RISE: PATRICK *enters. He is old and bent, and leans on a staff. A crowd of people, including* SHEILA, FERGUS, MICHAEL *and* FINN, *follow him, and stand in the background as he speaks.*

PATRICK: This is the place where the old snake hides. (*Indicating cave*) I'll just rest here and wait for Connal and Bennan. They'll help me catch the old snake. (*He moves toward rock beside cave.* SHEILA, FERGUS, MICHAEL *and* FINN *approach* PATRICK.)
SHEILA: That's not a very comfortable resting place, I'm thinking. You've walked many miles today, Patrick. You deserve better than a rock.
PATRICK: It'll do, Sheila. Until tonight when I'll go to your house to sleep.

SHEILA (*Pleased*): It'll be a great honor to have you stay with us, Patrick. Michael and I—and little Finn—will be very happy to have you.

MICHAEL (*Heartily*): We will that, indeed.

FINN (*Piping up*): Will you tell me one of your stories, Patrick?

PATRICK: I will, young lad. I will. (*Turning to people*) And now you may return to your homes, my good people. It was kind of you to come all this way. Thank you, Fergus and Michael, for leading them.

FERGUS: But, Patrick! We don't think it is safe for you to stay here alone.

PATRICK: It's as safe as houses. Don't worry. And Connal and Bennan, my two young followers, will be here soon.

SHEILA (*Fearfully*): Suppose the snake comes out before they get here?

PATRICK: In that case, the snake and I will have a little chat. Don't worry, Sheila. I have ways of coping with snakes. Don't forget, I've had dealings with the creatures before this! (*Crowd murmurs in assent*)

SHEILA: Yes, but this one is dreadful!

PATRICK: Now, now! It's time you went back to your homes. I will deal with the snake.

FINN (*Pleading*): Patrick, will you tell me how you're going to trick the snake?

SHEILA (*Warningly*): Finn!

PATRICK (*Kindly*): That I will, Finn—later on. Fergus. Michael. (*He beckons to them and speaks to them in a lower tone.*) I really think it would be better to go now. The noise of our talking may rouse the snake, and he may come out and frighten the women and children. Not that he'd mean to, poor fellow, but you know how women are about snakes.

FERGUS: You're right, Patrick. We don't want a panic.

MICHAEL: We'll start off, then. But we'll be back before

evening. (*Calls to the others*) Come, we will leave Patrick here for a little while. (TOWNSPEOPLE *move slowly off, looking back at* PATRICK. FINN *is pulled off firmly by* SHEILA, *but he looks back, pleading*)

FINN: Patrick, tell me how you'll trick the snake. Please tell me!

PATRICK: Yes, Finn, yes. Later, my boy. (*Raising hands to people*) Goodbye, and God bless you! (*When* TOWNS-PEOPLE *are offstage,* PATRICK *sits down wearily on rock on the other side of cave.*) That's better. They mean well, my good people, but it is wiser for them to go back down to the town, to their own homes. And now (*He stretches*), I think I'll rest for a while. It's true I have walked many miles today. I'm not as young as I once was. (*Leans back, and is soon asleep, his head nodding.* CONNAL *and* BENNAN, *two young men, enter.* CONNAL *is carrying a large box and* BENNAN, *a coil of rope. They see* PATRICK.)

BENNAN: Ssh. He's sleeping.

CONNAL: No wonder. The dear old man traveled a great distance today. (*He sets box down quietly, off to one side.*)

BENNAN: We'll let him rest a bit. (*They busy themselves coiling the rope*) It's too bad he had to come here all the way from Tara, and all because of a snake!

CONNAL: Indeed it is, Bennan.

BENNAN: Of course Patrick is used to traveling long distances. He's gone all over Ireland, preaching to the people, and seeing that churches are built.

CONNAL: Yes, that he has. No man knows this country so well. Nor loves its people so much.

BENNAN: He's like a father to us all.

CONNAL: He's done such great things for Ireland. Who but Patrick could have driven the snakes away from our shores?

BENNAN: Every last one of them—oop. (*He claps hand to mouth.*) With one exception, of course.

CONNAL: Yes, the granddaddy of all snakes, I'm thinking. Else he never would have outwitted us and escaped when the rest of them were sliding down the rocks to the sea.

BENNAN: The oldest, wiliest, most evil of them all. Or so they say.

CONNAL: Patrick says he feels sorry for this poor old fellow. All alone—the other snakes all gone.

BENNAN: Well, we'll catch the old snake today—I hope. But I wonder how Patrick means to do it.

CONNAL: I don't know, but I think Patrick is stirring now. Maybe he'll tell us. (PATRICK *stirs, stretches, raises his head; he is awake.*)

PATRICK: Ah, there you are, my lads. I wondered what had become of you.

CONNAL: We took a wrong turning and got lost for a time.

BENNAN: But now that we're here, Patrick, can you tell us what you propose to do about the last snake in Ireland?

PATRICK: Why, yes, my son. I intend to put him in that box you brought and drop him into the sea.

CONNAL (*Amazed*): What!

BENNAN (*Also amazed*): But how, Patrick? Surely he's not going to walk into the box! Why, he's the oldest and meanest of all the snakes. That's why he's still around.

PATRICK: He's old, that's true. But I'm old, too. And as for being mean, well, I guess anybody would be mean if he were all alone with nobody to talk to. That's why I think this old snake will be happier with his friends and relations, who are all in the sea now.

BENNAN (*Curiously*): But how are you going to make the snake go there?

CONNAL: He's a bold one, Patrick. You must be careful.

PATRICK: We have God on our side, Connal. A way will be

shown to us. Remember how the dogs of King Nial licked our hands when everyone said they would tear us apart?

CONNAL: We-ll. We must leave it to you, Patrick.

PATRICK (*Glances casually toward cave*): I think it's about time our snake came out of there. That's his home, you know. (CONNAL *and* BENNAN *jump back, frightened.*)

CONNAL: Oh, merciful heaven!

BENNAN (*Glancing wildly about*): Let's get out of here! It's dangerous!

PATRICK (*Calmly*): Now, now, my lads. Have I ever failed before? I told you—God is on our side. He will see to it. (*Raises hand in warning*) Ss-h! Listen! I hear something. No doubt the snake has heard us. (*There is a rustling noise in the cave.* SNAKE *crawls out, stopping when he sees the three men.*)

SNAKE (*Very coldly*): Who are you? What are you doing in my cave?

PATRICK: We're not in your cave, Snake. We were waiting outside here for you.

SNAKES Why? I don't know you. And I don't think I want to.

PATRICK: I am Patrick, and these are two of my followers, Bennan and Connal.

SNAKE (*Aroused*): Patrick? *You* are Patrick? The great Patrick who drove all my brothers into the sea? You— old man?

PATRICK (*Sadly*): Yes, I am old. And my work is almost done. But before I die, I want to make sure that all Ireland is free of snakes. That is why I came to see you.

SNAKE (*Sneeringly*): Do you suppose I'm going to go just because you say so?

PATRICK: I hoped you would. Reasonably and quietly.

SNAKE: Well, I'm not. So there. Put that in your pipe and smoke it. (*He turns his back on them, and stretches out on ground.* CONNAL *and* BENNAN *go up to* PATRICK, *and speak in low but urgent tones.*)

CONNAL: What are you going to do, Patrick? He's not going to go. You can see that as well as I.

BENNAN: And he'll bite and poison us if we try force. Besides (*He shivers*) I'm afraid to touch him.

PATRICK (*Soothingly, holding up hand*): Never mind, son. Patience. (*He addresses* SNAKE.) You know, Mr. Snake, when your brothers went into the sea, they turned into sea serpents, and they're all in the ocean somewhere, alive and happy.

SNAKE: What do I care? I've lived on land for a hundred years, and (*He turns and addresses* PATRICK *directly*) on land I'm going to stay! (*Mumbles*) Sea serpents, indeed!

PATRICK (*Changing his tactics*): I've heard great tales about you, Mr. Snake. Of course, I don't believe them. (SNAKE *starts to say something, but* PATRICK *goes on, musingly, almost dreamily.*) I've heard that you were the strongest and the quickest, and the cleverest of all the snakes.

SNAKE: *Were?*

PATRICK: Yes. Of course, you're old now. Like me. And even if the stories were true, you can't do the things you used to do—when you were young.

SNAKE: Name something I can't do.

PATRICK: Well, I don't think you can flip your tail in the air, while your head remains still. After all, it's only the young snakes who can do that.

SNAKE: Oh, can't I? (*He gives a quick flick of his tail.*)

PATRICK: You amaze me! A hundred years old, and can still do that? Well, I must try you on something harder.

SNAKE (*Impudently*): Go right ahead.

PATRICK: Can you roll over twice?

SNAKE: Just watch. (*He rolls over two or three times.*) There!

PATRICK: Oh, Mr. Snake, you well deserve your reputation. I thought those stories were exaggerated, but now I'm beginning to wonder. (*Puts hand to chin as if thinking.*) I am bound to try you on something you can't do. What will it be? Let me think. (*Raises head*) Ah! I think I have it.

SNAKE: I think you don't have it. (*As if bored*) But go ahead. What is it? I'll show you.

PATRICK: Do you see that box over there? That old wooden box? Now it's not very big, is it? (*He goes over to examine it.*) No—not big at all. So I don't think you could squeeze yourself into it. No, I don't think so. But try if you want to. Just for fun. (CONNAL *and* BENNAN *start forward, but* PATRICK *motions them back.* SNAKE *approaches box slowly.* PATRICK *continues off-handedly.*) It would take so much agility, you know. You'd almost have to be double-jointed to do it. In fact—

SNAKE (*Turning head towards him*): Stop talking, old man. Double-jointed, is it? Well, you don't know me! I'm the original double-jointed one.

PATRICK (*Shaking head*): No, it's not as easy as you think. In fact, I think I've got you this time, Snake. I really do.

SNAKE (*Drawing nearer to box*): Got me? Never! (*He is almost at box.*)

CONNAL (*Excitedly*): He's going to try it!

PATRICK (*Loudly;* SNAKE *is just about to enter box*): *Try it is right!* He'll never get all the way in! (*As* SNAKE *starts in, head first,* PATRICK *motions to* BENNAN *and* CONNAL. *They come up to him, and he whispers to them and motions toward box with his hands. They nod and quietly approach the box, one on each side.* PATRICK *continues to talk loudly to* SNAKE, *who is by now half way in box.*) Ready to back out, Snake? You can't make it all the way in. You might as well admit it.

SNAKE (*Muffled voice*): I don't admit anything to you, old man.

PATRICK (*To* CONNAL *and* BENNAN): Quickly now! As soon as he's all the way in. (CONNAL *and* BENNAN *strain forward, watching* SNAKE *wriggle into box. Just at this moment,* FINN's *voice is heard offstage, approaching.*)

FINN: Patrick! Patrick! Did you catch the old snake yet? (*Entering*) How are you going to trick the old snake? (SHEILA *rushes in behind* FINN, *angrily.*)

SHEILA: Finn, shame on you! (PATRICK, CONNAL, BENNAN *draw back, startled.* SNAKE *withdraws from box, growls.*)

SNAKE: What is this? What are you two doing here?

SHEILA (*Sees* SNAKE *and screams*): Oh! Patrick! Save me! Save me! (*Runs to* PATRICK)

FINN: Help! (*Hides behind* PATRICK)

PATRICK (*To* CONNAL *and* BENNAN): Dear, dear. What bad luck. (CONNAL *and* BENNAN *glower at* FINN *and* SHEILA, *muttering to each other.*) Now Sheila, Finn, there's nothing to be afraid of. Mr. Snake was just showing us how clever he is. (SNAKE *preens himself*) Now you both run along home. (*He nudges them gently toward exit.* SHEILA *and* FINN *leave.* CONNAL *and* BENNAN *are still muttering angrily.* PATRICK *is about to return to them when* SHEILA *pops her head in again.*)

SHEILA: I'm truly sorry, Patrick, about the interruption. Boys will be boys, you know, and Finn is so stubborn.

PATRICK (*Waving* SHEILA *away*): Yes, yes, it's all right, my dear. (*Clutches head in exasperation.* SHEILA *exits.*)

CONNAL: Women and children! They should be kept at home.

BENNAN: They spoiled the whole thing!

PATRICK (*Unperturbed, to* SNAKE): Well, Mr. Snake. Gave up, did you? I knew you couldn't do that last thing.

SNAKE (*Cunningly*): Gave up, did I? Oh, no! But I smell

a trick here, old man. I think those people came just in time.

PATRICK: Why, what do you mean? Trick? How silly and suspicious you are getting in your old age. Why should I have to trick you?

SNAKE (*Muttering*): Why not?

PATRICK: You're just finding excuses, my friend, because you couldn't make it into that box. But just to satisfy you, we'll go and we'll *leave* the box with you. Maybe you'd like to practice with it. Maybe next time we meet, you'll be good enough to get into it. Come, Connal. Come, Bennan. We're going now.

CONNAL (*Protesting, pointing to* SNAKE *and box*): But, Patrick—

PATRICK: Come, my sons. (*He draws them both with him, his arms around their shoulders. They move off,* PATRICK *talking to them in a low voice.*)

SNAKE (*Watching them as they disappear*): Well, well! So they're gone. (*He wiggles over to box and looks at it.*) Practice indeed! *Me* practice! Why, I was almost in it when that boy and his ma came on the scene. (*Slowly*) I wonder if it *was* a trick, after all. (*He moves away, seems to be thinking.*) But anyhow, there's nothing Patrick could *mention* that I couldn't do! No, sir! (*Looks back toward box.*) I believe maybe I'll do it again. Just to prove it. (*Goes slowly to box, begins to wriggle into it. As he does,* PATRICK, CONNAL *and* BENNAN *show their heads, just offstage. As the* SNAKE *goes further into the box, they emerge, keeping out of sight of* SNAKE. CONNAL *and* BENNAN *encircle box from back, waiting for* SNAKE *to get all the way in box.*)

PATRICK (*Coming nearer to watch.* SNAKE'S *head is now in box and* SNAKE *can't see or hear* PATRICK): Be ready, lads. I think he's almost in. (*Shakes head*) The vain fellow. He couldn't resist showing off—even to himself. (*At last,* SNAKE *is all the way in box.* CONNAL *slams down lid, and* BENNAN *holds it fast.*)

BENNAN: Quick, Connal! The rope! (CONNAL *runs to get rope.* SNAKE, *meanwhile, is making a loud noise, and* BENNAN *is straining to hold the lid.*)

SNAKE (*Muffled, but furious*): Let me out! You've tricked me! You've tricked me! I'll kill you all!

BENNAN: Tricked you is right! But I'll never let you out! You're in here for good! (CONNAL *quickly winds rope around box, two or three times, then* BENNAN *helps him to tie a huge knot.*)

CONNAL: There! That'll do it!

SNAKE (*Howling inside box*): Ow! Let me out! Let me out! Help!

BENNAN: Well, Patrick, you did it. Wait'll we tell the people how you drove the last snake from Ireland.

PATRICK (*Sadly*): By trickery it was, Bennan. But it was the only way. He'd never go any other way—that one.

CONNAL: Help me with the box, Bennan. We'll push it down the hillside and then carry it down to the sea.

BENNAN (*Goes to help* CONNAL; *addresses box*): So it's a sea serpent you'll be after all, my fine snake! (TOWNS-PEOPLE *enter excitedly, with* FINN, *pursued by* SHEILA, *at the head of the crowd.*)

ALL: Where's the snake? Did you get him, Patrick?

PATRICK (*Pointing to box*): Yes, my friends, there he is. All wrapped in a parcel—poor fellow.

ALL: Hooray! (*They gather in a circle around* PATRICK, CONNAL *and* BENNAN *and dance a jig, singing, as the curtains close.*)

THE END

St. Patrick Saves the Day

by Graham DuBois

Characters

JEAN	BOB
KATE	TOM
RUTH	BILL
HELEN	JIM
ELLA	MURPHY
CARL	

TIME: *Saturday. A week before St. Patrick's Day.*
SETTING: *The living room of Jean's home.*
AT RISE: JEAN *is seated on the sofa, an open book in her hands.* RUTH *sits beside her.* ELLA *is sitting in a chair to* RUTH'S *left, and* HELEN *in a chair down center left.* KATE *enters.*

JEAN: Hello, Kate. We've been waiting for you.
KATE (*Crossing to a chair*): Did you get that library book I told you about?
JEAN: I'll say we did. And it's just what we wanted. It has a complete account of St. Patrick. Listen. (*Reads*) "Perhaps the best-known tradition is that he cleared Ireland of its vermin."
KATE: Vermin? Doesn't *vermin* mean rats and bugs?
JEAN: Sure. But it also means snakes.

ELLA: And James Lester. (*All except* RUTH *laugh*.)

RUTH (*Bristling*): I don't see anything funny about that. You all know I'm dating Jim.

ELLA: Only for the moment. He's girl-crazy, you know. Boasts that he's dated every girl in the junior class. Mother says Jim has only two interests in life—girls and practical jokes.

RUTH: Well, he has never played a joke on me.

KATE: Give him time, Ruth, and he will.

RUTH: One reason Jim likes me is that I can laugh with him. He says he was first attracted to me because of my impersonations. Whenever I impersonate Old Lollipop, Jim laughs until the tears run down his cheeks.

HELEN: I wonder how Mr. Murphy ever got that nickname. Old Lollipop is a funny name for a school watchman.

ELLA: It's just another tradition, I suppose. They've been calling him that for years.

HELEN: I guess it's what Miss Rand would call irony— giving a name like that to an old sourpuss.

RUTH: Jim says Mr. Murphy's really a nice guy when you get to know him. And Jim is his favorite in the whole school.

ELLA: Well, he won't be if that Irishman ever finds out who it was that mixed those bits of old rags with the furnace coal.

JEAN: Let's get back to the entertainment we want to put on before the dance. (*Picks up book*) Where was I, now? (*Turns pages*) Here it is. (*Reads*) "One old serpent defied St. Patrick, refusing to leave Ireland. Then St. Patrick constructed a large box and invited the serpent to enter. When the serpent declined, saying it was too small, St. Patrick urged him to test the size by getting in. The serpent crawled into the box, St. Patrick clamped down the lid, and threw it into the sea." (*Closes book and lays it aside*) Girls, I have it. We can easily dramatize this story.

ELLA: How? It seems to me that—

JEAN: There's a large box in the cellar that Dad uses for moving heavy things. It has a strong wooden bottom, and handles at the front and back, like a stretcher. The top fastens down, too, but that's not important.

KATE: I don't see how such a little incident will give us enough to work on.

JEAN: Oh, it gives us plenty. We can surely elaborate on it. We'll have fairies dancing in the moonlight. They are terrified by the serpent and run to tell St. Patrick. We'll get one of the boys to play St. Patrick, and you and Helen and Ella and I can be fairies. Ruth, you can play the serpent. You're the only one who could imitate the hissing.

RUTH: I'm not very fond of snakes, but I'll do my best.

JEAN (*Rises*): First of all, Kate and I will go get the box. (KATE *rises*.) We've got to see if Ruth will be comfortable in it. (*Followed by* KATE *walks to door*) We'll be right back. (*They go out.*)

ELLA: I'm glad I don't have to play your part, Ruth. I wouldn't like to be shut up in a stuffy old box, and I hate snakes.

RUTH: Oh, I don't mind. Miss Parker is always saying in drama class it's good experience to have all kinds of roles. (CARL *enters, very much agitated.*)

CARL: Have you seen Jim Lester?

RUTH: No. What about him? You look upset.

CARL: I guess you'd be upset, too, if you had tried to ride a bike with deflated tires, and sealing wax in the air valves.

RUTH: Well, what has Jim to do with that?

HELEN: What has Jim to do with it, she asks!

RUTH: But, Carl, you told me that you always keep your bicycle in a locked garage.

CARL: I do, but this morning I was riding down town, and I stopped at White's for a Coke. I wasn't in the store more than five minutes. When I came out I had two flat tires. I tried to inflate them, and then I found the sealing wax. (*Clenches his fists*) Just wait until I catch up with that Great Lover! He won't be making any of his famous dates for a long, long time.

RUTH: You have no proof that Jim did it.

ELLA: Who else would do a trick like that?

RUTH: It burns me up the way everybody blames poor Jim for everything.

CARL: That's because of the silly practical jokes he's always pulling.

RUTH: Do you begrudge him a little innocent amusement? Have you no sense of humor? Can't you take a joke?

CARL (*Incensed*): Innocent amusement? Sense of humor? A joke? He's played the last one he'll ever play on me. When I find him I'm going to pin his ears back.

ELLA: Ears like his could do with some pinning. You'd better use spikes.

CARL (*Showing his fists*): These are the only spikes I'll need.

RUTH: You don't mean that—that you'd strike him?

CARL: You get the general idea. (*Shaking his fists*) And I don't mean love taps, sister.

RUTH: Carl! You don't know what a sensitive soul Jim is. If you struck him, you—you might hurt his feelings.

CARL: I'll hurt more than that. (*Moves toward door*) When I get through with him, his own mother won't recognize him. (*Turns to face them*) He will be in no condition to dance next Saturday night—just in case he invites any of you. (*Goes out*)

RUTH: What a nasty temper he has! Some people get upset over nothing. Maybe we ought to warn Jim.

ELLA: Where would you find him? You know he always goes into hiding after he's played a joke like this. (JEAN *and* KATE *enter with the box. They set it on floor down right center.*)

JEAN: Well, here it is. (*To* RUTH) How would you like to try it for size? (RUTH *rises and approaches box.*) We needn't fasten the lid. (*She and* KATE *help* RUTH *into box.* RUTH *sits*) It's a perfect fit. Now, Kate, you lift your end and I'll lift mine, and we'll carry this into the yard, just to see how heavy it is. (*They carry the box out.*)

HELEN (*Laughing*): Ruth looked like the Queen of Sheba being borne on a litter by her slaves. I really think she enjoys all this.

ELLA: Of course she does. What was that phrase Mr. Burton used in history class about Napoleon?

HELEN: "Delusion of grandeur"?

ELLA: That's it. Ruth is probably imagining that she is a ruler over vast empires and countless subjects. (JEAN *and* KATE *enter.*)

HELEN: What have you done with Ruth?

JEAN: We left her sitting in the box. (*Walks to sofa*) She's having the time of her life. (*Sits*)

KATE (*Crossing to sofa*): She hasn't been as happy since the night of the Christmas ball. (*Sits*)

HELEN: You mean she enjoys sitting out there in the yard, in a box?

JEAN: Well—under certain conditions. Bill and Tom came along. They were going next door for a minute, and they said they would carry Ruth back in here as soon as they came out.

ELLA: She'll love that!

JEAN: I thought it was a good idea, myself. It will give us

a chance to get the boys here for a rehearsal. They'll have to do the carrying next Saturday, you know. (BOB *enters, very much excited.*)

BOB (*Breathlessly*): I—I guess—the St. Patrick entertainment—and the dance are off.

JEAN: What's happened, Bob? You're all out of breath.

BOB (*Sitting in chair*): Has—has he been here?

JEAN: Has who been here?

BOB: Old Lollipop.

JEAN: Why should he be here?

BOB: He's going everywhere. Says he'll visit the homes of all the students in Glendale until he gets to the bottom of it.

KATE: The bottom of what? You don't make sense.

BOB: I don't know what he was talking about. I met him rushing down the street breathing fire and brimstone. His arms were swinging like windmills. He looked as if he had been in one fight and was looking for another, and his work shirt was all soaked with water. From what he was shouting I gathered that something terrible had happened at the school.

KATE: Why didn't you tell him to compose himself?

BOB: Did you ever try telling an angry Irishman to compose himself?

JEAN: But what has all this to do with our St. Patrick entertainment?

BOB: Remember the row he kicked up about those rags in the furnace? Principal Jones said that if he had any more trouble from the students, he would close the recreation hall. And without the recreation hall we can't put on any kind of entertainment.

JEAN: But we have everything planned. Couldn't you have a talk with Old Lollipop and explain?

BOB (*Holding up his hand*): Not me! What do you want to do—throw me to the lions? He's in no mood for explanations. (TOM *and* BILL *enter, carrying the box. They walk right center.*)

TOM (*Gaily*): Make way for the queen! (*Sets down his end of the box*) Gently.

BILL (*Setting down the box*): And a hefty old queen she is! Must weigh two hundred if she weighs an ounce. (*Draws out his handkerchief and mops his brow*) My back is about broken. I thought little Ruth Carson would be as light as a feather. Well, as the poet says, women were deceivers ever. (*Sits on lid of box*)

JEAN: Why did you close the lid?

TOM: It's just as we found it. And we let it stay like that purely as a precautionary measure. We were afraid our little Snow White might fall out.

JEAN: But I'm afraid she hasn't enough air.

BILL: Don't worry: there's a big hole on the other side.

JEAN: But I *am* worried. She hasn't said a word—even when you were talking about her weight. That's not like her.

TOM: I guess she's too comfortable to talk. Probably taking a nap.

JEAN: But I have to know that she's all right. (*Rises*) She's my responsibility. (*Calls*) Ruth! Ruth! (*Pauses*) You don't suppose she has smothered in there, do you? (*Calls*) Ruth! Speak to me, Ruth! (*Pauses*) Bill, get off that box and open the lid. (BILL *jumps off box and is about to raise the lid, when* RUTH *enters, out of breath. All look at her in amazement.*)

RUTH (*Angrily*): Just wait until I see that viper, that toad, that—

JEAN (*Sinking back into her chair*): Oh, what a relief!

RUTH (*Sitting in chair*): That miserable creature, Jim Lester, played one of his silly jokes on me. I was waiting for Tom and Bill, and he came along and fastened the lid. If Phil Carter hadn't happened to pass and heard me yelling, I guess I'd be in there yet. I ran all the way to the corner looking for Jim.

JEAN (*Bewildered*): Then, you—you're not in the box.

RUTH (*Testily*): Of course I'm not, stupid! Don't you see me sitting here?

JEAN: Well, who is? Who is in that box?

BILL (*Turning toward box*): We'll soon find out.

TOM: I bet that Jim Lester filled it with bricks.

BILL: If he has, I'll break every bone in his— (*He raises lid and* JIM LESTER *pops up.*)

JIM: Hello, folks!

JEAN: Jim Lester! What are you doing in that box?

TOM: To think we carried that dope all the way from the yard!

BILL: Another of his corny jokes! (*Advances menacingly toward* JIM) You have to learn that you can't get away with stuff like this.

JIM (*Holding up both hands*): One moment, please. I can explain everything.

BILL: Well, shoot! And it better be good.

JIM: This is no joke, fellows. I'm in hiding. I didn't know you would carry me in here. I thought you were taking me to the cellar.

BOB: You're in hiding? What are you hiding from?

JIM: From Carl Roberts. He's been on my trail all morning. When I passed by here the second time, Carl was only a half block away. I saw the box was empty, and so I jumped in and pulled down the lid.

BILL: Cold feet, eh? Afraid of good old Carl's mighty left hook.

JIM: You misunderstand me completely. Fear is an emotion unknown to me. Carl is one of my best friends, and in view of the long friendship existing between our families, I would—

TOM: Baloney!

JIM: I would hesitate to indulge in any hostilities with those I esteem so— (CARL *enters.* JIM *drops down into box.*)

CARL (*Looking about*): Where is he? I know he's here. I heard his voice as I came up the walk. There's no use trying to hide him. Sooner or later I'll—

BILL: Well, I, for one, am not hiding him. I think he deserves what's coming to him. (*Points to box*) He's in that box.

CARL (*Advancing toward box*): Jim Lester, come out and fight like a man.

JIM (*Pushing up lid and peering out*): Have you considered where you are? Does it occur to you that it is unmannerly to fight before ladies?

JEAN: He's right, Carl. Let's have no fighting here.

CARL: I have no intention of fighting here, Jean. I'm inviting him to go to Shiler's Woods with me.

JIM: Shiler's Woods? It's four miles. My feet are in no condition for such a walk.

CARL: You don't have to walk. I'll provide transportation. I have Dad's car outside.

JIM: Let's talk it over. I'm averse to fighting one whom I have always regarded with deep affection. Cowardice has no place in my make-up, but to inflict bodily injury on somebody—

BOB: Quit stalling!

TOM: And stop talking like an animated dictionary.

JIM: Stalling is foreign to my nature. I only want to—

CARL: Get him out of that box, boys. (TOM *and* BILL *advance toward box*)

RUTH (*Rising*): Wait just a minute. (*Walks up to* CARL) Carl, how would you like to go to the St. Patrick Dance with me? (*Puts her hand on his arm and looks coyly up into his face*)

CARL: I'd love to, Ruth.

BOB: If there *is* any dance.

RUTH: Well, then, will you do me a little favor?

CARL: You bet I will! Anything you ask.

RUTH: Call off this fight with Jim Lester.

CARL: Now, Ruth, that's asking a little too much.

RUTH (*In her most coquettish manner*): Please, Carl. For my sake?

CARL: I don't see how I — well, all right.

BILL: It's not all right with me. This blockhead has to be punished for the silly tricks he has been playing on our class.

BOB: I agree. He has probably broken up our St. Patrick Dance. Let's keep him in the box until we decide what to do with him. (BOB, TOM, *and* BILL *force* JIM *down into the box*) We'll close the lid. (*He closes the lid.*) Now, let's fasten it, just to make sure. (TOM *fastens the lid.*) That does it. (*He sits on lid, folding his arms.*) Any suggestions?

JIM (*In muffled voice from inside box*): I haven't enough air in here. I have to breathe, don't I?

BILL: I don't see the necessity.

TOM: I've thought of something. Remember that scene in *Merry Wives of Windsor* Miss Rand read us yesterday? How they took old Falstaff to the river in a clothesbasket and ducked him. Why not give Jim Lester the same treatment?

JIM (*Alarmed*): No, fellows, you mustn't! I can't swim. I'll drown.

BILL: Well, they drown kittens, don't they?

CARL (*To* JIM): You can't drown in eighteen inches of water.

JIM: But the water in March is like ice. I'm sensitive to cold. I'll catch my death of pneumonia. But before I die I'll run right to the principal and tell him everything.

RUTH: You had better listen to him, boys; he'll probably keep his word. Something happened at school this morning that may prevent our holding our dance, and if Jim squeals to Mr. Jones about your ducking him, we might as well call everything off.

BOB: Yes, that's right. And don't forget that we still have Old Lollipop to reckon with.

TOM: But we can't let Jim Lester go on getting away with stuff like this.

RUTH: Just leave everything to me. We'll give him a dose of his own medicine. We'll play a practical joke on him that he'll never forget. And I'm the little girl who can think something up.

BOB: It had better be clever. (*Walks to window*) And quick. (*Looks out*) Golly! Here comes Old Lollipop on the run. He looks madder than ever. I'll bet he's coming here.

BILL: You say something happened at school that made him mad? You think it may have been one of Jim's jokes?

BOB: Want to bet?

BILL: Maybe that solves our problem. We'll just turn Jim over to him and let nature take its course.

TOM (*Shaking his head*): No, fellows; we can't do that. You don't know Old Lollipop's temper. He'd tear Jim limb from limb. I don't admire Jim especially, but I wouldn't want to see him murdered.

JIM (*Thinking they are playing a joke on him*): You'll have to think up something better than this, Ruth. I happen to know that Old Lollipop can't leave the school on Saturdays.

TOM: Shut up! (*Walks back to box*) You'd better keep quiet unless you want your head knocked off. (*Sits on box*)

BOB: He's coming up the path.

JIM (*Laughs*): Stop trying to kid me.

BOB: You won't think we're kidding when Old Lollipop comes charging in here like an angry bull. You won't be able to see him, but, boy, will you hear him! (MURPHY *enters angrily.*)

MURPHY: Where is he? Let me get my hands on him!

JEAN (*Quickly*): Who is it you want to put your hands on, Mr. Murphy?

MURPHY: I don't know, but—

JEAN: How can you put your hands on him if you don't know who he is?

MURPHY: I'll find out. Nobody can play a trick like that on Patrick Murphy and get away with it.

JIM: Ruth, you're a riot! (*Laughs*) I always said Old Lollipop was your best impersonation. But why did you think I'd fall for anything like this?

MURPHY (*Looking quickly about him*): Who said that?

ELLA (*Trying to distract* MURPHY'S *attention*): What has happened, Mr. Murphy? Your shirt is soaking wet.

KATE: What have you been up to?

MURPHY: I've been trying to get the suds out of the lily pond.

JEAN (*Puzzled*): What?

MURPHY: Some joker put bubble bath into the lily pond.

JIM (*From inside box; scornfully*): You're certainly putting on an act, Ruth. You're more like Old Lollipop than Old Lollipop himself. I would swear the old goat was right here if I didn't know he had to be at school.

MURPHY: The old goat, indeed! That's the first time anyone ever called Patrick Murphy a goat. (*Clenching his fists*) Be a man and tell me who it was that insulted me with that name. (*Looks from one boy to the other*) There's a ventriloquist in this room. Will one of you boys admit it? (*Clenching and unclenching his hands*)

Or do I have to squeeze it out of you with these two hands?

JIM (*Laughing*): Stop it, Ruth! Stop it! You're killing me. I've laughed so much my sides ache. I can just see that old goat charging down the street.

MURPHY: Where is that voice coming from? Old goat, am I? When I find out who said that, I'll butt him clean through these walls.

JIM: Ruth, you're a genius! (*Laughs*) You make Old Lollipop sound just as he did when he stoked the furnace with all those bits of rags.

MURPHY: So? Now we're getting somewhere. I said to myself, "Pat, find the guy who monkeyed with the coal, and you'll find the guy who monkeyed with the lily pond." And I'm not leaving this room until I know who he is. (*Folds his arms and glares at boys*)

JIM: I say, fellows, this has gone far enough.

BILL: Shut up!

MURPHY: I know where the voice is coming from. (*Points to box*) There's somebody in that box.

JIM (*Knocking against box*): Let me out, I say. The joke is up. I knew it was Ruth all along.

TOM (*To* JIM): Do you realize that Mr. Murphy is in this room?

JIM: Ah, go on! Let me out. I'm not afraid of a dozen Old Lollipops like the one in this room. I'll welcome the sight.

MURPHY: And will you welcome the feel of my two fists against your jaw?

JIM: Of course I will, sweetheart. Dear, sweet little girl hands that couldn't crush a fly.

MURPHY: Old Lollipop! Old goat! And now he calls me a girl—the worst insult of all. Let me at him.

BOB: Restrain yourself, Mr. Murphy. (*Raises lid of box, and* JIM *stands up*)

MURPHY (*Amazed*): Jim Lester! I wouldn't have believed it!

JIM (*Staring at* MURPHY *in bewilderment*): It is—it really is—you!

MURPHY: Yes, it really is Patrick Murphy. (*Shows his fists*) And here are two things that will impress the fact on you. (*Takes a step toward* JIM)

BILL (*Seizing one of* MURPHY'S *arms while* TOM *seizes the other*): Be careful, Mr. Murphy. Remember, if you strike a pupil you may lose your job.

MURPHY (*Cooling off*): I guess you're right. But I won't lose my job if I report the whole thing to the principal.

JIM (*Imploringly*): Don't do that, Mr. Murphy. He would expel me. My parents would never forgive me.

MURPHY: You ought to have thought of all that before you monkeyed with the school lily pond. (*Turns toward door*)

BOB: One minute, Mr. Murphy. If you go to Mr. Jones, he'll close the recreation hall, and the whole school will suffer. Jim alone is responsible for all the jokes played on you and the rest of us, and he should be the only one to suffer.

MURPHY (*Pausing*): Right you are, my boy. (*Points to* JIM *who sits shamefacedly on the box*) But this idiot has to be punished. Never again will Patrick Murphy stoke the furnace with old rags or try to get bubble bath out of the lily pond! This young rascal must be taught a lesson.

CARL (*Showing his fists*): Well, there's a pretty good lesson in each of these.

JEAN: No, Carl; that isn't the answer.

TOM: The water of Maple Pond is fresh and invigorating. I still think it might cool his ardor for practical jokes.

KATE: That's out. He'd be at Mr. Jones' house before his

clothes were dry. We've got to find something that he can't run to Mr. Jones about.

JIM: I want you all to get something straight. I guess I've been an idiot, like Mr. Murphy says, but I didn't mean it a while ago when I said I'd go to Mr. Jones. I may be a silly dope, but I'm no tattletale.

RUTH (*Holding up her hand*): Wait! Leave it to the girls. We can punish him in a way that will really hurt.

MURPHY (*Chuckling*): How can delicate little colleens like you hurt a big lummox like that? (*Points to* JIM)

RUTH: We can boycott him.

HELEN: Boycott him? What do you mean, Ruth?

RUTH: No more dates for Jim Lester from any girl in the junior class from now until after commencement.

JIM (*Quickly*): Can't you punish me some other way?

ELLA (*Enthusiastically*): Ruth, I believe you have something there!

RUTH: But we will have to pledge ourselves to stand together. We'll just start with the girls in this room and I'll speak to the other juniors on Monday. Jim has played some of his crazy pranks on most of them, you know. I'll begin. (*Solemnly*) I pledge myself to have no dates with Jim Lester for the rest of the school year.

JIM (*Crestfallen*): I'd rather take the ducking in Maple Pond or . . .

JEAN (*Ignoring* JIM): I make the same pledge.

KATE: And so do I.

HELEN: And I.

ELLA: And I.

MURPHY (*Chuckling*): Knowing Jim Lester as I do, I'd say that's pretty stiff punishment.

JIM: I'll say it is! I know I had some punishment coming to me; I deserve it. I've been acting like a kid, but this will make me feel like a stranger in my own class.

RUTH (*To* MURPHY): And you won't go to Mr. Jones? (MURPHY *shakes his head*)

JEAN (*Clapping her hands*): Then we can have the recreation hall for next Saturday night. We are putting on a St. Patrick entertainment and dance, Mr. Murphy.

MURPHY (*Completely mollified*): Are you, now? Well, that's fine! St. Patrick! Never forget, kids, that St. Patrick lived in Ireland. And so did I. The greatest man who ever lived. St. Patrick, I mean. Named after him I was. If I can do anything for you, just call on Patrick Murphy.

JEAN: Well, you could help us with the decorations.

MURPHY: I'll say I could! I have all the green bunting in the world. I'll cover the walls with shamrock, and my wife, Bridget, will play Irish tunes on a green harp, and she and I and the children will sing Irish songs. And would you like me to dance an Irish jig?

JEAN: Oh, Mr. Murphy, it would be the hit of the evening.

MURPHY: I'll do it, then. (*Moves toward door*) I'll go back to school and get started on those decorations right away. (*Turns to face* JEAN) But there's one thing I'd like to know before I leave.

JEAN: What is that, Mr. Murphy?

MURPHY: Why do all the boys and girls call me Old Lollipop?

JEAN: Because—because you're so sweet. (MURPHY *is beaming as the curtain falls.*)

THE END

The Leprechaun's Pot of Gold

by Frances B. Watts

Characters

TIMOTHY LEPRECHAUN
PADDY PIXIE
GRANNY
SHARON
BRIDGET } her grandchildren
TERENCE
HUNTER
WOODCUTTER'S DAUGHTER
DANNY
KATHLEEN } village children

TIME: *St. Patrick's Day, a long time ago.*

SETTING: *A clearing in a forest in Ireland, in front of Timothy Leprechaun's cottage.*

AT RISE: TIMOTHY LEPRECHAUN *tiptoes out of his cottage, carrying a pot of gold. He sets the pot down at center and bends over it, running his hands through the gold.*

LEPRECHAUN:
Lovely gold! Lovely gold!
It's mine to keep. It's mine to hold.
I hoard it well. It's not to spend.
For gold's a leprechaun's best friend.

471

(*He laughs wickedly, then stands and looks about.*)
Let the village folk beware!
My gold today becomes a snare!
(PADDY PIXIE *enters.*)

PIXIE: Sure, and if it isn't Timothy Leprechaun. Why is your pot of gold out here in the open? I always thought you kept your gold in hiding, miserly creature that you are.

LEPRECHAUN: Enough of your impudence, Paddy Pixie. If you must know, I'm setting a snare for the village folk.

PIXIE: A snare? What wicked tricks are you up to now?

LEPRECHAUN: It's revenge I'm after, Paddy. For years now the greedy villagers have been trying to capture me, so that they might force me to tell them where I hide my gold.

PIXIE: They do it for sport. They mean no harm.

LEPRECHAUN: After today they will be afraid of such sport. Today my gold will be a trap. Whoever tries to take it will be captured and thrown into my dungeon.

PIXIE (*Laughing*): And how do you mean to do that? It's little and frail you are compared with human folk.

LEPRECHAUN (*Taking wand from pocket*): Frail I am, but my magic wand is strong.

PIXIE (*In disgust*): So it's black magic you'll be using.

LEPRECHAUN: And why not? I paid dearly for the wand. Three gold pieces I gave for it to a wily fairy in Dublin. Come, I'll show you how powerful it is. Pick up the pot and start to carry it away.

PIXIE: Very well. You've made me curious. (*He picks up pot and starts toward right.*)

LEPRECHAUN (*Waving wand*):
Hobbledy-hip! Hobbledy-hop!
Force him, magic wand, to stop!

PIXIE (*Stopping suddenly*): Help! I can't move! Set me free!

LEPRECHAUN: Don't get excited. I was merely showing you how I intend to capture those who try to rob me today. (*Touches* PIXIE *with wand*) There, you can move now. (PIXIE *puts pot down.*)

PIXIE (*Moving arms and legs*): How wicked you are to set such a trap! And on St. Patrick's Day, too. The happiest holiday of the year.

LEPRECHAUN: Holidays are the most troublesome. Folks have nothing to do, so they're quite apt to go leprechaun-hunting.

PIXIE: You misjudge people, Timothy. There are some who would not dream of robbing a leprechaun of his gold.

LEPRECHAUN: Nay. All humans are greedy. There is not one soul in the land of Ireland who would not take my gold, especially if he found it lying right under his nose.

PIXIE: It's wrong you are. There are many honest folks in this world.

LEPRECHAUN: A wager! Let's make a wager today!
Should we find *one* honest soul,
I'll give to you my pot of gold.
But should no honest soul we see,
Then *you'll* become a slave to me.

PIXIE: I agree to the wager. So strong is my faith in people, I'll risk becoming your slave to prove I am right.

LEPRECHAUN: Then our wager begins this very minute. (*They shake hands.*)

PIXIE: I'll run home first to tell my mother not to expect me for lunch, but I'll return soon. (*Exits*)

LEPRECHAUN (*Calling after him*): You do that, Paddy. It may take a long time to find an honest human. (*He goes to the cottage doorway.* GRANNY, SHARON, *and*

BRIDGET *enter, carrying baskets.* LEPRECHAUN *ducks into cottage, then peeks out, as* GRANNY *and the girls search for mushrooms.*)

SHARON: I do hope we find some mushrooms here, Granny. We've been hunting for over an hour.

GRANNY: Have patience, Sharon, lass. We'll find some soon. Then it's Irish stew with mushrooms for St. Patrick's Day dinner.

BRIDGET: Terence may find some across the brook. He said he would call us if he does.

GRANNY: Perhaps he will. Terence has a sharp eye for mushrooms.

SHARON (*Discovering pot of gold*): Granny! Bridget! Here is a pot of gold! I can hardly believe my eyes!

BRIDGET (*Running over*): It is! It is a pot of gold. Oh, wonderful!

GRANNY (*Examining pot*): A pot of gold it is. Sure, and it must belong to the leprechaun who, they say, lives in the forest hereabouts.

SHARON: I know. Kevin Riley's dad tried to capture the leprechaun once.

BRIDGET (*Clapping her hands*): Now the gold is ours, and we lifted not a finger to get it! What luck! (*Reaches for pot*)

GRANNY: Not so fast, Bridget, child. The gold is not ours. It belongs to the leprechaun. He just set it down for a minute, perchance, and intends to return.

SHARON: Oh, Granny! What do we care for a miserly old leprechaun? Think of the lovely things gold will buy!

BRIDGET: A fine new house! Pretty clothes!

SHARON: And roast beef every Sunday!

GRANNY: Hush! For shame. It's greedy thoughts you're thinking. (*Spies* LEPRECHAUN's *cottage*) That little cottage over there is the leprechaun's, no doubt. I'll take his gold to him before he loses it to less honest folks.

BRIDGET: Ah, Granny (*Sighs*), it would be such fun to be rich. (GRANNY *carries pot to cottage and knocks on door.* LEPRECHAUN *opens door, stands in doorway, scowling.*)

GRANNY: Mr. Leprechaun, this gold is yours, no doubt.

LEPRECHAUN (*Grudgingly*): Aye. (*Aside, to audience*) What a pesky old busybody she is!

GRANNY (*Handing him the pot*): Then you ought to be taking better care of it. Next thing you know, it'll turn up missing. (TERENCE *enters, carrying basket. Holds up mushrooms.*)

TERENCE: Granny! I found dozens of mushrooms across the brook! Come quickly! (*Exits running*)

GRANNY: Now, if you'll excuse me, sir, I must be going. My grandson has discovered mushrooms. They're elegant, sir, with Irish stew. (LEPRECHAUN *scowls at her.* GRANNY *and girls start to exit.*)

SHARON: What a rude old leprechaun, Granny. He didn't even say "Thank you, ma'am."

BRIDGET: Nor "Farewell," either.

GRANNY: We should not expect thanks for honesty. You see, my dears, honesty is its own reward. (*They exit.* LEPRECHAUN *returns pot to center of stage.*)

LEPRECHAUN: Whew! That was a narrow escape! Had Paddy Pixie been about, the wager would be lost already. Well, what he doesn't know won't hurt him. (*He stoops and fondles gold.* PIXIE *enters.*)

PIXIE: Did anyone come when I was gone?

LEPRECHAUN: Not a soul.

PIXIE: Then let us go into the cottage. No one will come near if you guard the gold too closely.

LEPRECHAUN: Very well. (*They stand in cottage doorway.*)

PIXIE: Hark! Here comes someone now! We must hide! (*They duck inside, then peek around doorway. The* HUNTER *enters, carrying gun over shoulder. He walks slowly to center.*)

HUNTER: What a luckless day! I've been hunting since daybreak and not so much as a rabbit has crossed my path. The luck of the Irish is a fairy tale, to be sure. (*He stops as he spies gold, then drops to his knees.*) A pot of gold! There is such a thing as luck, after all! My wife and young ones will be quite beside themselves with joy. (*He lifts pot and starts to exit.* LEPRECHAUN *and* PIXIE *rush out of cottage.*)

LEPRECHAUN (*Waving wand*):
Hobbledy-hip! Hobbledy-hop!
Force him, magic wand, to stop!

HUNTER (*Turning and stopping*): Help! Let me go, leprechaun!

LEPRECHAUN: Not on your life, thief. You intended to take my gold, so I intend to take *you* to my dungeon. There you shall live out the rest of your days in darkness.

HUNTER: Have pity! I only wished to take the gold to my wife and young ones. Hunting has not been good, and my family has been starving for weeks.

PIXIE: Aye. Have pity, Timothy.

LEPRECHAUN: Why should I have pity? (*He takes pot and sets it down at center, then pushes* HUNTER *into cottage.*)

PIXIE: Poor man. His concern for his family overcame his sense of honesty. (LEPRECHAUN *returns, dusting hands.*)

LEPRECHAUN: Sure, and that man will never see the light of day again. Am I right about people, or am I not?

PIXIE: 'Tis true that human beings are weak at times. But I still have faith that an honest soul will come this way today.

LEPRECHAUN: Hush! I do believe someone else is approaching! (*They hide in cottage and peek out. The* WOODCUTTER's DAUGHTER *enters, carrying a few pieces of wood. She sets the wood down and rubs her back.*)

DAUGHTER: Ah, me! 'Tis weary I am of gathering wood. Father hates to have me out in the forest to look for wood, like this. (*Sighs*) But how else can we earn our living while he is sick in bed? (*She picks up the wood and walks to center. She sees the pot and falls to her knees.*) A pot of gold! It's too good to be true! Now I will have money to summon doctors to make Father well again. (*She picks up pot and starts to exit.* LEPRECHAUN *and* PIXIE *enter from cottage.*)

LEPRECHAUN (*Waving wand*):
Hobbledy-hip! Hobbledy-hop!
Force her, magic wand, to stop!

DAUGHTER (*Turning and stopping suddenly*): Help! Set me free, leprechaun!

LEPRECHAUN: Nay. You intended to take my gold, so I intend to take *you* to my dungeon. There you shall live out the rest of your days in darkness.

DAUGHTER (*Weeping*): Have pity! I took the gold only to summon doctors for my father, the woodcutter. He has been ill these many months.

PIXIE: Do have pity, Timothy. She is just a young lass.

LEPRECHAUN: Young or not, she deserves no pity. (*He takes pot and sets it down, then shoves* DAUGHTER *into cottage.*)

PIXIE: Poor lovely lass. Her desire to help her father was stronger than her honesty. (LEPRECHAUN *returns.*)

LEPRECHAUN: I left the lass wailing like a banshee. How weak humans are! Do you still believe we'll find an honest one, today?

PIXIE: I do. Humans are often frail in spirit, but they are basically good and honest at heart.

LEPRECHAUN: Humph! You're wrong, Paddy. But, hark— others are coming. (*He and* PIXIE *hide in cottage.* DANNY *and* KATHLEEN *enter, and search the ground.*)

DANNY: We've been dawdling too long here in the forest, Kathleen. We'll miss the St. Patrick's Day parade, if we're not careful. Let's return to the village.

KATHLEEN: Just a few minutes more, Danny. I do hope to find a shamrock to wear on my frock. I have no green frock to wear to the parade. A green shamrock would make me feel so much gayer and more Irish.

DANNY: Another minute, then. What I'd like to have is a fine green shirt and a green balloon to carry.

KATHLEEN (*Discovering pot*): Danny! Come quickly! It's a pot of gold!

DANNY (*Running to center*): Sure, and it's the truth you're saying! There's enough gold here for a frock, a shirt, and a million green balloons!

CHILDREN (*Joining hands and dancing about, singing to the tune of "The Farmer in the Dell"*):
We found a pot o' gold.
We found a pot o' gold.
Heigh oh, the derry oh,
We found a pot o' gold.

KATHLEEN: Come, let's take it quickly and be gone. (DANNY *tries to lift pot.*)

DANNY: It's very heavy for a small boy, Kathleen.

KATHLEEN: Here, I'll help. (*They carry pot between them and start to exit.* LEPRECHAUN *and* PIXIE *enter.*)

LEPRECHAUN (*Waving wand*):
Hobbledy-hip! Hobbledy-hop!
Force them, magic wand, to stop!

CHILDREN (*Turning and stopping*): Help! Let us go, leprechaun!

LEPRECHAUN: That I will not. You intended to take my gold, so I will take *you* to my dungeon. There you shall live out your days in darkness.

KATHLEEN: Have pity! We meant no harm.

DANNY: Please have pity! We wished to buy some clothes and jolly balloons for the St. Patrick's Day parade. That's all.

PIXIE: I beg you to have pity, Timothy. They are but thoughtless and high-spirited children.

LEPRECHAUN: Bah! I have no pity for greedy little children. (*He roughly pushes children into cottage, as they squeal with fright.*)

PIXIE: Ah me, things are going from bad to worse. If I do not win the wager soon, the leprechaun may have half the village locked up before sunset. (LEPRECHAUN *returns, rubbing his hands with glee.*)

LEPRECHAUN: Things are going from good to better. Will you concede that you have lost the wager, Paddy?

PIXIE: Not yet. I still feel certain that we will meet an honest soul this day.

LEPRECHAUN (*Shading eyes*): Ah, I see some others approaching. (*Aside, to audience*) Drat it! It is the old granny and her grandchildren. The old busybody! What a piece of bad luck this is. (*He and* PIXIE *hide in cottage again, and peek out of the door.* GRANNY, SHARON, BRIDGET, *and* TERENCE *enter.*)

GRANNY: If we take a look about here again, we might find a few more mushrooms.

TERENCE: We should go back soon, Granny. The parade starts in less than an hour.

SHARON (*Spying pot*): Look! The pot of gold is here again!

TERENCE: You told me nothing about a pot of gold!

BRIDGET: There was no reason to tell you, for Granny gave it back to the old leprechaun.

SHARON: He's very careless with his gold. If he cares that little about it, he deserves to be robbed.

TERENCE: Let's take it, Granny! He's only a miserly leprechaun.

GRANNY: For shame! When will you children learn to have respect for all creatures who walk the earth? He is a lonely leprechaun, no doubt, and gold is his only comfort. How much luckier *we* are, who have each other. (*She carries pot to cottage.* LEPRECHAUN *and* PIXIE *come out.*)

LEPRECHAUN (*Whispering to* GRANNY): Go away, old woman. Go away, I say.

PIXIE: So you tried to pull the wool over my eyes, Timothy. I heard what the children said. This good, honest granny was here once before today.

GRANNY: I was indeed. Returned the gold to him, I did. Why he chose to set it outside again, I haven't the faintest notion.

PIXIE: It was a trap, Granny. Had you taken the gold, you and your grandchildren would have been locked in his dungeon with all the others. Furthermore, had it not been for you, I might have lost a wager and become his slave.

BRIDGET (*Shuddering*): What a narrow escape!

GRANNY: Saints preserve us! Why would the leprechaun do such wicked things?

PIXIE: Because he dislikes people and thinks only of revenge. He believes that everyone is out to steal from him, and he wagered his pot of gold on it. Thanks to you, Granny, I won the pot of gold. And now I'll give it to you to show my gratitude.

GRANNY: Begorra! That's very generous of you, Mr. Pixie.

CHILDREN: Hooray! We're rich!

GRANNY: Quiet children. Just one moment, Mr. Pixie. Did I hear you say that there were *others* in the leprechaun's dungeon?

PIXIE: You did, Granny. There are two young children, a woodcutter's daughter, and a hunter locked in his deep, dark dungeon.

CHILDREN: Oh, how dreadful!

GRANNY (*To* LEPRECHAUN): You must free them at once.

LEPRECHAUN: Not on your life, old woman. Paddy Pixie has his freedom. You have my pot of gold. The prisoners *I* will keep.

CHILDREN: Have pity, leprechaun!

LEPRECHAUN: I have no pity or love for people.

GRANNY: Then perhaps I can appeal to you another way. (*Holds out pot*) Set the prisoners free, and I'll give you back your pot of gold.

LEPRECHAUN (*Snatching pot*): Agreed!

PIXIE (*Taking gold and holding it away from* LEPRE-CHAUN): It's untrustworthy you've proven to be, Timothy. You'll get your gold when the prisoners are free.

LEPRECHAUN (*Pouting*): Very well. (*Exits into cottage*)

GRANNY: I do feel sorry for the poor leprechaun. He must get very lonely with nothing but his gold to keep him company.

PIXIE: Gold is his only companion. He has never known the joy of making friends. (LEPRECHAUN *enters with* HUNTER, WOODCUTTER's DAUGHTER, DANNY, *and* KATH-LEEN.)

DANNY *and* KATHLEEN: Are we free? Are we free?

PIXIE: Yes, thanks to Granny here, who paid your ransom.

DAUGHTER: Thank you, Granny. I took the gold only to help my sick father.

HUNTER: And I took it to buy food for my hungry family.

KATHLEEN: We took it to buy clothes and balloons for the parade.

DANNY: We meant no harm.

GRANNY: You owe me no apology. My own grandchildren here were sorely tempted to take the gold also. It is no easy matter for poor folks to be honest.

PIXIE: But some are honest against all odds. That is why we are all free now.

ALL: Hooray for Granny!

GRANNY (*Shyly*): Come, the parade will soon be starting. Let us all go together. Then, whoever wishes, may come back to my house for Irish stew with mushrooms.

TERENCE: Come, let's be on our way! (*All except* PIXIE *and* LEPRECHAUN *start to exit.*)

GRANNY: You're invited to join us, too, Mr. Pixie.

PIXIE: Thank you, Granny. It's kind you are. (*Hands pot to* LEPRECHAUN) Here, Timothy, have fun with your gold.

LEPRECHAUN: Ah, be off with you.

GRANNY (*To* LEPRECHAUN): If you've a mind to join us, Mr. Leprechaun, you are also welcome. (*He looks at her in surprise, then turns away.*)

LEPRECHAUN (*Gruffly*): I must keep watch over my gold.

GRANNY: Goodbye, then. Have a pleasant time. (*All exit, except* LEPRECHAUN, *who kneels beside pot and touches the gold.*)

LEPRECHAUN:
Lovely gold! Lovely gold!
It's mine to keep. It's mine to hold.
I hoard it well. It's not to spend.
For gold's a leprechaun's best friend.
(LEPRECHAUN *looks at gold sadly. He stands and paces back and forth.*) What I have long suspected is true. Alas, gold is not enough. It brings me no real happiness. It doesn't talk or laugh. It doesn't care about me. (*Pause*) Granny seemed almost friendly to me. Perhaps—(*He runs to exit and calls*) Come back! Please come back, everyone! (*All re-enter.*)

GRANNY: What is it, Mr. Leprechaun? Did you hurt yourself, perchance?

LEPRECHAUN: Yes, yes. I've been hurting myself for years. I have made my pot of gold my only friend. Now I know that gold is a loveless companion. And too much association with it makes one selfish and mean.

PIXIE: Now you are coming to your senses, Timothy.

LEPRECHAUN (*To* GRANNY): Do you truly wish me to join you all at the parade today? Are humans that forgiving?

GRANNY: We humans are not perfect. But most of us are forgiving and loving. Isn't that right, everyone?

ALL (*Ad lib*): Yes! Do join us, Mr. Leprechaun. Come! (*Etc. All exit, except* LEPRECHAUN.)

LEPRECHAUN: Aye! I'll be with you in a minute. (*He runs back, lifts pot.*) Perhaps this pot of gold will bring happiness yet. For it's happy my new friends will be, when they hear I intend to share it with them. (*Marches toward exit, singing to "The Farmer in the Dell"*)

I'll share my pot o' gold.

I'll share my pot o' gold.

Heigh oh, the derry oh,

I'll share my pot o' gold.

(*He smiles and waves to audience, and exits. Curtain.*)

THE END

Cinder-Rabbit

by Constance Whitman Baher

Characters

CINDER-RABBIT
CARONIA ⎫
LETITIA ⎭ *her stepsisters*
MRS. RABBIT, *her stepmother*
MAGGIE CHICK, *Cinder-Rabbit's Fairy Godmother*
PRINCE COTTONTAIL
JACK ⎫
SPEEDY ⎭ *his advisers*
FOUR WHITE MICE

SCENE 1

TIME: *The day before Easter.*

SETTING: *Cinder-Rabbit's home. There is a fireplace up right. Two large kettles are downstage. A table and chairs stand at center.*

AT RISE: CINDER-RABBIT *is sweeping ashes from the hearth into fireplace.*

CINDER-RABBIT (*As she finishes sweeping*): There! Every last cinder is back in the fireplace where it belongs. (*She puts down broom and rubs her back.*) At least my stepmother won't be able to scold me about the ashes again today. (*Looking at kettles*) Oh! The Easter eggs! I hope I haven't left them in the dye too long. Letitia and

484

Caronia will beat me if I have. (*Quickly takes eggs from kettles and holds them in her apron*) Thank goodness! They're just perfect! (*Carries eggs to table, where two baskets and ribbons are set out*) There, now. I'll put them in these baskets (*Arranging eggs in baskets*), and I'll add a pretty ribbon to each one. (*She ties yellow ribbon on one basket and purple ribbon on other.*) One of these is bound to win Prince Cottontail's Easter egg contest at the ball tonight—I just know it. (*Holds up baskets and gazes at them*) And maybe the Prince will choose either Letitia or Caronia to lead the Royal Easter festivities with him tomorrow. How exciting!

MRS. RABBIT (*Calling from off left*): Cinder-Rabbit!

CARONIA (*Calling from off right*): Where are you, Cinder-Rabbit?

LETITIA (*Calling from off left*): Cinder-Rabbit! (CINDER-RABBIT *quickly puts baskets down as* MRS. RABBIT, CARONIA, *and* LETITIA *enter wearing ball gowns.* CARONIA *carries comb and hairbrush and yellow bow;* LETITIA *carries purple bow.*)

MRS. RABBIT: Cinder-Rabbit, whatever have you been doing with yourself? The girls need you to help them dress, or we'll all be late for the ball.

CARONIA: Cinder-Rabbit, my whiskers need combing, and I think my fur is a little mussed. (*Hands* CINDER-RABBIT *comb and brush*)

LETITIA (*To* CARONIA): What a fuss-budget you are, Caronia. Besides, if you weren't always in such a hurry, you wouldn't get your whiskers so twisted up. Cinder-Rabbit, leave her fur alone and come help me lace my dress. (CINDER-RABBIT *does so.*)

MRS. RABBIT: Cinder-Rabbit, if you weren't my very own stepdaughter, I'd throw you right out of this rabbit hole. You are so lazy. Look at this place! How long has it been since you washed the floor?

CINDER-RABBIT: I washed the floor yesterday, Stepmother.

CARONIA: Cinder-Rabbit, are my ears pink enough inside? Perhaps my paws need a manicure. Well, I suppose we haven't time for all that now. (*Holding out bow*) Here, put this bow in my fur.

MRS. RABBIT (*As* CINDER-RABBIT *helps* CARONIA *with bow*): You washed the floor yesterday—humph! And the wood-work—I suppose it never occurred to you that the wood-work needs a good scrubbing.

CINDER-RABBIT: I did that last night.

LETITIA: Mother, leave Cinder-Rabbit alone. She can wash and scrub all night long while we're at Prince Cot-tontail's ball. I need her to help me dress. (*Holding out bow*) Here, Cinder-Rabbit, I want a bow in my fur just like Caronia's.

CARONIA: If you weren't a rabbit, you'd be a copycat, Letitia. (*As* CINDER-RABBIT *fixes bow*) Why don't you wear the bow on your big feet, Letitia?

LETITIA: Caronia, do you know why your nose twitches so much?

CARONIA: No, why?

LETITIA: Because you're so nosy!

MRS. RABBIT: Girls, stop it! You'll be late for the ball. Cinder-Rabbit, where are the girls' Easter baskets?

CINDER-RABBIT (*Bringing them*): Here they are, Step-mother.

MRS. RABBIT: Humph! (*Inspecting baskets*) Well, they'll do. (*Aside, to girls*) I told you not to waste your time dyeing the eggs yourselves.

LETITIA: They *are* pretty.

MRS. RABBIT: Pretty? Well, yes, I suppose so. Too pretty to give away to nasty children tomorrow.

CINDER-RABBIT: But tomorrow is Easter, Stepmother. All rabbits give their eggs away to the children on Easter Sunday.

MRS. RABBIT: Well, I've never thought it was a good idea. Spending all that time to make good Easter eggs, and then having to give them away.

CINDER-RABBIT (*To herself*): I wish I had some to give away.

MRS. RABBIT: What was that? *You* want Easter eggs? Fancy that! Cinder-Rabbit having her own Easter eggs—hah! Girls, you must tell that to Prince Cottontail when you dance with him. I'm sure he'll think it's very funny. (*Giving girls one last inspection*) Well, I think you're finally ready. (*Shooing them offstage*) Hurry along now. I'll be right there. (*Girls exit.* MRS. RABBIT *goes to fireplace and kicks at ashes.*) Look, Cinder-Rabbit, there are ashes on the hearth again.

CINDER-RABBIT: But, Stepmother, you just kicked them there!

MRS. RABBIT: I did nothing of the sort. Now, see that there's not a speck of dust in this entire house by the time we return, or I promise you, this time I shall throw you out, once and for all! (*She turns abruptly and exits.* CINDER-RABBIT *slowly starts to sweep ashes into fireplace, then stops and leans on broom.*)

CINDER-RABBIT: By now they must be at the gates of Prince Cottontail's castle. . . . (*Dreamily*) I can almost hear the orchestra. . . . (*Soft sounds of waltz music are heard.* CINDER-RABBIT *begins to dance about, holding broom.*) They say Prince Cottontail is the handsomest prince in all the world. (*She waltzes toward table and bumps into it.*) Oh! (*Sits down*) That's what I get for day-dreaming. *I'll* never get to see Prince Cottontail. (*Sadly she rests her head on her hand.*)

MAGGIE CHICK (*Entering*): What's this? Why all those gloomy thoughts about Prince Cottontail and the Easter ball? Why won't you get to meet the Prince? Why have you no basket to enter in the contest?

CINDER-RABBIT (*Frightened*): Who are you, and how in the world did you know what I was thinking?

MAGGIE (*Whirling about, waving her wand*): I know a good deal more than people give me credit for. I am Maggie Chick, your Fairy Godmother, and I have more than a touch of magic in me. Just follow my advice and all will be well.

CINDER-RABBIT: My Fairy Godmother? Oh, goodness. I never knew anyone gave a thought to a poor rabbit like me, even at Easter.

MAGGIE: Don't worry about a thing. Cheer up, girl. Say, do you know what one rabbit said to the other?

CINDER-RABBIT: No, Maggie. What?

MAGGIE: He said, "I'm so scared, my hare is standing on end." Ha! That's a good one. Get it—*hare*—rabbit? (CINDER-RABBIT *giggles*.)

CINDER-RABBIT: You're funny, Maggie, and you've already cheered me up.

MAGGIE: Well, I'm going to do more than that, my girl. Now look—you want to go to the ball and dance with Prince Cottontail, don't you?

CINDER-RABBIT: Oh, yes!

MAGGIE: And you'd like it if you won the Easter basket contest and were chosen to help Prince Cottontail lead the Easter festivities tomorrow—

CINDER-RABBIT: Oh, Maggie, that would all be too wonderful— (*Sadly*) but you know I can never do any of those things.

MAGGIE (*Shaking her finger*): Uh, uh, uh! Aren't you forgetting something?

CINDER-RABBIT: What?

MAGGIE: *I'm* your Fairy Godmother! You've heard of wishbones, haven't you? And they come from chickens, right?

CINDER-RABBIT: Yes.

MAGGIE: Well, I just happen to be one of those chickens with magic in every single bone. (*Snaps her fingers*) Now, let's get to work. First of all you need something to wear. (*Pointing to vegetable bin upstage*) What's that?

CINDER-RABBIT: Just our old vegetable bin. I went to the market yesterday, and it's full of lettuce and carrots.

MAGGIE: Perfect! (*Takes large head of lettuce from bin*) This will be just perfect. (*Sets it on table*) Now, what else have we here? (*Looks about room*) I'll need two carrots— (CINDER-RABBIT *brings them to her.* MAGGIE *reaches into her pocket.*) and a pinch or two of fairy dust. (*She sprinkles "dust" over lettuce and carrots.*) Now, Cinder-Rabbit, you take these (*Hands them to her*), and go to your room. I want you to stand very still, right in the middle of your room, cross your arms like this, bend down, and touch your toes. (*She demonstrates.*) They say rabbits' feet are lucky, and I don't want to overlook a single possibility in a case like this. So be sure you touch both feet. Now go, and don't worry —I'll just say a few little magic words out here and you won't feel a thing. (CINDER-RABBIT, *bewildered, exits left.* MAGGIE *faces left and recites.*)

Head of lettuce, carrot stick,
Quickly do this magic trick—
Make a dress of dazzling hues
And two dainty dancing shoes.

Cinder-Rabbit, cross your arms,
Touch both feet and hear my charms—
No sweeping, scrubbing floors or wall—
Tonight, you're going to the ball!

(MAGGIE *claps her hands together like cymbals.*) There, that should do it. (*Turns*) Now, while my little enchantment does its work, I'd better figure out some way to get her to the Prince's castle. Let's see— (*She paces back and forth.*) Wilhelmina the White Rabbit is sailing in on a boat made of watermelon, with six beavers pulling the oars. . . . Several of the guests are flying in on the Dragonfly Express. . . . At least one mole is running a subway direct to the palace. . . . And the ants are running buses all night long. . . . That will never do for Cinder-Rabbit. She must arrive in style. In something elegant. Something unusual. (*Suddenly*) I have it! We'll take that broken-down old coach outside the hutch, and we'll turn it into a pumpkin! (*Rubbing her hands with glee*) Oh, this is choice! I'll make wheels out of four radishes, and have four white mice to pull it. Oh, what a sight this will be! (*She stands in front of window and chants.*)

Carriage, carriage,
Hear my spell—
Turn into
A pumpkin shell!

(*Still looking out window*) Oh, it's marvelous! (*If desired, "pumpkin" made of a large drum covered with orange paper may be wheeled in by* FOUR WHITE MICE.) Cinder-Rabbit! Cinder-Rabbit! Are you ready?

CINDER-RABBIT (*Entering wearing beautiful green ball gown*): Yes, Maggie. All ready. (*Whirling about*) Maggie Chick, my gown is beautiful. (*Holding up orange slippers*) And my slippers —and the coach—and everything!

MAGGIE (*Pacing*): I know I've forgotten something. I just know it. Of course! You don't have an Easter basket.

CINDER-RABBIT: You're right. (*Worried*) And there are no Easter eggs left. I used all the ones we had here for Letitia and Caronia's baskets.

MAGGIE: Now, wait . . . wait. . . . Don't lose heart. (*She snaps her fingers quickly.*) Are you ready? Cross your arms and touch your toes. (CINDER-RABBIT *does so.* MAGGIE *faces upstage and chants.*)

Presto, change-o, tisket tasket,
Eggs, now make an Easter basket!

(*She claps her hands together like cymbals.*) Now look behind the vegetable bin. (CINDER-RABBIT *goes to bin and returns with golden Easter basket filled with large eggs covered with colored glitter.*)

CINDER-RABBIT (*Holding up one of the eggs*): Oh, Maggie, they're beautiful! How can I ever thank you?

MAGGIE: Don't worry about that, child, you just concentrate on getting yourself to the ball. (CINDER-RABBIT *starts right.*) Just one thing—you'd better not stay at the ball after midnight.

CINDER-RABBIT: What will happen, Maggie?

MAGGIE: Disaster. That's what will happen. At twelve o'clock all my magic will disappear. Your pumpkin coach will turn back into a broken-down carriage, and your beautiful dress will vanish and you will be in rags once more. Dance all you like, but before the clock strikes twelve, you must leave the ball. (*Claps her hands*) Now off with you, and have a wonderful time! (*As* CINDER-RABBIT *exits*) And remember, be back by the stroke of twelve! (MAGGIE *smiles. Waltz music is heard, rising to a crescendo.*)

CURTAIN

*   *   *

If desired, sound of a clock chiming twelve may be heard.

*   *   *

Scene 2

Time: *The next morning.*

Setting: *Same as Scene 1.*

At Rise: Letitia *and* Caronia *are sitting at table at center.* Cinder-Rabbit, *in her ragged clothes again, is preparing breakfast.*

Letitia: What an outrage! If I hadn't been there, I never would have believed it. (Cinder-Rabbit *pauses to listen.*)

Caronia: It was disgraceful.

Mrs. Rabbit (*Entering and sitting at table*): The whole thing was an utter catastrophe.

Letitia: I'm not even sure we'll have Easter this year.

Mrs. Rabbit (*To* Cinder-Rabbit): What's the matter with *you*, Cinder-Rabbit? Hurry up with our breakfast! We're hungry. You'd think *you* had been out dancing all night. (*To girls*) She's probably the only one of us who had a decent night's sleep. (As Cinder-Rabbit *serves breakfast*) I suppose we might as well tell you, Cinder-Rabbit—the girls were the hit of the ball!

Letitia: Caronia wasn't. She was batting her eyelashes as fast as she could, but she didn't get one dance with the Prince.

Caronia: Well, you didn't either. He probably knew you'd trip over your big feet the minute he started the bunny hop.

Letitia: It had nothing to do with my feet—even if they are big. It was that girl. That strange girl in the green dress.

Caronia (*Dejectedly*): I know. The minute she came in, he gazed only at her, and I don't think he asked another person there to dance. (Cinder-Rabbit *stops to listen.*)

Mrs. Rabbit: Cinder-Rabbit, what are you doing? Get

back to work. The whole thing is probably all your fault for doing a sloppy job on the girls' Easter baskets.

CINDER-RABBIT: I worked very hard on the Easter baskets.

MRS. RABBIT: Well, neither of the girls won the prize. In fact, no one did.

CARONIA: That's just the trouble. And now there's no one to help Prince Cottontail hide the first Easter eggs for the children today.

CINDER-RABBIT: You mean there wasn't any winner? No winner at all?

LETITIA: There would have been, only she ran away when the clock struck twelve. So now there's no winner, and no one to begin the Easter festivities. (*There is a knock on the door at right.*)

MRS. RABBIT: Cinder-Rabbit, answer the door. (*To girls*) It's probably some nosy neighbors wanting to hear all about the ball. (*To* CINDER-RABBIT, *as she and the girls turn their backs to the door*) Whoever it is, tell them we're not at home.

CINDER-RABBIT (*Opening door*): Oh, Your Highness! (*She curtsies, as* PRINCE COTTONTAIL *enters, followed by* SPEEDY, *who carries a slate and chalk.* JACK, *carrying a small chest, hops in after them.*)

MRS. RABBIT (*To girls*): Your Highness? Did she say, Your Highness? (*She turns, sees* PRINCE, *pokes* LETITIA *and* CARONIA *and they all curtsy awkwardly.*) Your Highness!

LETITIA *and* CARONIA (*Turning and curtsying*): Your Highness!

PRINCE: Please rise, good subjects. I am sorry to intrude upon you at such an early hour but, as you may know, the situation is desperate.

MRS. RABBIT: We know, Your Highness. My two girls were at the ball last night.

SPEEDY (*Writing rapidly on slate*): Did you say, two girls?

Two . . . two times two is four, two times four is eight, two times eight is—is—

JACK: Oh, don't mind him. Someone told him once that rabbits multiply quickly, and he's been like that ever since.

MRS. RABBIT: Yes, well, as I was saying (*Pointing*), Letitia and Caronia were there, but that one, my stepdaughter, was home, of course, cleaning and scrubbing.

PRINCE (*Looking carefully at* CINDER-RABBIT): Of course.

JACK: You see, the Prince has no one to help him start the Easter festivities. That is, he has—er—lost track of the fair maiden he would have chosen. She got the jump on him, as you might say. (*He tries with all his might, but makes only a small jump.*)

PRINCE (*Taking chest from* JACK): We do have one clue to this mysterious maiden. As the clock struck twelve and she ran from the castle, she dropped one of the beautiful eggs from her Easter basket. She picked up one of the broken halves, but in her haste, left the other half lying on the ground. (*Opens chest and takes out broken half of a large glittering Easter egg*) Whoever in my kingdom possesses the matching half of this broken Easter egg must be the lovely lady I seek.

MRS. RABBIT: You are indeed lucky, Your Highness, that you have come to our poor home, for I am sure that that egg came from the basket of one of my girls here. Come, girls, fetch your Easter baskets for the Prince.

LETITIA (*Aside*): But, Mother, none of our eggs are broken.

MRS. RABBIT (*Aside to* LETITIA): Well then, *break* some! Now hurry! (*Girls run off.*) The girls will be back in two shakes, Your Highness.

SPEEDY (*Scribbling rapidly*): Two shakes . . . two times two would be four, two times four would be eight, two times eight would be—would be—(CINDER-RABBIT, *unnoticed by others, takes her Easter basket from behind vegetable bin and sets it by fireplace where it can be seen by audience.*)

CARONIA (*Re-entering with* LETITIA): Here are our baskets, Your Highness. (*She curtsies and holds out broken half of an egg.*) I believe this is the missing half you are looking for.

PRINCE (*Taking egg and examining it*): Let me see . . .

LETITIA (*In a loud "whisper"*): Yours is much too small, Caronia.

CARONIA: Sh-h-h.

PRINCE (*Comparing two halves*): Your egg does not seem to be as sparkling as the one I have.

MRS. RABBIT: Some of the sparkle must have rubbed off on the way home, Your Highness. You know how that can happen.

PRINCE (*Trying to fit the two halves together*): No, I'm afraid this is not the one. It is too small to match with my half. (*Hands egg back to* CARONIA)

LETITIA (*Holding out broken egg from her basket*): Here, Your Highness. This must be the one, then.

CARONIA (*To* LETITIA): It's too big, like your feet!

PRINCE (*Examining egg and trying to make it fit with other half*): No, I'm afraid this egg is not the right one either. It is too big. (*Sadly, he hands egg back to* LETITIA.) I thought for sure we'd find the maiden here. (*To others*) I am sorry to have troubled you, and I'm afraid we must be going now. We don't have much time. . . . (*As* PRINCE *and his advisers start toward door,* PRINCE *sees basket with glittering eggs on hearth. He goes to hearth and points to* CINDER-RABBIT's *basket, excitedly.*) Why, here's another basket! Whose is it? These eggs sparkle like the broken one I found at the ball. (*JACK and* SPEEDY *hop back to fireplace.*)

JACK (*Picking up basket*): They certainly do shine.

SPEEDY (*Reaching into basket*): And it has a broken egg in it. (*As he starts to take broken egg from basket,* CINDER-RABBIT *snatches basket away and holds it behind her.*)

PRINCE (*Going to her*): Why are you trying to hide the basket? (CINDER-RABBIT *draws back, frightened, as* PRINCE *reaches behind her into basket.*) Come, don't be afraid. Let me see if that broken egg matches mine. (*He takes broken half of glittering egg from basket and holds it against his half.*)

JACK (*Looking on, amazed*): A perfect match!

SPEEDY: Then—then (*Points to* CINDER-RABBIT)—*she* must be the one!

MRS. RABBIT, LETITIA, *and* CARONIA (*Ad lib*): Cinder-Rabbit! It can't be! Impossible! But it is! That's her basket! (*Etc.*)

PRINCE (*Staring at* CINDER-RABBIT; *gently*): You are the one, then!

MAGGIE (*Entering*): Of course, she's the one. Naturally she looks a bit better dressed up, but she was the one who dropped the egg at the ball, all right.

PRINCE (*To* MAGGIE): Who are you? And how do you know about the egg and the ball and Cinder-Rabbit?

MAGGIE: I'm Maggie Chick, Cinder-Rabbit's Fairy Godmother, and I keep track of what goes on, as you'll soon see. (*To* CINDER-RABBIT) Go to your room, Cinder-Rabbit, and put on what you find there waiting for you.

CINDER-RABBIT (*Bewildered*): All right, Maggie. (*She exits.*)

MRS. RABBIT (*To* MAGGIE): It's you who spoiled my girls' chances . . .

MAGGIE: I'm afraid they just don't have what it takes to charm a prince. (CINDER-RABBIT *returns wearing the green gown and orange slippers she wore to the ball.*)

PRINCE: How beautiful you look!

MAGGIE (*Whirling around* CINDER-RABBIT): Splendid, my girl. You look even better in that outfit than you did last night.

PRINCE (*Going to* CINDER-RABBIT): Now I recognize you again. You are indeed the beautiful maiden I danced with all last night. (*Bowing*) Will you do me the honor of leading the Easter festivities today?

CINDER-RABBIT (*With a deep curtsy*): Oh, I will, Your Highness.

PRINCE: And when we have properly begun the Easter events, you must return with me to my castle and be my bride.

CINDER-RABBIT: Oh, Prince Cottontail! You have made my dearest wish come true! (PRINCE *takes* CINDER-RABBIT's *hand.*)

PRINCE (*To others*): We must hurry now, if we are to begin the Easter festivities on time. (*To* CINDER-RABBIT) Perhaps your sisters will agree to accompany my two advisers in the procession.

LETITIA *and* CARONIA (*Ad lib, excitedly*): Oh, Your Highness, how wonderful! We'd love to! (*Etc.*)

CINDER-RABBIT: And could they and my stepmother come to live in the castle, too?

PRINCE: If that is what you desire, it shall be so. They shall be ladies-in-waiting in our court.

MRS. RABBIT, LETITIA, *and* CARONIA: Oh, Your Highness, how generous you are!

PRINCE (*Offering his arm to* CINDER-RABBIT): Come, my princess, we must be off to start the Easter festivities. (*Takes basket of glittering eggs*) It shall be your official duty to hide the first of these beautiful eggs.

MAGGIE: Yes, all the children in the land are coming to the Easter egg hunt.

CINDER-RABBIT (*Taking basket and looking up at* PRINCE *happily*): Prince Cottontail, this will be the best Easter we ever had. (*An Easter song is heard.* PRINCE *and* CINDER-RABBIT *start off in stately fashion, followed by* JACK *and* LETITIA *arm in arm, then* SPEEDY *and* CARONIA, *and finally,* MRS. RABBIT *and* MAGGIE, *as the curtain falls.*)

THE END

The Choosing of Easter Rabbit

by Sally Werner

Characters

OLD RABBIT	BEAR
FIVE RABBITS	ROBIN
RAGGEDY RABBIT	RED DEER
SQUIRREL	EASTER FAIRY
SPARROW	

TIME: *Late afternoon, a few days before Easter.*

SETTING: *A clearing in the woods.*

AT RISE: *The* RABBITS *are gathered together, reading a notice on one of the trees.*

OLD RABBIT: Well, well, did you read this notice?

OTHER RABBITS: What does it say, Old Rabbit? What does it say?

OLD RABBIT (*Puts on glasses*): Hear ye, hear ye, rabbits and rabbits! A new Easter Rabbit will be chosen this year. Meet here at seven o'clock tonight. The Easter Fairy will be here to do the choosing. Signed, a rabbit who knows.

1ST RABBIT: A new Easter Rabbit!

2ND RABBIT: How exciting!

3RD RABBIT: It might be me.

4TH RABBIT: Or me.

5TH RABBIT (*Strutting about*): It could be me.

OLD RABBIT: Yes, it could be any one of you, if you do the right thing. Well—I must go now, but I'll be back to-night to see who is chosen. (*He leaves, and* RAGGEDY RABBIT *enters.*)

RAGGEDY: What's all the excitement about?

1ST RABBIT: Oh, it wouldn't concern you, Raggedy. They are going to choose a new Easter Rabbit tonight at seven o'clock. You'd better come to see which one of us is chosen.

2ND RABBIT: Yes—you could watch. They wouldn't choose you, of course.

3RD RABBIT: No, you're too ragged.

4TH RABBIT: And you're so plain.

5TH RABBIT: You have no glamour.

RAGGEDY: But—perhaps I could fix myself up a bit. I would so love to be the Easter Rabbit.

ALL (*Laughing and pointing at him*): You? Ha, ha!

1ST RABBIT: Oh, Raggedy, you wouldn't do at all.

RAGGEDY: No, I guess you're right. (*Sighs*) Anyway I'm going home to brush up. I've been helping Beaver fix his new house up. That's why I'm so raggedy-looking. (*Sighs again*) Oh, how I'd love to be Easter Rabbit.

2ND RABBIT: Oh, for goodness' sakes, Raggedy, quit day-dreaming. You know you could never be chosen. (SQUIR-REL *enters rubbing stomach.*)

SQUIRREL: Oh dear, oh dear, I am so hungry. I just can't remember where I hid those acorns last fall. Won't one of you rabbits help me find them?

1ST RABBIT: Not I. I must hurry home soon to get ready for the meeting tonight. My whiskers need a good comb-ing. Hope you find your acorns, Squirrel.

RAGGEDY: I should go home too, but first I will help you, Squirrel. Seems to me I saw you hide your acorns down near that old stump in the hollow. Come I'll show you. (RAGGEDY *and* SQUIRREL *leave.*)

2ND RABBIT: That silly Raggedy—always helping someone. Never thinks about himself.

3RD RABBIT: Can you imagine Raggedy being chosen as Easter Rabbit?

4TH RABBIT: Raggedy? Of course not. Ha, ha, ha. You make me laugh.

5TH RABBIT: Here he comes back on the run. (RAGGEDY *comes back.*)

RAGGEDY (*Puffing*): Poor Squirrel. He's very forgetful. He was so glad when I told him where one of his store-houses was located. Here comes Bear. (BEAR *enters, looking sadly about.*)

BEAR: My goodness, I certainly feel weak. I've been hibernating all winter and it seems I can't get filled up.

2ND RABBIT: You'd better get yourself some food.

BEAR: Yes, but it is hard to find—hard to find. (*Shakes head*) It's so early and I'm hungry.

2ND RABBIT: Well, don't come to me for help. I'm going to be at the meeting tonight. I might be chosen to be the Easter Rabbit. I must go home and slick my fur up.

RAGGEDY: I should go home too, Bear, but first I must show you the grubs I found in that old tree in the meadow. You look so thin, Mr. Bear. Come on. (BEAR *and* RAGGEDY *leave.*)

3RD RABBIT: That silly Raggedy. He never finds time to take care of himself.

4TH RABBIT: I don't think it would do him much good. He will always be the same old Raggedy.

5TH RABBIT: If he weren't always looking out for others, he might get himself looking decent.

1ST RABBIT: I doubt it.

2ND RABBIT: I wonder which one of us will be chosen to-night. (RAGGEDY *comes back.*)

RAGGEDY: Poor old Bear. He was so hungry. He hadn't eaten all winter. I'm glad I knew about those grubs. My goodness, here comes Sparrow, and does he ever look hungry! (SPARROW *enters looking about the ground.*)

SPARROW: Hello, Rabbits. Have you seen any grain? There isn't a thing to eat around here. If I could only find a little grain to tide me over until it gets warmer!

3RD RABBIT: Well, don't ask me. I am going home soon to get ready for the meeting tonight. Look at my tail. I need to fluff it up a bit.

RAGGEDY: I should leave, too, but first I will show you where you might find some grain. Over this way there is an old grain shed. Come on and I'll show you. (RAGGEDY *and* SPARROW *leave.*)

4TH RABBIT: That Raggedy! He has no pride in his appearance at all.

5TH RABBIT: Helping Sparrow. Honestly—he just can't stand to see anyone hungry.

1ST RABBIT: He's a queer one—that Raggedy. He'll never amount to anything.

2ND RABBIT: Just a plain old ragged-looking rabbit.

3RD RABBIT: Shh—here he comes back. (RAGGEDY *enters.*)

4TH RABBIT: Well, I suppose you have Sparrow taken care of.

RAGGEDY: Oh, yes. I'm so glad I happened to know about the grain shed.

5TH RABBIT: You're a funny one all right. Look, here comes Robin. He's early this year. (ROBIN *enters.*)

ROBIN: Dear me, no gardens yet, no worms. I wish I hadn't come so soon. I'd give anything for a worm. I really am hungry.

4TH RABBIT: Well, don't look at me, Robin. I'm much too busy. Anyway, you robins are always in a hurry to get back here. Why don't you stay away until later? I must go home and freshen up a bit for the meeting tonight.

RAGGEDY: I should go too, Robin, but first let me show you the field on the hillside where the snow has melted.

You might find a few worms or bugs there. I just happened by there today. (ROBIN *and* RAGGEDY *leave.*)

4TH RABBIT: That Raggedy sure does get around, doesn't he? But isn't he foolish? Here it is getting late and off he goes to help Robin.

5TH RABBIT: It will take him such a long time to brush up that tangled fur, too.

1ST RABBIT: Raggedy now, and Raggedy he will always be. (RAGGEDY *comes back puffing.*)

RAGGEDY: Well, I suppose I'd better go home and get cleaned up. (*All the others laugh.*)

2ND RABBIT: It's no use, Raggedy. You won't be chosen anyway. Look, here comes Red Deer. I haven't seen him in a long time. (RED DEER *enters.*)

RED DEER: Have you seen any nice green moss around here? There is so little to eat in the forest right now.

5TH RABBIT: Don't expect me to help you find it, Red Deer. I may be chosen to be Easter Rabbit tonight. Come on, Rabbits. Let's go home and primp up. We haven't much time. Come on, everybody. (*The five* RABBITS *leave.*)

RAGGEDY: I should go home too, but first, Mr. Red Deer, I will show you where I saw some moss. It is on the other side of the ravine. Come with me. (RED DEER *and* RAGGEDY *leave.* OLD RABBIT *enters.*)

OLD RABBIT: Well, this is the place. Wonder who the new Easter Rabbit will be this year. Too bad I'm not younger. I think I'd be just the type. Nice long whiskers, fluffy tail, long ears—hmm—not bad. Ho hum—well— here they come, all spruced up. (*The five* RABBITS *come back, chattering to each other.*)

1ST RABBIT: Is the Easter Fairy here?

OLD RABBIT: Not yet. But here comes that Raggedy. (RAGGEDY *enters.*)

2ND RABBIT: What a sight you are, Raggedy.

RAGGEDY: I know. I haven't had time to clean up. I'll just sit way back here and watch while the Fairy chooses one of you.

3RD RABBIT: Well, you'd better not let her see you.

4TH RABBIT: Keep down low and you won't be noticed.

5TH RABBIT (*Struts about*): How do I look? (FAIRY *enters, carrying Easter basket.*)

FAIRY: Good evening, Rabbits.

ALL: Good evening, Easter Fairy. We've been waiting for you.

FAIRY: You have? I have been here several times this afternoon.

ALL: Here? You have?

FAIRY: Yes. I came five times.

ALL: Five times!

1ST RABBIT: I didn't see you.

FAIRY: Did you see a hungry squirrel?

1ST RABBIT: Yes.

FAIRY: That was I. I came first disguised as a squirrel. (*To* 2ND RABBIT) Did you see a hungry bear?

2ND RABBIT: Yes.

FAIRY: I came the second time disguised as a bear. (*To* 3RD RABBIT) Did you see a hungry sparrow?

3RD RABBIT: Yes.

FAIRY: I came the third time disguised as a sparrow. (*To* 4TH RABBIT) Did you see a hungry robin?

4TH RABBIT: Yes.

FAIRY: I came the fourth time disguised as a robin. (*To* 5TH RABBIT) Did you see a hungry red deer?

5TH RABBIT: Yes, I did.

FAIRY: I came the fifth time as a deer. And now I am here to choose the Easter Rabbit.

1ST RABBIT: We are all brushed up and ready to be chosen.

2ND RABBIT: Yes, we have been busy getting ready for you.

FAIRY: The Easter Rabbit must be kind and good and

helpful. The children must love him. Have you been kind and helpful to others? (RABBITS *look at each other shamefacedly, but do not answer.*) Raggedy is the only one among you who could ever be a real Easter Rabbit.

ALL: Raggedy!!

FAIRY: Yes. Raggedy—where are you?

RAGGEDY (*In a timid voice*): Here I am.

FAIRY: Come here, Raggedy. You will be the new Easter Rabbit. (RAGGEDY *comes up to* FAIRY. *She gives him basket.*)

1ST RABBIT: I thought the Easter Rabbit had to be beautiful.

2ND RABBIT: And have his whiskers combed.

3RD RABBIT: And have his fur slicked smooth.

OLD RABBIT: Well then, why don't you help Raggedy get ready?

4TH RABBIT: Of course! Raggedy needs our help. All day he has been helping others.

5TH RABBIT: Let's help make him the most beautiful Easter Rabbit there ever was!

FAIRY: Thank you all. I choose all the rest of you to be the Easter Rabbit's helpers.

ALL: Hooray for Raggedy! Hooray! (*Curtain*)

THE END

Fiesta

by Jean McArthur

Characters

MOTHER	THERESA
MIGUEL ⎱	TEACHER
ROSITA ⎰ *her children*	SEÑOR MARTINEZ
MARIA	SEÑORA MARTINEZ
SEÑORA GONZALES	COUSIN MANUEL
PANCHO	DAVID
ALFREDO	NANCY
CARMEN	MAYOR
LOLITA	HORSE

TIME: *The day before Pan-American Day.*

SETTING: *The main room of a small Mexican house.*

AT RISE: MOTHER *is standing by the table, mixing something in a bowl.* ROSITA *is busy dusting and* MARIA *is sitting at the table, studying.* MIGUEL *rushes in.*

MIGUEL (*Excitedly*): Mother, Mother, there's someone outside.

MOTHER: Go see who it is, Miguel; and Rosita, finish your dusting. Maria, do your school work. (MIGUEL *exits.*)

MARIA *and* ROSITA: Yes, Mother.

MIGUEL (*Running back in*): It's Señora Gonzales and she has a—

SEÑORA GONZALES (*Entering and finishing his sentence*): A letter. A letter for you.

MOTHER: A letter for us? (*Begins to take off apron*) I cannot read a letter like this. Who would write to us? Suppose it's bad news! Oh, dear!

SEÑORA GONZALES: It's from your cousin in Mexico City. His address is on the back.

MOTHER: My cousin? Children, it's from Cousin Manuel. Maria, come read it to us. You read the best. Come. (*Pulls MARIA forward.*)

MARIA (*Reading*): My dear Cousin Rosa—

MOTHER: I know it's bad news.

SEÑORA GONZALES: Sh! Listen!

MARIA (*Reading again*): My dear Cousin Rosa. I am writing to tell you that I shall be in your village on Pan-American Day on business. I shall have with me two children from North America—the son and daughter of a very good friend of mine. I wish them to see how we celebrate Pan-American Day here in Mexico. I know that you will make them feel at home and that you will show them the true hospitality of Mexico. Your Cousin, Manuel Aroza.

MOTHER: I knew it, I knew it. Bad news!

ROSITA: It's *wonderful* news. Only, when is Pan-American Day?

SEÑORA GONZALES: Really! Everyone knows that Pan-American Day is, why it's, uh—

MARIA: It's on April 14th.

SEÑORA GONZALES: Of course! (*Suddenly*) But that's tomorrow.

MOTHER: What shall we do?

MIGUEL: How do we celebrate it?

MOTHER: That's just it. We don't.

SEÑORA GONZALES: We should. It's a day that all the American countries should celebrate—a day of friendship for all.

MIGUEL (*Jumping up and down*): Bravo, bravo!

MOTHER: You're right. We'll have a fiesta.

ROSITA: A fiesta?

MIGUEL: With games?

MARIA: And dancing?

SEÑORA GONZALES: With good things to eat, too!

ROSITA: Tortillas?

MIGUEL: And frijoles?

MARIA: And tamales?

MOTHER: Of course. Oh, the work to be done! Where's my apron?

MARIA: But what will the American children eat?

MIGUEL: Ice cream and doughnuts.

MOTHER (*Stopping*): Nonsense, Miguel! They would be a nation of stomachaches!

MIGUEL: I read it. And they ride horses after bad men. (*Demonstrates*) Bang, bang!

SEÑORA GONZALES (*Nodding her head*): It is so. I have read it, too.

MOTHER: Well, these children will eat frijoles, and there will be no shooting in my house. Come, Señora Gonzales, we have work to do. We must call all the other women together and tell them of the fiesta. (*They exit together leaving* ROSITA, MIGUEL *and* MARIA *alone.*)

MARIA: They have forgotten one thing.

MIGUEL: What?

MARIA: The letter said that we should make the children feel at home. They should have their own kind of food.

ROSITA: We don't have their kind of food.

MARIA: I know that! But there's a Yankee cookbook in the schoolteacher's house.

ROSITA: You can't cook!

MARIA: I can if you'll help me.

MIGUEL *(Eagerly)*: A horse! They must have a horse to ride so they can shoot the bad men. Bang, bang!

ROSITA: That is your problem. Horses are a man's concern. Maria and I have cooking to do. We need the cookbook. Come, Maria. (MARIA *and* ROSITA *go offstage talking excitedly.*)

MIGUEL: A man's concern? I am only a little boy. Where is the book that tells how to make a horse?

CURTAIN

* * *

SCENE 2

TIME: *Afternoon of the same day.*

SETTING: *The same.*

AT RISE: MIGUEL *and* PANCHO *are sitting by the table.* MIGUEL *seems to be doing some figuring on a scrap of paper.*

MIGUEL *(Licking pencil)*: Then there's hay. How much hay does a horse eat?

PANCHO *(Shrugging his shoulders)*: Who knows? Now, a burro—

MIGUEL: No burros. A horse! These are Yankees who are coming. They always ride horses. (*He is interrupted by the arrival of* ALFREDO. ALFREDO *comes in, turns a square corner, comes to attention and salutes* MIGUEL.)

ALFREDO: Alfredo reporting, sir.

PANCHO *(Eagerly)*: What did you find out?

MIGUEL: Let me ask. Have you completed your mission, Alfredo?

ALFREDO *(Still at attention)*: Yes, sir. There is only one horse in the entire village, and that belongs to Señor Martinez.

PANCHO: That old plow horse?

ALFREDO (*Relaxing*): I can't make horses, you know. I almost got into trouble as it was. Señor Martinez didn't like my being around. He thinks an awful lot of that horse. I don't think he'll let us have it.

MIGUEL (*Standing up*): He has to! It's his patriotic duty. I shall tell him so.

PANCHO: I wouldn't, if I were you. He has an awfully mean temper.

MIGUEL: Who? The horse?

PANCHO: No. Señor Martinez.

MIGUEL: I don't care. (*Briskly*) At-ten-tion! (ALFREDO *and* PANCHO *stand at attention*) About face! (*They turn*) Forward march! (*The three boys start toward the door but are interrupted by the arrival of* ROSITA, CARMEN *and* LOLITA.)

ALFREDO: Out of the way, girls!

ROSITA: Out of the way yourself, Alfredo! We have important business.

MIGUEL: Not as important as ours. Come, men! (MIGUEL, PANCHO *and* ALFREDO *march off in formation*.)

LOLITA: Boys, boys, they are so silly. Where is Maria?

ROSITA: She'll be right along. But hurry. Let's get everything ready for her. (*She runs to cupboard for dishes*.)

CARMEN: What do you think we'll make?

LOLITA: Whatever the cookbook says, of course. Look, Maria's coming! She has Theresa with her. (CARMEN *runs to look.* MARIA *and* THERESA *enter*.)

MARIA: Oh, what a time we had!

THERESA (*Holding up a book*): Here it is—the North American cookbook.

LOLITA: Did the teacher mind lending it to you?

MARIA: Well—

THERESA: We didn't see her. She wasn't there, and we were

in such a hurry that we couldn't wait. So we just borrowed it.

ROSITA: Maria!

MARIA (*Ignoring her*): Well, what shall we make?

CARMEN: What's in the book?

THERESA (*Reading from book*): Candy, cake, pies. What are pies?

LOLITA: But those are all sweets.

CARMEN: How about tortillas?

THERESA: They don't mention those, but there is something called popovers.

GIRLS (*All together*): What are they?

ROSITA: Let's make them and find out. What do we need, Theresa?

THERESA (*Reading*): Two eggs.

MARIA (*Running to cupboard*): Eggs, eggs. Oh, dear, we only have one.

THERESA: It says two in the book.

LOLITA: Haven't you just one more egg?

MARIA: Well, there's a duck egg.

ROSITA: Get it, Maria. (MARIA *goes to the cupboard and returns with the egg.*) Drop it in. Now what?

THERESA (*Reading*): One cup of milk.

MARIA: We have no milk.

CARMEN: Use some water then.

LOLITA: Will it work?

CARMEN: It's wet, isn't it? That's all that's necessary.

LOLITA: How much is a cup?

CARMEN: That's the Yankee word for bowl. Hurry, Maria, get a bowl of water and put it in. (MARIA *does as she is told*)

LOLITA: What now?

THERESA: One cup of flour. I wonder what kind.

CARMEN: What kind of flour do you have, Maria?

MARIA: We don't have any real flour, but we do have some corn meal.

CARMEN: Good! Get it, Maria. (MARIA *does*) Now what?

THERESA: One-fourth teaspoon salt.

ROSITA: We have that. (*Runs to get it*)

LOLITA: The book says such a little bit. Here, let me salt it. (*She shakes salt vigorously into the bowl.*) There, that ought to be enough!

THERESA: Shortening. Get it, Maria. (MARIA *does.*) Now it says, "Beat smooth with a rotary beater." What's that?

LOLITA: You could use a spoon to stir it, but—

CARMEN: What does "rotary" mean?

MARIA: I think it has something to do with round things.

THERESA: That's it! Something round. Haven't you anything round to stir it with?

ROSITA (*Peering into bowl*): I don't know. It doesn't look very good, does it?

CARMEN: That's because you're not a Yankee. If you were, it would look delicious.

MARIA (*Peering into bowl and wrinkling nose*): I doubt it. (*The others start to look at the mixture but are interrupted by the entrance of* MOTHER *and* SEÑORA GONZALES.)

MOTHER: Oh, I'm glad that the cooking is done! It was so nice of you to let us use your stove, Señora Gonzales.

SEÑORA GONZALES: It was nothing. And everyone has been so helpful. Isn't it strange, though, about the schoolteacher's house being robbed? Who would want to steal a cookbook?

THERESA (*Edging toward the exit*): Adios, Señora Gonzales.

CARMEN (*Following her*): We have to be going.

LOLITA: We've had a lovely time.

MOTHER (*Going to table*): Girls, what is this? (*She peers into the bowl.*) Have you been making glue?

MARIA: They're popovers.

SEÑORA GONZALES: What did you say?

MARIA: They're popovers for the Americans. We only wanted to help. But everything went wrong and—(*She is interrupted by the arrival of the* TEACHER.)

TEACHER: Girls, the Mayor said you were seen entering my house early today. Tell me, were you the ones who took my new cookbook?

ROSITA (*Hanging head*): Sí, Señora.

MOTHER: Children!

TEACHER: Why did you do such a thing? If you had asked, I would gladly have given the book to you.

CARMEN: You weren't home.

LOLITA: We wanted to make something good for the little North Americans.

MARIA: We didn't even do that. Look.

TEACHER (*Gingerly taking a taste*): Ugh! You certainly didn't! What is it?

SEÑORA GONZALES: Popunders.

TEACHER: What?

MOTHER: Popovers.

SEÑORA GONZALES: Over, under, those are neither.

TEACHER: I agree. (*Turning to girls.*) Next time, be sure that you ask before you borrow things. And I am sure your visitors will want to taste Mexican food anyway. (*There is the sound of running offstage and* MIGUEL, ALFREDO *and* PANCHO *race in and try to hide behind the others.*)

MIGUEL: Mother, protect me.

MOTHER (*Sternly*): Miguel, what have you been doing? (*Before he can answer* SEÑOR *and* SEÑORA MARTINEZ *appear.*)

SEÑOR MARTINEZ (*Angrily*): Where are they? Where are the scoundrels?

SEÑORA MARTINEZ (*Grabbing* MIGUEL): Here is one of them—trying to hide behind his mother's apron.

MIGUEL: Let me go, let me go!

ALFREDO *and* PANCHO (*Coming out of their hiding places*): Let him go. He didn't mean it.

SEÑORA MARTINEZ: A big boy like you. You should know better!

MOTHER: What has he done?

SEÑOR MARTINEZ: He tried to steal my horse.

SEÑORA MARTINEZ: He would have done it if I hadn't caught him.

MIGUEL: I just wanted to borrow the horse.

ALFREDO: We didn't know you were home.

PANCHO: We would have been more careful if we had known!

SEÑOR MARTINEZ: What is the world coming to? Horse thieves at their age!

SEÑORA MARTINEZ (*Angrily*): They should be whipped.

MOTHER (*Turning to* MIGUEL): Why did you do it?

MIGUEL: We did it for the visitors. So they could have a horse to ride and chase the bad men. Bang, bang.

TEACHER (*Stepping forward*): Boys, you should not have tried to take the horse without asking. Your visitors do not need it. They would rather see a real Mexican fiesta, I am sure. After all, the real meaning of Pan-American Day is to share your way of living with the other American countries.

ALFREDO: We wanted to make the strangers feel at home.

TEACHER: You can do that very easily. I have a perfect plan for making them feel right at home. Come with me and I'll tell you how to do it.

SEÑORA GONZALES: We will go, too. Perhaps we can help.

SEÑOR MARTINEZ (*Following her*): Wait for us. We would like to help, too. (*They all hasten off, leaving* MIGUEL *alone.*)

MIGUEL: Just the same I intend to get a horse. If I could just—that's it! That's it! (*Jumping up and down.*) Hey, wait for me. I have to get my horse!

CURTAIN

*   *   *

SCENE 3

TIME: *The next day.*

SETTING: *The same. The room has been decorated with crepe paper, and crayon drawings of the Mexican and American flags.*

AT RISE: COUSIN MANUEL, DAVID *and* NANCY *enter and stand looking at the decorations.*

COUSIN MANUEL: This is strange. The house is decorated, but there is no one here to meet us.

DAVID: Are you sure they knew we were coming?

COUSIN MANUEL: I wrote my cousin a letter.

NANCY: Perhaps they didn't get it. I like this little house. In fact, I like your whole country.

DAVID: So do I. Look, someone's coming now. (*The* MAYOR *enters, followed by all the others.*)

MAYOR: Welcome to our fair village and to your cousin's humble house.

COUSIN MANUEL (*Stepping forward to shake hands*): Thank you. (*To* MOTHER) I see that you got my letter, Cousin.

MOTHER: Sí, Manuel. And the celebration is ready to begin.

MAYOR: You must let me begin this joyous celebration. Señores and Señoras, we welcome you all. This is a true day of celebration, not only for Mexico but for our twenty sister republics, as well. (*All cheer.* MAYOR *holds up his hands for silence.*) Today is the day when we must pledge anew to help each other and to respect each other. And now to begin the fiesta, the people of the village will sing one of their own songs. (*All sing a Mexican song.*)

ALL: Bravo! Bravo!

DAVID: That was a good song.

NANCY: I liked that.

MAYOR: Gracias, Señorita. We are pleased, and now for you a special song, a song of your own country which the school teacher has taught us. (*They all sing an American folksong.*)

DAVID: That was fun!

NANCY: We will teach you more songs before we leave. Why, it almost seems like home to hear one of our own songs sung.

MAYOR: Gracias, amigos. Now, the best of all. For the very first time in the history of our village—(*He is interrupted by* MIGUEL, *who suddenly races to the front of the stage.*)

MIGUEL: Wait! Wait! Stop the fiesta!

COUSIN MANUEL (*Bewildered*): What is all this?

MIGUEL: I have a horse.

DAVID (*Looking around the room*): Where?

MOTHER (*Suspiciously*): Whose?

MIGUEL (*Going to the side of stage, whistles*): Come. (HORSE—*two children covered by a blanket and a paper horse's head—enters and stops in the middle of the stage.*) My motto is, "If you can't get it, make it."

DAVID (*Looking at the horse*): That's good! Did you really make it?

MIGUEL: Sí. It is for you to ride when you chase bad men.

DAVID (*Doubtfully*): Well, I don't know as I would ride that! But it is a nice one.

MAYOR (*Hurriedly*): Places all, places. The fiesta must go on. We shall now present for the very first time in the history of our village a genuine, North American square dance. After which, there will be refreshments for all.

NANCY: What a wonderful place this is! (CHILDREN *take their places and dance a simple square dance.*) That was wonderful. Hurrah for Mexico!

CHILDREN: Bravo for the United States!

MAYOR (*Not to be outdone*): Viva Pan-American Day!

ALL: Viva Pan-American Day!

NANCY: What a wonderful time we're having! I feel like dancing!

HORSE (*Solemnly*): Be my guest, Señorita. (*The square dance music begins again as* HORSE *and* NANCY *take their places as head couple. They begin to dance as the curtain closes.*)

THE END

The Bell of Dolores

by Camilla Campbell

Characters

MANUEL, *a Mexican Indian*
FRANCISCO, *an older Indian*
ROSA, *his wife*
ROBERTO, *a young Indian*
DON ALFREDO ELIZONDO, *a Spaniard*
TWO POLICEMEN
MIGUEL HIDALGO, *the village priest*
MARIA, *Roberto's mother*
OLD MAN
YOUNG GIRL
DON CAESAR, *a Creole*
HERNANDO, *the watchman*
ANTONIO, *the courier*
CAPTAIN ALLENDE *of the Spanish army*
CAPTAIN GOMEZ *of the Mexican army*
VILLAGERS

TIME: *September 15, 1810. Early evening.*
SETTING: *A street in the village of Dolores, Mexico.*
AT RISE: MANUEL *is dozing on the church steps, his head on his knees.* FRANCISCO *and* ROSA *enter from right and stand looking at him, shaking their heads.* FRANCISCO *sets down a bundle he carries.*

518

FRANCISCO: Ho! Manuel! Wake up, lazy dog.

MANUEL: Francisco! Good day, Rosa. You are back, then, from San Miguel?

ROSA: No, we are still there. You only dream us here. (*All laugh.*)

MANUEL (*Eagerly*): Did you bring the new rope for my bell?

ROSA: *Your* bell!

FRANCISCO: The best piece of rope from the best rope-maker in the state of Guanajuato, if not in all Mexico. (*Gives* MANUEL *a piece of rope, which he examines carefully*)

ROSA: And high time we brought something to put you to work, *amigo,* if you've nothing better to do than nap all afternoon. A soft job you have as bell-ringer of Dolores.

MANUEL (*Drawing himself up proudly*): That is what *you* think, Rosa. It is without doubt the most important job in the village. Without my bell . . .

ROSA (*Teasing*): You and *your* bell! You are more important, I suppose, than the good Father Hidalgo himself?

FRANCISCO: Now, Rosa . . .

MANUEL (*Deflated*): Well, no. Nobody in Dolores is more important than Father Hidalgo. That goes without saying.

ROSA: Then it is noble of you to say it. I am glad to know . . .

FRANCISCO (*Interrupting*): Tell us, Manuel, did anything take place while we were away?

MANUEL: All was quiet, with Rosa gone. But truly, there was not one thing to ring my bell for except the church services. No weddings, no funerals, no fires. . . .

FRANCISCO (*With excitement*): Ah, but *hombre!* We heard news in San Miguel!

MANUEL: In truth? And what was that?

Rosa: The Viceroy's soldiers came last week and tore out all the olive trees! (*Makes gestures of uprooting trees*)

Manuel (*Puts hands to head and rocks it*): *Ay, de mi!* How well I remember that day they rooted out our grapevines which Father Hidalgo had taught us how to plant.

Francisco: Yes, after all our work, and we could do nothing but stand by and watch.

Rosa: And not even the Father could say a word. Ah, but the anger in his eyes. That was wonderful, that anger. Because his poor people were in trouble.

Francisco: I do not understand these things that the soldiers of Spain do.

Rosa: We are not supposed to understand, we Indians. We live as we are told, and why bother about why?

Manuel: But Rosa, the reason is simple. Since our country belongs to Spain, we live for the good of Spain. We in Mexico must not grow grapes and olives, because the Spaniards wish to make money by selling us wine and olive oil from the mother country.

Rosa (*Bitterly*): And who has the money to buy wine and olive oil? Have you?

Francisco (*Ignoring* Rosa): It is God's law, then, that colonies must live only for the benefit of the mother country?

Rosa: I think it is man's law, not God's.

Francisco: Shush, wife! Let no Spaniard hear you say that!

Rosa: And why not, pray? My tongue, at least, is my own. I think I shall say it to Don Alfredo Elizondo himself, that old *gachupine!* (Francisco *tries to hush her.*)

Manuel (*Thoughtfully*): You should talk to the Father about this thing. But carefully, Rosa. He has ideas, too, on this business of nations owning other nations. (*Quickly*) Ay, he will be coming soon, and the rope not yet mended! *Adios.* A million thanks for bringing the rope. (*He goes into the church.* Francisco *picks up his bundle.* Rosa *adjusts her new shawl and they start to move toward left as* Roberto *enters.* Francisco *sets his bundle down while the boy walks up to them leisurely.*)

Roberto: Welcome home, *senora y senor.*

Rosa: Good afternoon, Roberto.

Francisco: How goes everything with you?

Roberto: All goes well with me, thank you. (*Moves on toward right exit slowly and lifts hand in farewell gesture.*) Adios.

Francisco *and* Rosa (*Looking after him*): Adios! Adios! (*They turn back and* Francisco *picks up his bundle. They start out left when they hear voices and footsteps.* Don Alfredo Elizondo *and two* Policemen *come in from left.* Francisco *puts the bundle down again. He and* Rosa *move back as far as they can against the church wall.*)

Don Alfredo: Imbeciles! Pigs! You can find him if you try. (*He goes beyond* Francisco *and* Rosa, *then turns back to look at them.*) Have you seen the boy, Roberto, son of the widow, Maria? (Francisco *starts to speak until* Rosa *pulls on his arm. They shrug and say nothing.*) Dogs! (*To* Police) They never talk! Find him! Find him! (*The three exit right.*)

Rosa (*In a hissing whisper*): Don Alfredo Elizondo, the *gachupine,* the so-proud Spaniard!

Francisco: Now why do the police want Roberto?

Rosa: It is something Don Alfredo has stewed up, you can be sure. He likes to see the jail filled. Come, Francisco. We will never get home. (Francisco *picks up his bundle and they are starting to leave when* Manuel *comes out of the church.*)

Manuel: There. It is good as new. Ha, you're still here?

Rosa: No, we're still in San Miguel, remember? How you dream! (*All laugh.*)

FRANCISCO (*Holding his bundle this time*): Don Alfredo has the police after Maria's son, Roberto.

MANUEL: *Ay de mi.* That is a good boy. He could have done nothing wrong.

ROSA: Tell that to Don Alfredo. Come, Francisco. (*They exit left. MANUEL looks after them and shrugs. He settles himself on the steps, facing right. In a moment FATHER HIDALGO enters left.*)

HIDALGO: Good evening, Manuel.

MANUEL (*Jumping up quickly and turning around, his face beaming*): Good evening, Father! I have waited to tell you the bell rope is mended. There will be no trouble to ring it now.

HIDALGO: That is good, then. Our bell in Dolores is neither large nor famous, but we would miss it were it not here, I think.

MANUEL: Yes, Father, very much. (*With a grin*) Maybe you would have no one at mass if it didn't ring?

HIDALGO (*Returns the grin companionably. The noise of a crowd of people coming toward them from the right drowns out his reply and causes both men to turn in that direction. The two POLICEMEN enter with ROBERTO between them. They are followed by a group of angry VILLAGERS. HIDALGO raises a hand and stops them. Several start talking to him at once*): Now, my children, calm yourselves. Roberto, what is happening here? (ROBERTO *hangs his head and remains silent.*)

MARIA (*Angrily*): They are taking him to jail!

OLD MAN (*Pushing his way to the front of the group and speaking bitterly*): Don Alfredo Elizondo says he stole a goat from him.

YOUNG GIRL: But I saw the very goat, Father, on the river bank. It had merely strayed.

MARIA: My son would not steal!

OLD MAN: But if Don Alfredo says he did, off to jail he goes. (*Makes gesture of shooing*)

HIDALGO: I shall see about this in the morning, Roberto. Go with them now and be patient.

ROBERTO (*Hopefully*): You will help me, Father?

HIDALGO: I will do what I can, my son. (*The crowd, less noisy but still mumbling, exits left.* DON CAESAR *stands looking after them.* MANUEL *remains on the church steps.* HIDALGO *moves toward* DON CAESAR.) It disturbs you, Don Caesar?

DON CAESAR: It troubles me to see injustice done. The *gachupines,* Father, are ruining New Spain. (MANUEL *comes closer to listen. He and* HIDALGO *exchange glances.*)

HIDALGO: Your father and mother are *gachupines,* Don Caesar, for they were born in the mother country, were they not? You speak against them?

DON CAESAR: I am *Creole,* Father, like yourself, being born here. Is my father a better man than I because he was born in Spain and I in New Spain? Is there some magic in the air of the mother country which makes her children nobler than those of her American colony? (*He stops and looks at* MANUEL.) As for that, is there magic in the Spanish blood which makes it nobler than that native to this land?

HIDALGO: Am I right in thinking, then, that you believe all men are equal in the eyes of God?

DON CAESAR: Exactly. Manuel is just as important as Don Alfredo, regardless of what Don Alfredo thinks.

MANUEL: Thank you, Don Caesar.

HIDALGO (*Chuckling*): And Don Alfredo is just as important as Manuel, no matter what Manuel thinks.

DON CAESAR (*Chuckling, too*): Ah, yes, Manuel, just because you ring the bell . . .

MANUEL (*Protesting*): Now, *senores* . . .

DON CAESAR: Truly, Manuel, you and I are stepchildren in our own country. (*He begins to stride back and forth.*) You, also, Father. Can you become a bishop in your church? No, the bishops come from Spain! Can I become the Viceroy, or a governor, or a judge? No! They, too, must come from Spain. They must be *gachupine!* (*He stops beside* HIDALGO *and lowers his voice.*) This is reckless talk and I could be punished for it. But I know your great sympathy for the poor people. Is there nothing we can do? The *gachupine* has the Indian thrown in jail, and we in the middle—we *Creoles*—stand by and do nothing!

MANUEL (*Touching* HIDALGO *on the arm*): Father, don't you think . . .

HIDALGO: That we should tell him?

MANUEL: Yes, Father. And there are two others, Rosa and Francisco. They are ready. Shall I bring them to you tonight?

DON CEASAR: Now I am curious indeed! What talk is this? (MANUEL *leaves with a parting salute which the two men acknowledge with nods.*)

HIDALGO: Spain has ruled this part of America for three hundred years. Some of that rule has been good and some bad. Right now it is bad. Many of us think it is time to end that rule. There are those of us, Don Caesar, bold enough to plan a revolution.

DON CAESAR: A revolution? Against Spain?

HIDALGO: Against Spain and against the *gachupines*. I can count on my faithful Indians and the peasants of mixed blood, but we need to enlist more *creoles*. Being that, and a lawyer, too, you could help us greatly.

DON CAESAR: Father Hidalgo, you found Dolores a wretched village, and look what you have done to give our people a better life, both inside the church and out.

The weaving and pottery factories, the tannery—they mean independence and self-respect for many families. If you wish to spread your good work to all New Spain, tell me what I can do to help.

HIDALGO: This is the story. The plot began in Querétaro, with a group calling itself a literary club. (*He chuckles.*) Our literature is that which Spain forbids us to read: the works of the liberals in the new United States and in France.

DON CAESAR: The smugglers keep busy! I have them, too, those books, in a wine barrel in my cellar. That Thomas Jefferson! What words!

HIDALGO: I have need of his eloquence. It is my part to write our declaration of independence, and to proclaim it next December 12 during the big fair at San Juan de los Lagos.

DON CAESAR: A good time and place. So many people . . . But already it is the fifteenth of September. How much is done? (*The stage begins to darken slowly except for one lighted window of the house*)

HIDALGO: Not enough. I have guns and iron pikes in my cellar, and lead for bullets behind the bookshelves. It is our hope that so many will rise with us there will be no need for battles. But if we must fight, we shall be ready.

DON CAESAR: Yes, that is the practical way. (*They are lost in thought for a moment or so.* HILDAGO *sighs.*)

HIDALGO: Tonight I have some letters to finish and work to do on the proclamation. Perhaps you would help me? (*He opens the door of his house. The light from inside shines on them.*) Do you recall the Declaration of Independence of the English colonies? "When, in the course of human events, it becomes necessary . . ."

DON CAESAR: ". . . for one people to dissolve the political bands which have connected them with another . . ."

HIDALGO: ". . . and to assume among the powers of the

earth the separate and equal status to which the laws of
Nature and of Nature's God entitle them, . . ."

DON CAESAR: ". . . a decent respect to the opinions of
mankind requires that they should declare the causes
which impel them to the separation."

BOTH: "We hold these truths to be self-evident; that all
men are created equal; that they are endowed by their
Creator with certain unalienable rights; that among
these are life, liberty and the pursuit of happiness; that
to secure these rights, governments are instituted among
men, deriving their just powers from the consent of the
governed."

HIDALGO: There is the key, Don Caesar: "the consent of
the governed." A startling idea, perhaps, to some.

DON CAESAR: But so beautiful, so logical, so utterly just.
(*They enter the house and outlines of figures are seen
passing the window. The village watchman walks slowly
across the stage right to left, carrying a lantern. He halts
a moment before the lighted window, peers into the
shadows of the church door and moves out left. A man
slips out of the dark at the right and taps on the door.
HIDALGO opens it.*)

ANTONIO: Are the letters ready, Father?

HIDALGO: I am sealing the last one now, Antonio. Wait
here but a minute. (*Closes door. ANTONIO slides into a
shadow by the house. Soon HIDALGO opens the door and
hands him some papers.*) This goes to Captain Allende
at the barracks in San Miguel. This to the mayor of
Querétaro. This note is for the mayor's wife, Doña
Josefa. Go with God, Antonio, for the freedom of
Mexico.

ANTONIO: Thank you, Father. I'll be back tomorrow night.
(*He slips out right as the watchman enters left. He peers
into the church door, stops before the lighted window,*

then goes out right. A man slips in from left, taps on door. HIDALGO *opens it.)*

HIDALGO: Ah, Manuel! What news?

MANUEL: I brought two men from the factory, Father, with a dozen more iron pikes. They are stacking them in the cellar.

HIDALGO: Good! Good!

MANUEL: Rosa and Francisco had visitors. I will bring them tomorrow night to talk with you.

HIDALGO: There's time enough. Now, say, who is this? (*A man runs in from the right.*) Captain Allende! I thought you would be in San Miguel!

ALLENDE: We are betrayed, Father! A list of our names was sent to the Viceroy. The mayor and Doña Josefa are in jail in Querétaro, along with others. The weapons we stored there were found and seized.

MANUEL: *Ay de mi!* What misfortune!

ALLENDE: Doña Josefa sent a warning to me at the barracks. I rode as hard as I could. Left my horse by the river. So noisy . . .

HIDALGO: Yes, yes. That was right. (*He steps into the street with* DON CAESAR *behind him.*)

ALLENDE: What shall we do?

HIDALGO: Action must be taken at once! There is no time to be lost!

ALLENDE: But we are not ready. We may not succeed.

HIDALGO: Better to do the best we can than to be captured and shot with nothing done. (*Watchman enters right.*) Hernando! Go quickly! Rouse all those who are with us. You know the ones.

HERNANDO: Yes, Father. I go. (*Sets down lantern and starts out left*)

HIDALGO: Don Caesar, the risk is greater than I had expected. It is not too late for you to withdraw. Your name was not on the list.

DON CAESAR: I shall see that it gets on the list, Father. I am with you to the end of this.

HIDALGO (*Putting an arm across his shoulders*): We shall yet see the oppressor's yoke broken and the fragments scattered on the ground.

ALLENDE: My regiment at San Miguel will join us. (*A handful of men and women, including* MARIA, *come quietly on stage, watching* HIDALGO. *He turns to* DON CAESAR *and points to a group of three men.*)

HIDALGO: Take these men and go to the jail. Release Roberto and the other peasants. The jailer is with us. He will give you the key. (*They exit left.*) Maria, show Captain Allende to the home of Don Alfredo Elizondo. Captain, arrest him in the name of the new Republic of Mexico. We must not let him spread an alarm.

MARIA: We will put the *gachupine* in the jail he so likes to see filled! (*They exit left as several others come on stage.*)

HIDALGO: Ho! Manuel! My bell-ringer! Now be thankful for your mended rope. Swing on it harder than you ever have before. Our bell must be the proclamation I had no time to write. Ring it till it calls all the people of Dolores, and of the *haciendas* round about; till it calls all the people of Mexico! (*The people on stage make way for* MANUEL *to run into the church. The stage begins to grow light with the coming of day. Soon the bell is heard, slow at first, then gaining in speed and volume. More people enter, including the* OLD MAN, FRANCISCO *and* ROSA. DON CAESAR *and a group including* ROBERTO *enter from left.* HIDALGO *goes to the church steps and stands there with an arm upraised as the bell continues to peal.* MARIA *and* CAPTAIN ALLENDE *enter from left,* ALLENDE *making a gesture to* HIDALGO *that their mission was accomplished. The bell slowly dies away.*)

OLD MAN: Why are we here, Father? It is too early for mass.

FRANCISCO: We see no fire!

HIDALGO: My children, this day comes to us a new dispensation. Are you ready to receive it? Will you fight for the land your forefathers owned three centuries ago? Will you defend your religion and your rights? Will you make New Spain free? (MARIA *hurries into the church.*)

ALLENDE: No longer New Spain!

ROBERTO: *Viva* Mexico!

ALL: *Viva* Mexico! (MARIA *returns with the banner of Guadalupe and puts it into* HIDALGO's *hand.*)

ROSA: Mexico's own saint! Our Lady of Guadalupe!

OLD MAN: She's no *gachupine!* She belongs to us!

DON CAESAR (*Going to stand by* HIDALGO): Long live Mexico! Long live our Lady of Guadalupe! Down with bad government! Down with the *gachupines!*

ALL (*Ad lib*): Long live our Lady of Guadalupe! Down with bad government! Down with the *gachupines!* (*Etc.*)

HIDALGO: With that as our *grito*, our battle-cry, how can we lose? Let us march to San Miguel, to Guanajuato, to Querétaro, to the City of Mexico! Come! We shall arm ourselves. (*Exit right, followed by all on stage repeating the grito until it fades away offstage. The curtain closes very slowly. Lights dim and rise as curtain opens very slowly.* MANUEL, *his hair now streaked with white, dozes on the church steps.* ROSA, *wearing a tattered shawl, and* MARIA, *bent and lame, enter left. Each carries flowers.*)

MARIA: That Manuel! Every year he becomes more lazy! Every year for, now, how many years, Rosa?

ROSA: Fourteen, Maria. It is a long time. Don't let your heart be hard against Manuel. He has had no joy since we lost the good Father Hidalgo.

MARIA (*Sharply*): And who in Mexico has had joy? Fight,

fight, fight. Win and lose. Fight some more. And my
Roberto shot down in the first battle.

Rosa: It's true my Francisco lived two years longer. But
never again did I see him after he marched away that
sixteenth of September. Hiding in the hills with Morelos. Knowing the revolution was lost, but not giving up
till he was captured and shot by the King's soldiers.
(Manuel *has roused and listened. He rises to stand
before the two women.*)

Manuel: In one way you are fortunate. Your son and
your husband, even in death, were returned to Dolores.
You can keep their graves fresh with flowers. Does anyone put flowers on the grave of Miguel Hidalgo, buried
in shame there in the wild north where he was betrayed
and ambushed? And me out of my head with fever and
not there to stand with him before the firing squad?
Why do I live while he lies in a traitor's grave? He who
died for us . . . (*He stops to listen to a voice offstage.*)

Gomez (*Off*): Hold my horse, boy. I'll not be long. (*Appears on stage from right, breathless and excited*) Good
afternoon. I am Captain Gomez of the Army of Mexico.

Manuel, Rosa *and* Maria: Good afternoon, Captain.

Gomez: I have news of the greatest importance! I look for
the mayor and the bell-ringer.

Manuel: I, Captain, am the bell-ringer of Dolores.

Gomez: Call the villagers together then, quickly.

Manuel (*Suspiciously*): And why, Captain? Is it new taxes
we must pay? (*The captain hands him a written message.*)

Gomez: This letter is from President Guadalupe Victoria
himself! Only to Dolores has he written a letter himself! Now will you summon your people to hear it?

Manuel (*Looking at the paper carefully*): Yes, Captain.

Rosa: I will show you the home of Don Caesar, our mayor.

It is just over here. (*She points to right and she and captain exit right.*)

MARIA (*Clutching* MANUEL'S *arm*): What did the letter say?

MANUEL: You know I can't read, Maria. But the Captain said *President* Guadalupe Victoria. And there was a seal this big!

MARIA: Hm-m. Guadalupe Victoria was a general in the revolution, I have heard. (*With mounting excitement*) Ring that bell, Manuel! I've a feeling . . . (*She stands with raised fist as* MANUEL *enters the church and she hears the bell ring softly.* DON CAESAR *enters right, wearing a cape and limping so that he appears to be older. He is followed by* ROSA *and* CAPTAIN GOMEZ. *Villagers begin to come on stage from left and right and walk toward the church listlessly.* DON CAESAR *faces them from the steps and raises a hand for silence.* MANUEL *comes out of the church and stands beside him.*)

DON CAESAR: Fourteen years have passed, people of Dolores, since Father Miguel Hidalgo stood here and lighted the torch of freedom in our land. Fourteen years ago, and six months later he was dead, shot as a traitor, and Captain Allende with him, and many others. (*The people stir about and whisper a little.*) Some thought the cause was lost and gave up. Others carried on the fight—Morelos—Guerrero—Iturbide. Now comes the news we have thirsted for: Mexico is a Republic! On October 10th the new legislature named Guadalupe Victoria our first president! (*The people stand still in amazement, then begin to shout.*)

ALL: *Viva* Mexico! Long live the President!

DON CAESAR: Here with me is the bearer of the news, Captain Andrés Gomez. (GOMEZ *bows.*) He brings a request from the President. (GOMEZ *hands the message to* DON CAESAR *and gestures to him to read it aloud.*) "Your beloved priest, although not the first to have the idea of independence, nor yet the one to see that idea succeed, nevertheless is truly the father of our republic. By his vision and his example he inspired others to continue the fight he began. The official holiday of the Republic of Mexico shall be the sixteenth of September, to commemorate the day the *grito* was first shouted in Dolores."

Rosa: Let us call our village Dolores Hidalgo!

ALL: Yes, yes! Dolores Hidalgo!

Don Caesar (*Waits for the excitement to simmer down, then reads*): "Since the holiday and the *grito* belong now to the nation, there is a request I would make of you. It is my wish that the bell of Dolores which rang out the call to arms should be hung in the national capital. (*The people shuffle and shrug and some shake their heads "no."*) Every year, on September 16, it will be rung for all the people of the Republic. The *grito* shall be repeated to keep us aware of the price of our deliverance, to remind us anew of the brave men who died for us." (Don Caesar *folds the paper.*) What is your wish? (*No one replies as all on stage turn toward* Manuel.)

Manuel: My bell? To leave Dolores? Here he stood, Father Hidalgo, with his face shining with a great light. He told me, "Manuel, ring that bell as it has never rung before." And I did. And not afterwards have I rung it so. Since the Father died its voice has been soft, for it mourned with the rest of us. (*He sighs.*) It would not seem right for the bell to be taken to the great capital while he lies in a forgotten grave.

Gomez: The President has ordered that Miguel Hidalgo be re-buried with honors in the City of Mexico. A fine monument is to be built there for him.

Manuel: Then, Don Caesar and my friends, you may give the bell to Mexico. Only let me ring it once more as I did that day in 1810, this time for success. Let me ring it

once more for Dolores, then you may have it for Mexico.
ALL: Ring it, Manuel, ring it! (*He bounds into the church.*
MARIA *throws her flowers into the air and embraces* DON
CAESAR. *Others embrace as the bell peals out strongly
and the curtain closes.*)

THE END

Weeping Willow's Happy Day

by Janice Auritt Oser

Characters

SUGAR MAPLE	HEMLOCK
MAGNOLIA	WEEPING WILLOW
PITCH PINE	FOREMAN
WHITE PINE	LUMBERJACKS, *four*
RED MAPLE	ARTIST
WHITE OAK	DAUGHTER
RED CEDAR	WINDS, *at least two*

SETTING: *Forest.*

AT RISE: WHITE PINE, RED MAPLE, WHITE OAK, RED CE-
DAR, *and* HEMLOCK *are grouped together towards the
center of the stage.* PITCH PINE *stands near a rock or two
on a slope, if possible. Other* TREES *are scattered at ran-
dom on stage.* WILLOW *droops pathetically, sniffling into
a handkerchief.*

SUGAR MAPLE: Poor Weeping Willow. I wish we could
make her happy.

WHITE PINE: We've tried everything we know.

SUGAR MAPLE: Isn't there anything we can do, Weeping
Willow?

WILLOW: You're sweet, Sugar Maple, but . . . (WINDS

534

rush on, run about whispering in ears of WHITE PINE
and other TREES *near him.*)

SUGAR MAPLE: Those winds are whispering among the
trees again.

MAGNOLIA (*With Southern accent*): I declare, won't they
ever learn it's not polite to whisper in public like that?

PITCH PINE: What are they saying, anyway?

WHITE PINE: They're whispering that the men from the
Company are coming to choose again.

WILLOW: What are they choosing?

RED MAPLE: Why trees, of course. Every year they come
and choose the trees they want and take them away with
them.

MAGNOLIA: I declare, and here I am not even looking my
best. It's too cold for me to bring out my lovely white
flowers. I'm sure their luscious fragrance would impress
them. (WINDS *run offstage, making whooshing sounds.*)

WHITE OAK: Oh, the men from the Company will hardly
look at you anyway. They'll be more interested in me.

PITCH PINE: And why will they be so interested in you?

WHITE OAK: Well, I don't want to brag, of course—

PITCH PINE: Of course.

WHITE OAK (*Frowning at* PITCH PINE): But I make very
valuable lumber. Yes sir, the birds and squirrels around
here will be doing without my acorns for their dinner
tables when the men from the Company take a look at
me.

WILLOW: Goodness, White Oak, do you think they'll take
me? I'm so bored here with nothing to do.

RED CEDAR: Can't you find anything to do, Weeping Willow?

WILLOW (*Sniffling, dabbing eyes with handkerchief*): No,
Red Cedar. I was planted here to keep the sandy banks
of the stream from slipping away, but it was such a small
stream and now it's all dried up. (*Sobs*)

RED MAPLE: There she goes, weeping again. I'll be glad when they take me away from here and make me into a chair or something. I make very nice chairs, you know. And other pieces of furniture, too. I—

WHITE PINE: Never mind, Red. Don't forget that they use you for fuel sometimes, too. And I'm not bad for furniture myself, I must say.

WILLOW: Is that all the men from the Company want? Wood to build furniture and houses and things?

HEMLOCK: I should say not. There are other uses for trees —look at me. People make something called "tannin" from my inner bark, and it's used in tanning leather. And my wood is made into wood pulp for making paper. Did you know that paper is made from hemlocks and other kinds of trees?

WILLOW: Goodness no, Hemlock, I didn't know that. (*Sadly*) I wish I could be used for something as wonderful as that.

RED CEDAR: Oh that's nothing; what good is paper without a pencil? The wood for lead pencils comes from me.

WILLOW: Oh my, are they going to take you away too, Red Cedar? Confidentially, a little birdie told me that he likes to perch on your branches because they're so close to your trunk, and he feels very cosy and safe. And he loves to eat your blue berries. The birds will miss you, Red Cedar.

RED CEDAR: I'm afraid the birds in the neighborhood will have to get along without me. My wood has other uses, too. Believe it or not, it keeps moths away; so people like to line closets and chests with it and keep their woolens there in the summertime. (WINDS *rush on and whisper in* WHITE PINE's *and a few other* TREES' *ears.*)

WHITE PINE (*To* WIND): What's that again? (WIND *whispers hurriedly.*) Oh, oh, she says the men from the Company are almost here. (WINDS *whirl around and exit.*) Get ready, everybody. Look your best.

WILLOW: Oh, they'll hardly look at me. (*Droops more.* PITCH PINE *twists body, holds arms in strange position for rest of play, if possible. Enter* FOREMAN *and* LUMBERJACKS.)

1ST MAN: Here's a likely spot.

2ND MAN: Some good-looking trees here. (TREES *beam, except for* WILLOW.)

FOREMAN: Oh, they're O.K., I guess. (TREES *look sad.*) But that Red Cedar should make a lot of lead pencils—or scare a lot of moths away. Take 'er away!

3RD MAN: O.K., Chief. (*Takes one of* RED CEDAR's *arms*)

4TH MAN (*Taking other arm*): Here goes! (*They march* RED CEDAR *offstage.*)

FOREMAN: Say, here's a White Oak. That'll bring a pretty penny. Take 'er away! (3RD *and* 4TH MEN *return.*)

1ST MAN: Anything you say, Chief. (*Takes one of* WHITE OAK's *arms*)

2ND MAN (*Takes other arm, shouts*): Timber! (*They nonchalantly lead* WHITE OAK *away.*)

3RD MAN: How about this White Pine, Chief?

FOREMAN: Take 'er away! (1ST *and* 2ND MEN *return.* 3RD *and* 4TH MEN *take* WHITE PINE's *arms.*)

3RD MAN: Easy now. (*They lead* WHITE PINE *away.*)

FOREMAN: Now the red maple—maple furniture is right in style right now. (RED MAPLE *beams.* 3RD *and* 4TH MEN *return as* 1ST *and* 2ND MEN *take* RED MAPLE's *arms.*)

2ND MAN (*Shouts mightily*): Timber! (*They casually lead* RED MAPLE *away.*)

FOREMAN: Just one more—take the Hemlock. They should get paper for a lot of copy books from that.

3RD MAN (*Taking one of* HEMLOCK's *arms*): Doesn't look much like a stack of copy books yet.

538 WEEPING WILLOW'S HAPPY DAY

4TH MAN (*Taking other arm*): It will. (*They lead* HEM-
LOCK *away.*)

FOREMAN (*Looking around*): I guess that's about it. Nothing else here for us. (*Exits*)

MAGNOLIA: Well, I like that! Nothing else here for him! If
my flowers were out he certainly would have noticed me.

SUGAR MAPLE: I don't care if he *did* pass me by. Who wants
to be a chair, anyway? I'd much rather have people come
and take my sap to make syrup and sugar candy.

PITCH PINE: I guess he thought I was too funny-looking.

MAGNOLIA: Why *are* you so funny-looking, Pitch Pine?

PITCH PINE: Well, I'm small because I don't get much food
up here on these rocky hills. And the wind twists me into
these funny shapes. But I don't care; I'd just as soon stay
here and keep the soil from sliding away.

WILLOW: It's very nice of you to feel that way about it,
Pitch Pine.

PITCH PINE: Aw, it's nothing. I just like to be useful.

WILLOW: And you are! And so is Sugar Maple, and even
Magnolia will have lovely flowers that everyone likes to
smell. But I don't do anything. . . . I'm no good to anybody . . . (*Voice trails off, dabs eyes with handkerchief*)

PITCH PINE: Gosh, don't cry!

MAGNOLIA: What else can a Weeping Willow do?

WILLOW: If only I were good for *something!* (WINDS *rush
on, whirl around* PITCH PINE, *each whispering first in
one ear and then in the other.*)

MAGNOLIA: Tell us what the winds are whispering now.

PITCH PINE: They're saying that somebody's coming.
(WINDS *rush off.*)

SUGAR MAPLE: Who's coming? Are they coming for my sap?

PITCH PINE: I don't know. The winds whispered that
they're strangers. (ARTIST *enters, carrying equipment.
He is followed by* DAUGHTER.)

DAUGHTER: There aren't many trees here, Daddy.

ARTIST: Yes, I see the Company has been here for some of its lumber.

DAUGHTER (*Pointing to* PITCH PINE): What a funny-looking tree!

ARTIST (*Smiles*): Oh, that's a Pitch Pine. Pitch Pines are often bent into strange shapes by the wind, but they're very useful.

DAUGHTER: And here's a Sugar Maple. That's useful, too. I love sugar candy. Why don't you paint this one?

ARTIST (*Looking around*): Perhaps, perhaps. (*Sees* WILLOW) Ah, look at that Weeping Willow! What a graceful, elegant tree!

DAUGHTER: Oh, that one. You can't make sugar candy from it.

ARTIST: I know. But trees are more than useful; they're beautiful. They're one of the great beauties of the Earth, and I think the Weeping Willow is the most beautiful of all. That's the one I'll paint. (*Starts to set up canvas*)

DAUGHTER (*Looking up*): Wait, Daddy! Look at that big black cloud!

ARTIST (*Looking up*): Oh oh, it looks as if we're going to have a storm. Too bad; we'd better hurry home. (*Gathers equipment*) I'll come back another day to paint that Weeping Willow; it's so lovely, it—it—it inspires me!

DAUGHTER: Hurry! (*They exit.*)

MAGNOLIA: Well, I declare! Passed right by me, too. (WILLOW *sniffles.*)

PITCH PINE: What's wrong, Willow? Didn't you hear all those nice things he said about you? He's going to paint a picture of you. This is your happy day!

SUGAR MAPLE: You can stop weeping now, Willow, and smile.

MAGNOLIA: Who ever heard of a Smiling Willow? A Weeping Willow can't be happy, or it wouldn't be a Weeping Willow.

PITCH PINE: That's not so. Aren't you happy now, Willow?

WILLOW: I'm so happy I could cry! (*Sobs.* TREES *smile and sigh exaggeratedly in exasperation. Curtain.*)

THE END

The Tree Friends

by Sara Sloane McCarty

Characters

MARY		CHIPMUNK
HARRY		RABBIT
CARRIE		BIRD
LARRY	aspen trees	SUN
CHERIE		NIGHT
JERRY		WIND
PABLO		THUNDER
PENNY		
PAUL		
PATRICIA	pine trees	
PETER		
PRISCILLA		

TIME: *Morning.*

SETTING: *In the forest.*

AT RISE: *Six* ASPEN TREES *stand in a row center stage. At their feet in the smallest possible heaps are six* PINE TREES. SUN *enters left, crosses slowly in front of* PINE TREES, *and stops at right of the last tree.*

SUN (*To the audience*): This is the Forest. Many trees are growing in this forest. There are big tall pine trees. (*He gestures and looks up high above his head.*) There are

541

spruce and fir trees. (*Again he gestures and looks up high toward imaginary trees.*) Down on the forest floor you see the baby pine trees, just starting to grow. (*He points to the* PINE TREES.) And, of course, there are aspen trees. (*He points toward the* ASPEN TREES.) Aspen trees aren't big and important like the pines and the spruces, but the forest could never get along without them. In a moment we are going to show you why. Listen. The aspen trees are talking together.

MARY ASPEN TREE (*Stretching*): Ho-hum. It looks like another very warm, sunny day.

HARRY ASPEN TREE (*Sleepily*): Why don't you say hot?

CARRIE ASPEN TREE (*Fluttering her hands to show that her leaves are green on one side and silver gray on the other*): We have a nice breeze in the afternoon.

LARRY ASPEN TREE (*Swaying*): It would be all right if we were closer to those big shady trees.

CHERIE ASPEN TREE (*Fluttering her hands*): No wonder we notice the heat of the sun. We're almost alone out here in this clearing.

MARY ASPEN TREE: Not really alone. Here comes Rabbit. (RABBIT *hops on and sits near* PINE TREE *babies.*)

CARRIE ASPEN TREE: And here is Chipmunk. (CHIPMUNK *scampers in. He is a very frisky fellow.*)

HARRY ASPEN TREE: Silly girls! Watch me. I'm going to make my leaves sparkle in the sunlight. (*He shakes his hands with palms up. All the* ASPEN TREES *shake their hands.*)

ASPEN TREES: Sparkle! Sparkle! (BIRD *comes by. He holds his arms wide, dips to the right, then to the left, as he runs.*)

JERRY ASPEN TREE: See the bird. He likes the sun.

SUN: All the forest stretches and grows in the sun. (ASPEN TREES *stretch and stand tall.* PINE TREES *lift their heads and move them restlessly.* BIRD, CHIPMUNK, *and* RABBIT *move about busily.*) The animals and birds are busy, too. But the day is soon over. Night is coming. Now it is time for the sun to shine on the other side of the world. (*He moves offstage right.* NIGHT *enters left.*)

NIGHT: I am Night. I bring rest to the world. It is time for me to cover the forest with darkness. Sleep! (*She touches the* RABBIT.) Sleep! (*She touches the* CHIPMUNK.) Sleep! (*She touches the* BIRD, *who puts his head under his arm.*) Sleep, trees! (*She waves her arm toward the* TREES. WIND *enters. Sound effects record may be used if desired.*)

WIND: Woo! Woo-woo-woo! I am the Wind. Here I come to sing in the forest. Woo! Woo-woo-woo!

NIGHT: But such a loud song! You will wake the forest.

WIND: They'll get used to me. I'm really a very nice wind.

NIGHT: Except when you play too rough.

WIND: Like this? (*He rushes at* ASPEN TREES, *who shrink from him in terror.*) Woo! Woo-woo-woo! I *love* to play rough.

NIGHT: Stop that!

WIND: All right. I'll go, but I'll be back.

MARY ASPEN TREE: I'm frightened.

CARRIE ASPEN TREE: I am, too. (*She clings to* MARY.)

CHERIE ASPEN TREE: I'm cold! (*She clings to* CARRIE.)

HARRY ASPEN TREE (*Trying to be brave*): Silly girls.

LARRY ASPEN TREE: We—we're not scared!

JERRY ASPEN TREE: Not—not much! (WIND *returns and rushes at them.*)

WIND: Woo! Woo-woo-woo! (THUNDER *enters, clapping cymbals or two large pan lids together. Sound effects record may be used.*)

THUNDER: Bang! Bang! I am Thunder. I like to make lots of noise! Bang! Bang!

ASPEN TREE GIRLS: Oh! (*They scream.*)

ASPEN TREE BOYS: Oh! (*They hide their faces in their hands. All the* ASPEN TREES *begin to shake and shiver.*)

NIGHT: No wonder they call those trees the trembling aspen trees. They are always shaking and quaking about something. What is the matter? Thunder can't hurt you.

THUNDER (*Laughing*): I sound awful, don't I? (*He claps the cymbals together and runs off yelling.*) Bang! Bang!

WIND: I enjoy this sort of noise. Woo! Woo-woo-woo! (*He rushes at the trees, bumping into the baby* PINE TREES. *They wake up again. When they speak, they use baby voices.*)

PABLO PINE: What was that?

PENNY PINE (*Crying*): I want my mother!

PAUL PINE: Don't be such a baby.

PATRICIA PINE: But we *are* babies—at least, we're very small.

PETER PINE: We're baby pine trees.

PRISCILLA PINE: It's cold and dark. I don't like the wind. (*All the baby* PINE TREES *begin to whimper softly.*)

HARRY ASPEN TREE: Did you hear a voice?

LARRY ASPEN TREE: Down there on the ground.

JERRY ASPEN TREE: Where? It's too dark to see.

MARY ASPEN TREE: I hear them. They're crying.

CARRIE ASPEN TREE: It's the baby pine trees.

CHERIE ASPEN TREE: Let's spread our branches over them. (*All the* ASPEN TREES *hold out their arms.*)

HARRY ASPEN TREE: I'll show them how brave I am.

MARY ASPEN TREE: Why don't we sing them a lullaby?

JERRY ASPEN TREE: What shall we sing?

CARRIE ASPEN TREE: Let's sing "Sleep, baby, sleep. Thy father watches his sheep." (*They sing this song, or any lullaby they all know, such as "Rock-a-bye Baby" or "Sweet and Low." All the* ASPEN TREES *sing.* PINE TREES *yawn, stretch, and curl up asleep.*)

NIGHT: Well! The aspen trees are beginning to learn why they are there. Those baby pine trees need them. (*She walks very slowly offstage. The* SUN *enters left as* NIGHT *goes out right.*)

SUN (*To the audience*): Here I am again, bright and early. I must ask you to imagine that twenty years are passing by. Yes, that's right, *twenty years.* Not that it makes much difference to me. I keep right on giving light, and the world keeps right on whirling around me. But it matters to the forest. A lot of things can change in the forest in twenty years. For one thing, little trees grow into big trees. (*While he is talking,* PINE TREES *get up very slowly, stretching a great deal, and making as little noise as possible.*)

CHIPMUNK (*At front stage*): My grandfather says he can remember when the pine trees were very small.

RABBIT (*At front stage*): It is hard to believe that. Just look at them now!

CHIPMUNK: My grandfather says the aspen trees used to be taller than the pine trees.

RABBIT: Don't be silly. Anyone can see the pine trees are taller.

CHIPMUNK: They *grew.* Every minute, every day, they grew.

MARY ASPEN TREE (*Swaying and fluttering her hands*): Who is mumbling?

HARRY ASPEN TREE: I think Rabbit and Chipmunk are talking about us.

CARRIE ASPEN TREE (*Bending to look between the tall pine trees*): I can't see them. Where?

LARRY ASPEN TREE: The pine trees are too tall. Do you remember—

CHERIE ASPEN TREE: When they were small? Of course I do.

JERRY ASPEN TREE: We used to sing to them so they wouldn't feel afraid of Wind and Thunder.

MARY ASPEN TREE: I can even remember—long ago—when we used to be afraid, too. We were always trembling.

HARRY ASPEN TREE: That's a funny thing. After we began taking care of those little pine trees—we were not afraid any more.

ASPEN TREES: Not afraid! We're strong and brave. (NIGHT *enters from the left.* SUN *goes off right.*)

NIGHT: It is time for darkness. Time for sleep. (WIND *and* THUNDER *enter, howling and banging as usual.* WIND *rushes at the trees, who pay no attention.*)

WIND: Woo! Woo-woo-woo!

THUNDER: Bang! Bang!

PERRY PINE: Do you hear the wind?

PENNY PINE: Yes. Remember when we were very small, we were afraid of Wind?

PAUL PINE: Afraid of Thunder, too.

PATRICIA PINE: The kind aspen trees took care of us.

PETER PINE: They sheltered us with their branches.

PRISCILLA PINE: They sang to us till we went to sleep.

PERRY PINE: Let's thank the aspen trees.

PINE TREES: Thank you, aspen trees.

ASPEN TREES: You're welcome.

HARRY ASPEN TREE: We're very proud of you, so tall and brave.

PERRY PINE: Thank you. We think you are very beautiful when the sun shines on your leaves.

ASPEN TREES: Thank you. (*They all flutter their hands, palms up.*)

NIGHT (*To the audience*): And so forever after, wherever you find tall, tall pine trees, you will find the aspen trees close by. And wherever there are baby pines, the aspens will be there to spread their branches over them, to sing them lullabies. For aspen trees, like everyone else, learn to be brave and strong by helping others. (*Curtain*)

THE END

May Witch

by Margaret Wylie Brydon and Esther E. Ziegler

Characters

JANE	MELANIE
GINNY	EMILY
CAROL	KRIS
MIMI	JULIA

TIME: *The eve of May Day.*

SETTING: *An upstairs study or playroom in* JANE's *home. Opposite the window is a desk holding drapes, artificial flowers, and odds and ends used for making May baskets. An armchair, which is partially decorated as a throne, holds a wreath.*

AT RISE: *The only light in the room comes through the window at left. There are sounds of happy voices and footsteps on the stairs.* JANE *enters up center and turns on a lamp. She is followed by* GINNY, JULIA, CAROL, MIMI, MELANIE, *and* EMILY, *who seat themselves comfortably around the room.* EMILY *carries a lopsided paper cornucopia filled with tulips, which she tosses on the desk.*

GINNY: That was fun! Let's do it again soon.

JULIA: When would you suggest—the Fourth of July?

CAROL: Whoever heard of leaving May baskets on doorsteps in July?

MIMI (*To* CAROL): Whoever heard of May baskets at all, until you gave your report in school? In New York we never celebrated this way.

MELANIE: In the South we didn't either. I wonder how it all started?

CAROL: May Day started with the Romans, when they were honoring the goddess Flora.

JANE (*Gathering up scattered bits of petals and greenery*): My mother says that when she was a child in England, people always celebrated on the first Saturday in May. That's why she let us have a slumber party this weekend —so that we could have fun the way she did.

EMILY (*Helping* JANE): Didn't she say something about putting some candy into her flower baskets?

JANE: Yes, but only as a surprise for her very best friends.

EMILY: Well, we're all best friends, aren't we? How would it be to surprise each other with fudge baskets?

MIMI: Really, Emily! You're so childish!

CAROL (*Reprovingly*): If you had listened to me in class, you'd know that this is "the time of year to celebrate the coming of spring with greenery and sweet-smelling blossoms."

EMILY: O.K., we've done that! Now what's wrong with a little sweet-tasting fudge?

JANE: Nothing. But first, we have the throne to finish. Help me clear off this desk, and we'll put it up here. (EMILY *and* JULIA *help* JANE *clear the desk and spread a large drape over it.* GINNY, CAROL, *and* MELANIE *pick up the partially decorated chair and lift it to the top of the desk.* MIMI *is toying with a wreath of flower-entwined vines.*)

CAROL: Put that down, Mimi. You know that's for the queen.

MIMI (*Putting the wreath aside*): If just *one* of you votes for me, I'll win by a landslide.

CAROL (*Pointedly*): I think the queen should be the one who contributes the most to the party. (*All diligently arrange artificial flowers around the throne.*)

MELANIE: Jane's idea of delivering flowers to everybody around here was super, wasn't it?—ringing doorbells after dark and hiding to watch people look surprised!

JULIA (*Dangling the battered cornucopia of tulips by its paper handle*): And now what are we going to do with Tulips Triumphant?

MIMI: I dared Emily to leave it at that old house on the corner, but she wouldn't.

EMILY: It was just too scary. I noticed that none of the rest of you volunteered to go up to that witch's den.

GINNY: Oh, it's not that bad. Jane passes that house every day on the way to school.

CAROL: She crosses to the other side of the street before she gets there, though. She said so herself.

JANE (*Defensively*): It's different when you're alone. Those vines and shrubbery make it awfully dark, and the lady who moved in there is very old and strange.

MELANIE: Yes, she hides in the shrubbery and stares when you go by. I've seen her.

MIMI: Have you ever talked to her, Jane?

JANE (*Placing a drape over one arm of the throne*): I should say not! But my mother and some of the other grownups in the neighborhood tried to call on her, and she just peeked out and jabbered some foreign words.

MELANIE: Oh, maybe it was an incantation!

EMILY: Do you think she's really a witch, Jane?

JANE: I don't know. She doesn't exactly jump out at people. But she does peer out from behind things and mutter to herself. And she has a big, black cat, too. I don't blame Emily a bit for passing up that house.

MIMI: A queer old person like that wouldn't have any use for a May basket anyway.

MELANIE: But everyone else loved them. I thought little Miss Blakely was going to cry over her rosebuds.

JANE: Now that we've done our good deeds for the day, let's plan what we'll do the rest of the time.

EMILY (*Eagerly*): If you want to have the refreshments now, I'll help.

MIMI: Relax. We had dinner just an hour ago.

JULIA: Yes, this is a slumber party, not an all-night picnic!

EMILY (*Worried*): Does that mean we can't eat?

CAROL: No, but we were only allowed to stay overnight because we made such a fuss about celebrating May Day as it used to be done. So I think we should try some of the customs I told you about.

GINNY: You mean put up a Maypole and dance and all that?

MIMI (*Scornfully*): I did that in kindergarten.

JANE: No. We'll choose a queen at midnight, and she can decide what we'll do.

GINNY: Swell, but I don't see how we'll ever choose.

JULIA: We might take the oldest.

MIMI (*Posing*): Shouldn't it be the most glamorous?

EMILY (*Hopefully*): Or the fattest?

CAROL: Well, if you're all going to speak for yourselves . . .

EMILY: If Kris were here, we'd know right away whom to choose.

MELANIE: That's right. Kris is pretty, and always a lot of fun. Why couldn't she come tonight, Jane?

JANE: I'm not sure. My mother called her mother after school on Tuesday, but Mrs. Van Derveen said that Kris was going to spend the weekend with her grandmother. Mother got the impression that Kris's parents didn't want her to come.

MIMI (*Indignantly*): What's wrong with us?

JANE: Mrs. Van Derveen was very polite, but she doesn't speak English very well, and Mother thinks she doesn't understand our ways. Kris and her family have been in this country for only two or three years.

GINNY: I didn't know that. Kris speaks just like the rest of us.

JANE: Let's start celebrating, shall we? Before it's too late to go out again.

CAROL: Yes, we don't want to stay up too late if we're going to get up before dawn to wash our faces.

EMILY (*Dismayed*): What's the big hurry? I took a good bath before I came.

MIMI: Don't you remember? Washing in dew before dawn on a May morning is supposed to make you ravishingly beautiful for a whole year.

EMILY: Oh, boy! Count me in. That's a big improvement over my mother's idea of giving up sweets.

MELANIE: There are lots of romantic things we can do this evening.

JULIA (*To* MELANIE): What do you suggest, Miss Heart-throb—waiting around for someone to put a tree on the roof?

EMILY: Golly! Are we going to do that?

CAROL: Of course not. Only Swiss boys do that. When they like a girl, they cut down the nearest pine tree and put it up under her window or on her roof on May Day Eve. It's supposed to bring her good luck and a long life.

EMILY: I know what it would bring me if my father saw it. And it wouldn't be anything lucky or life-preserving, I can guarantee that!

GINNY: If we want to do something romantic, there's that business of throwing a ball of yarn into an old cellar. What is that all about, Carol?

CAROL: You just keep one end of the yarn in your hand, and if you have patience and wind long enough, your true love will appear and help you.

MELANIE: Now that *is* an idea!

EMILY: Well, I don't think much of it. I'm the youngest. I'd be sitting around winding yarn for years.

JANE: Besides, the only old cellar I know of around here is the one at the witch's house.

CAROL: You know, that might be the perfect place to go. May Day Eve is the time when people are expected to go out "to dispel witches and monsters of winter darkness before ushering in the new spring."

JULIA: Quote—unquote!

MELANIE: I think the most thrilling custom was looking down an abandoned well through a dark glass, to see the reflection of your true love's face.

MIMI (*Eagerly*): Let's try that one. In New York I heard a lecturer say that there's a lot more to these old customs than just superstition.

GINNY: But where are we going to find a well?

JANE: Maybe an unused pool would do.

CAROL: Is there one around here, Jane?

JANE (*Hesitantly*): Yes. But you know where.

EMILY: Ooooh, not the witch's den again?

JANE (*Nodding*): There's an old lily pond in her backyard that has some rain water in it. You can see it from here. (*She points out the window.*)

MIMI: But how could we see a reflection in it at night?

JANE: Look down there. (*They join her at window.*) See? There's a street lamp lighting up that whole side of the yard.

MELANIE: Come on, let's go! This sounds exciting. I'm sure that May magic is more likely to work in a witch's pool than in any other place.

JANE: I can get sand out of Jimmy's sandbox and scatter it over the back steps, just in case!

EMILY: Sand? Now who's being childish?

CAROL: Sand is a protection against witches, in case they chase you. They can't cross over it. They have to stop and pick it up grain by grain.

MIMI: No wonder witches are thin!

EMILY: Fat or thin, any one of them could outrun me.

MELANIE: Everybody doesn't have to go—just the ones who want to look into the future to see who their own true loves will be.

EMILY: I can wait for that. I can wait a long while to meet the goon who is going to sit around in the bottom of an old lily pond waiting for me.

JANE: We can go in two groups. Some of us should stay here to keep a lookout for the witch. We'll see the light from here if she opens her back door.

JULIA: I'll be lookout first, if you want me to be.

JANE: I'll have to go with each group, I guess. I'm the only one who knows how to get into the yard from the alley.

GINNY: I want to go with the first group.

MELANIE: Me, too. I can hardly wait to look into the enchanted pool.

JANE: You'd better come with us, Carol, since you know the rules. Then I'll come back and take the other three.

JULIA: How will we signal you in case of danger? Whistle?

CAROL: Oh, no! Try a hoot owl's cry. Like this. (*She imitates a hoot owl.*)

MELANIE: Wonderful! A witch could never tell that from the real thing. You do it, Mimi.

MIMI (*With dignity*): I don't know how. We didn't have hoot owls in New York.

JANE: How about you, Emily? Can you do it?

EMILY: If I saw a witch I wouldn't be able to make a sound!

MIMI (*To* EMILY): Then you'll have to go with Jane this time and let Carol stay with Julia and me. I, at least, can run fast in case you need help.

CAROL: And it certainly will be necessary to have someone here who can be depended upon to keep her head and give warning in time.

GINNY (*As* EMILY *shakes her head*): Come on, Emily. Remember how brave you were on Halloween? Everybody said you were a wonderful ghost.

EMILY: Just the same, I don't want to be one permanently.

MELANIE: Oh, come along, Emily. It won't be any fun at all unless you're in on it. Be a good sport.

EMILY (*Reluctantly*): Oh, all right—if my legs will stop shaking long enough to get me there.

JANE: Let's take along a May basket, and then if that strange old woman catches us there, we can give it to her.

CAROL: We can take the one Emily made. How's that?

JULIA (*Picking up the battered cornucopia and handing it to* EMILY): For a witch's den, I'd say this is just about perfect!

JANE: Then let's get started. I'm sure we can find a piece of dark-colored glass in the trash cans in the alley. Come on. Follow me. (JANE *exits, followed by* MELANIE, GINNY, *and* EMILY.)

MIMI (*Climbing up to the throne*): How do you think I'd look as Queen of the May?

CAROL (*Busily readjusting cushions*): No fair sitting there! You have to wait until midnight for the choosing.

JULIA: We'll never make it past ten o'clock.

MIMI (*Loftily*): Oh, I don't know. When I lived in New York, I often stayed up until all hours.

JULIA (*Laughing*): Really? I'll bet you were a riot in your playpen! (*Turning to window*) Look, they're going down the alley.

CAROL: Watch under the streetlight, so we'll know when they get there. I hope that scaredy-cat Emily doesn't spoil everything.

MIMI (*Putting the wreath on her head*): It fits perfectly!

CAROL: Let's watch at the window. We have to know what's going on.

JULIA: There they are. See—coming out from behind those bushes. (CAROL *and* MIMI *join her at the window.*) Jane and Melanie and Ginny are almost at the pool. That's Emily back by the gate.

CAROL: Now look! Emily's up in front. She's right by the pool.

JULIA: How did that happen?

CAROL: They're all pushing her.

MIMI: Now they're in a huddle. What are they doing, for goodness' sake?

JULIA: Trying to look into the pool, I guess. But if they have only one piece of dark glass, they'll have to take turns. (*Faint shrieks are heard offstage.*)

MIMI: That's Emily yelling!

CAROL (*Alarmed*): What's happened?

JULIA (*Amused*): Probably saw her true love.

MIMI: Oh, no, Julia! She sounded terrified. I'm sure—Oh, look—the back-porch lights are on!

JULIA: Quick, Carol! Hoot!

CAROL (*Stammering in a faint voice*): Hoo . . . hoo . . .

MIMI (*Urgently*): Hoot, Carol, *hoot!* The witch is opening her back door!

CAROL (*Whispering*): I can't! I'm scared!

JULIA: Oh, for goodness' sake! (*She pokes her head out the window and yells.*) Hoot, hoot! Hoot, hoot!

MIMI (*After a pause*): They must have heard you. Somebody's running.

JULIA: Yes, I can hear them. They're coming down the alley. They got away!

MIMI: But look! There's the witch—no, two witches— out there in the yard. They're picking up something.

CAROL (*With a groan*): I'll bet it's Emily. It *must* be Emily. See? They're dragging her between them. They're taking her inside!

JULIA (*Turning toward the door*): Listen! Here come the other girls now. (*There is a sound of running feet outside, and* JANE, MELANIE, *and* GINNY *rush in.*)

JANE (*Gasping*): Hurrah! We made it!

MELANIE: It was a thrilling getaway!

JULIA: For you, maybe. But what about poor Emily?

JANE: What? (*Looking around*) That's right. Where is Emily?

GINNY: I thought she was with us.

MELANIE: So did I. She was all right when we pulled her out of the pool.

CAROL: When you did *what?*

MELANIE: There's no time now to explain. We'll have to go back after her. (*She starts out.*)

JULIA: Wait, Melanie. Tell us what happened.

JANE: Maybe I'd better go tell Mom and Dad.

JULIA: I think you'd better tell us everything that happened before you bother your parents, Jane. We got Emily into this, and we ought to think of a way of getting her back without disturbing them.

JANE: Well, when we got into the backyard, we had to push Emily up to the pool. We told her to look through the glass first.

MELANIE (*Nodding*): So she would stop being scared.

JANE: Yes. And then she started to shake and couldn't say a word. She was pointing into the water.

GINNY: It was terrible—down there shining up at us!

MIMI: What? What was?

MELANIE: Two big *green eyes!*

CAROL (*Weakly*): Oh, no!

MELANIE: And all of a sudden they seemed to jump out at us.

JANE: Emily lost her balance and fell into the pool, shrieking.

JULIA: What did you do then?

GINNY: It wasn't deep. We pulled her out, and just then some weird sounds came from somewhere.

MELANIE: It was a *goblin!* Remember? I said it was a goblin.

GINNY: So one of us yelled, "Run!" And we all did.

JANE: All but Emily. Something must have caught her.

MIMI: *Two* somethings! We saw them come out the door.

JANE (*To* CAROL): Why didn't you warn us?

CAROL: I couldn't, I just couldn't.

JULIA: I tried to hoot. Maybe I was that goblin you heard.

MELANIE: Well, come on! We'll have to go back for Emily.

CAROL: Sh-h-h! What's that sound? (*All listen.*)

JANE (*After a pause*): It's probably from the television set.

CAROL (*In a half-whisper*): No, it's a scrunching noise down there. (*She motions toward the window.*)

MELANIE: Maybe it's the witch trying to pick up the sand we threw on the back steps.

JULIA: No, listen! I'm sure I hear voices.

MELANIE: Then it's *two* witches. (*To* MIMI) You said there were two!

JULIA: If there are, your sand isn't going to stop them. That was the back door that just opened!

GINNY: They have Emily, and they're coming after us!

MIMI (*Frightened*): What'll we do?

JULIA: Come on, Jane. Let's see what it is.

JANE (*Reluctantly*): All right. But I still think I should have called my mother. (*As the others watch fearfully from the doorway,* JULIA *and* JANE *disappear into the hall. After a moment, a thumping noise is heard, apparently coming from below stairs, and* JULIA *and* JANE *dash back into the room, slamming the door behind them.*)

JULIA (*Her back against the door*): There *is* something down there!

JANE (*Gasping*): Coming up the back stairs, and—and it's all white with a great big *blob* for a head!

GINNY: Ohhh!

MELANIE: See? I told you. It *is* a goblin. The witch couldn't cross the sand, so she sent her goblin.

CAROL (*As the thumping sound comes closer*): What shall we do?

JANE: There's no lock on the door. We'll have to hold it shut. (*They crowd against the door.*)

MELANIE: But goblins can come right through doors. The only thing that can stop them is a winding sheet!

GINNY (*Grabbing the drape from the chair arm*): Here, can we wind it in this?

JULIA: We'll have to try it. (*Taking the drape*) Maybe we can get up on something and drop this down on whatever it is.

JANE: Here, help me get some chairs. (JULIA, JANE, MELANIE, *and* GINNY *set up four chairs, two on each side of the door, and stand on them, holding the four corners of the drape like a canopy over the entrance.*)

JULIA: Now turn off the light, Mimi.

MIMI (*Wailing*): But then it will be dark!

MELANIE: Oh, hurry up. Do you want the goblin to see us? (MIMI *turns off the light, but some light remains on-stage.*)

JANE (*Whispering*): Sh-h-h! It's coming closer. Hear the footsteps?

GINNY (*Anxiously*): It does sound like two of them, doesn't it?

MELANIE: Maybe it has *four legs!*

JULIA (*In a whisper*): Get ready! It's coming in! (*The door is opened slowly by a strange white figure, not yet distinguishable as* EMILY, *which gropes its way into the room. It is followed closely by* KRIS, *who is unseen by the others. When* EMILY *is directly beneath the canopy,* JULIA *speaks.*) Now! (*They drop the drape over* EMILY, *who collapses to the floor. The girls jump squealing from the chairs, and pin their prisoner to the floor.*)

JANE: We have it! We have it!

GINNY (*Fearfully*): But what are we going to do with it?

EMILY (*Her voice muffled by the drape*): Let me out of this!

MIMI (*Astonished*): That's Emily's voice!

KRIS: What on earth are you playing?

JULIA: Turn on the lights! (*When* CAROL *obeys,* KRIS *is seen standing in the doorway holding a basket which contains a large thermos and paper cups.* EMILY *is seated in the middle of the floor, still covered by the drape.*) Why, Kris! How did you get here?

KRIS: I walked over with Emily.

EMILY (*Flapping her arms wildly under the drape*): Get this thing off me! (*The girls quickly uncover* EMILY, *who is clutching a cookie jar. She is dressed in a white bathrobe many sizes too large for her, and her head is tied up in a turban made of a huge Turkish towel.*) You know, I'm getting rather tired of these happy May Day customs.

MELANIE (*Helping* EMILY *to her feet*): But, Emily, we thought you were a goblin. Where did you get that outfit?

KRIS: It's my grandmother's bathrobe. Emily can hardly walk in it, but she had to have something. She was dripping wet.

JANE: Your grandmother? Do you mean the . . .

EMILY (*Hastily*): The *lady* on the corner is Kris's grandmother. And she's not at all what you thought!

KRIS: I was just as surprised as you are to find out that Grandma's house is so near yours. You probably think that she's not very friendly. She's only been in this country a few months, and she's ashamed to speak to anybody because of her bad English. (*Laughing*) But she was so tickled with Emily and her tumble into the pool that she certainly wasn't afraid to talk to her.

EMILY (*Incredulously*): She says I'm the prettiest little girl she's seen in a long time.

KRIS: That's right! Grandma is pleasingly plump herself and proud of it. She says that when she was a child in the Netherlands, plumpness was greatly admired. I hope you'll all get to know her. She's very jolly, and she likes to have people around her. I guess she's been pretty lonely since she's been here, with only a cat for company most of the time.

EMILY (*To* JANE, *accusingly*): And it's not black at all. It's a dark gray Persian with green eyes.

GINNY: Green eyes? Do you suppose that's what we saw in the water?

JULIA: Oh, come now! You can't make me believe the cat was sitting in the pool!

JANE: I guess he must have been overhead on a branch, and we just saw his reflection.

EMILY: Anyway, he plopped down beside me and scared me and I couldn't run.

KRIS: Grandma and I heard the commotion and came out.

JANE (*Embarrassed*): I'm very sorry we broke into her yard that way.

KRIS: Well, I'm not! When Emily explained what you were doing, Grandma understood. (*She puts down her basket.*)

EMILY (*Hastily*): You know—about the *pool,* and the *May basket?* (*Dolefully*) Only it wasn't a basket anymore— just a soggy bunch of tulips.

KRIS: Grandma loved them. They reminded her of her old home in Holland. She loves May Day celebrations. (*Turning to* EMILY) The reason she laughed at you, Emily, when you were sitting there all wet, was that the same thing happened to her once when she was a child in Holland. While she and her friends were up to one of their May Day tricks, sprinkling people with wet branches, she reached into the canal to get some water and tumbled in. (*Happily*) She says you girls must be a lot like the ones she used to play with. That's why she let me come over.

JANE: Oh, good! Will you be able to stay all night after all?

KRIS: Not this time. I must have Mother's permission first.

EMILY: But she may stay for refreshments. (*Holding up the jar*) Her grandmother sent over these homemade ginger cakes and some hot chocolate.

KRIS: Grandma has invited all of you over in the morning for a big Dutch breakfast with us. She says that's a must after May Day celebrations.

MELANIE (*Joyfully*): Do you hear that, girls? (*To* KRIS) And we thought you didn't like us.

KRIS (*Embarrassed*): I've always wanted to be friends with you, honest I have, but my parents are a little hesitant about some American ways—for young people, that is.

JULIA: I don't blame them. We certainly acted silly to-night.

KRIS: Never mind, Julia, because everything turned out so well. After tonight, Grandma is going to tell Mother that girls are about the same everywhere.

MELANIE: Isn't it wonderful? I have an idea that fate must have intended from the first that we all become friends, and the May Witch was just . . .

JULIA (*Hastily stuffing a pillowcase over* MELANIE's *head*): Hoot! Hoot!

EMILY (*Coming to the rescue*): Let's eat.

JANE: I think we should crown the queen now while Kris is here. (*To* KRIS) We agreed to choose as queen the one who did the most to make this a good party.

MELANIE (*Struggling out of* JULIA's *grasp*): I say Kris has done that by joining our group.

EMILY (*Nodding*): And by providing the refreshments. Let's crown her!

KRIS: Oh, no. I'm not the one.

GINNY: Then who?

KRIS: Why, Emily, of course. If it hadn't been for all she went through tonight, we might never have become friends at all.

JANE: That's right. Hurrah for Emily!

JULIA: Come on, Emily. Get up there. (JANE *takes the cookie jar.*)

EMILY (*As the girls help her up to the throne*): I'm a queen! (JULIA *puts some gay music on the record player, as* MIMI *takes the drape from the floor and places it about* EMILY's *shoulders.* KRIS *presents the thermos to* EMILY *with a flourish, as if it were a royal scepter.*)

CAROL (*Solemnly placing the wreath upon* EMILY's *turbaned head, where it hangs at a rakish angle*): We hereby crown Emily Queen of the May!

MELANIE (*Dramatically*): Begone, May Witch and all creatures of darkness! A new sovereign reigns! (EMILY *promptly seizes a cup from the picnic basket and pours herself a cup of hot chocolate.*)

JULIA: She not only reigns but she pours!

EMILY (*Beaming*): Heavens! And just a few minutes ago I was a goblin!

GINNY (*Kneeling*): What is your first command, O Glorious Goblin—I mean—O Glorious Queen?

EMILY (*Grandly*): Pass the cakes! (JANE *bows and hands*

the cookie jar to EMILY, *who takes a cake and munches happily. Chattering gaily, the others join her in the feasting, as the curtains close.*)

THE END

Mother's Choice

by *Mildred Hark McQueen*

Characters

MR. HENRY JOHNSON
MRS. VERA JOHNSON, *his wife*
LUCILLE ⎫
PAT   ⎬ *their children*
BOBBY   ⎭

TIME: *The Saturday before Mother's Day. Late afternoon.*
SETTING: *The living room of the Johnson family. There is a table in one corner with a newspaper and a telephone on it. The room is comfortably furnished.*
AT RISE: LUCILLE, *about twelve years old, sits in chair at left holding pad of paper and a pencil. She is writing. PAT, about ten years old, sits curled up in chair right. BOBBY, eight years old, is sprawled on the floor working with a model rocket.*

PAT: Lucille, how are you coming with the poem for Mother?
LUCILLE: I don't know. I have some verses, but—(*She reads.*)
Here's to Mother,
She's queen of our realm.
We feel safe and secure

565

With Mom at the helm.

PAT: What's wrong with that? I think it's terrific.

LUCILLE: It isn't true, though.

BOBBY (*Looking up*): Sure it is. We like Mom.

LUCILLE: Of course, but I doubt if she ever feels like a queen. Mom leads a wretched life. (*Writing again*) What rhymes with slave?

BOBBY: Who's a slave? I though you were writing a poem about Mother.

LUCILLE: Most mothers are slaves to their families, but we wish we could make her a queen. That's the idea of the poem.

BOBBY (*Going back to his model*): Mom doesn't seem like a slave to me.

LUCILLE: Oh, Bobby, you just don't understand. If you'd read this article in the newspaper—(*She picks up newspaper from table as* MRS. JOHNSON *enters left.*)

MRS. JOHNSON: Children, are there any more dirty clothes in your rooms?

PAT: Mother, you aren't *washing?*

MRS. JOHNSON (*Calmly*): Yes, dear. You sound as if there were something unusual about it. You know I didn't get all the washing done on Monday.

LUCILLE: But it's the day before Mother's Day.

MRS. JOHNSON: So it is. (*She smiles a little.*) Well, the world must go on in spite of it.

BOBBY: There are some dirty socks in my room, Mom.

MRS. JOHNSON: Yes, I imagine there are, Bobby. (*She starts left, then stops.*) So Mother's Day is almost here. My, I suppose I should have planned a special dinner for tonight.

PAT: Oh, no, Mom.

MRS. JOHNSON: Well, we'll have a nice Sunday dinner to-morrow. We'll just have to take potluck tonight. There are always so many chores to do on Saturday. No time at all for creative living. Sometimes I think this house is more like a factory than a home. (*She goes out.*)

LUCILLE: There, you see, Pat. Mom's been reading the article in the newspaper, too! (*She picks up newspaper and reads.*) Is the mother at your house a slave or a queen? Is your home a cold efficiency unit—an industrial miniature? Does your house present a factory image or a palace image?

PAT (*Looking around*): This house certainly doesn't look like a palace.

BOBBY: It doesn't look like a cold efficiency unit, or a factory, either.

LUCILLE: But it is. It's a factory where Mom slaves from morning till night—cooking, sewing, washing. Oh, if there were only something we could do.

BOBBY: Maybe you and Pat could help her more.

PAT: Look who's talking, Bobby Johnson! Who didn't take out the garbage this morning when he was asked, and who gets his clothes so dirty Mom can't get them clean?

LUCILLE (*Dramatically rising*): Dirty clothes, garbage, clutter—those are the things that make up Mom's life! (*Reading from paper again*) Listen. "In the factory home Mother feels enslaved, doing menial chores in which she finds little satisfaction. But in the palace home, the mother of the house becomes a queenly, important person. Every woman now and then has the urge to transform her home into a palace."

BOBBY: That's silly. Nobody lives in a palace except a queen.

LUCILLE (*Sitting down and placing newspaper on table*): Bobby, it's symbolic. It just means that we ought to make Mother *feel* like a queen and feel that her home is a palace. She ought to have more glamour and beauty in her life.

PAT: Well, Lucille, we did get her a corsage to wear to church tomorrow.

BOBBY: I have a box of candy for her.

LUCILLE: And you'll probably eat most of it yourself. It's Dad's present I'm counting on. He's getting the big present.

PAT: And we told him over and over to get something glamorous. (*The phone rings.*)

LUCILLE: Oh, maybe that's Dad now!

BOBBY (*Getting up and rushing to phone*): I'll get it. (*Picking up receiver*) Hello? Hi, Dad . . . Are you buying the present for Mom?

PAT: Ask him what it is, Bobby.

BOBBY: What did you say, Dad? Oh, boy, that sounds like fun . . . What? O.K., I'll tell them, and Mom, too. (*He hangs up.*)

LUCILLE: Has Dad bought the present? What is it?

BOBBY: He didn't tell, but he says it's something wonderful. Just what Mom's been wanting for ages.

LUCILLE: Oh, I can hardly wait to see what it is.

BOBBY: He'll be right home, and what do you think? He says to tell Mom he's taking us all out to dinner tonight.

PAT: Out to dinner? How terrific. (*She rushes to door left.*) Mom, Mom, listen! (MRS. JOHNSON *comes to the doorway, carrying some socks and other dirty clothes.*)

MRS. JOHNSON: What's happened?

PAT: Dad just called. He's taking us all out to dinner.

MRS. JOHNSON: Now, wasn't that sweet of your father to think of that? I don't know when we've gone out to dinner. (*Looking at dirty clothes*) You know, I don't think I'll wash these things, after all. I'd better get myself fixed up a little. My hair and my nails—and I wonder what I'll wear. Oh, this is such a nice surprise. We'll just sit there and order our food, and we won't have to worry about cooking it or washing the dishes. (*She goes out.*)

LUCILLE (*Looking after her*): Poor Mom. You can just see how she feels most of the time. Enslaved. It's kind of pathetic how thrilled she was, all because of a little thing like going out to dinner.

BOBBY: You're goofy, Lucille.

PAT: I don't think we should feel so discouraged, Lucille. This is the first step toward making Mom feel like a queen, and think how she'll feel when Dad gets home with her present.

LUCILLE: You're right, Pat. We ought to accentuate the positive. Oh, I wonder what the present will be. I suggested a beautiful negligee—satin or velvet, maybe, that Mom can wear when she relaxes.

BOBBY: But you talk as if she never *does* relax.

PAT: Or something different for the house. I suggested silver candlesticks or a real fancy lamp.

LUCILLE: A new lamp might be good. It might shed a soft rosy glow over everything and make this old junky furniture look better. Well, I'd better finish this poem. (*She starts writing as* MR. JOHNSON *enters right, beaming.*)

MR. JOHNSON: Hi, family. Am I ever pleased with myself! (*They all rush toward him and he grins.*)

PAT: But Dad, where's the present?

MR. JOHNSON: Now, now, don't rush me. You just wait until you hear what I've bought for your mother.

BOBBY: Do you have it in your pocket, Dad?

PAT: Or is it going to be delivered?

MR. JOHNSON (*Looking around and walking left*): Is your mother around? I don't want her to overhear this. I just want to see her face when I tell her what we're giving her. (*He walks right.*) She's never had a present like this for Mother's Day. (*He sits down right and stretches his legs expansively.*)

LUCILLE: Oh, Dad, please, there's no reason to keep us in suspense.

MR. JOHNSON: Now, wait, there's a big secret I didn't tell you. I know you children thought we were going to spend—oh, maybe twenty or twenty-five dollars at the most. I told you we could go a little higher this year—but I wanted to surprise you, too.

PAT: Dad, you mean you broke the bank?

MR. JOHNSON: A few days ago, I got a bonus I didn't expect, for my monthly sales. And I blew every bit of it on your mother's present. All two hundred and fifty dollars of it.

BOBBY: Two hundred and fifty dollars. Wowie!

LUCILLE: Oh, Dad, I can't believe it. It must be something wonderful.

PAT: Something beautiful that Mother's always wanted!

MR. JOHNSON (*Rising and making his announcement*): You bet it is. It's a dream present—dear to every woman's heart. It's a brand-new, modern, super-speed, double-action washing machine!

PAT: What? (*She falls into a chair.*)

LUCILLE (*Also sitting down*): A washing machine? How horrible, Dad. How perfectly horrible!

PAT: Dad, how could you?

LUCILLE: It's a cold efficiency unit, an industrial miniature, a factory symbol.

MR. JOHNSON (*Bewildered*): A factory what? What are you girls talking about? You must be out of your minds.

BOBBY: You tell 'em, Pop.

LUCILLE: Hush up, Bobby. Oh, Dad, I told you to get something beautiful and glamorous. And you end up with a washing machine!

MR. JOHNSON: But it's what your mother needs. She's been having trouble with the old one. Just last Monday it broke down again.

PAT: But you fixed it, Dad.

MR. JOHNSON: I know, but that old machine won't last.

LUCILLE: Dad, listen, a washing machine will make Mom feel more like a slave than ever, chained to this house.

MR. JOHNSON: Nonsense, she can do the wash in a third of the time. I wish the store could have delivered the new machine today, but there wasn't time. But here's my receipt. (*He takes slip of paper from pocket and holds it up.*) I thought we could give her this along with a card. Weren't you kids going to make a card or write a verse or something?

LUCILLE: I have a verse, but I'll never give it to Mom with a washing machine. I won't be a party to such a thing.

MR. JOHNSON: Now, now, you girls don't know what you're talking about. Wait and see how pleased your mother will be. The machine will be here bright and early Monday morning, in time for her to do the washing.

LUCILLE: In time for her to do—oh, how awful to remind Mom of the washing on Mother's Day. Dad, listen, you'll just have to cancel it.

MR. JOHNSON: But I can't do that.

PAT: Dad, please. Mom was so thrilled when we told her you were taking us out to dinner. We can't spoil everything now.

MR. JOHNSON: But I—I don't know what to think. I felt sure your mother would be thrilled with the washing machine. I still feel—

LUCILLE: Dad. You just don't understand women.

MR. JOHNSON: No man does, but just the same I've lived with your mother a lot longer than you children have. What do you think, Bobby? Man to man, tell me.

BOBBY: I don't know, Dad. Lucille and Pat get crazy ideas, but I did hear Mom say just a few minutes ago that this house seemed like a factory.

MR. JOHNSON: A factory, huh? Well, I must say I'm very much disappointed, after buying just what I thought your mother wanted. Besides, it's too late now to get anything else.

LUCILLE: No, it isn't, Dad. Call them up right away. Cancel the washing machine.

PAT: Yes, Dad, hurry. Before Mom gets dressed. She's getting dolled up for the dinner.

MR. JOHNSON (*Going slowly toward phone*): But now we won't have any present for her, except the usual flowers and candy.

LUCILLE: Dad, I have a wonderful idea! Cancel the washing machine and tell the store you want a gift certificate!

MR. JOHNSON: I could do that, I suppose—

PAT: A gift certificate for $250. Then Mom can choose anything she wants in the whole department store.

MR. JOHNSON: Let's see, is the phone number on the receipt here? (*He looks.*) Yes, here it is. (*He dials.*) I hate to do this, but—

LUCILLE: Oh, Dad, you're doing the right thing. I know you are. Why, if we gave Mom a washing machine, she —she might—leave home or something.

MR. JOHNSON (*On phone*): Hello? Let me speak to the adjustment department please.

LUCILLE: Oh, Mom will be thrilled. All that money to get something she really wants.

MR. JOHNSON (*Into phone*): This is Henry Johnson. I bought a washing machine from you a short while back —a Super Queen, I think it was called. . . . It cost $250, and I want to cancel the order. . . . Well, I've changed my mind. I'd like to have a gift certificate instead . . . I'll hold on while you check. (*To children*) She's going to take care of it.

LUCILLE: Oh, wonderful! And I'd better finish this poem. I still have a line or two. (*She writes again.*)

PAT: I do hope Dad gets this settled before Mom shows up. Bobby, go see if you can keep Mom busy for a little while.

BOBBY (*Getting up*): But I thought you wanted her to relax.

PAT: Don't argue. You're always losing things. Can't you ask her where something is? Or, I know, ask her what you ought to wear out to dinner.

BOBBY: But I don't want to get dressed up.

PAT (*Firmly*): Bobby—

BOBBY (*Going out left*): O.K. O.K. (*Calling as he goes off*) Mom! Oh, Mom!

MR. JOHNSON (*Into phone*): Fine, fine. If you'll just cancel the slip for the washing machine and make out a gift certificate for $250 to Mrs. Henry Johnson. Say, I don't suppose you could get it out here this afternoon, could you? By special messenger? It's a Mother's Day present. I'll be glad to pay extra, whatever it costs.

PAT: Oh, Dad, how terrific if they could. It will be so much more exciting to *see* the gift certificate than just to have you tell her about it.

LUCILLE: Of course it would. (*Looking at her piece of paper*) If I do say so, I think this is a pretty good Mother's Day poem.

MR. JOHNSON (*Into phone*): Thank you—thank you, that's wonderful. (*He hangs up.*) A very nice young lady. When I told her the present was for Mother's Day, she said she understood. She has a mother, too.

PAT: How sweet.

MR. JOHNSON: And she's sending the gift certificate right out by special messenger. It should be here shortly.

LUCILLE (*Running and kissing* MR. JOHNSON): Dad, I love you. You're the greatest.

PAT: I'll say you are, Dad. And you just wait and see how pleased Mother will be. (MRS. JOHNSON *enters with* BOBBY, *who now wears a jacket over his shirt.* MRS. JOHNSON *has changed her dress and fluffed out her hair. She wears earrings and necklace.*)

MRS. JOHNSON (*As she enters*): Girls, whatever have you done to your brother? He actually *wants* to get dressed up in his best jacket. (*Sees* MR. JOHNSON *and smiles*) Henry dear, you're home. I'm so glad. And I'm thrilled we're going out to dinner.

MR. JOHNSON: Vera, my dear, you look very nice—very nice indeed.

LUCILLE: Yes, like a queen, doesn't she, Dad?

MR. JOHNSON: Yes, yes, indeed. Queenly and regal. It must be your hair.

MRS. JOHNSON (*Pleased*): Why, Henry. I did change my hairdo a little. Fluffed it out more.

MR. JOHNSON: Well, whatever it is, you look positively beautiful. Here, sit down, Vera, right here, where we can all look at you. (*He leads her to chair right and she sits down, looking a little bewildered.*)

MRS. JOHNSON: Well, I don't know what's gotten into all of you. But I must say it's very pleasant. Bobby wanting to dress up, you paying me all these compliments, Henry.

MR. JOHNSON: You deserve them, my dear. Isn't that a new dress?

MRS. JOHNSON: New dress? My goodness, no. It's three years old. But I've dressed it up with jewelry.

LUCILLE: You may have a new dress very soon, Mom. Who knows?

MRS. JOHNSON: Well, I know our budget, Lucille. Unless there's a fairy godmother around—

PAT: How about a fairy godfather? Dad, for instance?

MRS. JOHNSON: My, you do all look pleased with your-selves. Do you have another surprise? I've already had one. We're going out to dinner.

MR. JOHNSON: As a matter of fact we *do* have a surprise. That is, we will have.

LUCILLE: More than one, Mom.

MR. JOHNSON: Yes, I believe the children have written a special poem for you in honor of Mother's Day.

PAT: Lucille really wrote it, but we all thought of the idea. You know, Mom, something different, instead of the same old card with "Happy Mother's Day."

MR. JOHNSON: And a splendid idea. Now, Miss Poet Laureate, will you do the honors?

LUCILLE (*Rising and smiling*): Thank you, Dad. (*She reads.*)

Here's to Mother,
She's queen of our realm.
We feel safe and secure,
With Mom at the helm.

MRS. JOHNSON (*Nodding and smiling*): Why, how lovely. How perfectly lovely.

LUCILLE:

We wish we could give her
A palace or two;
We would like to make
All her wishes come true.

We would place a crown
Upon her hair;
Give her ermine and diamonds
To show her we care.

MRS. JOHNSON: My goodness.

BOBBY: Lucille must have been up on Cloud Nine when she wrote this.

PAT: Sh-h.

LUCILLE:

>But alas, it's a dream
>That will not come true;
>We can't do for Mom
>What we'd like to do.

>And a queen's life is different
>From our mother's life;
>Her life's full of trouble
>And toil and strife.

>She slaves for her family
>From morning till night;
>She keeps our modest home
>Shining and bright.

MRS. JOHNSON (*Looking around*): Our modest home?

LUCILLE:

>She cooks and she sews,
>Hears the problems we face;
>And all of our troubles,
>She tries to erase.

MR. JOHNSON: This poem is sad, Lucille, and getting sadder by the minute.

LUCILLE:

>So the only crown
>We can give Mom today
>Is a crown of love
>For Mother's Day.

MRS. JOHNSON (*Dabbing at her eyes*): Why, that's beautiful—just beautiful.

LUCILLE: Did you like it, Mom?

PAT: And you *are* going to get a present, too. Lucille didn't know when she wrote the poem.

MRS. JOHNSON: But I don't deserve any more. My goodness,

a crown of love, and I'm the queen of your realm. I wish I felt and acted more like a queen. I'm afraid I'm very cross sometimes—not really the way you pictured me.

LUCILLE: But Mom, you have to put up with so much.

MRS. JOHNSON: Nonsense. (*The doorbell rings.*)

BOBBY: Here's the present, I'll bet. Here's the present. (MR, JOHNSON *rises quickly.*)

MR. JOHNSON: I'll take care of it. (*He goes off right.*)

MRS. JOHNSON: My, I can't stand much more excitement. I suppose it's a messenger, with flowers maybe.

LUCILLE: No, you're wrong, Mom. You'll never guess—never.

MR. JOHNSON (*Enters smiling, with a long white envelope.*): Well, well, well. Here's your present, my dear. And we hope you'll like it.

MRS. JOHNSON (*Smiling and taking envelope*): But what on earth is it? Another special message? (*She opens envelope and takes out gift certificate, staring at it.*) Why, why—it's a gift certificate from Porter's. How nice. What! What? Oh, no, it can't be! Not two hundred and fifty dollars!

MR. JOHNSON: That's it, my dear, that's it. You're not seeing double.

PAT: Aren't you thrilled, Mom?

BOBBY: Isn't that a lot of dough?

MRS. JOHNSON: But I can't take it. It's too much. Henry, please—

MR. JOHNSON: Now, Vera, we'll have no arguments. It's all yours. I got a special bonus, and we all agreed it should go to you. That's your present for Mother's Day. Buy anything you want.

MRS. JOHNSON: Anything I want? Really?

LUCILLE: Sure, Mom. (*Breathlessly*) What are you going to get?

MRS. JOHNSON: Well, it seems selfish to get something just for myself. I ought to get something all of you could enjoy.

LUCILLE: Absolutely not. This is just for you, Mom.

MR. JOHNSON: Yes, my dear, it certainly is.

MRS. JOHNSON: All right then, I'll be selfish. Because I know what I want.

PAT: A new sofa?

MRS. JOHNSON: More than anything in the world I want—

LUCILLE: That expensive coat and suit you admired in Porter's window?

MRS. JOHNSON: I hope you won't mind, but—

PAT: Those silver candlesticks?

MRS. JOHNSON: What I really want is a—

LUCILLE: A new set of china?

MRS. JOHNSON: Is a brand spanking new automatic washing machine! (*They all stare at her in stunned silence.*)

BOBBY (*Grinning*): Say, Dad, what do you know?

MR. JOHNSON (*Shaking his head at* BOBBY *but grinning, too*): Well, this is very interesting, my dear. So that's what you're going to get?

MRS. JOHNSON: Yes, and Porter's have just what I want. I saw an ad in the paper. Double action, super speed—

LUCILLE: But, Mom, we thought—well, we thought you'd want something—well, beautiful and glamorous—

MRS. JOHNSON: You don't understand how beautiful a new washing machine can seem to a woman who's been struggling along with an old one for years. Why, I was beginning to feel like a slave to that old machine, but now—well, I'll feel like a queen, the way you said in the poem. In fact, I think that's the name of the machine— the Super Queen.

MR. JOHNSON: Yes, it is, my dear.

MRS. JOHNSON: Did you see the ad, too, Henry?

MR. JOHNSON: I happened to, yes.

MRS. JOHNSON (*Goes to table and picks up newspaper*): The ad's here in the paper somewhere. My, what's this? Oh, someone's been writing an article about mothers. It says: "Is your mother a slave or a queen?" Well, there's no doubt what *I'll* be when I get my new washing machine. Look, here it is. Here's the picture. The Super Queen! Oh, Henry, call the store right away and tell them to deliver it first thing Monday morning. (MR. JOHNSON *smiles and goes toward phone.*) Oh, and look, here's a little verse in the ad. It's kind of cute. It fits right in with your poem, Lucille. (*Reading, as they all listen*)
Monday's a dream day
With the Super Queen;
Mom's home is her castle,
And she is the queen.
(MRS. JOHNSON *holds up picture of washing machine.*) Isn't that a beautiful Mother's Day present? My, I can hardly wait until Monday morning! (*Curtain*)

THE END

Time for Mom

by Aileen Fisher

Characters

KEVIN
PHYLLIS
CARTER
DEBBIE
KAY
BOYS AND GIRLS
JANIE
MOTHER
FATHER

SCENE 1

TIME: *Early May.*

SETTING: *A street.*

AT RISE: *All* BOYS *and* GIRLS *(except* JANIE*) enter gaily.* BOYS *may have marbles;* GIRLS, *roller skates and jump ropes. They sing to the tune of "My Bonnie Lies Over the Ocean" while playing with their marbles, etc.*

BOYS *and* GIRLS:
  Oh, May is a wonderful season,
  Oh, May is as gay as a rhyme,
  There's more than one jolly good reason
  Why May is a jolly good time.

May brings spring things (*They jump rope, etc.*)
And school soon is over and through, and through,
May brings spring things
And May brings us Mother's Day, too.

KEVIN (*Stopping his play*): Mother's Day! And I can't think of anything different to give my Mom. I've worn out my brains.

PHYLLIS: Which brains do you mean, Kevin? (*She giggles*)

KEVIN: Well, you can laugh if you want to. But I can't think of a single good present to get with *thirty-seven cents*.

PHYLLIS: Oh, that's different. What about Janie? Has she thought of anything?

KEVIN: No. We're both in the same boat, and it's about to sink. But Janie is six cents better off than I am. She has forty-three. Last year we went together and bought Mom a box of candy. But even putting our money together again, we can't get much of a box for eighty cents.

CARTER: What about fish-hooks? You can get plenty of those for eighty cents, with a couple of sinkers thrown in.

KEVIN (*Ignoring* CARTER): Anyway, my mother's on a diet this year, trying to keep her weight down.

DEBBIE: So's mine. But I'm giving her candy anyway. *I'm* not on a diet!

CARTER: I have my eye on a model airplane kit for my mother.

KAY: You would, Carter! She'll just love that. About as much as fish-hooks. Why don't you think of something *she'd* like for once?

CARTER: You mean she wouldn't like fish-hooks?

KEVIN: Can you think of something *my* Mom would like for eighty cents, Kay? Something different?

KAY (*Hesitating*): Well . . . I'm giving my mother flower seeds. You could get all kinds of them for eighty cents. And your mother could have flowers all summer.

KEVIN: Sure. Only we live in an apartment, remember. On the third floor. We don't have a yard.

CARTER: That's easy. Get a flower box and stick it on the windowsill.

KEVIN: We might get a *piece* of a flower box for eighty cents. Then what would we put in it?

DEBBIE (*Helpfully*): Well, there are always handkerchiefs . . . or perfume from the dime store . . . or a memo pad for the telephone or something.

KEVIN: But Janie and I want to give Mom something different. Something special.

DEBBIE: You have awfully big ideas for such a flat pocketbook, Kevin. (*Turns to* PHYLLIS) What are you giving your mother, Phyllis?

PHYLLIS: A scarf. A silk scarf with flowers and things. My Aunt Elizabeth helped pick it out. She works at the store, so we got a discount. (*To other* GIRLS) Come on home with me and I'll show it to you. It's *beautiful*. (*They jump rope or skate out.*)

KEVIN (*With a sigh*): Thinking's the hardest thing I do. And I don't seem to get anywhere.

CARTER: Cheer up, there's always fish-hooks. Or what about something in the camping line? A canteen! Or a couple of those adventure stories at the supermarket?

KEVIN: My mother doesn't have much time to read. We've a big apartment and she does all the work and takes care of the baby and everything.

CARTER: Well, don't try to be so different, Kevin. You won't have a brain left in your head. (*Looks offstage*) Here comes your sister! Maybe Janie's thought of something. I'll be seeing you. (*He saunters out. If there are other boys, they go with him. In a moment* JANIE *enters.*)

KEVIN: Did you get any good ideas, Janie?

JANIE: Did you?

KEVIN: Plenty of ideas, but none of them very good.

JANIE: I've thought of something Mom would like more
than anything else!

KEVIN: You have?

JANIE: It's something we can't buy.

KEVIN: That's a help.

JANIE: But we can give it to her without buying it.

KEVIN: You mean we wouldn't have to spend even eighty
cents?

JANIE (*Mysteriously*): We just have to spend some time
and thought on it, that's all. And it'll go a long way, in
small portions.

KEVIN: What do you mean—small portions? Do we give it
to her on the installment plan or something? So much a
month?

JANIE (*Nodding mysteriously*): Sort of. Anyway, it will be
a different kind of present. Come on home, Kevin, and
we'll work it out! (*They hurry out.*)

CURTAIN

*   *   *

SCENE 2

TIME: *The morning of Mother's Day.*

SETTING: *The dining room.*

AT RISE: MOTHER *is heard offstage, as if in the kitchen,
making noise with dishes.* KEVIN *and* JANIE *tiptoe in
carefully, look around, put small wrapped parcels at*
MOTHER'S *place.* JANIE *goes to kitchen.*

JANIE (*As she goes*): Need any help, Mom? (FATHER *enters
with large package.*)

KEVIN: What did you think of, Dad? You said you wanted
to get her something different. Something other than
flowers.

FATHER: Wait till you see what I have. (*Pats package*) Books, Kevin! Art books.

KEVIN: Art books?

FATHER: Your mother is very clever, son. I am sure she could draw and paint if she'd just put some time on it. I have a hunch she's always had a secret desire to do something in the art line. Now we'll see.

KEVIN: Does it take much time?

FATHER: Well . . . yes, I suppose it does. Why?

KEVIN: Mom's awfully busy, Dad. Mondays and Thursdays she goes down to the basement and washes. She has to keep her eye on the baby, too. Tuesdays and Fridays she irons. Wednesdays she cleans the apartment real well . . . though she cleans it some every day. Saturday she bakes. She has to stop besides, and make three meals a day and keep our clothes mended and . . .

FATHER (*Taken aback*): How do you know all this?

KEVIN: Janie figured it out. It has something to do with our presents. (*Nods at little packages*)

FATHER: I'm afraid I was carried away. I thought of something she'd like to do . . . but I didn't think of where she was going to find time to do it. I'm afraid I went haywire on those art books, Kevin. (*He is quite depressed.*)

KEVIN: Wait till you see what Janie and I have for her. Cheer up, Dad.

FATHER (*Scolding himself*): Thoughtless of me! Not to think of how busy she is! Maybe the books will just make her feel bad. I should have bought her some labor-saving gadget instead . . . (MOTHER *and* JANIE *come in with dishes.*)

JANIE, KEVIN, *and* FATHER: Happy Mother's Day!

MOTHER (*Seeing gifts on table*): What's all this? For *me*?

ALL: Happy Mother's Day!

KEVIN: Dad's is the big one. You have to open that last.

JANIE: Ours are the little ones, and they're sort of alike. Open them, Mom!

MOTHER (*Taking up one of the little packages, reading the tag*): To Mother from her loving daughter Janie. (*Begins to open it.* FATHER *is as curious as she is.*)

FATHER: Looks like tickets of some sort! What kind of tickets?

KEVIN: You'd be surprised, Dad.

MOTHER: Not one ticket, but a number of them. What in the world? (*She holds up strips of cardboard with writing on them.*)

KEVIN: Read what it says.

MOTHER (*Reading first one*):
Dear Mom, this ticket you will see
Is worth two meals, to you from me.

MOTHER (*Puzzled*): Two meals?

JANIE: Whenever you want time for something, Mom, I'll get dinner—from beginning to end. You just tell me what to get. That ticket is worth two meals. Doing dishes, and everything. Kevin will help.

MOTHER: How wonderful! (*Takes another ticket, reads*)
Dear Mom, you have some things, I trust,
That you would rather do than dust.
This ticket will entitle you
To seven dustings—good ones, too.

JANIE: See the numbers 1 to 7 along the bottom? Every time you want me to dust, I'll punch out a number. Just like a conductor.

MOTHER (*Happily*): I can't think of anything I'd rather have than time to do a few things I never get around to. (*Looks at other tickets*) And here are tickets for baby-sitting . . . and washing dishes . . . and baby-sitting

again . . . and straightening up the living room . . .
and setting the table . . . and sewing on buttons . . .
and . . .

KEVIN: Open mine, Mom!

MOTHER (*Taking other small package*): Oh, I hope it's
more tickets, Kevin! I hope it's a present of more time!
How did you ever think of it?

KEVIN: We wanted to give you something different. And
Janie figured out if you had some time to yourself that
would sure be different.

MOTHER (*Reading one of* KEVIN's *tickets*):
Dear Mom, this ticket means I'll run
Twenty errands, not just one.

KEVIN: You see the twenty numbers around the edges to
punch out?

MOTHER (*Reading another*):
Dear Mom, the grass could not be greener.
Go look . . . I'll run the vacuum cleaner.
(*Laughing*) Why, you're going to spoil me completely!
I'll have so much time on my hands I won't know what
to do with it.

FATHER (*Beaming*): Oh, yes you will! (*Pats package of
books*) Look and see.

MOTHER (*Opening package*): Books! Art books! Oh, *how*
did you know I've always wanted to try to draw and
paint?

KEVIN *and* JANIE: Now you'll have some time. Tickets,
please!

FATHER: I must confess if it hadn't been for our brainy
children, I'd have been sunk! I . . . I just didn't think
of the time angle. Thank goodness, they did.

MOTHER: I think you all had a brainstorm, that's what I
think. And I can't tell you how happy I am!

KEVIN, JANIE, *and* FATHER (*Singing gaily*):
Oh, May is a wonderful season,

Oh, May is as gay as a rhyme,
There's more than one jolly good reason
Why May is a jolly good time.
May brings gay things
And presents for people like you, like you. (*Nod at*
    MOTHER)
May brings spring things
And May brings us Mother's Day, too! (*Curtain*)

THE END

A Hat for Mother

by Marguerite Kreger Phillips

Characters

JILL, *a teen-ager*
BONNIE, *age 12*
LOIS ⎫
LOLA ⎬ *twins, age 10*
CINDY, *age 8*
MRS. LANGLEY, *their mother*

TIME: *Late one afternoon in May.*
SETTING: *The Langley living room.*
AT RISE: LOIS *and* LOLA *are rushing about putting the finishing touches to the room.* LOIS *has a gay scarf tied around her hair, and she stops pushing the dust mop about every foot or two to adjust the scarf.* LOLA *is swinging a dustcloth in and out of the chair rungs.*

LOLA: Why don't you take that rag off your head, Lois? You stop every half second to tie it. How can you get the dusting done?

LOIS: You just tend to your part of the work, Lola, and I'll take care of mine. Mother will be home from the office before we're ready if we don't hurry up.

LOLA: She can't do that. Jill has to get here with the hat.

LOIS (*Stops pushing the mop and leans on it gazing into space*): Oh! I hope Mother will like it.

588

LOLA (*Startled*): Why shouldn't she like it? We put enough things together and Jill is doing the trimming.

LOIS: That's just it. Did we put too *many* things together?

LOLA (*Blustering*): We did the best we could with what money we had.

LOIS: I'm just hoping the rayon I gave Jill for the crown will be enough.

LOLA: Now you have me worrying. I dyed that blue ribbon myself, but I followed the directions my art teacher gave me.

LOIS (*Reassuring herself as well as* LOLA): Jill passed judgment on everything we contributed and her Home Ec teacher considers her an "A" student, a judge of what is good style even if she is only fourteen. Now, empty that wastebasket and stop making me nervous about Mother's hat. It just has to turn out beautiful!

LOLA (*As she gets the basket from upstage*): If you're finished with the mop, why don't you put it away? (*Begins dusting again.*) By the way, what about supper?

LOIS: It has to be warmed up. We want to give Mother her hat first, then we can all enjoy our meal. If we had to sit and worry about whether she was going to like the hat, we wouldn't be able to eat a thing.

LOLA: I would! I'm hungry now. (*She leaves the dustcloth on chair*)

LOIS: Oh, you! (LOLA *now rushes off with wastebasket, and* LOIS *starts to follow with mop when* CINDY *comes running on with a Parcel Post package about a foot square.*)

CINDY: Look what they left at our door. A package for Mom.

LOIS (*Rushes to her as* CINDY *reaches table and throws package down*): What is it?

CINDY (*Grinning*): A package. Can't you see?

LOIS (*Bending over it*): And I can read. It's for Mother.

CINDY: That's what I said.

LOIS (*Studying label*): Cindy, it has the word Paris on it.

LOLA (*Entering in time to hear this last remark*): Did I hear someone say "Paris"?

CINDY: You sure did. Does Mom know somebody in Paris?

LOIS: I don't think so—she never told us about anybody.

LOLA: You mean the stamps are French? (*Now looks closely at package*) That looks like John Tyler on those stamps. He was no Frenchman.

LOIS: Ahem! Ahem! The family philatelist speaks!

LOLA (*Pointing*): You have eyes. Use them.

LOIS (*Takes another look*): I hate to admit it, but you're right.

LOLA (*A bit boastfully*): Naturally—I know my stamps. Those are ten-cent stamps and they have the picture of John Tyler on them.

CINDY: What do they have Paris on it for, then?

LOIS (*Spelling aloud*): P-a-r-i-s. (*Then spots another word and is excited*) And what's this? M-i-l-l-i-n—Oh dear, the rest of the word is rubbed out.

LOLA: Let's wait for Mother to figure it out.

LOIS (*They both turn from table leaving* CINDY *with package*): I have to put this mop away.

LOLA: I wish Jill would come.

CINDY: And what do I do with this? (*Slaps the package*)

LOIS (*Waves to chair*): Dump it on the chair, and let's all hope it is something nice for Mother.

CINDY: She'll have enough to make her happy when she sees the hat we've made. She won't need anything else.

LOIS (*Pointedly*): Jill really did all the trimming.

CINDY: How could she trim it if I hadn't found those blue-jay feathers? (*Moves down to chair with package*)

LOIS (*A bit grudgingly*): Jill did say they were perfect.

LOLA: Bonnie should be coming soon. (*Grabs up dust-*

cloth from chair and tosses it to Lois) Put this away with the mop, will you? (Lois *exits with both, as* Bonnie *rushes on.*)

BONNIE: Oh dear, am I late? I hope Mother isn't home yet.

CINDY: You're late, but Mother isn't here.

BONNIE (*Looks around*): Where is it? I don't see the hat.

LOLA: For the simple reason that Jill hasn't brought it yet.

BONNIE: I'll simply swoon if my roses don't look right.

LOLA: That would be a big help, especially when it's your turn to get supper! Lois and I want the surprise first, then food.

BONNIE: That's O.K. I just have to light the oven and set the things in to warm—Mother got everything ready before she left this morning. (Lois *enters*)

LOIS (*To* BONNIE): Oh good! I was afraid you'd be late.

CINDY: She is.

BONNIE: Shush, don't tell anybody. (*Spies package*) Oh, what's that?

LOIS (CINDY *and* LOLA *wink at each other*): Just a package for Mother.

BONNIE (*Instantly excited*): For Mother?

CINDY: And it's from Paris.

BONNIE (*Picking it up hurriedly*): Paris?

LOIS: Oh, Bonnie, let it be. Go wash and take a look at the food. We don't want you out in the kitchen when Mother gets here.

BONNIE (*Shakes it curiously*): Hm-m, that word "Paris" isn't part of the postmark.

LOLA (*Gives her a poke*): How about the food? The package won't run away.

BONNIE (*Drops the package back on the chair*): You're too young to understand the significance of "Paris," but I guess I can wait. (*She exits as* JILL *rushes on waving a good-sized hatbox in the air.*)

JILL *(Marching downstage with the others following eagerly)*: Wait until you see it!

CINDY *(As* JILL *still holds it up in the air)*: How about bringing it down to my level? (JILL *laughs, places it on table, opens the box slowly and takes out a very stunning all-blue hat.)*

LOLA *(Delightedly clapping her hands)*: My ribbon looks new!

BONNIE *(Sticks her head in at door)*: Oh, Jill, you got home. Let me see the hat. (JILL *holds it out for her to see.)* Those roses are great. Now if this hat only looks right on Mother.

JILL: And see what a lovely crown that blue rayon made, Lois.

LOIS *(Warmly)*: Jill it's your artistic work that makes the hat what it is. Your fingers did it.

BONNIE: She's right, Jill, we couldn't have managed it alone. I'll be back in two seconds. I still have to put the vegetables in to warm. (BONNIE *exits.)*

JILL *(Gazing at hat)*: Now, where shall we have it when Mother gets here?

LOLA: How about right in the middle of that table, but inside the box so she has to dive for it.

JILL: Fine! *(Puts hat back in box and moves box to table center)*

CINDY: And when Mom shows up we'll all shout, "surprise!" We'll give her our surprise first, then show her the other package.

JILL *(Surprised)*: What other package?

LOIS *(Indifferently)*: On that chair.

JILL *(Moving down to it)*: When did this come?

LOIS: A little while ago.

JILL *(Balancing it on one hand)*: It doesn't weigh much.

BONNIE *(Returns and sees* JILL *with package)*: Take a look at the words near the postmark.

JILL (*Aloud*): Paris?

LOIS (*Leans over and points*): And see that other word? (*Spells it out*) M-i-l-l-i-n-

BONNIE (*Anxiously*): Jill, that could be the beginning of the word millinery.

JILL (*Gasps*): Millinery? You mean this could be a hat?

CINDY (*As all seem drawn together in anxiety*): Don't let Mom see it if it is, at least until she has a chance to look at the one we made her.

JILL: Mother wouldn't send away for a hat. She has to watch her budget too closely with five of us to support.

BONNIE (*Near tears*): And the one we made is so beautiful.

JILL (*Sighs deeply*): Still, we'll have to tell her about this package.

CINDY (*Bravely*): I know my Mom. She won't even look at it until she's seen what's in that box on the table.

LOLA (*Gives CINDY a shove*): Go see if she's coming. (CINDY *exits*)

BONNIE: Oh, I do want Mother to have beautiful things and if that's a hat from Paris—

LOIS (*Cutting in*): How could it be a hat from Paris?

CINDY (*Dashing in*): She's coming up the steps. (*Looks back*) She's on the porch. (*Again looks back*) She's coming in the door.

JILL (*Pushes package back on chair and rushes to left of table*): Ready, everybody. Let's all get over on this side. (CINDY *moves to back of table but* LOIS, LOLA *and* BONNIE *all crowd left.* MRS. LANGLEY *enters.*)

ALL (*Shouting*): Surprise!

MRS. LANGLEY (*Gasps and stares*): I'm surprised, but what for? Is it my birthday?

LOLA: No! But it will soon be Mother's Day.

JILL: The surprise is in the box. (CINDY *pats it.*)

LOIS (*Blurting*): And over on that chair is another package that came for you by mail.

Mrs. Langley (*Surprised*): For me?

Cindy: Shall I get it for you?

Mrs. Langley: I don't remember ordering anything. . . . Oh, let it wait. Your surprise is what I'm interested in.

Jill (*Wanting to be fair*): Maybe it's important.

Mrs. Langley (*Beaming at them all*): Nothing is more important than what you have in that box. (*Moves down to right of table and reaches for box. All girls are tense as she lifts out the hat.*) Oh! A hat! Isn't it beautiful! (*Holds it out in front of her*) Those feathers—those roses—it's all just perfect. I'm so thrilled, I'm absolutely weak.

Lola (*Quickly brings a chair from left*): There, Mother, sit down.

Mrs. Langley (*Holding her hat, sits down*): Just see how perfectly that ribbon blends with these feathers and such darling roses—(*She looks at their happy faces as they bend towards her.*) How did you ever do this? How could you, with the little allowance I'm able to give you?

Lois: You have smart children! (*All laugh.*)

Cindy: Smart? We're *super!*

Jill: You really like it, Mother?

Mrs. Langley (*Holds hat out to* Jill): I love it. Now, you put it on me— (*They all stand back to admire it.*)

Bonnie (*Rushing off*): I'll get you a mirror.

Cindy (*Looks at* Mrs. Langley *from all angles*): I never thought it would turn out that pretty.

Lois: You forget that the pretty face under the hat helps.

Mrs. Langley: Don't spoil me, children.

Lola (*Very solemnly*): Now, you'd better look at the other package.

Mrs. Langley (*Seems hesitant*): I suppose so, but—

Bonnie (*Dashes back with mirror and holds it for* Mrs. Langley): How do you like the back? (Mrs. Langley *strives to see herself from all angles.*)

MRS. LANGLEY: Why, this hat does things for me!

JILL: Now, shall I take it off?

MRS. LANGLEY (*Playfully pushes her hand away*): I just got it on. Don't you dare try to take it off.

LOIS (*Gets the package from chair*): Here's the package, and it has the word Paris on it.

MRS. LANGLEY (*Takes one look and gasps*): Oh, no!

JILL (*Staring at her*): What's wrong, Mother?

MRS. LANGLEY (*Smiling and getting control of herself*): I'm all right . . . just a little startled.

JILL: You act as if you know what it is.

MRS. LANGLEY (*Protestingly*): But I don't need what's in that package, if it's what I think it is. (*Changes the subject as she turns suddenly to* BONNIE) How is dinner coming, Bonnie?

BONNIE: Mother, you're trying to put us off.

MRS. LANGLEY: I'm not. I'm perfectly content with your surprise, and I don't need what's in *that* package.

BONNIE (*Tragically*): I knew it! I knew it! It's a hat. And if it's a hat from Paris, you're afraid you'll hurt our feelings—

MRS. LANGLEY (*Breaking in*): Bonnie! Stop that nonsense. It can't be better than the one I have on. Now, I guess I have to tell you how I know what's in that package.

LOIS (*Studying package*): It's postmarked Cleveland, Ohio. I can just make it out.

MRS. LANGLEY: Yes, I know.

LOLA: You know?

JILL: Oh, Mother, do open it. This suspense is awful.

MRS. LANGLEY: First I must tell you something, something that will surprise you and make me feel very foolish.

LOIS: Why, Mother!

CINDY: I don't know what you mean, Mom, but you're tops with me.

MRS. LANGLEY: I entered a contest about two months
   ago—

JILL (*Interrupting*): And this is a prize?

MRS. LANGLEY: I'm afraid so.

CINDY: Hurrah! My mother won a prize!

LOIS: What's wrong with winning a prize, Mother? You
   don't look a bit happy about it. If you won it, it's yours.
   What kind of kids do you think you have? We'll all
   be proud of you.

MRS. LANGLEY: Even if it's a hat?

JILL (*Pausing, then looking at others*): Even if it's a *hat!*

MRS. LANGLEY: What darlings you are.

JILL: What did you do to win a prize?

MRS. LANGLEY: I had to write some poetry.

BONNIE: Poetry? My very own mother a poet!

MRS. LANGLEY: Not good poetry, I'm afraid. That's why
   I'm embarrassed. It was really only a jingle.

CINDY: All poetry jingles. (JILL *sits in chair beside* MRS.
   LANGLEY. BONNIE, LOIS, LOLA *and* CINDY *sit on the floor
   as close to her as they can get.*)

MRS. LANGLEY: Promise you won't laugh at me. Laugh at
   the jingle if you wish, but not at me.

JILL: Shouldn't you open the package first?

MRS. LANGLEY (*Shakes her head*): When I entered the
   contest I specified the third prize and that was a hat
   from Paris.

JILL *and* BONNIE (*Aghast but thrilled*): From Paris!

CINDY: I still like the one we made.

MRS. LANGLEY (*Taps her blue hat*): Good for you, Cindy.
   This is the work of all of you—I have faith in it. And
   it is the most becoming hat I've ever had.

JILL: Oh, Mother, we'll try not to be jealous if it turns
   out that you like the hat you won better than ours.

LOIS: How about the poetry?

BONNIE: You should have told us you were a poet.

MRS. LANGLEY: You won't call me a poet when you hear it, but it had to be something silly about a hat. (*Clears her throat, recites*)
Can it be the birds I hear
When you walk down the street?
Or flowers of the early spring
  I smell as you pass by?
No! 'tis just that hat
  Above your brow
Suggests these things to me
  I vow!
(*They all laugh and scramble together to help* MRS. LANGLEY *open the package. She pulls out a flat odd-shaped piece of millinery and turns it from side to side*) I'll appreciate having you masterminds tell me just what this is supposed to be.

BONNIE: Mother, you know very well it's a hat.

JILL (*Trying to be very brave*): Of course it's a hat.

BONNIE: It has to be. That's what the prize was.

MRS. LANGLEY (*Holding it out and making a face at it*): Yes, the third prize was to be a hat from Paris.

BONNIE: And a millinery firm wouldn't give a hat for a prize that wasn't a hat.

JILL (*Takes a turn at scrutinizing it*): I'll have to admit I can't tell front from back.

CINDY (*Snatches it and flattens it down on her head*): Now what does it look like above my brow?

MRS. LANGLEY: Not a hat, I *vow*! (*They all laugh.*)

JILL: Mother, you should give it a chance. Try it on.

MRS. LANGLEY: I wouldn't be seen under it. (*Jumps up suddenly*) I've got the hat I like right on my head, and there it's going to stay! Bonnie, when do we eat? (*Curtain*)

THE END

We, the People

by Myriam Toles

Characters

NARRATOR

DOLLY CARRELL
ANN SAFFORD
EMMA REED
FAITH GOODWIN } *in Philadelphia*

NELS, *a lumberman*
PIERRE, *a lumberman* } *in a forest*

MARTIN, *a storekeeper*
JOHN, *a cooper* } *in a New England village*

NATHAN, *a farmer*
DANIEL, *a tanner* } *in a New Jersey town*

ELLEN HARDWICK
NANCY FORTIN } *on a Southern plantation*

MR. MASON,
  from Virginia
MR. ELLSWORTH,
  from Connecticut } *at the Convention*
MR. DAYTON,
  from New Jersey

TOWN CRIER
HENRY GOOD,
  a messenger
JOHN PATRICK,
  a messenger } *in a Massachusetts town*
TOWNSPEOPLE
THREE CITIZENS

SETTING: *There is a lectern on one side downstage, behind which the Narrator reads from a large book. The various scenes may take place at different parts of the stage.*

AT RISE: NARRATOR *enters and goes to lectern. Spotlight shines on him. A few strains of "Yankee Doodle" are heard offstage.* NARRATOR *stands quietly for a moment before speaking.*

NARRATOR: Today, we have come together to recall, as Americans, some of our nation's beginnings, and to share with each other a bright vision of our country's future.

Look back with me and see us as we first came, three thousand miles across the sea, to this rich and open land. We came with fire in our eyes and hope in our hearts for a new life in which a man could think and worship and develop as he wished. We were the common men, but men with a destiny—Englishmen, Scots, Swedes, Germans, Irish and French. We came and built new homes, new villages, new cities. We fought and won a war to free us from the Old World.

Look again. It is now September in the year 1787. In the city of Philadelphia, in Convention Hall, the chosen delegates of this new nation are making the laws that will keep us free forever. Throughout the land, anxious men and women wait to hear the results of the Convention. From the sawmills and streams of our forests, from the billowing whitecaps of our seas, from the rich black earth of our farms, from town and city factories, traders, trappers, farmers, farm wives and women of wealth, statesmen and merchants gather eagerly in little groups, waiting for messengers from Philadelphia.

Let us take a closer view of some of these gatherings. Let us look first at a group in Philadelphia itself. Dolly Carrell is hostess to a sewing circle of wealthy merchants' wives, Ann Safford, Emma Reed and Faith Goodwin. Their fingers fly as they sew and visit. Let us open the door and listen, as they discuss this great Convention and the talk that's going round. (*Spot on* DOLLY CARRELL *and* ANN SAFFORD, *who enter from opposite side.* DOLLY *places a chair for* ANN.)

DOLLY: I'm so glad you could come today, Ann. We've such exciting things to talk over.

ANN: Indeed we have. (*She sits down.*) I'm simply dying to hear what everyone has to say. Emma and Faith should be along any minute. I saw their carriage stopping. (*Opens sewing bag*)

DOLLY: Here they are now. (*Goes upstage center to greet them*) Come in, come in. Ann is here already. (EMMA *and* FAITH *enter.*)

EMMA: That's good. I've brought you that dress pattern, Ann. I almost forgot it in all this excitement. (*Gives pattern to* ANN *and sits down to knit.*)

ANN: Oh, thank you, Emma. Look, Faith, it's almost the same as the one you lost.

FAITH (*Taking pattern*): Yes, it is. I'll borrow it from you later.

ANN: See, I can use this blue cashmere. It will make a darling dress for my little Susan. (*Takes blue cloth from bag*)

DOLLY: Just the thing. (*Moves her chair closer*) Now if you are all comfortable, let's settle down and talk as we work. I want you to tell me everything you have heard about the Convention. I understand that the meetings are supposed to be a complete secret.

EMMA: Oh, Dolly, everyone knows that the members are arguing about changing the old laws of our Confederation.

DOLLY: Of course, Emma, but no one can find out what is actually being said at the Convention.

FAITH: I'll be surprised if fifty-five men can keep the whole thing secret. My husband says that Mr. Franklin is the one they have to watch.

ANN: My dear Faith, that isn't surprising. He is eighty-two years old, the oldest member there. He just can't keep from talking outside the meeting.

EMMA: He does have such queer ideas! He feels that the common people should know what is being done at the Convention.

ANN: He even believes in having schools where the common people can be educated!

FAITH: Fancy that! I can see him now, talking about it and hobbling along with that old crabtree stick.

EMMA: Don't forget the spectacles on his nose, or that plain brown suit! And he *never* wears a wig!

ANN: We may laugh at him, but just the same, we know that Mr. Franklin is a wonderful old man. When he was our ambassador to France, he made friends for us everywhere. He will be a peacemaker at the Convention, and that's so important.

DOLLY: That is true, Ann. All the others are young men, and so fiery! Of course, many are very brilliant, too, but they need Mr. Franklin's older, wiser head.

FAITH: And Mr. Washington's, too. He also is older than most of the delegates. I believe he is fifty-five.

DOLLY: How fortunate we are to have Mr. Washington at the head of the Convention!

EMMA: He wrote my husband last April that we must be a united nation under one strong government, or else we would become thirteen little nations quarreling with each other.

ANN (*Goes to look over* EMMA's *shoulder*): Who taught you to knit so fast?

EMMA: My mother. When the soldiers were at Valley

Forge, Mother worked very hard to knit the warm things they needed.

FAITH: What a great man Mr. Washington is! He was first in war, and now he is first in making a peaceful settlement of all our problems.

ANN: I wonder how all those men with so many different ideas about government can possibly reach a peaceful agreement.

DOLLY: We shall soon know. They've been meeting for fifteen weeks already, and I hear they expect to end the Convention next week.

EMMA: What excitement there will be when the results are made public. I can hardly wait.

FAITH: Nor can I. Dear me, it's almost time for supper. I must be going. (*Puts away her work and stands*)

ANN: I must run along, too. Let us meet together after the news is out.

FAITH: Why not come to my house the day the Convention is over? Our husbands can tell us all about it. And I'll send Timothy, my carriage boy, with a note to each of you so you can all come together.

ANN: Thank you, Faith. I'd love to come.

DOLLY: And I, too.

EMMA: We'll all be there. And now, goodbye, Dolly. It has been a lovely afternoon. Goodbye, all! (*Exits*)

FAITH: Wait for me, Emma. (*She hurries out, followed by* ANN, *and calls back.*) Goodbye, Dolly. I'll see you next week.

DOLLY: Goodbye, goodbye. (*Spot shifts back to* NARRATOR *as* DOLLY *exits.*)

NARRATOR: Word of the Convention has traveled far, even to the deep forests where strong men cut and saw the lumber for our growing towns, and float it down the rushing rivers. Let us listen now to Nels and Pierre, two lumbermen, who rest from their work in a little clearing. In this quiet spot, they are confiding their fears and hopes. (*Spot off* NARRATOR; *shifts to* NELS, *who enters, idly holding a small piece of a branch.* PIERRE *follows, holding an axe over his shoulder.*)

NELS: We can stop a bit now, Pierre. We have enough lumber to load that last raft.

PIERRE: Fine, sound boards, too, and more where these came from. (*Sits on ground and examines blade of axe*)

NELS: There's no end to the trees. And the pines are so sweet and fresh smelling, too. Ah, Pierre, this is a wonderful new country! (*He stretches, then sits and whittles.*) Good clean work for all! A man can make a new life here. It's not like the old country.

PIERRE: I'm not so sure of that, Nels. What chance have the common people when our laws are almost the same as when we were under the King? The common man is still at the bottom of the ladder.

NELS: Wait a bit, Pierre! You Frenchmen get excited too soon. The Convention at Philadelphia is even now changing the laws of the Confederacy to make them more equal and just.

PIERRE: Bah! Just a lot of rich men—merchants, shipowners, and planters meeting to patch up a set of old laws that have given justice to none but the wealthy people.

NELS: They are men of learning, Pierre. They will think straight. Besides, they well know it was the common folk who fought and bled for liberty. They dare not keep it from us now.

PIERRE: I say that changes alone won't do. This government is like a house built with rotten timbers—the rotten timbers of unjust laws. We need to throw out the old laws entirely and make a whole new set.

NELS: There's sense to that, Pierre. That's an idea I never thought of. Who knows? Perhaps that idea will come to the gentlemen of the Convention. I know that some of them want changes that give more rights to the common man. There is talk that they may even let us elect a President.

PIERRE: And why not? Free men are worth more to a country than money or land. Unless these fine gentlemen give us our rights and make a strong government that is fair to all the people, we will refuse to obey the laws.

NELS: I have faith in the Convention. But enough of this. (*He throws branch away.*) Come, let's get on with our work, Pierre, or we'll have no profits ourselves, and then what good will a new government do us?

PIERRE (*Stands up*): We'll load the raft now. I'll ride it down to the settlement. I may stay there a while and hear the talk that's going round.

NELS (*Slowly and thoughtfully*): Well, now, Pierre, that's not a bad idea. I think I'd like to get the news firsthand. I'll help pole the raft, too. Somehow I feel this Convention is a big thing. It may better the lives of all us common folk, maybe of the whole world—who knows?

PIERRE: I hope you are right, but I'll have to see for myself. We'll go together. Two of us will get the raft there sooner. Come, friend. Let's start while it is light. (*They exit. Spot shifts back to* NARRATOR.)

NARRATOR: In 1787, tradesmen traveled far to do business. They found that each state used different money. It made one's head spin to try to buy and sell. Let us see what Martin, a storekeeper, and John, a cooper, think about it, as they meet in a village street in New England. (MARTIN *and* JOHN *enter from opposite sides of the stage. Spot shifts to them as they meet in the center and shake hands.*)

MARTIN: Good morning, John. Welcome home!

JOHN: Ah, Martin, it's good to see you, neighbor. It's good to be back here in this peaceful spot.

MARTIN: So, you didn't like the city?

JOHN: Truly I did not! I sold my casks and barrels for a fair price, but I tell you, Martin, I had a sore time getting any real money. Rhode Island prints its own money, and it is worthless. They do the same in New Hampshire. If a man trades in those states, he gets a handful of paper money that no one wants. Why, some sell their paper dollars for ten and fifteen cents in real coin!

MARTIN: I have had a few customers in my store here who tried to buy my goods with that cheap, worthless paper, but I refused to sell to them.

JOHN: Better be careful, Martin! They now have a law that a man has to accept the printed money, or he can be clapped into jail.

MARTIN: Bah! I'll do as many others have done. I'll close my store and refuse to trade. But tell me, how did you get around the law? You say that you were paid in real money.

JOHN: I was lucky. The merchants needed my barrels. I pretended that I was not eager to sell, and only agreed when I saw coins, real money, offered to me. (*He shows handful of coins.*)

MARTIN: Good, John, good! I'm only an ordinary man with little learning, but I think that trade would grow if we had one kind of money for all the states. We would prosper if we worked together as we did when we fought the British.

JOHN: Aye, Martin, you're right! The states need such laws to hold them together, just as my barrels need hoops to hold them together.

MARTIN: Maybe this Convention will make a change, and business will be better.

JOHN: That's what I am hoping. Well, Martin, it's been good to talk with you.

MARTIN: Come in again soon, John. We may hear news any day now from Philadelphia.

JOHN: The only news I want to hear is that money and trade laws are the same for all the states, big or small. Unless I hear *that,* I'll take to the woods and live on bear meat. (*He laughs.*) Goodbye, Martin.

MARTIN (*Laughing*): I may join you! Goodbye, John. (*They exit. Spot shifts back to* NARRATOR.)

NARRATOR: Now let's go to a small town in New Jersey, on a clear and sunny September day. Daniel, a tanner, and Nathan, a farmer, stand outside the tannery and talk of the unjust laws that keep a man from earning money. (DANIEL *enters during speech. Spot shifts to* DANIEL *holding up a hide to inspect it, as* NATHAN *enters.*)

NATHAN: Hello there, Daniel.

DANIEL: Hello. I hear that you want to work in my tannery, Nathan.

NATHAN: That I do, Daniel. Times are hard, and money is very scarce.

DANIEL: I'll be pleased to have another helper. Two wagon-loads of fresh hides came in yesterday, and I'll need help to make them into good shoe leather.

NATHAN: I'll be glad to work for you, Daniel, even though the wages are small.

DANIEL: If I can sell the leather for real money, I'll pay you fairly. But tell me, Nathan, how is it that you are asking for work? Why are you not on your farm?

NATHAN: Because of the shameful trade laws of New York. I was doing well with my little farm, even though taxes are so heavy. Each week I took a wagonload of chickens and vegetables to the city people of New York. They liked our fowls and green things and paid me well. Then New York passed a law that charged duty on everything that came from another state.

DANIEL: Think of that! Did you have to pay this tax, just to sell in New York?

NATHAN: Yes, and when I had paid the duty, I was forced to put a price on my fowl that was so high that no one would buy them. And I had to throw my vegetables in the river. My trade is gone, and I must make a living some other way.

DANIEL: I have heard that New York has no love for New Jersey, but it should not deal with us as though we were a foreign country, like France or Spain.

NATHAN: It is indeed a foolish business. The New York people cannot have my good food, and I cannot have their payment. If the thirteen states are to be one country, it is foolish and wrong to make laws that keep people from trading with each other.

DANIEL: Let's hope the gentlemen of the Convention propose one law for all the states. Then trade can go on. Until then, Nathan, why not come work for me in my shop? I'll pay in coin.

NATHAN: You're a good friend, Daniel. (*Claps him on shoulder*) It's a bargain. Let me start work now.

DANIEL: Good! I've a barrel with dry hides out back. You can fill it with water. Come, I'll show you. (*Spot back on* NARRATOR *as* DANIEL *and* NATHAN *exit.*)

NARRATOR: Let us go now to the deep South, to a great plantation, rich in slaves and land, but poor in money. Here, in a fine home, Ellen Hardwick and Nancy Fortin, wives of planters, are having tea and discussing the problems of unequal trade laws and slavery. (ELLEN *and* NANCY *enter during speech. Spotlight shifts to them, sitting and drinking tea.*)

NANCY: Oh, Ellen, I've had such wonderful news!

ELLEN: You have? What is it, Nancy?

NANCY: The *Fair Wind* came to Charleston Port on Tuesday, loaded with goods, and among the boxes was one for me. There were lengths of scarlet cloth and twelve yards of gold lace.

ELLEN: From London? Real gold lace?

NANCY: Yes. I never expected it. The agent who sells my husband's rice crop in London is so difficult, my dear.

ELLEN: Yes, I can believe he is. The agent who sells my husband's tobacco crop never fills all my orders either. He always says that the crop didn't pay well. With the last cargo my husband sent to England, I ordered all the things that we just can't get here—pins and needles and a clock and some plates and cooking pots. He sent me nothing but two iron pots!

NANCY (*Pours more tea*): I sometimes wonder, Ellen, if these men are honest. They pay so little for our crops and charge so much for the things they send us.

ELLEN: I wonder, too. It seems our crops are never enough to give us any profit.

NANCY: My husband says that unless we bring in more slaves, we can't expect to have any real profit from our plantation for another twenty years.

ELLEN: Twenty years! Imagine!

NANCY: William says the northern states think the slave trade should stop entirely. He is afraid that the Convention will vote to put an end to it.

ELLEN: But what would South Carolina do then?

NANCY: William is worried over the outcome. You know, Ellen, how he usually looks on the bright side of things, but now he is afraid the northern states will make it impossible for the South to live.

ELLEN: Those members from the North simply don't know the South. I wish women could go to the Convention. We could tell them a thing or two!

NANCY: We have no say in the government. All we can do is to encourage our husbands. (*Puts cup down, rises*) We'll just have to wait and hope. But I must run now. My children will wonder where I am.

ELLEN: Goodbye, Nancy, and do let me hear what goes on. I'll be waiting.

NANCY: Goodbye, dear. (NANCY *and* ELLEN *exit. Spot shifts back to* NARRATOR.)

NARRATOR: Let us hear what some of the delegates at the Convention are saying. As Mr. Mason from the great State of Virginia pauses outside the hall during a recess to talk with Mr. Ellsworth from Connecticut, Mr. Dayton from New Jersey rushes up. (*Spot on* ELLSWORTH *and* MASON, *who have entered during speech.*)

ELLSWORTH: Today's session was very encouraging, wasn't it?

MASON: At last we are rid of the Articles of Confederation!

ELLSWORTH: Now we can write a new set of laws that will make our government stronger than that of any of the individual states.

MASON: A good thing, too, if we hope to keep our country united!

ELLSWORTH: The arguments were very bitter today, but I fear tomorrow's session will be even worse. Here comes Mr. Dayton of New Jersey. He looks ready for an argument already. (MR. DAYTON *enters, a sheaf of papers in his hand, a scowl on his face.*)

DAYTON: Ah, gentlemen! I am glad I caught you before you departed. I want to talk to you. The first big question to come up tomorrow is whether Congress is to be made up of one body or two.

MASON: Any sensible man knows that one lawmaking body is enough.

DAYTON: Mr. Mason, you are wrong! We need two houses. Each will then act as a check upon the other.

ELLSWORTH: Many people believe that such a plan will give all the people more say in our new government.

MASON: That's nonsense, Mr. Ellsworth. I am prepared to debate the question tomorrow.

ELLSWORTH: You may possibly win on this issue, Mr. Mason, but you will not get far with the second question, about how many representatives in Congress each state shall have. The small states are determined to have as many as the large states.

MASON: More nonsense! The largest and most wealthy states should have the most representatives. Our Virginia plan will settle this matter.

DAYTON: That is not fair to the small states! They would have little voice in the new government. I intend to present the New Jersey plan for two houses of Congress and equal representation for all states. I shall fight for it, and so will all the common people.

MASON: Mr. Dayton, the small business people deserve no voice in this. Why, three-fourths of them haven't even paid their taxes.

DAYTON: That's because you rich men made unfair laws in the Articles of Confederation. (*Speaking loudly and gesturing vigorously*) Now, at last, we'll make a constitution that will give the same opportunities to the rich and poor alike.

MASON: The poor have no judgment. Virginia will fight against this outrage.

ELLSWORTH: Gentlemen, gentlemen! Let us not quarrel. Let us debate the question at the meeting. I feel sure we can come to a compromise.

DAYTON: There *is* no compromise possible between right and wrong.

ELLSWORTH: We shall see. Now it is getting late, and we must find our way through these dark streets before the daylight is gone. Tomorrow I shall present a plan which may help us to reach an agreement. Good night, gentlemen. (*Turns and starts to exit*)

DAYTON (*Still angry*): It will be useless, Mr. Ellsworth.

The small states will never compromise! (*He stalks out.*)

MASON: Nor will the large states. Spare your efforts, Mr. Ellsworth. I bid you good evening. (*He, too, stalks out. ELLSWORTH gazes after them, shakes his head and exits. Spotlight shifts back to NARRATOR.*)

NARRATOR: It is early evening in a small town in Massachusetts. Nels and Pierre have tied their raft safely and wander about in search of news. As they come to the square, they hear the Town Crier and see two messengers, Henry Good and John Patrick, arrive from Philadelphia. Behind them three citizens shout their opinions, in loud excited voices. Other townsmen follow with anxious faces and anxious thoughts. Little do they know that this news will echo down the ages, that this set of laws will be ratified by the people of state after state. Little do they know that this Constitution will be the pattern and the dream for freedom-loving people of all the world.

TOWN CRIER (*Offstage, ringing bell and calling*): Hear ye! Hear ye! Town Meeting tonight. Come one, come all. (*Spot on TOWN CRIER as he enters, crosses stage, and exits, continuing to call.*) Town Meeting tonight in the square. Hear ye! Hear ye! (*Spot on NELS who runs in, calling loudly*)

NELS: Pierre, Picrre! Why, the fellow's lost. Pierre, Pierre!

PIERRE (*Offstage*): Here I am. (*Walks in tiredly*) I've been lost for an hour.

NELS: Cheer up, my friend. After tonight, we can go back to the woods we know.

PIERRE: I'll not go back until we've been promised fair laws.

NELS: I feel in my bones the news will be good. Here come the townspeople. (HENRY GOOD, JOHN PATRICK, THREE CITIZENS, *and other* TOWNSPEOPLE *enter.*)

1st Citizen: Congress has forgotten we are men, not slaves.

2nd Citizen: We fought seven years at Valley Forge, and for what?

3rd Citizen: We want justice, not fine words.

Henry Good: Wait, wait until you hear before you go wild. (*Claps his hands for attention*) Friends and neighbors, the work of the Convention is ended. Mr. Patrick will explain what has been done.

Patrick (*Steps forward*): My friends, after sixteen weeks of secret meetings our delegates agreed it was better to have half a loaf than none. Each side gave up something. We now have a new Constitution. It is not perfect, but its laws are the same for big and little states, for rich and poor alike.

Townspeople (*Shouting and waving*): Hurrah! Hurrah!

1st Citizen: Mr. Patrick, tell us—is it true the common people can elect the President?

Patrick: It is true.

Townspeople (*Shouting*): Hurrah! Hurrah!

Patrick: Not only that, but we are to have two bodies of lawmakers so that neither one can exceed its rights. In the Senate every state will have the same number of members. In the House of Representatives, the number of members from each state will depend on population.

2nd Citizen: Wait, Mr. Patrick. Won't that give the states with large numbers of slaves too much power?

Patrick: No, the delegates found a way around that problem. Every five slaves are to be counted as only three.

3rd Citizen: I, for one, think the Convention should have abolished slavery and made free men of all.

Patrick: That will cure itself in time. The new law forbids bringing any more slaves into the country after the year 1808.

1st Citizen: Mr. Patrick, I can see that these laws are good

for the country as a whole, but what about the laws that
help us make a living? What about our trade and money?

TOWNSPEOPLE (*Ad lib*): Yes, what about them? (*Etc.*)

PATRICK: It seems to me that things will be better in every
way. The new government will make trade the same for
every state. It will place the same tax on all and will
coin only one kind of money.

NELS (*Shouting*): You see, Pierre, I was right. The new
laws are just.

PIERRE (*Throwing his hat in the air and shouting*): Liberty! Justice!

TOWNSPEOPLE: Hurrah! Liberty! Justice!

HENRY GOOD: Wait, wait. Let me speak. I believe that in
giving equal rights to all men, we will become a great
nation, and will give hope to men in other lands. I believe this Constitution will throw a beam of light over
the whole world.

TOWNSPEOPLE: Hurrah! Hurrah! Hear! Hear!

PATRICK: And now, fellow citizens, we must go to our
homes and think all this over with great care. For the
states must now vote on whether or not to accept this
Constitution. I, for one, will vote to accept. The most
important part of this new Constitution lies in its beginning words. These are proud, proud words. Their
meaning will go deep into your hearts as they have into
mine. (*Takes out copy of Constitution*) Let me read:
"We, the people of the United States—" Think of this
my friends. We, the people—all of us. "We, the people
of the United States, in order to form a more perfect
Union, establish justice, insure domestic tranquillity,
provide for the common defense, promote the general
welfare, and secure the blessings of liberty to ourselves
and our posterity, do ordain and establish this Constitution for the United States of America." (TOWNSPEOPLE

shout and clap as the opening bars of "America" are played offstage. All join in singing the first verse, as curtains close.)

THE END

The Yankee Doodle Kitten

by Deborah Newman

Characters

JUDY
SUE
PENNY
FRITZY ⎫
MITZY ⎬ kittens
BITSY ⎭
SAMUEL, *a cat*
MAJOR
ELLEN
ELLEN'S MOTHER
JANE
JANE'S FATHER
THREE RATS
VENDORS
CHILDREN
PARENTS
PATRIOTIC CATS

TIME: *Just before the parade.*

SETTING: *A street near the parade grounds. At center is a booth containing flags, candy, boxes of peanuts and popcorn, and balloons.*

AT RISE: VENDORS, *carrying flags, candy and balloons, are*

walking about, selling their wares to CHILDREN *and* PARENTS.

1ST VENDOR (*Carrying flags*): Flags! Flags! Get your flags here before the parade. (*He sells a flag to a girl.*)

2ND VENDOR (*Carrying balloons*): Balloons! What color balloons do you like? How about a red one for you, little girl? (*He sells a balloon to another girl.*)

3RD VENDOR (*Carrying a basket filled with boxes of popcorn and peanuts*): Peanuts, popcorn—have something to eat while you watch the parade. (*He sells boxes of popcorn to some boys.*)

1ST VENDOR: Flags! Have a flag to wave when the parade goes by. Flags! (*The* VENDORS *continue to call their wares and make sales as* JUDY, SUE *and* PENNY *enter, followed by the 3 kittens,* FRITZY, MITZY, *and* BITSY. FRITZY *wears a blue bow,* MITZY, *a pink bow, and* BITSY, *the smallest kitten, a white bow.* JUDY *carries a sign: "Free—Kittens."*)

JUDY (*To* 1ST VENDOR, *who is standing near the booth*): Good morning, sir.

1ST VENDOR: Good morning, girls. Are you bringing your kittens to the parade?

SUE: Well, no—not exactly. We have too many kittens at home right now, and Mother says we have to give these three away.

PENNY: We thought there might be some people at the parade who would want kittens.

JUDY: May we stand near your booth with the kittens?

1ST VENDOR: Go right ahead. (*The girls put up the sign and then stand with the kittens near the booth. The* VENDORS *call their wares.*) Flags for the parade! Flags for the parade!

2ND VENDOR: Balloons! Balloons! Get your balloons right here.

3RD VENDOR: Peanuts! Popcorn!

JUDY (*Suddenly calling out in a loud voice*): Kittens! Free kittens!

SUE (*Calling*): Kittens! Free kittens for pets. (ELLEN *and her* MOTHER *enter.*)

PENNY (*Calling*): Kittens! Cute little kittens. (ELLEN *runs over to the kittens and then calls to* MOTHER.)

ELLEN: Mother! Come see the wonderful kittens. (MOTHER *comes to her.*)

JUDY: We're giving the kittens away. Would you like one?

ELLEN: May I have a kitten, Mother?

MOTHER: Well, I did say you could have one for your birthday.

ELLEN: My birthday's only three months away. Oh, please say yes, Mother.

MOTHER: All right, dear. Pick out your kitten.

ELLEN: Oh, goody! (*Taking* FRITZY) I'll take this one. He's the biggest. (FRITZY *bows.*)

SUE: We call that one Fritzy. He's very strong.

ELLEN: Come on, Fritzy. You're my kitten now. (FRITZY *bows, and meows to* MITZY *and* BITSY.) Thank you for the kitten. (FRITZY *marches off with* ELLEN *and* MOTHER.)

1ST VENDOR (*Calling*): Flags! Have a flag to wave at the parade. (JANE *and her* FATHER *enter.*)

PENNY: Kittens! Free kittens! Have a kitten for a pet.

JUDY: Free kittens! Free kittens! (JANE *comes over to the kittens, pulling her* FATHER *along with her.*)

SUE (*To* JANE): Would you like a kitten?

JANE: Let's take one of these kittens, Dad.

FATHER: Now, Jane, we already have a dog.

JANE: But Mom wants a kitten. I know she does. (*Points to* MITZY) Mom would love that kitten with the pink bow. Oh, please, let's bring home a kitten.

FATHER: Well, all right—if you promise to help take care of the kitten.

JANE: I promise. (*She takes* MITZY.) I want this kitten.

JUDY: That's Mitzy. She's a very graceful cat. (MITZY *meows and twirls around in a dance step.*)

JANE: Come on, Mitzy. You'll have a new home now. (*To girls*) Thank you for the kitten. (MITZY *meows to* BITSY *and then follows* JANE *and her* FATHER *off.* BITSY *meows sadly and waves.*)

SUE (*Patting* BITSY): Poor Bitsy. You're the only one left. (BITSY *meows sadly.*)

1ST VENDOR (*Coming to booth and arranging flags on booth*): Well, girls, I see two of the kittens have new homes already.

PENNY: Yes. Only Bitsy is left. Would you like a kitten? (BITSY *goes to* VENDOR, *meows at him pleadingly.*)

1ST VENDOR: Oh, no, thank you. I'm afraid I don't need a kitten. (BITSY *hangs head. The sound of whistles and drums comes from offstage.* BITSY *runs and hides behind the booth. The whistles and drums stop.*)

JUDY: The parade! It's going to start.

SUE: Let's go!

PENNY (*Looking around*): Where's Bitsy?

JUDY (*Calling*): Bitsy! Where are you? Oh, dear! I don't see Bitsy anywhere.

SUE (*Pointing*): I think I see Bitsy over there, near the soldiers.

PENNY: Let's go catch her. (*They run off. Parade music begins offstage. All* VENDORS, CHILDREN *and* PARENTS *go off.* BITSY *peers out from behind booth, then comes slowly out and sits down in front of the booth, crying and meowing sadly. The music gradually becomes softer as* SAMUEL *enters, strutting proudly in his Uncle Sam costume. The music stops, and* SAMUEL *marches around*

*the stage, singing "Yankee Doodle." He stops suddenly
when he sees* Bitsy.)

SAMUEL: Powder my whiskers and curl my tail! What's a
cat doing crying when there's a parade going on up
ahead? Come on, my friend. Let's go to the parade.

BITSY: Leave me alone. I don't want to go to the parade!

SAMUEL: Well, then, my friend, why don't you go home?

BITSY: I can't go home. I don't have any home. The girls
were trying to give me away, but no one wants me.

SAMUEL: Oh, ho, so that's the way the fur flies, is it?
Well, my friend, just let me tell you that you can't sit
around and cry on today of all days. Today's the day
we honor our American heroes. (*He takes a flag from
the booth.*) Now, my friend, you may think that American heroes are all men—soldiers, sailors, and marines.
Hmph! That's all a kitten knows. Why, I tell you, we
cats are also heroes of America. (*Gives flag to* BITSY)
Now, you hold this, and I'll tell you about the cats
who were American heroes, too. (*The music of "Yankee
Doodle" is heard, and a parade of* PATRIOTIC CATS
*enters. One is dressed as George Washington, one wears
the Lincoln shawl and black top hat, one wears a Daniel
Boone cap and carries a gun, one wears a nurse's uniform
with a Red Cross insignia, and several others are dressed
in red, white and blue costumes. They line up at the
center of the stage, and sing to the tune of "Yankee
Doodle."* CATS *in special costumes sing the individual
verses, and then all march in a circle and sing the
chorus.*)

WASHINGTON CAT:

When Gen'ral George at Valley Forge
Found mice who ate the flour,
The cats got rid of all the mice:
It was their finest hour.
    (*Chorus*)

Yankee Doodle cats are we,
Yankee Doodle dandy.
When a hero needs some help
We cats have come in handy.

DANIEL BOONE CAT:
Daniel Boone found out quite soon
That he was very lucky.
His cat could help him hunt and fish,
And guide him to Kentucky.
(*Chorus*)

LINCOLN CAT:
When times were bad and Lincoln sad,
We took his shawl and top hat,
And cheered him up by playing tricks—
He never made us stop that.
(*Chorus*)

RED CROSS CAT:
Clara Barton hated mice.
We never let one past her,
So she could lead our great Red Cross
That aids us in disaster.
(*Chorus*)
(*When the song is over, the* CATS *march off, repeating the chorus.*)

BITSY (*To* SAMUEL): I never knew all that! Are cats really heroes of America?

SAMUEL: That we are, my friend. We're Yankee Doodle cats. We're first-class, true, red-white-and-blue heroes. Now, come along to the parade with me.

BITSY (*Shaking her head*): No. I think I'd better stay here where the girls can find me. But I'm glad you told me about the Yankee Doodle cats. It makes me feel brave —and very important.

SAMUEL: Farewell, my friend. Remember what I've told you. (SAMUEL *exits.* BITSY *goes to booth to return flag as three tough-looking* RATS *enter, dressed in black and wearing black masks.*)

1ST RAT: This is the place. I told you there wouldn't be anyone around.

2ND RAT (*Pointing to booth*): Say, look at that! Popcorn and peanuts! A real feast!

3RD RAT: Wow! Are we in luck. All the popcorn we can eat. (*The* RATS *open boxes of popcorn and peanuts and eat.* BITSY *clenches her fists angrily and stands at one side of the booth so that the* RATS *don't see her.*)

1ST RAT: Say, just look at all those flags.

2ND RAT: I wonder what a flag tastes like.

3RD RAT: Aw, flags are no good to eat.

1ST RAT: I'm not so sure. (*He takes a flag and almost lets it touch the ground.*) Let's find out how a flag tastes.

BITSY (*Running to* 1ST RAT): Go away! Don't you dare touch the American flag.

2ND RAT (*Sneering*): Well, well. Look who's in charge of the flag. A kitten!

BITSY: Put that flag back.

3RD RAT (*Pushing* BITSY *aside*): Get out of the way, kitten, if you know what's good for you.

BITSY: I won't get out of the way. Now, put back that American flag.

1ST RAT: Aw, forget about her. She's only a kitten.

BITSY: I'll show you who's only a kitten. (*She meows and holds out her claws.* RATS *scream as she chases them around the stage, hitting them.* 1ST VENDOR *and the* MAJOR *enter, followed by* SAMUEL.)

MAJOR: Here now! We can't have this noise during the ceremony. Stop it! (BITSY *snatches the flag from the* 1ST RAT *as the* RATS *run out.*)

1ST VENDOR: Why, it's the kitten. She scared the rats away from the booth and saved the flag.

MAJOR: So she saved the American flag, did she? (BITSY

nods and purrs.) That makes her a real Yankee Doodle kitten. (JUDY, SUE *and* PENNY *enter.*)

JUDY: Bitsy! There you are! We've been looking for you.

MAJOR: Is this your kitten, girls?

SUE: Yes, sir. That's Bitsy. She was lost.

MAJOR: You should be very proud of Bitsy, girls. She just did a real patriotic deed. She saved that flag from some rats.

PENNY: Good for you, Bitsy!

MAJOR: Yes, indeed, Bitsy's a fine kitten. I'd like to have a kitten like that myself.

GIRLS (*Delighted*): You *would?*

JUDY: Please take her, sir. She's yours. We brought her to the parade to try to find a new home for her. (SAMUEL *enters.*)

MAJOR: All right, Bitsy. You're my kitten now. Come up on the reviewing stand with me.

SUE: Hooray for Bitsy!

PENNY: Hooray for the Yankee Doodle kitten! (BITSY *marches around the stage and goes to* SAMUEL. SAMUEL *winks and bows.* BITSY *salutes him.*)

MAJOR: Come on, everyone. Let's get back to the parade. (*All go off except* SAMUEL, *who comes forward and bows to the audience as the curtains close.*)

THE END

America Is a Song

by Paul T. Nolan

Characters

UNCLE BRUNO STRAUSS, *a German cabinetmaker*
ALBRECHT, *his young nephew*
SAM WILSON, *the wagon master*
MAJOR HART, *the cavalry officer*
THE PIONEERS
BRITISH SOLDIERS
AMERICAN COLONIAL SOLDIERS
DAN EMMETT
SOUTHERN SOLDIERS
MRS. JULIA WARD HOWE
MRS. FREDERICKS
NORTHERN SOLDIERS
JOE SWEENEY ⎫
LONG JIM ⎪
MOLLY, *his wife* ⎬ *pioneers*
REVEREND TUCKER ⎭
MOUNTAIN BEN ⎫
COMANCHE CHARLIE ⎬ *the three scouts*
LONESOME ⎭
MALE AND FEMALE EXTRAS, *for the families of Joe Sweeney,*
   Long Jim, and Reverend Tucker.

623

TIME: *Evening. Sometime after the end of the Civil War.*

SETTING: *A wagon train camp, east of the Rocky Mountains.*

AT RISE: PIONEERS *are sitting around the campfire, upstage left, singing "The Old Chisholm Trail."* UNCLE BRUNO, ALBRECHT, SAM WILSON, *and* MAJOR HART *stand near wagon upstage right, and work on wagon wheels or reins.*

MAJOR HART (*As singing stops*): We'll take you as far as the Fort with us, Mr. Strauss.

UNCLE BRUNO: Thank you, Major. We should be able to find a wagon train going back East from the Fort.

MAJOR HART: There're a lot of folks who go back. It's easier going back.

SAM WILSON: For some—and for some it's harder. There's nothing wrong with the East, but a man ought to go where he has a mind to. We'll be needing furniture makers out in Oregon.

UNCLE BRUNO: If you ever get to Oregon. Oh, if it were just me, I'd go on. I'm old, and I would like to see the western edge of this great new country before I die. But the boy can wait. Soon there will be railroads . . .

SAM WILSON: And there won't be a new country any more . . . But you do what you think is best, Mr. Strauss. I know this has been a hard trip for you—losing the boy's folks that way.

ALBRECHT: If you want to go on, Uncle Bruno, I am not afraid.

UNCLE BRUNO: I know you're not, Albrecht, but sometimes courage is not enough. We need common sense, eh?

MAJOR HART: You think about it, Mr. Strauss. If you want to go back, my men will give you safe escort to the Fort. Until tomorrow morning, then.

UNCLE BRUNO: Thank you, Major Hart. We'll be ready in the morning. (MAJOR HART *exits right.*)

SAM WILSON: Maybe we'll have good word from the scouts by then.

UNCLE BRUNO: If there was a safe way, I would go. But I don't know. I don't know.

SAM WILSON: We'll just wait and see.

UNCLE BRUNO: Yes, it is foolish to try to make up my mind until the scouts return. (*Looks off right*) Isn't that one of your scouts coming?

SAM WILSON: It sure is. It's Mountain Ben, or if it isn't, then some bear has Ben's clothes on. (MOUNTAIN BEN *enters.*) Did you find anything, Ben?

BEN: Snow, and more a-coming. The passes are already filling up. Might get through on a horse, but a wagon would never make it. And we're not going to be able to stay here much longer when the snows start coming down from the mountain. We have to move.

SAM WILSON: O.K., Ben. Go get some grub. (BEN *goes over to campfire.*)

UNCLE BRUNO: What will you do, Mr. Wilson?

SAM WILSON: I don't know yet. We'll move, but I'm not sure in what direction.

UNCLE BRUNO: Maybe you could go to the Fort.

SAM WILSON: We're moving West, Mr. Strauss. I'm not sure how, but that's where we're going. (*There is silence, and then* THE PIONEERS *sing "Tenting Tonight."*)

UNCLE BRUNO: They sing well.

SAM WILSON: That's one of the lonesome songs. Both the boys in blue and the boys in gray sang that one. I guess many of them figure things haven't changed much since they sat around campfires waiting for the war to be over.

UNCLE BRUNO: I wonder why they keep going on, if they feel that way.

SAM WILSON: They keep going on because they have to,

and they sing to get all the lonesomeness out of them. It probably doesn't make good sense, but if you sing about being lonesome, after a while you don't feel so lonesome any more.

ALBRECHT: Americans do a lot of singing, don't they, Mr. Wilson?

SAM WILSON: They sure do, Albrecht, and they always have. (*Lights go out in campfire area of stage.*) Things sort of started that way when we got to be a country. My pappy told me we started the Revolution with a song. Kind of funny the way it happened, too. (*Lights go out at wagon and come up in campfire area. Several* BRITISH SOLDIERS, *who have just entered, are standing there, and some* AMERICAN COLONIAL SOLDIERS *enter.*) Back when we were still a colony of England, the colonists fought with the British against the French and the Indians. The British were mighty glad to have our help, but their soldiers just couldn't help but make fun of the Colonial irregulars, as they called us.

1ST BRITISH SOLDIER: Hey there, Yankees, are you going squirrel hunting?

1ST AMERICAN SOLDIER: Shucks, no, Redcoat. We just thought you might need some help fighting the French and Indians. They don't fight according to the books over here, you know.

1ST BRITISH SOLDIER: How King George ever expects us to win a war over here with these Yankee Doodles to worry about, I'll never know.

2ND BRITISH SOLDIER: Yankee Doodles is right. (*Starts singing the song "Yankee Doodle." Other* BRITISH SOLDIERS *join in. The lights go down on campfire area as* BRITISH SOLDIERS *exit, and come up again on wagon area.*)

SAM WILSON: And that's how Americans first heard the song, but they picked it up and they liked it. They were glad to be Yankees—doodles or not. When the British finally surrendered to the Americans at Yorktown in 1781, the same Colonial irregulars were there—only they were trained soldiers now. (*Lights out in wagon area and up in campfire area. A row of* AMERICAN SOL-DIERS *stands at attention.*)

1ST AMERICAN SOLDIER: Now, men, the war is over. The British soldiers are returning to England. We have won more than the war; we have won a nation. In a minute the British soldiers will be passing. I expect you to show what kind of soldiers you have been. Stay at attention.

2ND AMERICAN SOLDIER: Is it all right if we sing?

1ST AMERICAN SOLDIER: Sing?

2ND AMERICAN SOLDIER: Sure. The British soldiers gave us a song when we started this revolution. We want to let them know that we consider we won ourselves a song, too.

1ST AMERICAN SOLDIER: I think that would just show them how grateful we are. (*The* BRITISH SOLDIERS *start marching across the stage from left to right.*) Attention! (*The* AMERICAN SOLDIERS *come to attention.*) Company sing! (*The* AMERICAN SOLDIERS *start singing "Yankee Doodle," and they continue singing until the* BRITISH SOLDIERS *have crossed the stage and the lights go out, then* AMERI-CAN SOLDIERS *also exit. The lights come up on wagon scene.*)

SAM WILSON: That's the way it was. That's how we got "Yankee Doodle." North and South, we Americans have done about as well at capturing songs as we have in winning battles.

ALBRECHT: They captured songs in the Civil War, too?

SAM WILSON: Lots of songs were taken by both sides. If old Dan Emmett were here, he'd tell you about one.

ALBRECHT: Dan Emmett?

SAM WILSON: Yes. Old Dan was a minstrel. Born in Ohio,

I think. But he was in New York one time in winter, doing a show. And he needed a new song, but old Dan was so cold, all he could think about was how cold it was. (*Lights out, then up as* DAN *enters downstage center in a minstrel costume.*)

DAN: Jolly Dan, they call me. But I sure don't feel jolly now. It must be ten below zero, and I'm so cold I can hardly move, and I have to think of a song. What is there to sing about? I sure wish I was down south in Dixie. Yeah, I sure do. Now! That would make a song. "I wish I was in Dixie." (DAN *speaks the first lines of* "Dixie"—*haltingly, as if he were making them up. As he speaks,* SAM WILSON's *voice can be heard.*)

SAM WILSON: And that's the way *Dixie,* the song of the sunny South, was born in the cold North. The North tried to keep that song for itself, and Dan Emmett even wrote some new words, but though the South lost the war, they won a song. (SOUTHERN SOLDIERS *come onstage behind* DAN EMMETT *and sing* "Dixie." *Then lights go out, and come up on wagon scene.*) Of course, the North got its turn at song-borrowing, too. The North offered a cash prize of two hundred and fifty dollars for a good song, and within a year, twelve hundred songs were submitted. But it takes more than money to get a good song. It takes something else. A little Boston lady, Mrs. Julia Ward Howe, wanted to write a poem about the war— what it meant to those who were trying to end slavery. And she did. It was called "The Battle Hymn of the Republic," and when it was published in *The Atlantic Monthly,* she was sent a check for five dollars. (*Lights come up on* MRS. JULIA WARD HOWE *sitting in a rocker, upstage center.* MRS. FREDERICKS *enters.*)

MRS. FREDERICKS: Mrs. Howe?

MRS. HOWE: Yes, Mrs. Fredericks?

MRS. FREDERICKS: You know that poem you had published in *The Atlantic Monthly?*

MRS. HOWE: A poem? Oh, yes, the one they titled "The Battle Hymn of the Republic." I had almost forgotten it. Why do you ask?

MRS. FREDERICKS: Some of the boys are home from the war, and they are outside asking for you. They want to sing it for you. They sing your words to the song, *John Brown's Body.*

MRS. HOWE: I remember them singing that song when I was in Washington to see Mr. Lincoln. It has a fine tune.

MRS. FREDERICKS: And it has some fine words now, too. Would you let them sing them for you?

MRS. HOWE: I would be very much honored. (*The* NORTHERN SOLDIERS *come onstage, stand behind* MRS. HOWE's *chair and sing, "The Battle Hymn of the Republic."*) It is a fine song. My poem has done some service in this war. I wish very much that it may do good service in peace. (*Blackout;* MRS. HOWE, MRS. FREDERICKS *and* NORTHERN SOLDIERS *exit, then* SAM WILSON's *voice can be heard as the lights come up on the wagon scene.*)

SAM WILSON: Mrs. Howe had her wish, and America had another song. And that's the way it's been right from the beginning, Albrecht. Songs just pop out whenever they seem to be needed.

ALBRECHT: It is a fine country that can tell its history with such songs.

SAM WILSON: It's more than that, Albrecht. The songs *are* history. (*Looking off right*) Here comes a rider.

ALBRECHT: He looks like an Indian.

SAM WILSON: He is. It's Comanche Charlie. Comanche's mother was the daughter of a chief, and his father was a mountain man. So I guess he's one hundred percent

Indian and one hundred percent mountain man, too. I know he's about two hundred percent man. (*Enter* COMANCHE CHARLIE.) Can we get through, Charlie?

CHARLIE: Cold weather's coming.

SAM WILSON: I know that, Charlie, but what about the chiefs? Will they let us take the wagon train through?

CHARLIE: Cold weather coming. Game scarce. Snow high. Indians hungry. Wagon train not get through.

SAM WILSON: Not a chance?

CHARLIE: No chance. If snow keeps falling, Indians will attack here.

SAM WILSON: Well, go get some chow, Charlie. (CHARLIE *goes over to campfire.*)

UNCLE BRUNO: What do we do now, Mr. Wilson? We can't go over the mountains, and we can't go around them. If we stay here, the snows and the Indians will attack us. I am only a cabinetmaker, Mr. Wilson, but if I can help, you can count on me.

SAM WILSON: You mean you're going with us, Mr. Strauss?

UNCLE BRUNO: No, I do not think so. But I won't leave if I can be of help—though what help a poor old cabinetmaker can be, I don't know.

SAM WILSON: Mr. Strauss, we sure do thank you. But I want to tell you something. Except for me and the scouts, there's nobody on this wagon train who works at being a pioneer. Old Joe Sweeney there was a canaller back in New York. There are no canals where we're going, but he figures he might learn something new. That long tall fellow over there was an acrobat with a circus, but he and his family sure don't aim to do any shows between here and Oregon. The Reverend there is a preacher, but he did some plowing in Iowa before he joined us.

UNCLE BRUNO: I am sorry, Mr. Wilson. I am slow to learn. When my brother and his family asked me to come to the New World with them, I thought it would be a new world just for me. I see that it is a new world for everybody all the time. I will not say I am just a poor cabinet-maker again. At least I bring with me skills and tools that I can use where I go. But these people—a canaller, an acrobat, a preacher—they must learn everything new.

JOE SWEENEY (*Coming over from campfire*): Just wait one minute there. It may be true that I have no trade or tools to bring with me, but I have my mule, Sal, and a fellow learns a lot of things on the Erie Canal.

UNCLE BRUNO: I did not mean to say you didn't know anything. I do not even know what a canaller does.

JOE SWEENEY: You don't? Then I'll just have to educate you. (*Turns toward campfire and calls*) Ma, you and the kids come over, and let's tell this fellow what it means to work on the Erie Canal. (JOE *is joined by his* FAMILY, *and they sing "The Erie Canal" song.*)

ALBRECHT: That is a fine song.

JOE SWEENEY: It's more than that, sonny. It's a work song. You set your muscles to that tune and you can work all day loading and unloading and never strain a muscle. (LONG JIM, MOLLY *and their* CHILDREN *come over.*)

LONG JIM: I guess maybe you're right about me, Mr. Strauss. Circus life sure didn't prepare us for the kind of life we're moving to. Did it, Molly?

MOLLY: Oh, I wouldn't say that, Jim. When I first saw you floating through the air with the greatest of ease, I knew that you were the man for me. Children, shall we tell your papa what it is like to sit out there and watch him on the flying trapeze?

CHILDREN: Sure, Mama. (MOLLY *and* CHILDREN *sing "The Daring Young Man on the Flying Trapeze."*)

MOLLY: There, and any man who can please all the girls from Jersey's shore to the Mississippi can sure find something to do in a land that's new. Making people laugh and be happy may be old, but there isn't any land so new that it doesn't want that talent.

LONG JIM: Thank you, Molly and children. If we aren't taking anything else with us, at least as our friend here, Albrecht, says, we're taking a fine song.

ALBRECHT: It's a very fine song. (REVEREND TUCKER *and his* FAMILY *come over.*)

REV. TUCKER: I guess folks would say that I was like Long Jim here, too—very nice to have around after everything gets settled. But I have a feeling that it's when things are getting settled that a preacher's needed most. And I have less than you to bring to a new land, Mr. Strauss. In fact, we haven't anything to bring except a little hope . . . and a song, too.

ALBRECHT: Another song! This is the singingest place in the whole world.

REV. TUCKER: Would you like to hear our song?

ALBRECHT: Very much.

REV. TUCKER: Maybe some of you folks know it, too. It's pretty famous in my part of Iowa. Folks there built a church a few years back, and when they finished, they asked Dr. Pitts to come over and speak. The church meant a lot to the folks. It took five years to build—and three of the years were war years. So we were all pretty anxious to hear what Dr. Pitts would say. And we were all pleased, because he didn't say it—he sang it. This is what he sang: (REV. TUCKER *and his* FAMILY *sing* "Little Brown Church in the Vale," *and* OTHERS *join in.*)

1ST PIONEER: That sure is a fine song, preacher.

2ND PIONEER: We'd like to hear you sing another one.

3RD PIONEER: How about *Old Dan Tucker?* We like it in Arkansas.

4TH PIONEER: Why not *John Henry?* It's a favorite in Carolina.

5TH PIONEER: How about *The Ballad of Jesse James?*

6TH PIONEER: I like *My Old Kentucky Home.*

SEVERAL PIONEERS (*Ad lib*): *Listen to the Mocking Bird. The Old Oaken Bucket.* (*Etc.*)

SAM WILSON: Now, wait a minute! Wait a minute! America is just full of songs. And everybody has his favorite. If we tried to sing them all, we'd be here till the end of the century. So, I'll tell you what we'll do . . . (LONESOME *comes running in shouting "Yippee, Yippee."*) I said wait a minute! We can't have singing if everybody's just going to shout all by himself. Lonesome! You're not singing. You're trying to say something. So, stop sputtering and get it out.

LONESOME: I'm trying to say everything. I've found a route to Oregon. We don't have to go over the mountains; we don't have to go through Indian territory; and we don't have to cross the Columbia River. I've found a route through the canyon. We'll be there by Christmas!

SAM WILSON: Why, you old rascal! You saved us. If you hadn't shown up soon, we'd have been nothing but a blasted opery company. All right, folks, you heard Lonesome. He's found us a way to Oregon, and we start moving as soon as it's light. Check your wagons and your stock. We're on our way!

UNCLE BRUNO: Mr. Wilson, do you think you still have room for an old broken-down cabinetmaker?

SAM WILSON: Mr. Strauss, if you hadn't come with us, I don't know what I would have done. My Aunt Lois is making the trip just because I promised her that you would make all new furniture for her once we got to Oregon.

ALBRECHT: Hooray, we're going! Now I'll get to hear all the rest of the songs of America.

SAM WILSON: You know, folks, we've heard some good singing here. Now even though we haven't much time, don't you think we ought to let the scouts sing one song for us? It will probably sound terrible, but they've done a good job for us today. What do you say?

ALL: Yes! Yes!

CHARLIE: Lonesome, you found the way. You pick the song.

BEN: Sing us some of those songs that made the cattle stampede when you were wrangling in Texas, Lonesome.

LONESOME: I know one song, and I think we all ought to sing it now together. It seems like the right time—just before we head for home. You all know it. It's *The Battle Cry of Freedom.* (*They all stand and sing as the curtains close.*)

THE END

Production Notes

BEYOND MUTINY

Characters: 10 male; as many male extras as desired for Seamen.
Playing Time: 20 minutes.
Costumes: The Seamen, Pedro, and Chachu, wear simple ragged clothes and red stocking caps; they are barefoot. Columbus, Juan, and Peralonso wear more dignified clothes, appropriate to the period.
Properties: Pail of water; wet tree branch.
Setting: The deck of the *Santa Maria.* Barrels and coils of rope are lying about. The quarter-deck is a raised platform at left of stage. (NOTE: A few large wooden boxes might serve as quarter-deck if no better platform is available.) There is a railing marking the quarter-deck's edge, and two or three barrels just to the right of the quarter-deck. An exit at upstage center leads to Columbus' cabin. Another exit, at right, leads to other parts of the ship.
Lighting: If possible, lights should be dim at rise of curtain, brightening to full light later on, as indicated in the text.

FOR THE GLORY OF SPAIN

Characters: 5 male; 1 female.
Playing Time: 20 minutes.

Costumes: The King and Queen are dressed in royal robes and wear crowns. The Queen wears many bright jewels and the King carries a scepter. Talavera wears a dark flowing robe with a cowl and a small skull cap. Columbus wears a dark doublet and breeches and hose. The Chancellor and Juan are dressed in court clothes.
Properties: Books, paper, maps, globes, letter, quill pen, inkstand, long sheet representing contract.
Setting: There is a large table at the center of the Council Chamber. Around it are a number of chairs, two throne-like ones, one at each end of table, for the Queen and the King. At the left is a small table with books, papers, inkstand, quill. On the large table are maps and globes.
Lighting: None required.

THE GHOST FROM GENOA

Characters: 3 male; 2 female.
Playing Time: 25 minutes.
Costumes: Everyday modern dress is worn by all characters. When Bob and Sam become Columbus and Mendoza, they wear Genoese doublets, capes, stockings, hats with feathers. Mendoza has a large mustache, earrings, and a

dagger. Queen Isabella wears an elaborate gown and a crown.

Properties: Magazines; watch; briefcase; afghan (see note in text).

Setting: A living room. Down right is a large sofa. At the center is a table with magazines on it, and a comfortable chair at the left. Between the windows up left and up right is a bookcase. A door left leads into another room.

Lighting: Dim lights as indicated in the text.

TEST FOR A WITCH

Characters: 4 male; 7 female; male and female extras.

Playing Time: 15 minutes.

Costumes: Polly and Peter wear everyday modern dress. The witches may wear the traditional black capes and pointed hats, the goblins, any weird dark costumes.

Properties: Two books; a large kettle; a bottle; a large basket containing some wrapped beef, potatoes, onions, string beans and carrots; a large paper bag containing bottles of milk; knives; dishes; spoons; cups. (NOTE: Polly and Peter should pretend to cut the vegetables. Except for a few vegetables that Polly holds up, the vegetables should be pre-cut. Most of the stew could be already cooked— or else the cast could pretend to taste it.)

Setting: A small park. At center is a picnic table and some benches. A stone fireplace is at the rear of the stage. It should have a grill for holding the kettle. Near the fireplace is a faucet for water.

Lighting: No special effects.

NOBODY BELIEVES IN WITCHES!

Characters: 3 male; 3 female; as many as desired for Courtiers.

Playing Time: 20 minutes.

Costumes: Matilda Witch and Lilly wear witches' costumes. In Scene 1, Matilda has "cat whiskers" in her pocket. In Scene 2, she wears a bright-colored cloak. Others wear appropriate court dress.

Properties: Newspaper, pad, pencil.

Setting: Scene 1 takes place in the witches' den. The room contains a stove with a kettle on it, and two chairs; various bottles, jars, a broomstick, a tree limb, a book, a bucket of water, and other ingredients for potion are placed about room. Scene 2 is the castle dining room. The table is set for dinner. There is a window on one side of the room.

Lighting: No special effects.

THE WONDERFUL WITCHWARE STORE

Characters: 2 male; 3 female; as many female extras as desired.

Playing Time: 20 minutes.

Costumes: Mr. Goblin wears a brownie suit with bright peaked cap. Mrs. Goblin also wears a brownie suit, with a bright apron and a bow at her neck. Ghost wears sheet. Witches wear traditional black costumes with black pointed hats.

Setting: The Witchware Store. The counter is at back of stage, with some paper jack o'lanterns at one end and a large pile of bandages rolled up at the other. A row of brooms stands along left side of the stage, with a large sign marked "SPECIAL."

Properties: Paper jack o'lanterns, bandages, brooms, doorbell, gallon jug of "Serpent's Tooth," folded colored sheet, folded white sheet.

Lighting: No special effects.

THE HAUNTED BOOKSHOP

Characters: 12 male; 1 female; male and female voices.

Playing Time: 25 minutes.

Costumes: Hank and Chet wear everyday clothes. The characters from *Treasure Island* wear knee breeches, long coats, cocked hats, long white stockings and buckled shoes. They have cutlasses at their sides. Old Pew wears a cloak with a hood, a black mask over his eyes and carries a crude walking stick. Long John should appear to have a wooden leg; he carries a crutch. Tom and Huck are barefooted and wear overalls. Injun Joe wears tattered clothing and an old felt hat over a straggly black wig. Aunt Polly wears a long-skirted dress with a high collar and long sleeves, and a big apron. Her gray hair is parted in the middle and drawn back into a tight knot, and she wears steel-rimmed spectacles. Penrod is dressed in knickers, long stockings, belted jacket and cap. He wears a badge on his shirt. Jody is barefoot, his clothes clean but very ragged. In his second appearance he wears a jacket and fur cap.

Properties: Books, wad of black paper, pick and shovel, cardboard cut-out of a large treasure chest bursting with gold coins, magnifying glass, megaphone.

Setting: Before rise the drop is painted to represent a row of shops. As indicated in the text, two street lights flank a large sign. The interior of the shop has walls covered with well-filled book shelves. Books are also stacked on the counters at downstage left and right, and on the floor. Between the shelves at upstage center is a fireplace. Upstage left and right, a few feet from the rear wall, are large book covers, two on either side. The covers should be tall enough to hide cast, and should have titles and authors printed clearly on them. The rear covers should point towards the center of the stage, but should be slightly overlapped by the front covers so that the whole grouping is adjacent to the wings for easy exit of the cast.

Lighting: No special effects.

THE BOOK THAT SAVED THE EARTH

Characters: 6 male; 1 male offstage voice. If desired, parts may be taken by girls.

Playing Time: 20 minutes.

Costumes: Historian wears a cap and gown, and has a long white beard. Think-Tank wears a robe decorated with stars and circles. He has a huge, egg-shaped head, and around his neck he wears a pair of huge goggles on a chain. Noodle and spacemen wear tunics, tights, and beanies with antennae. Spacemen have silver belts with small boxes containing pills, and Omega has a disc on a chain around his neck.

Properties: Hand mirror; large book with *Mother Goose* on cover in large letters, containing picture of Humpty Dumpty which resembles Think-Tank; microphone; books, pills.

Setting: Down right, in front of curtain, are a table and chair. A movie projector is on the table. Beside table is an easel with a sign: MUSEUM OF ANCIENT HISTORY: DEPARTMENT OF THE TWENTIETH CENTURY. Down left, in front of curtain, are a raised box and an elaborate switchboard with knobs and levers. A sign on an easel reads: MARS SPACE CONTROL. GREAT AND MIGHTY THINK-

TANK, COMMANDER-IN-CHIEF. BOW LOW BEFORE ENTERING. At back of stage is a backdrop of library shelves. A sign reads: CENTERVILLE PUBLIC LIBRARY. A card catalogue is at center and bookcases containing books are at right and left. On one shelf is a large copy of *Mother Goose.*

Lighting: Spotlights on Historian and Martians, as indicated in text.

Sound: Electronic buzzes and beeps.

BOOKS A LA MODE

Characters: 7 male; 6 female.

Playing Time: 20 minutes.

Costumes: Modern dress. Boys and girls wear school clothes and raincoats. Miss Kendall, Miss Brown, and the Woman wear dresses or suits. Mr. Gregg, Professor Martin, and the Man wear suits.

Properties: Schoolbooks and movie magazines, for boys and girls; paper and cards, for Miss Brown; stamp pad and stamp, for Miss Kendall; money and books, for Man; wallet for Bob; library cards for boys and girls, Man and Woman.

Setting: A library in a medium-sized town. There is an entrance downstage left. The right wall shows the ends of stacks with entrance between them. The upstage wall has large windows. At left is a large reading table with straight chairs around it. At right facing left are two desks with chairs. The downstage one has a typewriter on it and the upstage one a phone. Running upstage in front of the desks is a counter. On the counter is a bell. Upstage center is a table with a display of books with fresh bright jackets and with signs telling what the different kinds of books are.

Lighting: No special effects.

RUNNING THE COUNTRY

Characters: 6 male; 5 female.

Playing Time: 10 minutes.

Costumes: Modern everyday dress. Tim may wear a patrol badge.

Properties: Newspapers, pennies and nickels, ball.

Setting: A street corner. A street sign may be placed in the center of the stage, and a backdrop depicting houses or stores may be used.

Lighting: No special effects.

THE THREE ROYAL R'S

Characters: 8 male; 6 female; extras.

Playing Time: 30 minutes.

Costumes: Characters wear clothes of the period.

Properties: Black crayon, large handkerchief, reticule, large account book, long feather.

Setting: The walls of the room are made of chinked-in boards (a curtain background will be sufficient); and a door at up center leads to the outside. If a realistic setting is used, though this is not necessary, a small-panel window is on each side of the door. Two rows of benches, made of unfinished boards and without arms or backs, fill in the left side of the room. A row of nails is in the wall back of the benches, for hats and coats. A large plain table stands at right facing the benches; behind it is the teacher's chair. A fireplace may be used, if desired, placed in middle of wall right. On the wall at right of door hangs a large sheaf of heavy white paper, attached to a thin strip of wood so that the

sheets of paper may be turned over as used. The alphabet—small letters and capitals in the ornate script of the time—has been written carefully on the top sheet by the master, to serve as a model. A substantial birch rod stands near the teacher's chair. On the table are an old-fashioned inkwell, some quill pens in a holder, papers, books, a stack of slates with slate pencils, and a large bell.
Lighting: No special effects.

WELCOME, PARENTS

Characters: 4 male; 8 female.
Playing Time: 10 minutes.
Costumes: Everyday modern dress. Mr. Smith wears a bathrobe over his trousers. Mary and Jane wear coats. Nancy has on a paint-spattered white shirt, and David enters wearing shorts and a fur stole. Alice has three socks in her pocket.
Properties: One and one-half egg cartons, yellow material, fur stole, club for David, three pairs of socks, milk cartons for Jane, huge box for Mary, long sign saying WELCOME, PARENTS.
Setting: The dining room of the Smith home. At center is a large table with breakfast things on it. Around the table are eight chairs.
Lighting: No special effects.

THE PILGRIM PAINTING

Characters: 5 male; 4 female.
Playing Time: 25 minutes.
Costumes: Modern dress for the Brown family. Bonnie wears a dress of many colors; Eddie, a bright red sweater; and Mrs. Brown, an apron. Mr. Marks wears an overcoat and hat. The Pilgrim family is in conventional Pilgrim garb, dark brown or gray.
Properties: Tablecloth and place settings for four; bowl of fruit with bananas and oranges; simulated cooked turkey; paper wrapping or box for turkey; a doll and a rubber ball, for Bonnie and Eddie; a check, for Mr. Marks; and a palette and brush, for Mr. Brown.
Setting: The Brown living room. A table and four chairs are at stage left and an armchair and end table at stage right. Other plain furnishings may be used as desired. A door down right leads outside and a door center left leads to the kitchen. At center back are two folding screens. Behind the screens is the Pilgrim tableau, enclosed in a frame of wood or cardboard. It may be set on a platform, if desired. A heavy wooden table, set for a Thanksgiving dinner, and four chairs are in the tableau.
Lighting: A spotlight may be used on the tableau, if desired.

IN THE NAME OF MILES STANDISH

Characters: 7 male; 4 female; male extras.
Playing Time: 20 minutes.
Costumes: Pilgrim dress, such as found in old pictures. Men wear dark coats, knee breeches, shoes with buckles and large hats with buckle trim. Boys are dressed similarly, but without hats. Miles Standish wears doublet, knee breeches, heavy boots, soldier's cap, and carries a sword. Squanto is dressed in Indian costume. Pilgrim girls wear long, full-skirted dresses, white aprons and caps.
Properties: Large box or small barrel, fishing poles, artificial fish, bouquet of flowers.

Setting: Scene 1: A street. This scene may be played before the curtain. No special setting is necessary. Scene 2: Interior of Brewster cabin. A very plainly furnished room with benches placed around the sides, a spinning wheel and stool downstage center, and a fireplace upstage center. (There were no windows in the early cabins.)
Lighting: No special effects.

TURKEY, ANYONE?

Characters: 2 male; 6 female.
Playing Time: 30 minutes.
Costumes: Sally, Pam and Linda wear everyday dresses. Mrs. London wears an apron over a simple dress, and Mr. London wears slacks and a sport shirt. Dick wears a bright blue band uniform. Aunt Augusta may be comically dressed in a long black dress, a funny hat, and a large purse. Mrs. Parker should carry a purse.
Properties: Carving set, cookbook, movie magazine, knitting, heavy book, purse, money, ticket book, tickets, a package that looks like a wrapped-up turkey, a suitcase, an umbrella.
Setting: The Londons' simple, "lived-in" looking living room. The furnishings include some comfortable easy chairs, a desk, some book cases, tables, lamps, etc. There is a telephone on one of the tables.
Lighting: No special effects.

THE THANKSGIVING SCARECROW

Characters: 5 male; 4 female.
Playing Time: 15 minutes.
Costumes: Modern clothes. The Scarecrow wears a traditional costume of straw hat, worn trousers and coat and has a pipe in his mouth. The Farmer wears overalls, white shirt, and farmer's hat. Farmer's Wife wears a large white apron over her dress.
Properties: Stick, ball.
Setting: A road by a fence. On the other side of the fence stands the Scarecrow. Near him, but on the side of the fence nearest the audience, is a shade tree.
Lighting: No special effects.

GOVERNOR BRADFORD'S SCISSORS

Characters: 5 male; 4 female.
Playing Time: 30 minutes.
Costumes: Traditional Pilgrim dress.
Properties: Two bowls of apples, two small knives, four pumpkins, a sack of meal tied with a string, a bit of ribbon, and a pair of scissors.
Setting: The main room of Prudence's home in Plymouth, Massachusetts. A table is down center. There are two chairs behind the table and one at each end. A chair is down left center and another directly opposite it, down right center. A door in the left wall opens on the street. The doors of two closets, one right and the other left, open on the room.
Lighting: No special effects.
Sound: Shouting and laughter of Indians, offstage.

HAND-ME-DOWN HILDY

Characters: 14 female.
Playing Time: 15 minutes.
Costumes: Modern everyday dress. Hildy wears a shabby blue coat. Underneath are a pair of red flannel pajamas, with bottoms rolled up. All others wear coats over their clothes during Scene 1. Sue wears a hat with a bell on it; Pat, a hat with a red pompon;

Jill, a hat with a tassel; and Jane, an old, shapeless hat.
Properties: Christmas packages and toys, large Christmas bag, two plain shopping bags, a cloth sack, an old pair of mittens, an old scarf, an old muff, and new hat, mittens, scarf, muff and blue coat.
Setting: A living room, decorated for Christmas. There is a door leading to the street at left and a door leading to the rest of the house at right. The room is furnished comfortably.
Lighting: The lights are dimmed and raised as indicated, or a placard reading "Later that night" may be substituted.
Sound: Doorbell.

ONE NIGHT IN BETHLEHEM

Characters: 3 male; 5 female; there are 5 Shepherds and 5 Wives indicated, but more or less may be used if desired.
Playing Time: 15 minutes.
Costumes: Traditional Biblical clothing.
Properties: Broom, bowl of apples, jewel cases, large ruby on gold chain, and water jug.
Setting: The innyard at Bethlehem. At the rear is a stable, with doors that open wide to reveal manger scene. At right is the wall which encloses the yard. There is a gate in the center of the wall, and beside the gate is a rope attached to a bell. At left is the inn, with a door leading into it.
Lighting: No special effects.
Sounds: Carols, as indicated in text.

SANTA AND THE EFFICIENCY EXPERT

Characters: 2 male; 2 female; 6 male or female for Elves.
Playing Time: 15 minutes.

Costumes: Santa wears traditional costume, over an ordinary business suit. Sarah wears long dress and apron. Elves have appropriate bright-colored costumes, and the Speedwells wear ordinary, everyday dress. When they first enter, they wear coats.
Properties: Doll's dress, dolls, two teddy bears, purse, suitcase, briefcase, bottle of capsules, two whistles, certificates, pens.
Setting: The living room of the Claus home. A table is down center. At right is a rocker, and other chairs are placed about the room. There is a window in wall at right. Exit to outside is at right, and exit at left leads to rest of house.
Lighting: No special effects.

THAT CHRISTMAS FEELING

Characters: 6 male; 4 female; extras for carolers, if desired.
Playing Time: 20 minutes.
Costumes: Modern dress for all. Father wears suit, and later puts on overcoat and hat. Mother wears a pretty dress and a hat with veil and sequins. Louise, Dave, and Irene wear everyday clothes. Johnnie wears pajamas, and later puts on a snowsuit over his pajamas. Firemen wear uniforms.
Properties: Packages and white box, for Dave; book, for Johnnie; earrings, for Mother; packages and phone book, for Louise; paper with recipe, loaf of bread, and white box, for Ruthie; glass bowl and packages, one of which holds Christmas tree decorations, for Tom; fire extinguishers, for Firemen; Christmas paper and stickers, for Louise and Irene; artificial snow, for characters coming in from outside.
Setting: The living room of the

Jackson family. A door at right opens outside, and one at left leads to the rest of the house. At center in the upstage wall is a fireplace with a mirror over it. There may be pine branches, Christmas cards, and other decorations on the mantel. In the right wall is a window with a wreath in it. Upstage left is a large Christmas tree with lights, but no other decorations. In front of the fireplace are a card table and chair. On the table are packages, wrapping paper, ribbon, and seals. Upstage right is a small table with a telephone and telephone book on it. The rest of the room is comfortably furnished with a sofa, chairs, lamps, etc.

Lighting: No special effects.

TWO STRANGERS FROM NAZARETH

Characters: 5 male; 5 female.
Playing Time: 20 minutes.
Costumes: Appropriate dress of the period. The Wise Man wears lavish Oriental clothing.
Properties: Broom, tray, two cups of milk, bread, sewing materials, piece of wood, knife, silver coins.
Setting: The interior of a peasant's hut near Bethlehem. Down center is a table, with two stools behind it and a stool at each end. Down left, a fireplace, with a bench in front of it. Against right wall, center, is a bench, and down center, a stool. A part of the backdrop should be so constructed that it can be drawn aside at the end of the play to reveal a tableau of the manger. A door right leads outside and a door left leads to another room.
Lighting: No special effects except at the end of the play, when the tableau may be brightly illuminated.

LONG LIVE CHRISTMAS

Characters: 13 male; 6 female; 7 Spirits of Christmas and 6 Pages may be male or female. As many extras for townspeople and carolers as desired.
Playing Time: 25 minutes.
Costumes: Grandfather Lorenz, Peter, and Barbara wear modern dress. People of Camerovia wear simple peasant costumes. Bert has a red nose, a large walrus mustache, and a derby hat. Pages, Chamberlain, and King wear court costumes; King has a train and wears a crown. Christmas Fairy wears a white, frothy costume and carries a wand. Fun is dressed as a jester. Peace wears white and silver, Love white with scarlet hearts, Hope green, Kindness flame color, Faith yellow, and Childhood light blue. Fun carries a jester's stick and bells; Childhood carries a large colored ball; the others carry wands. Each Spirit of Christmas wears a ribbon with his name on it.
Properties: Large scrolls wound on sticks, reading "This is the Kingdom of Camerovia" and "Christmas Eve in Camerovia"; Christmas wreaths and decorations; tiny parcel and large pile of Christmas packages; long list; sandwich boards reading "Joe's Meats. Christmas Turkeys" and "Joe's Meats. Hamburger"; trumpets; two small trays, with a scroll on one and white gloves on the other; bulky brown packages; mop; pail; newspaper.
Setting: A public square. The stage is bare, except for an arch upstage center and a bench at left. On the apron of the stage, at right, is another bench.
Sound: Offstage music for Christmas Fairy and the Spirits of

Christmas. Record of trumpets may be used, if desired.

THE BROWNIE WHO FOUND CHRISTMAS

Characters: 7 male; 4 female; male extras. (If desired, Brownies may be female.)
Playing Time: 15 minutes.
Costumes: Santa Claus wears the traditional red suit. The Brownies wear brown costumes. Belinda wears a dress. The other children wear night clothes and have pieces of blanket around their shoulders.
Properties: Bulging sacks of toys for Brownies; wooden mixing spoon for Belinda; seven little pies; sled, blankets, skates, sewing box, doll, jumping jack, toy bird, woolly lamb with bell, and seven boxes of candy for Santa Claus.
Setting: The interior of a poor cottage. There are no Christmas decorations in the room. A bed stands at left, a table with benches and stools at right, and an old cookstove up center against the back wall. A clock is on the table. (A door and window should be played as if they were situated in the imaginary "fourth wall" of the stage, down on the apron.)
Lighting: No special effects.
Sound: Sleigh bells, bell of lamb, as indicated in the text.

LOOKING FOR LINCOLN

Characters: 7 male; 7 female.
Playing Time: 15 minutes.
Costumes: Plain clothes of the period. Graham and Stuart may wear suits; the rest of the men wear work clothes. Lincoln has a straw hat. The women and girls wear long skirts.
Properties: Book, letters (folded sheets of paper), three poles with fish hanging from the ends, man's shirt, jug of maple syrup.
Setting: A store in New Salem, Illinois. There is a door, up center. Over the door is a sign: "General Store—Sam Hill, Prop." A counter at left has a display of vegetables, seed, furs, cheeses and bolts of material. A counter at right has a sign: "Post Office, New Salem, Illinois—A. Lincoln, Postmaster." Guns and tools hang on the walls. Down right is a rocking chair. Several wooden kegs may be placed around the store.
Lighting: No special effects.

VISITOR TO GETTYSBURG

Characters: 4 male; 3 female.
Playing Time: 30 minutes.
Costumes: All of the characters wear clothes of the Civil War period. When Lincoln enters in Scene 1, he wears the traditional stove-pipe hat and coat. In Scene 2 he has a shawl draped over his shoulders, and slippers on his feet. In Scene 2, Mr. and Mrs. Holmes wear dressing gowns.
Properties: Scene 1: Dust cloth, paper for Lincoln. Scene 2: Valise, piece of paper, pencil.
Setting: The Holmes living room is attractive and comfortably furnished. At center on the upstage wall is a door which opens onto the veranda. There are windows on either side of this door. At center is a table; a large family Bible and an oil lamp are on the table. At either side of the table are comfortable chairs. At right is a door leading to the kitchen. In the right wall, downstage, is a fireplace, and before the fireplace is a sofa. At left is a door leading to the upstairs

rooms. Downstage left is a comfortable easy chair.

Lighting: Scene 1: The lighting should be dim until Mr. Holmes lights the oil lamp, when the whole stage becomes fully lighted. Scene 2: The stage should be in semi-darkness, perhaps lighted only by a light from the fireplace, until Johnny turns on the lamp. When Lincoln turns off the lamp at the end of the play, the stage becomes dim again.

YOUNG ABE LINCOLN

Characters: 8 male; 9 female; male or female extras for crowd.
Playing Time: 25 minutes.
Costumes: Simple settlers' clothing of the 1820's and 1830's. Boys may wear rough trousers and sports shirts; girls may wear blouses and long skirts or long gingham dresses. Harriet, Augustus, and Mrs. Lincoln as an old woman may wear slightly more dressy clothing of the 1860's. Mrs. Lincoln also wears a black shawl.
Properties: Two candles, shawl, blankets and pillows, basket, knitting or sewing, broom.
Setting: At one side of the stage is a window with a rocking chair beside it. The other side of the stage is furnished simply as a cabin room, with a table and two or three wooden chairs, plus a wooden shelf or two on which properties can be set.
Lighting: Stage is at first dimly lighted. In flashback scenes, stage lights go out completely and a spot lights the opposite corner. Candles which are lighted electrically can be used.

THE VALENTINE TREE

Characters: 3 male; 2 female; 3 male or female for Twinklets; male or female extras as desired.

Playing Time: 15 minutes.
Costumes: Jiggers wears a traditional jester's costume. Madam Snap wears a short dress and apron. Snip wears an elf suit with watches strapped and pinned all over him. Elf Twinklets wear elf suits. Fairies wear filmy white or pastel costumes. Joan wears everyday school clothes. All characters except Joan wear cardboard or cloth wings.
Properties: Silver penny, for Jiggers; rhyming dictionary, for Snip; pincushion, tinsel, and white cheesecloth scarf, for Madam Snap; tape measure, for King Twinkem; strings of hearts, paper hearts, balloons, and confetti, for Fairies.
Setting: The edge of a fairy wood. At the left is a Valentine Tree and at the right are Valentine bushes, covered with gold hearts. Behind the bushes at right is a screen. Two stools or tree stumps are on the green ground.
Lighting: No special effects.

VALENTINE STARDUST

Characters: 4 male; 5 female; plus Sugar Bun and Cream Puff, who may be either male or female.
Playing Time: 20 minutes.
Costumes: Albert Clack is dressed in a cook's apron and tall white hat. Rowena Clack wears an apron. Sugar Bun, Pie Crust and Cream Puff wear large cardboard cutouts front and back, painted to represent what they are and attached with strings at the shoulders. The rest of the characters wear everyday clothing.
Properties: Rolling pin, dough, pastry cutter, large gold key, heart-shaped pan, large shaker labeled "Stardust," small burnt cake, iced cake decorated with

lemon slices, umbrella for Mrs. Nibble, cake iced with powdered sugar and containing the gold key, key to the city for Miss Prim.
Setting: The Sugar and Spice Shop. Upstage right is a door to the outside; on the door are some bells which jingle when the door opens. Another door at upstage left leads to the kitchen. The shelves on the upstage wall and the counter, upstage center, are covered with gay shelf paper and filled with baked goods. There is a work table downstage left, and a bench near the table. A large gold key hangs on the wall beside the shelves. The shop is decorated with red paper hearts and streamers. A large sign suspended over the counter reads "Cupid's Headquarters. Sweets for the Sweet. Place Your Orders Today."
Lighting: No special effects.

THE TINIEST HEART

Characters: 5 male; 1 female; 9 male or female, for children.
Playing Time: 20 minutes.
Costumes: The Heart family may resemble the hearts in a deck of cards. Placards may be hung over their shoulders, with appropriate numbers and designs on each placard. Uncle Diamond may also wear a placard with diamonds. The King, Queen, Jack and Uncle Diamond wear crowns. Messenger may wear colorful tights and a long belted overblouse.
Properties: Wild flowers for girls; letter for Messenger; knitting and tray of tarts for Queen; fishing rod for Jack.
Setting: A room in the shabby castle of the Royal Heart family. There may be a backdrop, indicating stained and cracked walls. There are two modest thrones in

the room, and at least one easy chair. Other shabby furniture may be added. The entrance is at right.
Lighting: No special effects.

THE HANDWRITING ON THE WALL

Characters: 4 male; 4 female.
Playing Time: 25 minutes.
Costumes: Sue, Don and the twins wear colonial costumes. Their mother and Judge Hendrick wear modern dress. George and Martha Washington are costumed to look as much as possible like their pictures. George carries a sword.
Properties: Flashlights, red rose, button.
Setting: The colonial parlor of a country inn. Upstage left is a large fireplace with a crane and kettle and other fireplace accessories. The room is attractively furnished with antiques. There are candlesticks on the mantel with a row of plates between them. A spinning wheel, a cradle and some antique chairs could also be used for atmosphere. There are chintz curtains at the windows. An old sofa stands near the fireplace. An arch or door to the right of the fireplace opens into a hall where the registry desk can be seen with a bell and lamp on it. The door at left leads to the kitchen and dining room, the door at right to a bedroom. On the right wall beside the fireplace there should be a swinging panel, big enough to allow the actors to exit into the "secret passage." The panel may be worked from backstage.
Lighting: No special effects.

MARTHA WASHINGTON'S SPY

Characters: 5 male; 2 female.
Playing Time: 20 minutes.

Costumes: Silas, Caleb and Sam wear battered mufflers, jackets, ragged pants and boots with cloths wrapped around them. Betsy wears a man's coat, a muffler, and a cocked hat. Benjamin is well dressed and wears a cocked hat. Washington is dressed in a greatcoat, a cocked hat and a muffler. Martha is also bundled up in a cape.

Properties: Musket.

Setting: No particular furnishings are required. Backdrop might depict a winter scene, with snowy trees, etc. A fence, snow-covered bushes, some logs, etc., might be placed around stage. Exits are at right and left.

Lighting: No special effects.

George Slept Here, Too

Characters: 3 male; 5 female.

Playing Time: 25 minutes.

Costumes: Modern, everyday dress. All except Nadine and Babsy have winter coats. Mrs. Dale has a handbag containing a compact. Later, Jim and Frank dress as George Washington, with white wigs. Moira puts on long nightgown, robe, and small cap, and Larry puts on nightshirt, wig, and nightcap.

Properties: Blue suitcase containing two Washington costumes, identical suitcase, shoe tote, small bag, poster, paints, brushes, etc., pan, wooden spoons, flashlight, sign reading FOR SALE, candles.

Setting: The living room of the Dale home in Eastern Pennsylvania. A sofa is at right center, and an easy chair and stool are at left. Near the chair is a lamp. A desk with chair and telephone is at one side. A card table is set up at center at beginning of play. Exit down left leads to the outside, and exits up right, up left and up center lead to various parts of the house.

Lighting: Lamp is turned off and flashlight and spotlight are used for lighting indicated in text.

The Other Side of the Wall

Characters: 4 male; 3 female; male and female extras.

Playing Time: 20 minutes.

Costumes: Traditional royal costumes for King, Queen, Primrose, and Nicholas, including crowns and trains; the King and Prince wear swords. The Queen wears an apron over her gown. John and the boys and girls are dressed in simple country clothes.

Properties: Two books, a doll, wooden whistle, knife, small basket.

Setting: The courtyard of King Ethelbert's castle, surrounded by a wall too high to see over. On one side is an exit leading to the castle and on the other is a pair of gates with the royal seal and a heavy bar running across. A few branches show above the wall near the gate. There is a ladder behind the wall for John to stand on. Two benches, one on each side of the stage, face each other; a small basket is on the ground upstage.

Lighting: No special effects.

Sound: Gong.

The Last Snake in Ireland

Characters: 6 male; 1 female; Snake may be male or female; male and female extras for Townspeople.

Playing Time: 20 minutes.

Costumes: Peasant costumes for Townspeople, Connal and Bennan. Patrick wears dark robe and carries a staff. Snake wears narrow bag-like costume, dark in color.

Properties: Large box with lid; coil of rope; staff.

Setting: A hillside outside a cave in Ireland. A painted backdrop of trees may be used, with cave painted around exit upstage center. There are rocks to either side of cave. There are exits right and left.

Lighting: No special effects.

SAINT PATRICK SAVES THE DAY

Characters: 6 male; 5 female.

Playing Time: 25 minutes.

Costumes: Modern everyday dress. Murphy wears a white shirt which seems wet.

Properties: Book, a large sturdy box with handles so it can be carried, and a lid which can be fastened, handkerchief.

Setting: A comfortable living room. A sofa is at center, and two chairs on either side of it. There is a door in the middle of the right wall, and two windows in the upstage wall at right and left.

Lighting: No special effects.

THE LEPRECHAUN'S POT OF GOLD

Characters: 5 male; 5 female.

Playing Time: 25 minutes.

Costumes: Leprechaun wears a quaint green suit, and a deep crowned hat, and has a long beard. The Pixie wears appropriate costume. Granny and the girls wear long, old-fashioned dresses and aprons. Hunter and the boys wear rough shirts and trousers. The Hunter may carry a gun.

Properties: Pot containing pieces of gold; wand, baskets, mushrooms, pieces of wood, toy gun for hunter.

Setting: A clearing in a forest in Ireland. There is a cottage up left, facing on the clearing, with a doorway where Leprechaun and Pixie can hide. If desired, a backdrop of trees may be used to represent the forest, and other trees may be placed about the stage. There is an exit at right.

Lighting: No special effects.

CINDER-RABBIT

Characters: 3 male; 5 female; 4 boys or girls for white mice, if desired.

Playing Time: 25 minutes.

Costumes: Cinder-Rabbit wears ragged costume with an apron, then changes to green ball gown and orange slippers in Scene 1. In Scene 2, she is again in rags, then changes back to her green gown and orange slippers. Stepmother and stepsisters wear ball gowns in Scene 1, and appropriate plain rabbit costumes in Scene 2. Maggie is dressed as a chicken and has pockets in her costume which contain "fairy dust". She carries a wand. Prince, Jack, and Speedy wear rabbit costumes with appropriate courtly trimmings.

Properties: Easter baskets, purple and yellow hair ribbons, hairbrush and comb, slate and chalk, small chest with broken Easter egg in it, broom, drum draped with orange crepe paper for pumpkin, head of lettuce, carrots, breakfast food and dishes, golden Easter basket with glittering eggs for Cinder-Rabbit.

Setting: Cinder-Rabbit's home. A fireplace is up right; a table and chairs are at center, and there is a vegetable bin upstage. In Scene 1, two large kettles with Easter eggs in them are downstage; two Easter baskets are on table and beside them are ribbons, one yellow and one purple.

In Scene 2, the table is set for a meal. Cinder-Rabbit's basket is hidden behind vegetable bin in both scenes. A window is in right wall; right exit leads outside; left exit leads to rest of rabbit hole.
Lighting: No special effects.
Sound: Clock chiming twelve, appropriate Easter song, as indicated in text; waltz music.

THE CHOOSING OF EASTER RABBIT

Characters: 1 female; all other characters may be male and/or female.
Playing Time: 10 minutes.
Costumes: The Fairy wears long, flowing, light blue robes. The animal costumes may be as elaborate as desired. The animals might all wear appropriately-colored cotton knit pajamas. To this basic costume the rabbits may add a puffy cotton tail and long ears; the squirrel, a long bushy tail; the sparrow and robin, a beak and a tail; the red deer, antlers made from branches; and the bear, short ears and paws. Raggedy Rabbit should be dressed similar to the other rabbits, but his costume should be frayed and his tail bedraggled-looking.
Properties: A notice, glasses for Old Rabbit, Easter basket for Fairy.
Setting: A clearing in the woods. There are some cardboard trees upstage center. Other greens and cardboard bushes complete the setting.
Lighting: No special effects.

FIESTA

Characters: 7 male, 10 female. The horse may be either two girls or two boys; male and female extras for the fiesta scene.

Playing Time: 20 minutes.
Costumes: Girls wear cotton skirts with white blouses and may have flowers in their hair. Mother wears an apron. Boys wear jeans and white cotton shirts with a sash of bright-colored material around the waist. The Mayor has a sombrero, if possible. David, Nancy and Cousin Manuel wear everyday clothes. A blanket and a paper horse's head are needed for the horse.
Properties: Paper, pencil, dustcloth, a letter, several bowls, cookbook, two eggs, corn meal, salt, shortening, crepe paper decorations as desired.
Setting: The main room of a small Mexican house. There is a table upstage center. There is a cupboard to the right and several chairs of various sizes. A few dishes are on the table.
Lighting: No special effects.

THE BELL OF DOLORES

Characters: 13 male; 3 female; male and female extras.
Playing Time: 30 minutes.
Costumes: Most of the men wear loose white shirts tied at the waist, and white trousers. They wear sandals or go barefooted. The women wear peasant blouses and skirts. Rosa wears a new shawl in the first part, and a tattered one in the second part. Maria wears a shapeless black shawl. Don Alfredo and Don Caesar wear knee-high boots, tight trousers, frilly white shirts and long colored coats. Hidalgo wears a black suit with boots and cape, and a wig which is bald on top with a fringe of white hair. The policemen, Captain Allende and Captain Gomez wear uniforms.

Properties: Bundle, piece of rope, lantern, letters, bell to be rung offstage, banner of the Virgin of Guadalupe, flowers for Maria and Rosa, message.

Setting: A village street crosses the stage. An arched door at upstage left leads into the church. There are steps in front of it. Upstage right is a house with a door and window.

Lighting: The lights dim and brighten as indicated in the text. If possible, the watchman's lantern should be lighted, and there should be lights inside the house.

WEEPING WILLOW'S HAPPY DAY

Characters: 6 male; 4 female; 8 male or female (some actors may double).

Playing Time: 10 minutes.

Costumes: All trees except Weeping Willow wear large facsimiles of their leaves pinned onto the front of their costumes and labels with their names. They may be dressed in the colors of their barks: Reddish brown for Pitch Pine, Hemlock, and Cedar; purplish brown for White Pine; light gray for White Oak and Magnolia; dark gray (with white or silver sleeves) for Red Maple; gray for Sugar Maple. Weeping Willow wears gray with silver streamers; her costume should be nice looking. She carries a handkerchief. The Foreman and his Men wear colorful lumber jackets; the Artist and his Daughter wear everyday dress and the Artist carries appropriate equipment; the Winds wear any appropriate costume.

Properties: None.

Setting: If possible, Pitch Pine

should stand on an incline with a large rock or two.

Lighting: No special effects.

THE TREE FRIENDS

Characters: 7 male; 12 female. All-girl or all-boy cast may be used, if desired.

Playing Time: 15 minutes.

Costumes: If desired, characters may be identified with appropriate signs. For more elaborate production, aspen trees wear white caps, white skirts or trousers, and white shirts with green and silver paper leaves sewn on. The Leaves extend down over the hands, so that when the children hold their hands palms up, the palms look silver. Pine trees wear green caps, brown skirts or trousers, and green blouses with stiff green paper fringes sewn on. Animals wear appropriate animal costumes. Bird wears bright blue leotards and blue paper wings on a wire frame. Night wears black clothing and black peaked cap with a silver crescent moon on it. Sun wears yellow clothing, a headdress representing golden shafts of light, and a large golden sun, which hangs from his shoulders like a sandwich board. Wind wears a flowing white or blue cape and headdress, and a mask representing a fat-cheeked old man with puckered lips. Thunder wears grey clothing and a gray headdress with silver lightning bolts on it.

Properties: Cymbals or large pan lids, for Thunder.

Setting: The forest may be represented by a green backdrop.

Lighting: Change of daylight to shadows.

Sound: The wind and thunder may

be augmented with records, or by a chorus of children backstage.

MAY WITCH

Characters: 8 female.
Playing Time: 25 minutes.
Costumes: Modern everyday dress. On her second entrance, Emily wears a white terry cloth robe many sizes too large for her. Her head is wrapped in a turban made of a white Turkish towel. Kris wears dark clothes.
Properties: Paper cornucopia filled with tulips, reading lamp, 4 straight chairs, 2 large colored drapes, flower wreath for the queen's crown, artificial flowers, cookie jar with cake squares, picnic basket containing a thermos and paper cups, pillowcase, record player and a recording of gay folk music.
Setting: An upstairs playroom. There is a door up center leading to the hall and back stairs. At left there is a window overlooking the neighboring yards. Comfortable chairs or divans with cushions are arranged about the room. Opposite the window is a desk holding the drapes, artificial flowers, and odds and ends left from making the May baskets. An armchair, partially decorated as a throne, holds the wreath for the queen.
Lighting: As the play begins, the stage should be dark or dimly lit. The stage lights should go on and off as the lamps are turned on and off during the play, as indicated.

MOTHER'S CHOICE

Characters: 2 male; 3 female.
Playing Time: 20 minutes.
Costumes: Modern dress. Mother wears everyday clothes at beginning and later changes to a pretty dress, with necklace and earrings. Bobby wears shirt and trousers, and later puts on jacket. Father wears a business suit. The girls wear casual dresses.
Properties: Pad of paper and pencil, model airplane, newspaper, socks and dirty clothes, receipted bill, long white envelope.
Setting: The living room of the Johnson home. Entrances right and left lead to front door and to the rest of the house. There are two easy chairs, a rather shabby couch, a table with magazines and a newspaper, and a telephone on a table.
Lighting: No special effects.

TIME FOR MOM

Characters: 3 male; 5 female; male and female extras.
Playing Time: 10 minutes.
Costumes: Modern everyday dress. Mother wears an apron.
Properties: Marbles for boys; roller skates and jumping ropes for girls; 2 gift-wrapped packets of "tickets"; 2 or 3 large books, gift-wrapped; breakfast dishes.
Setting: Scene 1: a street. No scenery is required. Scene 2: the dining room. A table with tablecloth and 4 place settings surrounded by 8 chairs stands near stage center. A baby's high-chair may be added, if desired. There is an exit leading to kitchen.
Lighting: No special effects.

A HAT FOR MOTHER

Characters: 6 female.
Playing Time: 20 minutes.
Costumes: Everyday dress. Lois and Lola wear bluejeans. The other girls wear cotton dresses.

Mrs. Langley is dressed in a simple spring suit.

Properties: Mop, dustcloth, waste basket, parcel post package, hat box, all-blue hat trimmed with feathers and pink roses, hand mirror, bag-shaped hat.

Setting: The Langley living room. The furniture is worn but clean. There is a library table at center with straight chairs at either side. Several armchairs are placed at various positions around the room. Additional lamps, small tables, bookcases, etc., give the room a lived-in look. There are three exits: a doorway, up center, leading outside; an exit at left to the kitchen; a door at right leading to the rest of the house.

Lighting: No special effects.

WE, THE PEOPLE

Characters: 15 male; 6 female. Narrator may be male or female. Male extras for Townspeople.

Playing Time: 35 minutes.

Costumes: Dress of the late eighteenth century. Nels and Pierre wear heavy, outdoor clothes. The women are well dressed.

Properties: Sewing bags and equipment, knitting for Ann, piece of blue cloth, and dress pattern, in first episode; branch and knife for Nels; axe for Pierre; coins for John; piece of hide or brown cloth for Daniel; teapot, tea cups and saucers for Nancy and Ellen; sheaf of papers for Mr. Dayton; bell for Town Crier; copy of Constitution for John Patrick.

Setting: There is a lectern on one side downstage, with a book on it from which the Narrator may read his part. A few chairs and tables are in appropriate places, or the characters may carry in chairs as they enter, if preferred. The various episodes may take place on different parts of the stage.

Lighting: A spotlight alternates between the Narrator and the other characters, as indicated. If a spotlight is not available, the Narrator may exit or move to one side during the action.

Sound: Music, as indicated.

THE YANKEE DOODLE KITTEN

Characters: 7 male; 8 female; male and female extras for Children, Parents, and Patriotic Cats; male extras for Vendors.

Playing Time: 15 minutes.

Costumes: Modern everyday dress for all children and parents. Vendors wear colorful striped shirts and blue jeans. The Kittens wear cat costumes and colored bows as indicated in text. Samuel is dressed as Uncle Sam. Patriotic Cat's costumes are described in text. Samuel and Patriotic Cats may wear paper tails and whiskers or cat masks. The Rats are dressed in black, wear black masks, and may have paper ears and tails. The Major is dressed in an appropriate uniform.

Properties: Flags, balloons, candy, boxes of peanuts and popcorn, baskets for Vendors, sign reading "Free—Kittens" for Judy, gun for Daniel Boone Cat.

Setting: A street near the parade grounds. At center is a booth containing flags, candy, boxes of peanuts and popcorn, and balloons.

Lighting: No special effects.

Sound: Whistles, drums and parade music as indicated in text.

AMERICA IS A SONG

Characters: 11 male; 3 female; male extras for soldiers; male and female extras for Pioneers and families of Rev. Tucker, Joe Sweeney, and Long Jim. (Actors may play more than one part.)

Playing Time: 30 minutes.

Costumes: Traditional costumes of the period after the Civil War, for pioneers, scouts, etc. Dan Emmett wears minstrel costume. Soldiers wear uniforms.

Properties: Campfire utensils, pots, etc.; a wagon; rocking chair, cane for Dan Emmett, and guns for the soldiers.

Setting: A wagon-train camp. The upstage wall is a backdrop of a mountain range. A part of a wagon can be seen upstage right; upstage left is a campfire, with usual camping equipment: pots, kettles, blanket rolls, etc. A flashlight covered with red crepe paper and logs in tepee style make an effective campfire.

Lighting: If available, there should be two spotlights—one for the wagon scene, stage right, and the other for the campfire scene, stage left. Blackouts should be used for scene changes.

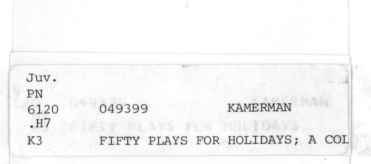